**Creative Publications**

# ALGEBRA

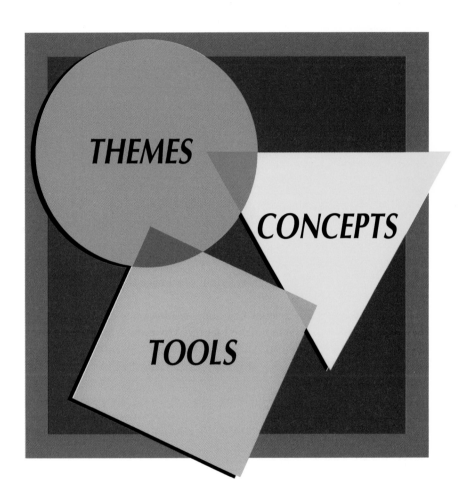

THEMES

CONCEPTS

TOOLS

**Anita Wah**
**Henri Picciotto**

**Creative Publications**

Mountain View, California

# ACKNOWLEDGEMENTS

| Page | Credit |
|------|--------|
| Cover (girl on bicycle) | Lori Adamski Peek/Tony Stone Worldwide |
| Cover (aircraft in flight) | Randy Jolly/Comstock |
| Cover (planet earth) | Terje Kveen/The Image Bank |
| Cover (money symbol) | Michel Tcherevkoff/The Image Bank |
| 2 | Linda Dufurrena/Grant Heilman Photography, Inc. |
| 42 | ©Comstock, Inc. |
| 80 | Science Source • Division of Photo Researchers |
| 122 | James H. Carmichael/The Image Bank |
| 164 | Garry Gay/The Image Bank West |
| 204 | Peter Grumann/The Image Bank West |
| 244 | Chris Bjornberg/Science Source • Division of Photo Researchers |
| 284 | Barry Runk, Stan Schoenberger/Grant Heilman Photography, Inc. |
| 326 | ©W. Cody/West Light |
| 366 | Don Landwehrle/The Image Bank West |
| 396 | ©Jim Zuckerman/West Light |
| 424 | Gabriel Covian/The Image Bank West |
| 456 | Chris Collins/The Stock Market |
| 482 | Michael Sciulli/The Image Bank West |

Text excerpt "When Mrs. Frederick C. Little's second son ... cigarette box," from *Stuart Little* by E. B. White. Copyright 1945 by E. B. White. Text copyright renewed (©) 1973 by E. B. White. Selection reprinted by permission of HarperCollins Publishers.

Managing Editor • George William Bratton III
Project Editor • Ann Roper
Project Art Director and Graphic Designer • Hyru Gau
Production Manager • Vickie Self
Art Director • JoAnne K. Hammer
Math Content Editor • Lyn Savage
Solutions Editor • Terry Whittier
Technical Illustrator for Solutions • Joseph Parenteau
Indexer • Steven Sorensen
Cover Design • Hyru Gau
Composition and Prepress • GTS Graphics, Inc.

1300 Villa Street
Mountain View, California 94041-1197
©1994 Creative Publications

ISBN: 1-56107-251-6
4 5 6 7 8 9 10 K 99 98 97

# AUTHORS

**Anita Wah** received her Bachelor's Degree in Mathematics from Oberlin College and a Master's Degree in Biostatistics from Harvard. She attended and taught as a master teacher at the Woodrow Wilson Algebra Institute and has over ten years of teaching experience at the high school and college levels. She has been involved as a curriculum consultant and staff development trainer for the State of California.

**Henri Picciotto** has been teaching mathematics for over twenty years at every level from counting to calculus. He has developed curriculum for the Lawrence Hall of Science at the University of California and has consulted for many schools, districts, and university departments of education across the country. He received his Bachelor's Degree, as well as his Master's Degree in Mathematics from the University of California at Berkeley. He is currently the mathematics coordinator for The Urban School of San Francisco, California.

## A Word From the Authors

We would like to acknowledge the many people without whom this book would not have been possible.

These math teachers and authors had a significant influence on our teaching or on the ideas that led to this book: Abraham Arcavi, Richard Brown, G.D. Chakerian, Calvin Crabill, Zoltan Dienes, Lew Douglas, Martin Flashman, Paul Foerster, Donna Gaarder, Martin Gardner, Harold Jacobs, Mary Laycock, Sidney Rachlin, Peter Rasmussen, Sherman Stein, Daniel Teague, Joel Teller, Zalman Usiskin.

We also learned a lot from the following curriculum development projects: Change from Within, the Hawaii Algebra Learning Project, the Interactive Math Project, the Lane County Mathematics Project, the Shell Centre for Mathematical Education, and the Quantitative Literacy Project.

We received valuable suggestions from Phil Mallinson, Neil Picciotto, and especially Lyn Savage.

These teachers used the preliminary version of this book in their classes, and helped us iron out the difficulties: Alan Fishman, Mark Gordon, Richard Lautze, Kem Morehead, Hoang Nguyen, and Beau Leonhart. We are grateful to have had their enthusiastic support as the course was being developed.

And of course, our spouses: Alan Fishman and Irva Hertz-Picciotto.

Heartfelt thanks to all!

# DEDICATION

This book is dedicated to our students and colleagues at The Urban School of San Francisco, a great place for involvement, collaboration, and challenge. ✒

**Dear Parent,**

This book is different from the book you used if you took algebra. It certainly is different from the books we used. We have taught from many algebra textbooks over the years, and are well acquainted with the traditional algebra course. The course had many problems: there were many Ds and Fs, and even students who got good grades often did not really understand what they were doing. In addition, the development of calculator and computer technology has made it imperative to change the emphasis of the course. Moreover, as a profession, math teachers now have a better understanding of how students learn.

This book is based on three big ideas, which have been guiding principles in our teaching:

- In order to learn to reason flexibly and independently about the abstract concepts of algebra, students need tools to think with. These tools should be designed to support students' work with the main ideas of algebra: variables, operations, equations, functions, and so on. We use manipulative, electronic, and old-fashioned pencil-and-paper tools.

- Learning mathematics should be based on solving interesting problems. Students' skills develop best if they are given an interesting context to practice them in. Look through the book at the wide variety of problems we address: air travel, get-rich-quick schemes, telephone billing plans, children's growth rates, making cranberry-apple juice, car and bicycle trips, and on and on.

- Most students will not remember concepts if they are explained once or twice by a teacher and practiced in isolation over a short period of time. Students must be involved in their own learning, and have experience with ideas in many forms and formats over an extended period of time. They must experiment, conjecture, discover, and write about what they are thinking. In this book, important ideas are returned to over and over, and much work is expected of the student — hard work, but work that is more varied and interesting than the traditional drill and practice.

After using this book, your child will be exceptionally well prepared for future courses, because we have made a point of giving extra emphasis to the areas that are most important to the rest of secondary school math and science: square roots, proportions, scientific notation, functions, and symbol sense. In addition, the emphasis on thinking, communication, and writing skill will help across the whole curriculum.

If you have any questions about this course, we are sure your student's teacher will be glad to help answer them. The biggest help you can provide is to make sure that your student does algebra homework every day.

Sincerely,

Anita Wah and Henri Picciotto

**Dear Student,**

In arithmetic you have learned to work with numbers. Algebra is an extension of arithmetic, where you learn to work with symbols. It is the language of all of mathematics and science, and a tool for solving problems in business and engineering.

In the future more and more algebra will be done by computer. But what good would it do you to have a computer ready to do the algebra for you if you didn't understand what algebra is? It would be as useful as a calculator to someone who didn't know the meaning of numbers.

Algebra is difficult to learn, but it is the key to so many possibilities in your life that it is worth the effort. You cannot learn algebra just by listening to your teacher. You need to be much more involved: do your homework every day, read the book carefully, and if necessary, get help from your teacher. Good work habits are essential if you want to succeed in this class.

Most importantly, be ready to discuss difficult problems with your classmates, sometimes to help them, and sometimes to get help from them. Talking is the best way to sort out what you understand from what you don't understand, and explaining is the best way to improve your understanding. While learning math and problem solving, you will also be improving your ability to communicate with other people.

You may be surprised at how much writing will be expected from you. Almost every lesson requires you to explain something, and you will have to write reports on a regular basis. This is difficult at first, but it will help you in the long run, by making you not only a better mathematician, but also a better thinker, and a better writer.

Good work habits, communicating, thinking, and writing will help you no matter what you do in the future. But of course, as math teachers, we would like you to stick with it, and take many more math classes. To convince you of this, we have tried to write a book that you will find interesting and that puts you, the student, in the center of the action.

Sincerely,


Anita Wah and Henri Picciotto

# C O N T E N T S

CHAPTER **3** WORKING BACKWARDS ...... 80

# CHAPTER 4 — INTERPRETING GRAPHS ............ 122

**CHAPTER 5 | SUMS AND PRODUCTS** .................................................................................. **164**

## CHAPTER 6  MAKING COMPARISONS ....................................................204

**CHAPTER 7  PRODUCTS AND POWERS** .....................................................................................**244**

## CHAPTER 8 GROWTH AND CHANGE ....................................................................284

## CHAPTER 9   MEASUREMENT AND SQUARE ROOTS .................................................326

# CHAPTER 10 SATISFYING CONSTRAINTS .......................................................366

# CHAPTER 13 MAKING DECISIONS .................................................456

# CHAPTER 14 RATIOS AND ROOTS .................................................482

![Creative Publications logo] Creative Publications

# ALGEBRA

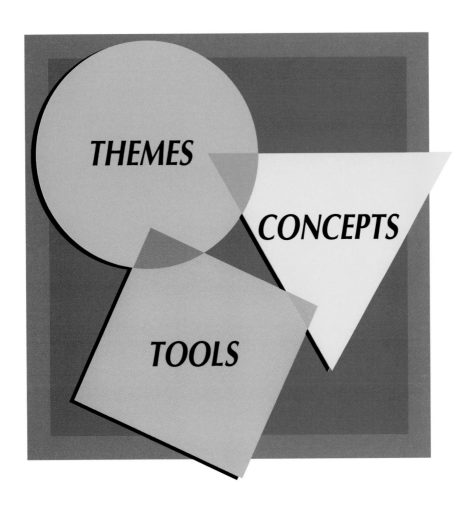

THEMES

CONCEPTS

TOOLS

Anita Wah

Henri Picciotto

# CHAPTER 1

The spiral shape of a ram's horn

## *Coming in this chapter:*

**Exploration** If you draw a closed shape by following the lines on graph paper, you can find its area and perimeter by counting. For a given area, what perimeters are possible?

# PERIMETER AND AREA PATTERNS

**LESSON 1.1**

# Polyominoes

**You will need:**

graph paper

**Definition:** *Polyominoes* are shapes that are made by joining squares edge-to-edge. The best known example is the *domino*.

Using three squares, you can find two different *trominoes*, the straight one and the bent one.

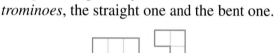

There are only two trominoes. The bent one is shown in different positions.

The following shapes are *not* polyominoes.

1. What part of the definition do they violate?

**DISCOVERING POLYOMINOES**

2. *Tetrominoes* are made up of four squares. There are five different tetrominoes. Find all of them.

3. Guess how many squares make up a *pentomino*. Find all twelve pentominoes. Make sure you do not "find" the same one more than once!

4. 💡 Find as many *hexominoes* as you can.

**AREA AND PERIMETER**

Large polyominoes may have holes in them, as in this 11-omino (i.e. polyomino of area 11).

In this book, we will not discuss polyominoes with holes.

**Definitions:** The *area* of a two-dimensional figure is the number of unit squares it would take to cover it. The *perimeter* of a figure is the distance around it.

For example, the area of the domino is 2, and its perimeter is 6.

In this book, area and perimeter will provide you with many opportunities to discover and apply algebra concepts.

5. Here is a 10-omino. What is its area? What is its perimeter?

6. Draw some 10-ominoes, and find the perimeter of each one. It would take too long to find all of the 10-ominoes, but try to find every possible 10-omino perimeter.

7. Repeat problem 6 for 16-ominoes.

8. Draw as many polyominoes as you can having 10 units of perimeter, and find the area of each one.

9. Find some polyominoes having perimeter 16. It would take too long to find all of them, but try to find every possible area.

**10.** Summary Describe any patterns you noticed when working on this lesson.

**11.** ☞ Have you found any polyominoes having an odd-number perimeter? If you have, check your work. If you haven't, explain why.

Area and perimeter of polyominoes are related. It is not a simple relationship: for a given area, there may be more than one perimeter possible. For a given perimeter, there may be more than one area.

**12.** Project The words *polyomino, tetromino, pentomino, hexomino* all end the same way, but they start with different prefixes.

a. Find other words (not just from mathematics) that start with the prefixes *poly-, tetr-, pent-,* and *hex-*. Tell the meaning of each word.

b. What are the prefixes for 7, 8, 9, and 10? Find words that begin with those prefixes. Tell the meaning of each word.

c. Write a story using as many of the words you found as possible.

---

PREVIEW **DIMENSIONS**

- The following are one-dimensional: a line, the boundary of a soccer field.
- The following are two-dimensional: the surface of a lake, the paper wrapped around a present.
- The following are three-dimensional: an apple, a person.

An object like a sheet, while it does have some thickness and therefore is three-dimensional, can be thought of as a model of a two-dimensional surface with no thickness. Similarly, a wire or even a pencil can be thought of as a model of a one-dimensional line.

**13.** Divide the following into three groups: one-, two-, or three-dimensional.

a. a book
b. a lake
c. a map
d. a piece of paper
e. a piece of string
f. an algebra student
g. Mickey Mouse
h. the boundary of a county
i. the water in a glass
j. the paint on a house

**14.** Name three objects of each kind.

a. one-dimensional
b. two-dimensional
c. three-dimensional

Getting comfortable with the concept of dimension will help you with some of the algebra concepts that you will study later in this course.

**15.** Draw a picture that incorporates several of your objects of different dimensions.

**16.** Write a short paragraph explaining what 3-D glasses are used for.

# 1.2 Perimeter of Polyominoes

**You will need:**

graph paper

## SHORTEST AND LONGEST PERIMETER

For polyominoes with a given area, there may be more than one perimeter. In this section, you will try to find the shortest and the longest perimeter for each given area.

1.  Copy this table, extend it to area 24, and fill it out. (A few rows have been done for you.) Experiment on graph paper as much as you need to, and look for patterns.

| | Perimeter | |
|---|---|---|
| **Area** | **Shortest** | **Longest** |
| 1 | 4 | 4 |
| 2 | 6 | 6 |
| 3 | | |
| 4 | 8 | 10 |
| 5 | | |
| ... | | |

2.  ☞ What patterns do you notice in the table? Explain.

3.  💡 Describe the pattern for the perimeter of a polyomino of area *A*, having:
    a. the longest perimeter;
    b. the shortest perimeter.

4.  For a polyomino having a given area, what perimeters are possible between the shortest and longest? (For example, for area 4, the minimum perimeter is 8, and the maximum is 10. Is it possible to have a perimeter of 9?)

5.  What perimeters are possible for area 9?

## MAKING PREDICTIONS

Mathematics is the science of patterns. Discovering a pattern can help you make predictions.

6.  Predict the longest possible perimeters for polyominoes having these areas. If the number is not too big, experiment on graph paper to test your predictions.
    a. 36          b. 40          c. 100
    d. 99          e. 101         f. 1000

7.  ☞ Explain your method for answering problem 6.

8.  Predict the shortest possible perimeters for polyominoes having these areas. If the number is not too big, experiment on graph paper to test your predictions.
    a. 36          b. 40          c. 100
    d. 99          e. 101         f. 1000

9.  ☞ Explain your method for answering problem 8.

## MAKING A GRAPH

10. On graph paper, draw a horizontal axis and a vertical axis. Label the horizontal axis *Area* and the vertical axis *Perimeter,* as in the following graph. Extend them as far as you can, to at least 25 units for area and 55 units for perimeter.

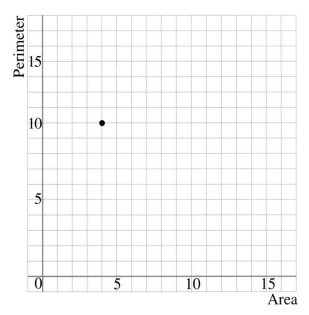

**Definition:** The point where the axes meet is called the *origin*.

For the following problems, you will need the numbers you found in the table in problem 1.

**11.** For each area, there is one number for the longest perimeter. For example, the longest perimeter for an area of 4 is 10. This gives us the number pair (4, 10). Put a dot on the graph at the corresponding point. (Count 4 spaces to the right of the origin, and 10 spaces up.) Do this for all the *area and longest perimeter* points on the table.

**12.** Describe what the graph looks like.

**13.** Using the same axes, repeat problem 1 with the numbers for area and shortest perimeter. One dot would be at (4, 8).

**14.** Describe what the graph looks like.

INTERPRETING THE GRAPH

**15.** Explain why the first set of points is higher on the graph than the second set.

**16.** As the area grows, which grows faster, the longest perimeter or the shortest perimeter? What happens to the gap between the two?

**17.** Use the graph to figure out how many different perimeters are possible for an area of 25. Explain how you did it.

**18.** Use the table you made in problem 1 to answer problem 17. Explain how you did it.

**19.** Use the graph to check whether there is a polyomino having area 15 units and perimeter 20. Explain how you did it.

**20.** Use the table you made in problem 1 to answer problem 19. Explain how you did it.

In this lesson you used patterns, tables, and graphs to help you think about a problem. This is an important skill which you will develop throughout this course.

**PREVIEW** **UNITS AND DIMENSIONS**

Length is measured in linear units, such as the inch (in.) or centimeter (cm). Length refers to one dimension.

Area is measured in square units, such as the square inch (in.$^2$, or sq in.) or square centimeter (cm$^2$). Area refers to two dimensions.

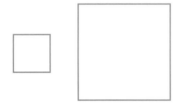

Volume is measured in cubic units, such as the cubic inch (in.$^3$, or cu in.) or cubic centimeter (cm$^3$, or cc). Volume refers to three dimensions.

21. Divide the following units into three groups according to what they measure: length, area, or volume.
    a. acre          b. fluid ounce
    c. foot          d. gallon
    e. kilometer     f. liter
    g. meter         h. mile
    i. pint          j. quart
    k. yard

22. For each unit listed in problem 21, name something that might be measured with it. For example, for (a), the area of a farm could be measured in acres.

LESSON

# Introduction to the Lab Gear

the Lab Gear

The Lab Gear blocks come in two colors, yellow and blue.

### THE YELLOW BLOCKS

The yellow blocks represent whole numbers, such as 1, 5, or 25.

1.  Use the Lab Gear to represent these quantities. Write down what blocks you used.
    a.  13          b.  21

2.  Find as many different numbers as possible that can be represented by using exactly three yellow blocks.

3.  🗝 Write some numbers that *cannot* be represented by the Lab Gear. Explain why you believe this to be true.

You will soon learn to use the Lab Gear for negative numbers. Later, you will use the Lab Gear to work with fractions.

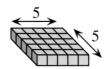

Notice that the block that represents 25 is a 5-by-5 square.

**Notation:** In algebra, the multiplication 5 times 5 is written $5 \cdot 5 = 25$, or $5(5) = 25$. Do not use x to indicate multiplication—it could be confused with the letter x. When handwriting, use a dot, and when typing or using a computer, use an asterisk: $5 * 5 = 25$. In this book, we will use the dot.

### THE BLUE BLOCKS

The blue blocks represent *variables*. All the Lab Gear variables are related to these two blocks.

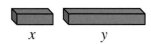

Variables are usually named by letters. Since the names $x$ and $y$ are used most often in algebra, they have been chosen to name the variables in the Lab Gear.

4.  Write a way to remember which block is $x$ and which block is $y$.

$5x$

This block represents $5 \cdot x$ (which is usually written as $5x$). The reason it is $5x$ can be seen by counting the number of $x$'s that make it. Another way to see it is to notice that it is a rectangle. In a rectangle, the area is equal to the length times the width. Using the corner piece, we can measure the $5x$ block, and see that its dimensions are 5 and $x$, and its area is $5x$ square units.

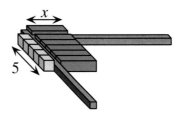

*1.3 Introduction to the Lab Gear*                         **9** ▲

_1.3 Introduction to the Lab Gear_

**5.** Using the corner piece, find the measurements of each of these blocks in terms of $x$ and $y$. Sketch each block. Label each one with its dimensions and area.

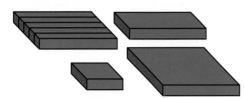

> **Notation:** In algebra, $5 \cdot x$ is written $5x$, and $x \cdot y$ is written $xy$. (When no operation is indicated, multiplication is understood.) $x \cdot x$ is abbreviated $x^2$, and read $x$ *squared*, or *the square of x*.

**6.** Explain why $x^2$ is read *the square of x*.

The following figure shows $x \cdot x \cdot x$ in the corner piece. There is a block whose measurements in three dimensions (length, width, height) match those shown.

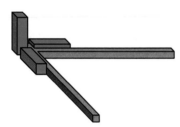

**7.** Which block would fit in the corner piece with those measurements? What shape is it?

**8.** In algebra the quantity $x \cdot x \cdot x$ is read $x$ *cubed*, or *the cube of x*. Why do you think it is called that?

**9.** Use the corner piece to find the length, width, and height of each of the remaining blocks in terms of $x$ and $y$.

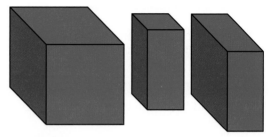

**10.** **Summary** Sketch each Lab Gear block, and label it with its name. Keep these labeled sketches in your notebook for future reference. (However, if you forget the name of a block, you don't need to look it up. Just measure it, using the corner piece.)

**11.** Sketch what each of the following would look like with the Lab Gear. If an expression is impossible to show with the Lab Gear, explain why.
   a. $x^2 + x^2 + 3$
   b. $x^2y + xy$
   c. $x + x^2 + x^3$
   d. $x^3 + x^4$

---

**DISCOVERY** *HANDSHAKES*

**12.** There are nine teachers at a math department meeting. They decide to shake hands with each other before starting the meeting. Each teacher is to shake hands exactly once with each other teacher. How many handshakes does it take? Explain your answer and how you arrived at it.

(Hint: You may use sketches to help you solve the problem. A good approach is to start out by counting the handshakes if there are two, three, four, five people at the meeting, and by looking for a pattern.)

# Variables and Constants

*Variables* are one of the most important concepts of algebra. A variable can stand for different numbers at different times. For example, *x* could be a positive or a negative number or 0. It could be greater than *y*, less than *y*, or equal to *y*.

Because they do not change, numbers are called *constants*.

## SUBSTITUTING

**Definition:** Replacing a variable by a constant amount is called *substitution*.

**Example:** The figure shows how the Lab Gear can be used to show the substitution $x = 2$ for the expressions $x$, $x + 2$, $3x$, $x^2$, and $x^3$.

$x$:

$x + 2$: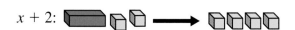

$3x$: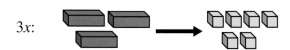

$x^2$:

$x^3$:

1. Sketch what $x + 2$ looks like modeled with the Lab Gear. Then sketch what it looks like if the following substitution is done.
   a. $x = 5$   b. $x = 1$
   c. $x = 3$   d. $x = 0$

2. Repeat problem 1 for $x^2$.

3. Repeat problem 1 for $x^3$.

4. Repeat problem 1 for $3x$.

An expression that involves $x$ can have many different values, depending on the value of $x$.

## EVALUATING

**Definition:** To *evaluate* an expression means to find its value for a particular value of $x$.

Looking back at the figure in the previous section, you can see the value of each expression when $x = 2$. The figure shows that $x + 2 = 4$, $3x = 6$, $x^2 = 4$, and $x^3 = 8$.

In the following problems:
- Put out blocks to match each figure.
- Replace the variables (represented by blue blocks) with the given constants (represented by yellow blocks).
- Evaluate each expression by counting what you have.

5. Evaluate for :
   a. $y = 1$;   b. $y = 2$;   c. $y = 0$.

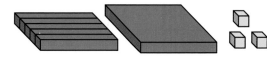

# ▼ 1.4

**6.** Evaluate for :

a. $x = 1$;  b. $x = 5$;  c. $x = 0$.

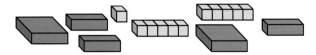

**7.** Evaluate for :

a. $x = 5$ and $y = 4$

b. $x = 4$ and $y = 0$

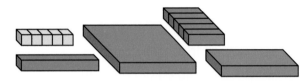

Evaluate these expressions without using the Lab Gear. You may want to use your calculator.

**8.** $y^2 + 5y + 3$ if $y = 1.3$

**9.** $y^2 + xy + 5x + y + 5$ if $x = \frac{1}{2}$ and $y = 4$

Evaluating expressions is important in many walks of life, from science and engineering to business and finance. It is usually done with the help of calculators and computers. In this course you will learn some of the ideas that are built into calculators and computers.

## FINDING X

Use trial and error for these problems.

**10.** If $x + 2 = 18$, what is $x$?

**11.** What is $x$ if

a. $3x = 18$?  b. $x^2 = 64$?

c. $x^3 = 64$?

In a sense, finding $x$ is the reverse of substituting. In future chapters you will learn many methods for finding the value of a variable.

## THE SUBSTITUTION RULE

In the following equations, there are two place-holders, a diamond and a triangle. The **substitution rule** is that, within one expression or equation, the same number is placed in all the diamonds, and the same number is placed in all the triangles. (The number in the diamonds may or may not equal the number in the triangles.)

For example, in the equation

$$\Diamond + \Diamond + \Diamond + \Delta = \Delta + \Delta$$

if you place 2 in the $\Diamond$ and 3 in the $\Delta$, you get

$$2 + 2 + 2 + 3 = 3 + 3.$$

Note that even though the diamond and triangle were replaced according to the rule, the resulting equation is *not* true.

**12.** **Exploration** The equation

$$\Diamond + \Diamond + \Diamond + \Delta = \Delta + \Delta$$

is not true with 2 in the $\Diamond$ and 3 in the $\Delta$. Find as many pairs of numbers as possible that can be put in the $\Diamond$ and in the $\Delta$ to make the equation true. For example, 0 in both the $\Delta$ and $\Diamond$ makes it true. Arrange your answers in a table like this:

| $\Diamond$ | $\Delta$ |
|---|---|
| 0 | 0 |
| ... | ... |

Describe any pattern you notice. Explain why the pattern holds.

For the following equations, experiment with various numbers for ◊ and Δ. (Remember the substitution rule.) For each equation, try to give three examples of values that make it true. If you can give only one, or none, explain why.

**13.** ◊ + ◊ + ◊ = 3 · ◊

**14.** ◊ + ◊ + ◊ = 4 · ◊

**15.** Δ + Δ + Δ = 3 · Δ

**16.** ◊ + ◊ + 2 = 3 · ◊

**17.** ◊ + ◊ + 2 = 2 · ◊

**18.** ◊ · Δ = Δ · ◊

**19.** ◊ · Δ = Δ + ◊

**20.** ◊ · ◊ · ◊ = 3 · ◊

**21.** ◊ · ◊ · Δ = ◊ + ◊ + Δ

**22.**  Say that ◊ is $x$ and Δ is $y$. For each equation above, show both sides with a sketch of Lab Gear blocks. In some cases, the sketches may help you explain whether the equations are always true or not. For example, for problem 13 both sides would look like this.

But, for problem 14 the right side would look like this. Write an illustrated report about what you did.

# 1.A Graphing Rectangle Areas

How does the area of a rectangle change if you vary either the length or the width and leave the other dimension unchanged? How does the area of a rectangle change if you vary both the length and the width? Tables and graphs will help you investigate these questions and notice patterns.

1. What is the area of a rectangle having the following dimensions?
   a. 1 by 9
   b. 2 by 9
   c. 3 by 9
   d. 9 by 9

2. What is the area of a rectangle having the following dimensions, if $x = 10$?
   a. 1 by $x$
   b. 2 by $x$
   c. 3 by $x$
   d. $x$ by $x$

3. Make a table like this, extending it to $x = 6$.

| $x$ | Area of rectangle having dimensions: | | | |
| --- | --- | --- | --- | --- |
| | 1 by $x$ | 2 by $x$ | 3 by $x$ | $x$ by $x$ |
| 1 | 1 | 2 | 3 | 1 |
| 2 | ... | ... | ... | ... |

4. Draw axes, with $x$ on the horizontal axis, and area on the vertical axis. Plot the points you obtained in problem 3 for the area of 1-by-$x$ rectangles. For example, (1, 1) will be on the graph.

5. Does it make sense to connect the points you plotted? What would be the meaning of points on the line, in between the ones you got from your table? Label your graph *1 by x.*

6. On the same axes, graph the data you obtained for 2-by-$x$, 3-by-$x$, and $x$-by-$x$ rectangles. For more accuracy on the last one, you may use your calculator to find points for $x = 0.5, 1.5$, and so on. Label your graphs *2 by x, 3 by x....*

7. Report Write about the four graphs. Describe them and compare them. Your report should reflect what you learned in the above investigation. It should consist of three parts: a problem statement, a detailed explanation, and a conclusion. It should include, but not be limited to, answers to the following questions.
   - What is the shape of each graph?
   - Which ones are alike? Different? Why?
   - How do the first three graphs differ from each other? What is the meaning of that difference?
   - What is special about the fourth? Why?
   - Do the graphs ever intersect each other? What is the meaning of the points of intersection?
   - Where do they cross the vertical axis, and what is the meaning of that point?
   - Where does the fourth one cross the others, and what are the meanings of those points?
   - Which area grows the fastest? Why?

# 1.5 Dimensions

**You will need:**

the Lab Gear

## DIMENSIONS AND THE LAB GEAR

Of course, all the Lab Gear blocks are three-dimensional, (as are all objects in the real world). However, we sometimes use the $x$-block, or the 5-block as a **model** of a one-dimensional object. That is, as a model of a line segment of length $x$, or 5. Similarly, we can use the $x^2$- or $xy$-blocks as models of two-dimensional, flat objects.

1. Some blocks, such as the $x^3$, cannot be used as models of one- or two-dimensional objects. Make a list of these blocks, which we will call the 3-D blocks.

When making sketches of the Lab Gear, if 3-D blocks or three-dimensional arrangements are not involved, it is much more convenient to work with two-dimensional sketches of the blocks **as seen from above.**

2. Which blocks do these figures represent?

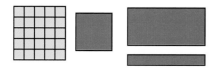

3. Make a 2-D sketch of each of the ten "flat" blocks as seen from above.

4. On your sketch, write *1* on the blocks that model one-dimensional line segments, and *2* on the blocks that model two-dimensional figures.

5. Which block can be thought of as a model of a zero-dimensional point?

6. Sketch the following:
   a. four $x$-blocks arranged to model a one-dimensional line segment;
   b. four $x$-blocks arranged to model a two-dimensional rectangle;
   c. four $x$-blocks arranged to model a three-dimensional box.

7. Sketch the following:
   a. three $x^2$-blocks arranged to represent a two-dimensional rectangle;
   b. three $x^2$-blocks arranged to represent a three-dimensional box.

## FACES OF THE LAB GEAR

The $x^2$-block, **as seen from the side**, looks just like the $x$-block seen from the side, since in either case you see an $x$-by-1 rectangle.

8. a. Make an $x$-by-1 rectangle by tracing an $x$-block.
   b. Place the $x^2$-block on the rectangle you traced. For it to fit, you will have to stand it on edge.
   c. Which other two blocks can be placed on the rectangle?

9. a. Using a block, trace another rectangle (or square).
   b. Find all the blocks that fit on it.

10. Repeat problem 9, until you have found five more groups of blocks. List each group. Some blocks will appear on more than one list.

In the next sections, when putting blocks next to each other, join them along matching faces.

**MAKE A RECTANGLE**

**11.** **Exploration** Build each shape and sketch it, showing which blocks you used.

  a. Use only blue blocks; make a rectangle that is not a square.

  b. Use both yellow and blue blocks; make a rectangle that is not a square.

  c. Use both yellow and blue blocks; make a square.

  d. Use only blue blocks; make a square. ■

**12.** Use 1-blocks to make as many different rectangles as you can, having area:

  a. 12     b. 13     c. 14

  d. 30     e. 31     f. 32

**13.** Make and sketch as many Lab Gear rectangles as you can having area:

  a. $8x$     b. $6xy$

You can rearrange the blocks $2x^2 + 12x$ into a rectangle like this.

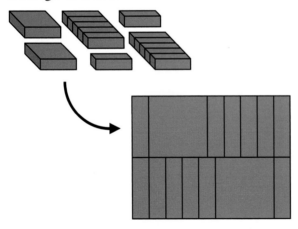

The length and width of this rectangle are $x + 6$ and $2x$, which can be seen better if you organize the blocks logically and use the corner piece, as shown. (Notice that you could also turn the rectangle so that the length and width are exchanged. This is considered to be the same rectangle.) The area of the rectangle $2x^2 + 12x$ can be found by just counting the blocks.

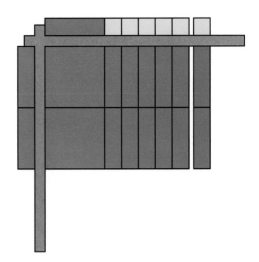

**14.** There is another rectangular arrangement of the same blocks which has different dimensions. Find it.

For each problem:

  a. Arrange the given blocks into a rectangle in the corner piece.

  b. Sketch it (as seen from above).

  c. Write the length, width, and area.

Find two different solutions for problem 17.

**15.**

**16.**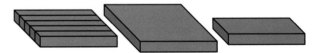

**17.**

By now you should be able to find the length, width, and area of any Lab Gear rectangle. This will be a useful skill throughout this course.

For each problem, the area of a rectangle is given.

    a. Get the blocks that are named.

    b. Make the rectangle.

    c. Write the length and width.

One problem is impossible. Explain why.

**18.** $3x^2 + 9x$    **19.** $3xy + 2x + x^2$

**20.** $4x^2 + 9y$    **21.** $x^2 + 5x$

---

**MAKE A SQUARE**

For each problem, the area of a square is given.

    a. Get the blocks.

    b. Make the square.

    c. Write the side length.

One problem is impossible. Explain why.

**22.** 36        **23.** 49

**24.** 40        **25.** $4x^2$

**26.** $9x^2$     **27.** $x^2 + 2x + 1$

---

**PREVIEW**  *THE ZERO MONSTER*

The Zero Monster eats zeroes. However, all I have to feed it are cups (∪), and caps (∩). It will not eat cups or caps, but it can put one ∪ together with one ∩ to create a zero, which it eats.

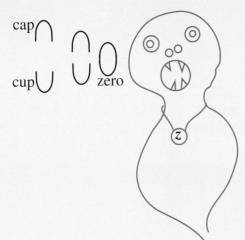

For example, if there are three cups and five caps, it will make and eat three zeroes, leaving two caps. This can be written like this:

$$∪∪∪ + ∩∩∩∩∩ = ∩∩$$

or like this:

$$3∪ + 5∩ = 2∩$$

**28.** Find out how many zeroes the Zero Monster ate. What was left after it finished eating? Fill in the blanks.

    a. $9∪ + 6∩ =$ \_\_\_

    b. $9∪ + 6∪ =$ \_\_\_

    c. $9∩ + 6∩ =$ \_\_\_

    d. $9∩ + 6∪ =$ \_\_\_

**29.** Fill in the blanks.

    a. $4∪ +$ \_\_\_ $= 8∩$

    b. $4∪ +$ \_\_\_ $= 8∪$

    c. $4∩ +$ \_\_\_ $= 8∩$

    d. $4∩ +$ \_\_\_ $= 8∪$

**30.** Fill in the blanks.

    a. $7∪ +$ \_\_\_ $= 1∩$

    b. $7∪ +$ \_\_\_ $= 1∪$

    c. $7∩ +$ \_\_\_ $= 1∩$

    d. $7∩ +$ \_\_\_ $= 1∪$

$2∩$ and $2∪$ are examples of *opposites,* because when you add them, you get zero. The concept of opposite is important in algebra, and we will return to it in Chapter 2.

# Coming to Terms

1. Name a Lab Gear block that can be used as a model for an object with:
   a. three dimensions;
   b. two dimensions;
   c. one dimension;
   d. zero dimensions.

> **Definitions:** In the expression
> $$x^3 + 2xy - 3x + 4,$$
> four quantities are added or subtracted, so we say that there are four *terms*: $x^3$, $2xy$, $3x$, and 4. Note that a term is a product of numbers and variables. The sum or difference of one or more terms is called a *polynomial*.

Note that polynomials do not involve division by variables. For example, $(1/x) + x$ is not a polynomial.

## DEGREE

The *degree* of an expression, in terms of the Lab Gear, is the **lowest dimension** in which you can arrange the blocks. For example, take the expression $3x$. These blocks can be arranged in a rectangle (two dimensions) or in a line (one dimension).

The lowest dimension is one, so the degree of $3x$ is one.

2. Show how the term $2xy$ could be arranged as a box (three dimensions) or as a rectangle (two dimensions). What is the degree of $2xy$?

Of course, $x^3$ cannot be shown in less than three dimensions, so its degree is 3.

3. Write the degree of each blue block.

The degree of a constant expression (any combination of yellow blocks) is considered to be 0. The reason for this is that the yellow blocks can be separated into 1-blocks, which model zero-dimensional points, with no length, width, or height. See the figure below, which shows how the number 8 can be shown in three ways.

Three dimensions

 or

Two dimensions

 or

One dimension

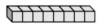 or

Zero dimensions

4. What is the degree of these terms?
   a. $4y$         b. $5x^2$
   c. $2xy^2$       d. 7

The degree of a polynomial can be found in the same way. For example, the figures below show how the blocks $x^2$ and $y$ can be arranged in figures of two or three dimensions. However note that they cannot be arranged into figures of zero or one dimension.

Three dimensions

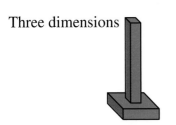

Two dimensions

**5.** What is the degree of $x^2 + y$?

**6.** What is the degree of these polynomials?
   a. $4y + 3$      b. $x^3 + 5x^2$
   c. $2xy^2 + x^2$   d. $xy + 7$

**Definition:** The 2 in the term $2xy$ is called the *coefficient*. A term like $x^3$ has an invisible coefficient, a 1, since $1x^3$ is usually written just $x^3$.

**7.** Generalizations If two terms differ only by their coefficients (like $2x$ and $5x$) what can you say about their degrees?

**8.** ⚷— How can you find the degree of a term without using the Lab Gear? Explain, using examples.

**9.** ⚷— How can you find the degree of a polynomial without using the Lab Gear? Explain, using examples.

### HIGHER DEGREE

**10.** Why is it impossible to show $x^2 \cdot x^2$ with the Lab Gear?

**11.** What is the product of $x^2$ and $x^2$?

**12.** Even though there are only three dimensions in space, terms can be of degree 4. Write as many different terms of degree 4 as you can, using 1 for the coefficient and $x$ and $y$ for the variables.

**13.** Which of these expressions cannot be shown with the blocks? Explain.
   a. $5x^2$   b. $2x^5$   c. $\frac{2}{x^5}$   d. $\frac{5}{x^2}$

### COMBINING LIKE TERMS

There are many ways you can write an expression that names a collection of Lab Gear blocks. When you put blocks of the same size and shape together and name them according to the arrangement, you are combining *like terms*. Look at these examples.

This quantity is written $x + x + x$,

or $3x$, after combining like terms.

This quantity is written $y + x + y$,

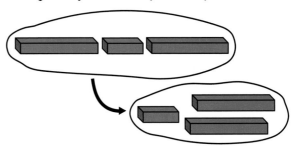

or $x + 2y$, after combining like terms. This quantity is written
$x^2 + 5 + x + x^2 + x + x^2$,

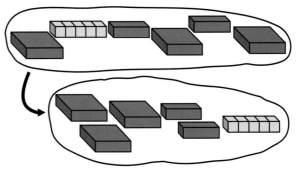

or $3x^2 + 2x + 5$, after combining like terms.

Of course, a 5*x*-block, when combining like terms, is equivalent to 5 separate *x*-blocks. For example, it can be combined with two *x*-blocks to make 7*x*.

For each example, show the figure with your blocks, combine like terms, then write the quantity the short way.

**14.**

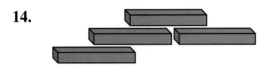

**15.**

**16.**

**17.**

**18.**

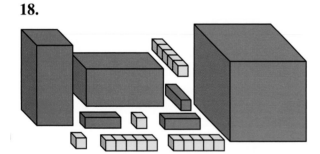

**19.**

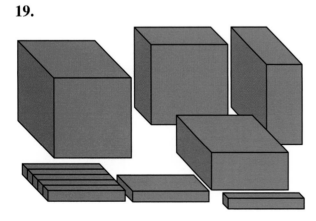

**20.**

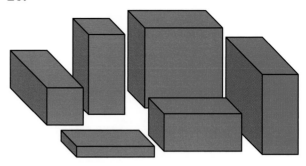

**21.** What terms are missing? (More than one term is missing in each problem.)
   a. $3x^2 + 4x + $ ___ $= 9x^2 + 8x + 7$
   b. $x^2y + 6xy + $ ___ $= 9x^2y + 8xy$

**22.** Summary Explain, with examples, the words *degree, coefficient, polynomial,* and *like terms.* Use sketches of the Lab Gear as well as explanations in words and symbols.

# LESSON
## 1.7
# Perimeter

**You will need:**

the Lab Gear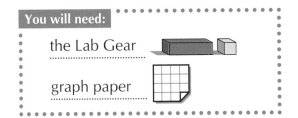

graph paper

### PERIMETER OF LAB GEAR BLOCKS

When we discuss the perimeter and area of the Lab Gear blocks, we will be thinking of the tops of the "flat" blocks, which are two-dimensional figures. For example, if you look at the 5-block from above, you would see this figure. Its area is 5 cm², and its perimeter is 12 cm.

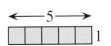

Area: 5 cm²
Perimeter:
5 + 1 + 5 + 1 = 12 cm

Find and write the area and perimeter of these figures, which are the top faces of groups of yellow blocks.

**1.**

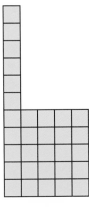

**2.**

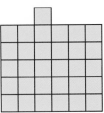

**3.**

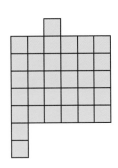

To determine the area and perimeter of the blue blocks, we will not use the actual measurements. Instead, we will consider their dimensions in terms of $x$ and $y$.

For example, this figure, the top of an $x$-block, is a 1-by-$x$ rectangle. So its area is $x$ (since $1 \cdot x = x$), and its perimeter is

$$x + 1 + x + 1$$

which, by combining like terms, can be written $2x + 2$.

Find and write the area and perimeter of the following rectangles, which are the top faces of blue blocks. Be careful when combining like terms.

**4.**

**5.**

**6.**

**7.**

**8.**

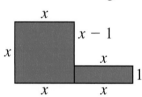

**9.**

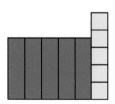

---

### PERIMETER OF LAB GEAR FIGURES

In these problems, assume that $x$ and $y$ are positive. In fact, assume that $x$ is between 1 and 5, and $y$ is between 5 and 10.

Find the perimeter of these figures.

**10.**

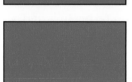

**11.**

**12.**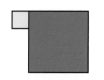

**13.**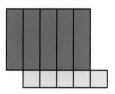

**14.**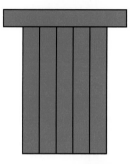

**15.**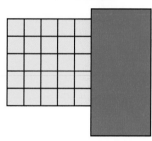

---

### MAKING FIGURES

Use an $xy$-block and a 5-block to make figures having these perimeters. (These can be any shape. They do not have to be rectangles.) Sketch the figure in each case.

**16.** $2x + 2y + 2$

**17.** $2x + 2y + 10$

**18.** $2y + 12$

**19.** Repeat the last three problems using a $y$-block and a $5x$-block.

*Chapter 1 Perimeter and Area Patterns*

**20.**

   a. Use another combination of blocks to get a perimeter of $2x + 2y + 2$.

   b. Use another combination of blocks to get a perimeter of $2x + 2y + 10$.

   c. Use another combination of blocks to get a perimeter of $2y + 12$.

**PENTOMINO STRIPS**

**21.** What is the perimeter of the L pentomino?

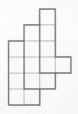

**22.** Draw a strip of L pentominoes, as shown in the figure above. What is the perimeter if you've used 3 L's?

**23.** Make a table like this, extending it to 7 rows.

| L's | Perimeter |
|-----|-----------|
| 1   | ...       |
| 2   | 16        |
| 3   | ...       |

**24.** Explain how you would find the perimeter of a 100-L strip without drawing it.

**25.** How many L's were used if the perimeter was 92?

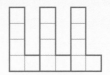

**26.** Repeat problems 22-25 for an arrangement like the one above.

**27.** ⬤━ You can use graphs to compare the perimeter patterns for the two pentomino strip arrangements.

   a. Draw a pair of axes. Label the horizontal axis *Number of L's* and the vertical axis *Perimeter*.

   b. Graph all the number pairs from your first table. For example, since the 2-L strip has a perimeter of 16, you would plot the point (2, 16).

   c. On the same pair of axes, graph all the number pairs from your second table.

   d. Compare the graphs. How are they the same? How are they different?

**28.** Repeat problems 22-25 using another pentomino.

**POLYOMINO AREA AND PERIMETER**

**29.** Arrange three blocks so that the perimeter of the resulting figure is $6x + 2y$. Find all the solutions you can.

**30.** Arrange four blocks so that the perimeter of the resulting figure is $8x + 18$. Find all the solutions you can.

**31.** Arrange five blocks so that the perimeter of the resulting figure is $2y + 2x + 12$. Find all the solutions you can.

# Window-Shopping

On weekends, Lara works at the A.B. GLARE window store. One day a customer, Mr. Alvin Cutterball, asked for an explanation of how the prices were chosen. Lara did not know. Later she asked her supervisor. The supervisor looked very busy and told her not to worry about it. Lara concluded that he probably didn't know and decided she would figure it out herself.

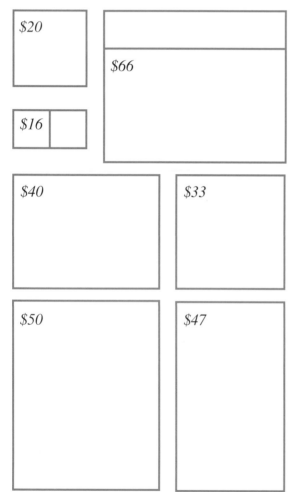

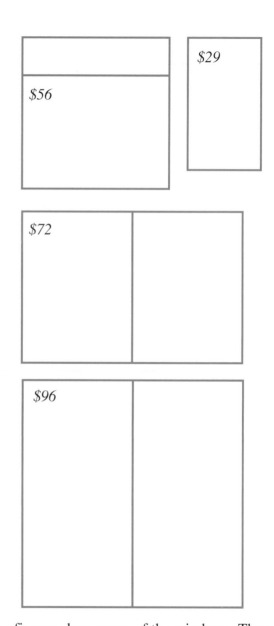

The figures show some of the windows. They are scale drawings, with one centimeter representing one foot.

*Chapter 1  Perimeter and Area Patterns*

1. **Exploration** The price of almost all the windows was calculated by following the same principle. Figure out how it was done.

   Important hints:
   - Work with other students.
   - Think about what numbers might affect pricing. (Some possibilities: length, width, area of glass, perimeter of window, number of panes, etc….)
   - Keep an organized record of the numbers you come across in your exploration.
   - Keep a record of ideas you try, even if they end up not working.

2. One window is on sale and priced below what the system would indicate. Which one is it? How much does it cost when not on sale?

3. Draw scale models of windows that would cost the amounts below. Explain how you got your answers.
   a. $32          b. $84

4. **Report** Summarize your solutions to problems 1, 2, and 3 by writing an explanation of how window prices are calculated. Make it so clear that even Lara's supervisor could understand it. Explain how you figured out the pricing system, showing tables, lists, calculations, diagrams, or anything else that helped you solve the problem.

**DISCOVERY** *A DOMINO PROBLEM*

The figure shows all the ways to cover a two-by-four strip with dominoes.

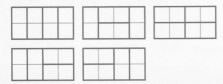

| Length of strip | Number of ways to cover it with dominoes |
|---|---|
| 0 | 1 |
| 1 | 1 |
| 2 | ... |
| 3 | ... |
| 4 | 5 |
| 5 | ... |

5. Find out how many ways there are to cover a two-by-five strip with dominoes. Sketch each way, making sure that you do not show the same way more than once.

6. Make a table like this one about strips of width 2, extending it to length 8. Note that there is only one way to cover a strip of length zero, and that is not to cover it!

7. Look for the pattern in the numbers in the second column. Use the pattern to extend the table to length 10.

# 1.B Drapes

The A.B. GLARE window store also sells drapes. They stock full-length drapes that go down to the floor, as well as window-length drapes that just cover the window.

One day a customer, Ms. Phoebe Tall, came in with a list of the windows for which she needed drapes.

---

**Window-length drapes:**
three 2-by-3-ft windows
two 3-by-3-ft windows

**Full-length drapes:**
two 3-by-7-ft door-windows

**Undecided:**
four 3-by-4-ft windows
six 3-by-5-ft windows

(The second number represents the height.)

---

The material Ms. Tall selected is priced at $3 per square foot. All her windows (except the door-windows, of course) are 3 feet above the floor.

She asked Lara to help her figure out what the cost of various options would be. She wanted to know the smallest amount she could spend. She also wanted to know how much it would cost if she used full-length drapes for all the "undecided" windows. After listening to Lara's explanations, she revealed that she was planning to spend no more than $800. Figure out what Lara should advise her to do.

1. Figure out the smallest amount Ms. Tall could spend, assuming that all the undecided windows are covered with window-length drapes. (Hint: First find the total area. Drawing sketches might help.)

2. Figure out the largest amount she could spend, assuming that all the undecided windows are covered with full-length drapes.

3. If she were planning to spend no more than $800, how many of the undecided windows could she cover with full-length drapes?

4. **Report** Write a full explanation of the results of your investigation. Include sketches that Lara could use to explain the options to Ms. Tall. Your report should consist of three parts: a problem statement, a detailed explanation, and a conclusion.

5. **Project** Find out how drapes are actually sold, and answer Ms. Tall's questions with information from a store in your area.

# Adding and Multiplying

## ADDITION

Using the Lab Gear, the addition $y + 5$ can be modeled in two ways. You can show two collections of blocks, $y$ and 5. Or you can line up the blocks to get a figure that has length $y + 5$. Both methods are shown here.

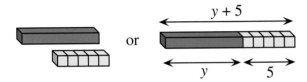

**1.** Sketch this addition both ways, $3x + 2$.

## MULTIPLICATION

The multiplication $3 \cdot (2x + 1)$ can be modeled in two ways. One way is to show three collections of $2x + 1$.

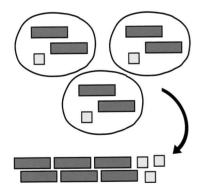

As you can see in the figure,
$3 \cdot (2x + 1) = 6x + 3$.

The other way is to use the corner piece. First set up the factors (3 and $2x + 1$) on the outside.

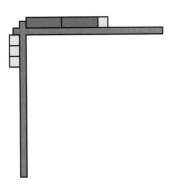

Then make a rectangle having those dimensions.

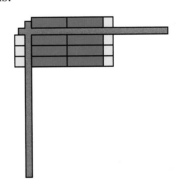

The rectangle represents the product. Again you see that $3 \cdot (2x + 1) = 6x + 3$. This is the familiar *length* $\cdot$ *width* = *area* formula for a rectangle.

**2.** Sketch this multiplication two ways,
   $2 \cdot (x + 3)$.
   a. Use collections of blocks.
   b. Use the corner piece.

**3.** What were the length, width, and area of the rectangle in problem 2?

With any factors of degree 0 or 1, you can model the multiplication in the corner piece.

4. What multiplication is shown in this figure?

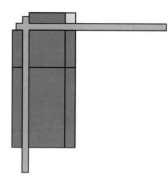

5. 🔑 Multiplying the $x$ by the $x$ gave $x^2$. What other multiplications do you see in the figure above?

6. Multiply with the corner piece.
   a. $3x \cdot 2$
   b. $3 \cdot 2x$
   c. $2x \cdot 3$
   d. $2x \cdot 3y$

7. Multiply with the corner piece.
   a. $5(x + 1)$
   b. $x(x + 3)$

8. Find the area of a rectangle having the sides given below. For each write an equation of the form *length times width = area*.
   a. 5 and $x + 3$
   b. $x$ and $2x + 5$

9. Find the sides of a rectangle having the given area. Each problem has at least two solutions. Find as many of them as you can and write an equation for each.
   a. $6x$
   b. $6x^2 + 3x$

10. These equations are of the form *length times width = area*. Use the Lab Gear to help you fill in the blanks.
    a. $y \cdot \underline{\quad} = y^2 + xy$
    b. $(x + 2) \cdot \underline{\quad} = 3x + 6$
    c. $(\underline{\quad} + 3) \cdot x = 2xy + 3x$

Understanding the area model of multiplication will help you avoid many common algebra errors.

### ORDER OF OPERATIONS

The figure above showed a multiplication. Some students write it like this: $x + 1 \cdot x + y$. Unfortunately, someone else might read it as *add the three terms*: $x$, $1 \cdot x$, and $y$. Simplified, this would be $x + x + y$, or $2x + y$. But the intended meaning was equivalent to $x^2 + xy + x + y$, as you can see on the figure. To avoid this kind of confusion, mathematicians have agreed on the following rule.

**Rule:** When the operations of multiplication and addition (or subtraction) appear in the same expression, *multiplication should be performed first*. If we want to change this order, we have to use parentheses.

This means that one correct way to write the multiplication in the figure is $(x + 1)(x + y)$, which can mean only *multiply $x + 1$ by $x + y$*.

11. a. Show $2 \cdot x + 5$ with the Lab Gear. Sketch.
    b. Next to your sketch show $2 \cdot (x + 5)$ with the Lab Gear. Sketch it. Keep the blocks on the table for the next problem.

12. a. Copy both collections of blocks from problem 11, substituting 1 for $x$. What is each expression equal to?
    b. Repeat, using 5 for $x$.
    c. Repeat, using 0 for $x$.

13. Can you find a value of $x$ for which $2 \cdot x + 5 = 2 \cdot (x + 5)$? If so, what is the value? If not, why can't you find a value?

**14.** **Exploration** Insert parentheses in each expression, so as to get many different values. What are the greatest and smallest values you can find for each one?

a. $0 \cdot 1 + 2 \cdot 3 + 4 \cdot 5 + 6 \cdot 7 + 8 \cdot 9$

b. $0 + 1 \cdot 2 + 3 \cdot 4 + 5 \cdot 6 + 7 \cdot 8 + 9$

## THE SAME OR DIFFERENT?

Students sometimes confuse $3 + x$ with $3x$. With the Lab Gear, it is easy to see the difference. $3 + x$ involves addition.

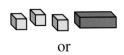

or

$3x$ involves multiplication.

 or

**15.** Find the value of $3 + x$ when:

a. $x = 0$      b. $x = 5$

c. $x = 0.5$

**16.** Find the value of $3x$ when :

a. $x = 0$      b. $x = 5$

c. $x = 0.5$

**17.** For most values of $x$, $3x$ does not equal $3 + x$. In fact there is only one number you can substitute for $x$ that will make $3 + x$ equal to $3x$. Use trial and error to find this number.

**18.** Build these expressions with the Lab Gear. Sketch. Which two are the same?

a. $6xy$      b. $2x + 3y$

c. $2x \cdot 3y$      d. $5xy$

**19.** Build and sketch these two expressions with the Lab Gear.

a. $2x + 3y$      b. $2xy + 3$

**20.** Use trial and error to find a pair of values of $x$ and $y$ that will make the two expressions in problem 19 have the same value.

**21.** Use the Lab Gear to show each expression. Sketch.

a. $5 + x + y$      b. $5 + xy$

c. $5x + y$      d. $5xy$

**22.** Choose values for $x$ and $y$ so that all four expressions in problem 21 have different values.

# Three Dimensions

**You will need:**

the Lab Gear

## VOLUME

**Definition:** The *volume* of a solid is the number of unit cubes it would take to build it.

1. What is the volume of this box? Explain how you got your answer.

You can find the volume of a Lab Gear building by just adding the volume of each block. For example, both of these buildings have volume $x^3 + x^2$.

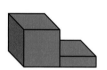 or

2. What is the volume of each of these buildings?

**a** 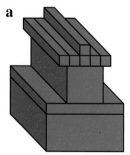  **b**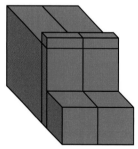

## MAKE A BOX

**Example:** This box has volume $y^3 + xy^2 + y^2 + xy$, length $y + x$, width $y$, and height $y + 1$.

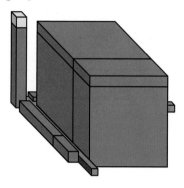

For each problem, the volume of a box is given.

    a. Get the blocks.

    b. Use them to make a box.

    c. Write the length, width, and height.

3. $3xy + x^2y + xy^2$

4. $xy^2 + 2y^2$

5. $x^2y + 2xy + y$

6. $x^2y + xy^2 + xy + y^2$

7. $y^3 + y^2 + xy^2$

8. $x^3 + x^2y + 2x^2 + xy + x$

We will return to the volume of boxes in a future chapter.

## SURFACE AREA

**Definition:** The *surface area* of a solid is the number of unit squares it would take to cover all its faces (including the bottom).

In simple cases, to figure out the surface area it helps to think of a paper jacket that would cover the whole block. The area of such a jacket is the surface area of the block.

For example, the surface area of the 5-block is 22 cm². Its volume, of course, is 5 cm³.

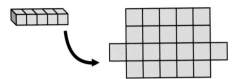

9.  Find the surface area of the 25-block.

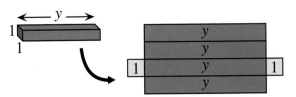

The surface area of the blue blocks can also be figured out by thinking of their jackets. For example, the $y$-block has a surface area of $4y + 2$.

10. Find the surface area of each of the other blue Lab Gear blocks.

### DISCOVERY  *POLYCUBES*

**Definition:** *Polycubes* are obtained by joining cubes together face-to-face. They are the three-dimensional equivalent of polyominoes. Here is a *tetracube.*

There is just one *monocube,* and one *dicube.* There are two *tricubes* and eight *tetracubes.*

All of these polycubes look just like the corresponding polyominoes, except three of the tetracubes, which are really three-dimensional.

11. Find all the polycubes, monocube to eight tetracubes, with your blocks and try to sketch them. Hint: Two of the three-dimensional tetracubes are mirror images of each other.

12. Find the surface area of the polycubes you found in problem 11.

13. Find polycubes having volume 8 and as many different surface areas as possible. There are five different solutions.

14. Were any of your surface areas odd numbers? If yes, check your work. If no, explain why not.

15. ☞ For a given number of cubes, how would you assemble them to get the largest surface area? The smallest?

16. What would the largest possible surface area be for a polycube having volume 100?

17. ☞ Explain in words how you would find the largest possible surface area for a given volume.

18. For each of the following volumes, find the smallest possible surface area.
    a.  12         b.  18         c.  20
    d.  24         e.  27         f.  30

19. ☾ Explain in words how you would find the smallest possible surface area for a given volume.

▼ 1.10

**MORE ON POLYCUBES**

**20.** Find all the polycubes having volume less than 5. Put aside all the ones that are box-shaped. The remaining pieces should have a total volume of 27. Using wooden cubes and glue, make a set of puzzle pieces out of these polycubes. Assemble them into a 3-by-3-by-3 cube. (This classic puzzle is called the Soma® Cube.)

**21.** 💡 There are 29 pentacubes. Twelve look like the pentominoes, and 17 are "truly" three-dimensional. Find them all and sketch them.

**REVIEW** *PERIMETER*

Find the perimeter of each figure.

**22.**

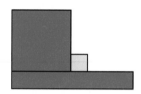

**23.**

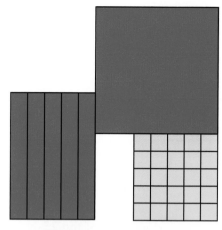

**24.**

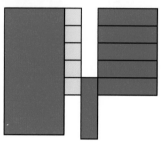

▲ 32

*Chapter 1  Perimeter and Area Patterns*

# Word Figures

## WORD TRIANGLES

Imagine you have a supply of letter tiles, and you use them to make word triangles like this one.

```
A
L A
A L E
R E A L
```

**Rules:** Each row contains the letters of the previous one, plus one more. It's OK to scramble the letters from one row to the next.

1. Extend this word triangle.

2. Make a word triangle with your own letters.

3. How many letter tiles are used in a five-row word triangle?

4. Make a table like this, extending it to ten rows.

| Rows | Tiles |
|:----:|:-----:|
| 1 | 1 |
| 2 | 3 |
| 3 | 6 |
| 4 | ... |

5. The numbers you found in problem 4 (1, 3, 6, ...) are called the *triangular numbers.* Explain how they are calculated.

6. ♀Extend the above word triangle up to **ARGUABLE.** (Along the way, you might use **ALGEBRA.**)

## WORD LADDERS

**Rules:** From one row to the next, change one letter only. It's OK to scramble the letters.

For example:

```
R E A L
L E A D
L O A D
F O L D
F O O D
```

7. Make up a word ladder with your own letters. Choose your word length, and use as many rows as you need. It's fun to choose related words for the beginning and end of the ladder, like **CAR** and **BUS.**

The above example, from **REAL** to **FOOD,** took four steps (and five rows). It is an example of a *perfect* word ladder. For a word ladder to be called perfect, two things must be true:

a. Every letter from the original word must be changed in the final word.

b. If the word has *n* letters, the ladder must take exactly *n* steps.

For a five-letter word, a perfect ladder would take five steps (one per letter) and therefore six rows.

8. How many tiles would a five-letter perfect word ladder require?

9. Make a table of the number of tiles required for perfect word ladders, extended to word length 10.

| Word Length | Tiles |
|---|---|
| 1 | 2 |
| 2 | 6 |
| 3 | 12 |
| 4 | ... |

10. The numbers you found in problem 9 (1, 6, 12, …) are called the *rectangular numbers*. Explain how they can be calculated.

11. 💡 Make up a word ladder from **MATH** to **GAME**.

PUTTING IT TOGETHER

12. This figure shows the third triangular number.

Draw a sketch of two copies of this triangle, arranged together to make a rectangle.

13. This figure shows the fourth rectangular number.

Show how you could divide it into two equal triangular numbers.

14. Summary Describe the relationship between triangular numbers and rectangular numbers.

15. 🔑
   a. Explain how to calculate triangular numbers by first calculating rectangular numbers.
   b. Calculate the 100th triangular number.

POLYOMINO PUZZLES

16. Using graph paper and scissors, or interlocking cubes, make a set of polyominoes having area greater than 1 and less than 5. You should have one domino, two trominoes, and five tetrominoes, for a total of eight puzzle pieces with no duplicates.

17. Using the same unit as you used for the puzzle pieces, draw staircases with base 3, 4, 5, 6, and 7. The first one is shown here.

Now cover each staircase in turn with some of your puzzle pieces. Record your solutions on graph paper. For the last staircase, you will need all of your pieces.

18. Make a list of all the rectangles, including squares, having area 28 or less. Their dimensions (length and width) should be *whole numbers greater than 1*. (In other words, the shortest sides should be 2.) There are 25 such rectangles.

19. Draw these rectangles, and use the puzzle pieces to cover them. Record your solutions on graph paper. (It is impossible to cover one of the rectangles.)

POLYOMINO AREA AND PERIMETER

Think of the monomino. Its area is 1 and its perimeter is 4. Think of the domino. Its area is 2 and its perimeter is 6.

**20.** Exploration  Is the number representing the perimeter of a given polyomino always greater than the number representing its area, or can it be equal to it, or even smaller? Look over your notes and sketches from Lesson 2, and experiment some more on graph paper if you need to. Then write a paragraph to answer this question fully, with examples and graph paper illustrations.

**21.** Find out if there are polyominoes having both area and perimeter equal to

    a. 14      b. 15      c. 16

    d. 17      e. 18      f. 20

### WORD SQUARES

This is a word square.

```
      a  b  c  d
  a [ M  A  T  H ]
  b [ A  C  R  E ]
  c [ T  R  E  E ]
  d [ H  E  E  L ]
```

Note that the words can be read across or down. The largest word square in the English language took years of hard work to discover. It is made up of obscure ten-letter words.

**22.** How many letter tiles are used in the word square above?

**23.** Make a table showing the number of tiles required for word squares, extended to word length 10.

| Word Length | Tiles |
|:-----------:|:-----:|
| 1 | 1 |
| 2 | 4 |
| 3 | 9 |
| 4 | ... |

**24.** The numbers you found in problem 11 (1, 4, 9, …) are called the *square numbers*. Explain how they can be calculated.

**25.** There is an interesting pattern based on adding pairs of consecutive triangular numbers (1 + 3, 3 + 6, …) Explain it.

**26.** Draw a sketch of the third triangular number put together with the fourth triangular number (upside down) to show a square number.

**27.** What do you think the 100th triangular number and the 101st triangular number add up to?

**28.** 💡 Make a word square using these clues. The answer words are all four letters long and can be read both across and down.

    a. Made to be played.

    b. You learned about it in this chapter.

    c. Don't make one!

    d. A piece of cake.

# Area on the Geoboard

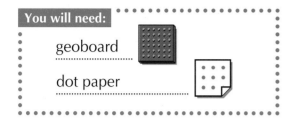

**You will need:**

geoboard

dot paper

This geoboard shape has area 18.

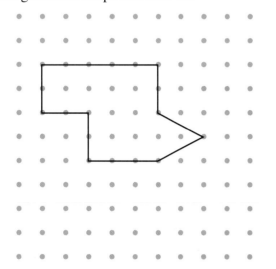

1. **Exploration** Find as many geoboard shapes having area 18 as you can. They do not need to be rectangles. You are allowed to stretch the rubber band in any direction whatsoever, including diagonals. Sketch each shape on dot paper.

## TRIANGLES

2. On your geoboard make three triangles, each one satisfying one of the following conditions. Sketch each triangle on dot paper.
   a. One side is horizontal, and one is vertical.
   b. One side is horizontal, no side is vertical.
   c. No side is horizontal or vertical.

3. Repeat problem 2 for these conditions.
   a. Two sides are of equal length, one horizontal and the other vertical.
   b. Two sides are of equal length, but neither is horizontal or vertical.

## VERTICES

**Definition:** The corners of geometric figures such as triangles and rectangles are called *vertices.* (Singular: *vertex.*)

4. Make a figure on the geoboard having vertices in order at (4, 6), (7, 5), (8, 3), (8, 2), (6, 0), (2, 0), (0, 2), (0, 3), (1, 5).

5. Do not remove the rubber band from problem 4. Using another rubber band, make a figure having vertices in order at (2, 2), (6, 2), (5, 1), (3, 1).

6. Add eyes to the face. What are the coordinates of their vertices?

## AREA TECHNIQUES

7. Make a triangle having vertices at (0, 0), (0, 10), and (10, 0). What is its area? Explain how you figured it out.

8. Make a triangle having vertices at (0, 10), (0, 6), and (3, 6).
   a. With another rubber band, make a rectangle that shares three of its vertices with the triangle. What are the coordinates of the fourth vertex of the rectangle?
   b. What is the area of the rectangle?
   c. What is the area of the triangle?

9. Find the area of a triangle having vertices at (0, 10), (0, 5), and (7, 5).

*Chapter 1 Perimeter and Area Patterns*

**10.** On your geoboard, make two different-shaped triangles that satisfy these conditions: one horizontal and one vertical side, and area 10. Record your solutions on dot paper.

**11.** Repeat problem 10 for area 9.

**12.** ☞ Copy these figures on your geoboard (or on dot paper). Find the area of each one. Explain how you did it.

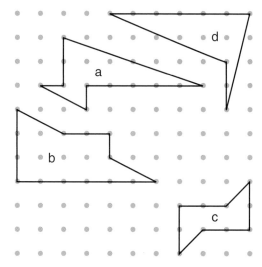

**13.** On your geoboard, make the triangle having vertices at (0, 10), (0, 4), and (3, 6).

a. With another rubber band, divide the triangle into two smaller triangles, such that they each have one horizontal and one vertical side. Find the area of all three triangles.

b. With another rubber band, make the smallest rectangle that covers the original triangle. What is the area of the rectangle?

**14.** Find the area of the triangle having vertices at (0, 0), (0, 7), and (3, 5).

**15.** Record your solutions on dot paper.
   a. Make five triangles having a horizontal side of length 6 and area 15.
   b. Make five triangles having a horizontal side of length other than 6 and area 15.
   c. Make five triangles having a vertical side of length 7 and area 10.5.

**16.** ♀ Find the area of the triangle having vertices at (0, 0), (0, 5), and (3, 7).

**17.** Summary Explain how one finds the area of a geoboard triangle having one horizontal or vertical side.

# 1.C More Window Prices

In Lesson 8 you figured out how window prices were determined in an imaginary store. Real prices are probably not determined this way.

Window manufacturers use a special four-number code for describing the size of standard two-pane windows like those shown below. The first two numbers give the width in feet and inches, and the last two numbers give the height. For example, the code 2636 means that the window is 2 feet 6 inches wide and 3 feet 6 inches high.

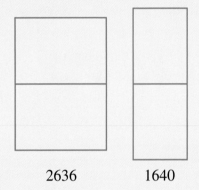

2636          1640

The prices for some windows are given below. You will investigate how the price depends on the dimensions of the window.

| Code | Price |
|------|-------|
| 3030 | $108.00 |
| 4030 | $135.00 |
| 3040 | $130.50 |
| 4040 | $162.00 |

1.  What are the dimensions of a 1640 window?

2.  Use the code to figure out the dimensions of the windows. Make a table showing the code, the dimensions, and the price. You may also want to include other measurements, like the perimeter or area.

3.  Experiment to figure out how the prices were determined. (The formula is not the same as the one used by the A.B. GLARE window store.) Try to find a pattern. According to your pattern, what should a 3050 window cost?

4.  **Report** Write a report about this problem.
    - First, clearly state the problem you are solving.
    - Next, explain the results of your investigation. Include the table you made and explain how you used it to find a formula relating the code to the price. Include sketches and show your calculations in a systematic way. Give a couple of examples to illustrate that your formula really works. Explain why the order of the numbers in the code is important. For example, compare the cost of a 3050 window with the cost of a 5030 window. Make another price list showing what some other windows should cost.
    - Write a brief conclusion commenting on your results. Explain why this method of pricing makes sense. Would it still make sense for very large or very small windows? If you do not think so, can you think of a better way?

# Essential Ideas

1. Explain, with examples, how to figure out the names of the other blue blocks by using 5-blocks, $x$-blocks, $y$-blocks, and the corner piece.

If $x = 5$ and $y = 3$, we can use the Lab Gear to think of $xy$, $x^2y$, $xy^2$.

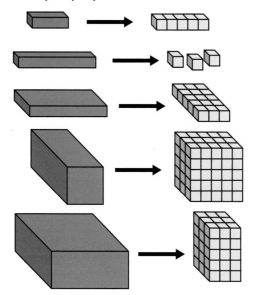

Here is $x^3 + x^2 + 3x + 5$, if $x = 2$.

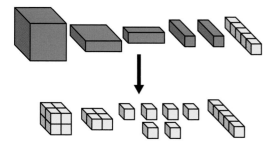

For each problem, write what the blocks show in terms of the variables $x$ and $y$, then use substitution to evaluate them for:

    a. $x = 0$ and $y = 2$;

    b. $x = 5$ and $y = 1$;

    c. $x = 2$ and $y = 3$.

2.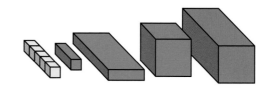

3.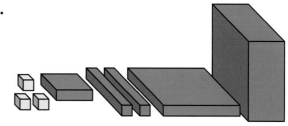

LIKE TERMS

Combine like terms.

4.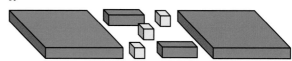

5.

6.
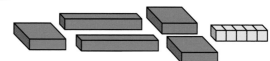

7.
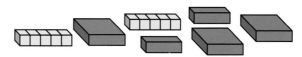

8.
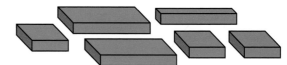

**9.**

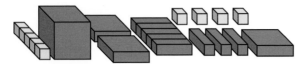

**10.**

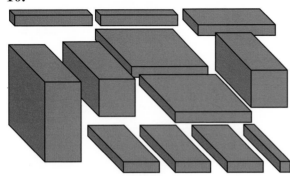

**11.**

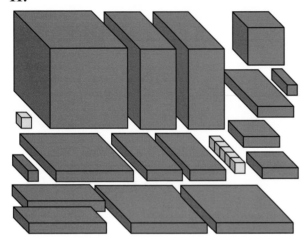

**12.** My student Al *doesn't* like terms. He missed every problem on the Algebra Quiz. Please help poor Al with his algebra. For each problem, give the correct answer and explain what Al did wrong. Use Lab Gear sketches when possible.

a. $x^2 + x = x^3$

b. $3x + x = 3x^2$

c. $x^2 + x^2 + x^2 + x^2 = x^8$

d. $y \cdot 6 = y^6$

e. $2x + 3y = 5xy$

**13.** Use the Lab Gear to show each expression. Sketch.

a. $2 + x + y$

b. $2 + xy$

c. $2x + y$

d. $2xy$

**14.** a. Find values for $x$ and $y$ so that all four expressions in problem 13 have different values.

b. Find values for $x$ and $y$ so that as many as possible of the given expressions are equal to each other.

**15.** Use the Lab Gear to show each expression. Sketch. (Hint: Use the corner piece for the last one.)

a. $x + y^2$

b. $x^2 + y$

c. $x^2 + y^2$

d. $(x + y)^2$

**16.** Find values for $x$ and $y$ so that all four expressions in problem 15 have different values.

**17.** Use the Lab Gear to show $2 + 5y$ and $(2 + 5)y$. Sketch each one.

**18.** a. Use trial and error to find a value of $y$ such that $2 + 5y = (2 + 5)y$.

b. If $y = 0$, which is greater, $2 + 5y$ or $(2 + 5)y$?

c. If $y = 2$, which is greater, $2 + 5y$ or $(2 + 5)y$?

## AREA AND MULTIPLICATION

Use the corner piece for problems 19-21.

**19.** Find the area of a rectangle having the sides given below. For each problem write a multiplication of the form *length times width = area*.

a. 3 and 5          b. 3 and $x$

c. 3 and $x + 5$    d. $x$ and $x + 5$

**20.** Find the sides of a rectangle having the following areas. Each problem has at least two solutions. Find as many of them as you can and write an equation for each.

a. $4x$          b. $4x^2 + 8x$

c. $3xy + 6x^2 + 9x$

**21.** These equations are of the form *length times width = area*. Use the blocks to help you fill in the blanks.

a. $x \cdot$ _____ $= x^2 + xy$

b. $(y + 1) \cdot$ _____ $= 5y + 5$

c. (_____ $+ 3) \cdot y = 2xy + 3y$

d. $2x \cdot$ _____ $= 4x + 2xy + 6x^2$

**22.** Use the Lab Gear to build all the rectangles (or squares) you can find having the following perimeters. For each one, sketch your answer and write the length, width, and area.

a. $8x$

b. $6x + 2y$

c. $4x + 4y$

**23.** What is the area of the triangle in the figure if

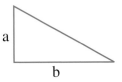

a. $a = 7$ and $b = 9$?

b. $a = 4x$ and $b = y$?

# CHAPTER 2

The equiangular spiral of a nautilus shell

## Coming in this chapter:

**Exploration** 1, 1, 2, 3, 5, 8, 13, 21, 34, 55, 89, 144, 233, 377...
There are many patterns in this sequence of numbers. Find as many as you can, using addition, subtraction, multiplication, and division.

# OPERATIONS AND FUNCTIONS

# Minus and Opposites

**You will need:**

the Lab Gear

## THREE MEANINGS OF MINUS

The *minus* sign can mean three different things, depending on the context.

- It can mean **negative**. In front of a positive number, and only there, it means negative. Example: -2 can mean negative 2.

- It can mean **opposite**. The opposite of a number is what you add to it to get zero. Example: -2 can mean the opposite of 2, which is negative 2, since $2 + -2 = 0$. Likewise, $-x$ means the opposite of $x$, and $x + -x = 0$.

- It can mean **subtract.** Between two expressions, it means subtract the second expression from the first one. For example, $x - 3$ means subtract 3 from $x$.

1.  For each of the following, write an explanation of what the minus sign means.

    a. $y - 5$    b. $-(5x + 1)$

    c. $-2$    d. $-x$

2.  Write the value of $-x$ if:

    a. $x = 2$;    b. $x = -3$.

3.  💡 True or False? (Explain your answers.)

    a. $-x$ is always negative.

    b. $-x$ can be positive.

**Notation:** In this book, the minus sign meaning *negative* or *opposite* will be smaller than the one for subtract. In handwriting, this is not necessary. However some calculators use different keys for the two meanings: ⊟ for subtraction, and (−) or +/− for *negative* or *opposite*.

There are two ways of showing minus with the Lab Gear: upstairs and the minus area.

## UPSTAIRS

**Rule:** Any blocks placed on top of other blocks are preceded by a minus sign.

This figure shows $5 - 2$. Notice that the *uncovered* part of the bottom block equals 3. If you remove matching upstairs and downstairs blocks, you will be left with three downstairs blocks. This is how we show $5 - 2 = 3$ with upstairs and downstairs blocks.

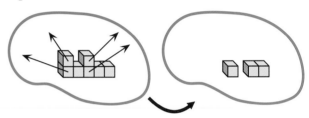

This figure shows $2 - 5$. If you mentally remove matching blocks downstairs and upstairs, you are left with 3 upstairs blocks, or -3. We can only do this mentally, however, since blocks cannot float in mid-air.

 $2 - 5 = -3$

Do not stack Lab Gear blocks more than two levels high. Two levels are enough to illustrate many ideas of algebra and will keep things clear. More would be confusing.

Subtraction with variables is shown in the same way. The amount being subtracted must be placed upstairs. Note that upstairs blocks are shaded in the 2-D sketch.

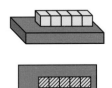

The upstairs method of showing minus is important and useful, but it is limited; it cannot easily be used to show minus when it means *negative* or *opposite*.

### THE MINUS AREA

Look at your workmat. The rectangles with rounded corners represent the **minus areas**. The whole collection of blocks inside the minus area is preceded by a minus sign. For example, $2 - 5$ can be shown this way. (Here the minus sign means *subtract*.)

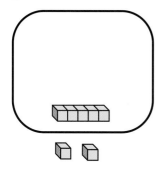

If you remove the matching blocks inside and outside the minus area, you will be left with three blocks inside the minus area, or -3. (Here the minus sign means *negative*.)

**4.** Sketch how you would show each quantity on the workmat. You may need to use upstairs in some of the problems.
   a. $5 - x$   b. $x - 5$
   c. $-(x + 5)$   d. $-(5 - x)$
   e. -5

**5.** **Summary**
   a. Explain, using examples, how the minus area can show all three meanings of minus.
   b. Which of the three meanings does the upstairs method show best? Explain.
   c. Put some blocks in the minus area, including some blocks upstairs. Sketch. What quantity does this arrangement represent?

### REMOVING OPPOSITES

When the quantities inside and outside the minus area are the same, they add up to zero and can be removed. For example, the figure shows that $5 + x + 1 - (x + 1) = 5$.

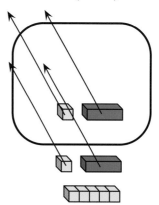

Similarly, matching upstairs and downstairs quantities add up to zero, and can be removed.

**6.** Two of these four figures represent the same quantity. Which two? Explain.

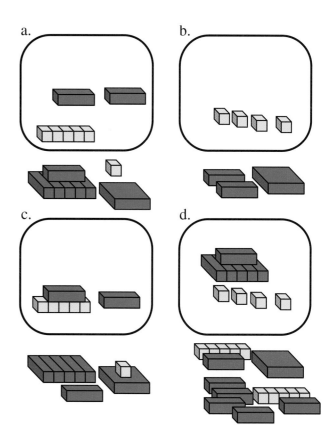

## ADDING ZERO

The number 2 can be shown most simply with two 1-blocks outside the minus area. However, sometimes it is useful to show the number 2 using more blocks.

For example, after adding a five-block in the minus area and a five-block outside, the figure still shows 2. Since 5 and -5 are opposites, their sum is zero, so we really added zero. The technique of adding zero is useful in many situations.

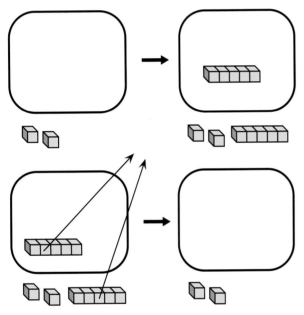

**7.** Sketch two other ways to show the number 2.

**8.** Sketch or explain how to show -9 with:
  a. three blocks;  b. five blocks;
  c. seven blocks.

**9.** Sketch or explain how you would show 5 with:
  a. 3 blocks;  b. 11 blocks.

**10.** Can you show 5 with any number of blocks? Can you show it with 100 blocks? With 101 blocks? Explain your answers.

**11.** a. Show $x - 1$ in at least three different ways. Sketch or explain.
  b. Show $1 - x$ in at least three different ways. Sketch or explain.

## MINUS PUZZLES

**12.** Nineteen numbers can be shown with exactly two yellow blocks. What are they?

**13.** Find three ways to show -4 using only a 5-block and a 1-block. Sketch or explain.

**14.** Find four ways to show 3 with three blocks. Sketch or explain.

**15.** Find four ways to show -8 with four blocks. Sketch or explain.

**16.** Make up a puzzle like the above for a classmate. Solve a classmate's puzzle.

*Chapter 2  Operations and Functions*

# Adding and Subtracting

 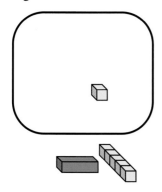

## ASSOCIATIVE AND COMMUTATIVE LAWS

As you know, addition can be modeled with the Lab Gear by putting together collections of blocks on the workmat. For example, $x + 5$ means *put together x and 5* and $(x + 5) + -1$ means *put together x + 5 and -1*. This expression can be simplified by removing opposites, which would give us $x + 4$.

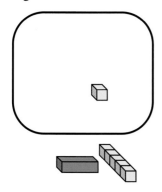

Note that the same figure could have been used to represent $x + (5 + -1)$. This is because, in an addition, quantities can be grouped in any way. This is called the *associative law for addition.*

The same figure could have been used to represent $-1 + (x + 5)$, or $(5 + x) + -1$. This is because in an addition, you can change the order of the terms. This is called the *commutative law for addition.*

Finally, because of the commutative and associative properties, the -1 could have been shown upstairs on top of the $x$, or on top of the 5, instead of in the minus area. In every case, the expression would simplify to $x + 4$.

1. After simplifying these expressions, one will be different from the rest. Which one? Explain.

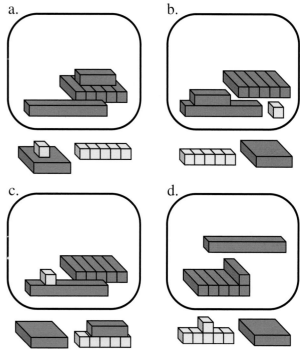

a.   b.

c.   d.

Add these polynomials. (In other words, remove opposites and combine like terms.) It may help to use the Lab Gear.

2. $(xy + 3x + 1) + (2x + 3)$

3. $(xy - 3x + 1) + (-2x - 3)$

4. $(xy + 3x - 1) + (-2x + 3)$

5. $(3 - 2x + xy) + (3x - 1)$

6. ⚷— What do you notice about problems 4 and 5? Explain.

**UPSTAIRS BLOCKS IN THE MINUS AREA**

Here is a useful technique. To simplify upstairs blocks in the minus area, you can add zero, then remove opposites. For example, this figure shows how to simplify

$$-(y^2 - y).$$

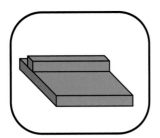

- **Add zero** by adding $y$ inside and outside the minus area.

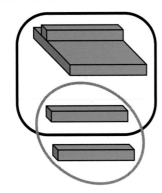

- **Remove opposites,** the matching blocks upstairs and downstairs.

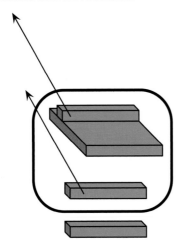

- The simplified form is $-y^2 + y$. All the blocks are downstairs.

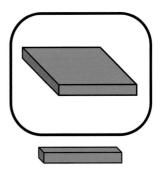

When working with the Lab Gear on the workmat, *simplifying* usually means
- removing opposites;
- combining like terms; and
- getting everything downstairs.

7. Model each expression using the Lab Gear. You will have to use both the minus area and upstairs blocks. Then simplify.
   a. $-(5 - x)$    b. $-(x - 5)$
   c. $3 - (x - 2)$    d. $(x - 2) - 3$

For problems 8–11 below:
- Build the first expression with the Lab Gear on the left side of the workmat.
- Next, compare each of the expressions a, b, c, and d to the original expression. (To make the comparison, build the expression on the right side of the workmat and simplify as needed.)

8. Which of these expressions are equivalent to $-(x + y)$?
   a. $-x + (-y)$    b. $-x - y$
   c. $-x + y$    d. $y - x$

9. Which of these expressions are equivalent to $-(x - y)$?
   a. $-x + y$    b. $-x - y$
   c. $-(y - x)$    d. $y - x$

10. Which of these expressions are equivalent to $-(y - x)$?
    a. $x - y$  b. $-x + y$
    c. $-y + x$  d. $-y - x$

11. Which of these expressions are equivalent to $-(-x + y)$?
    a. $-x + y$  b. $-y - x$
    c. $x - y$  d. $y - x$

12. **Generalization** For each expression below, write an equivalent one without parentheses. Do not use the Lab Gear.
    a. $-(a + b)$  b. $-(a - b)$
    c. $-(-a + b)$

### SUBTRACTION

The figure shows the subtraction
$$(x + 5 - 1) - (5x - 2).$$

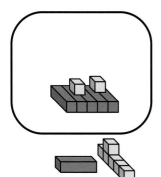

13. Use what you learned in the previous section to simplify it.

14. Simplify, using the Lab Gear.
    a. $x - (5x + 2)$  b. $x - (5x - 2)$

15. Simplify, with or without the Lab Gear.
    a. $(6x + 2) - (3x + 1)$
    b. $(3x - 2) - (6x + 1)$
    c. $(6x - 1) - (3x - 2)$
    d. $(3x - 2) - (6x - 1)$

16. In (a-c) find the missing expression. It may help to use the Lab Gear.
    a. $-3x -$ _____ $= -4x$
    b. $-3y -$ _____ $= -6y$
    c. $-3y -$ _____ $= -2x - 4y$

17. **Summary**
    a. Write a subtraction problem that you could model with the Lab Gear by putting blocks upstairs in the minus area.
    b. Simplify this subtraction without using the Lab Gear. Explain the rule you are using.

18. 💡 How could you show the subtraction
    $$y - -x$$
    with the Lab Gear? (Hint: Remember about adding zero.) What would it look like after it is simplified? What is a rule you could use without the blocks to simplify this kind of expression?

19. 💡 Simplify without the blocks, $-(-a - b)$. Explain your answer.

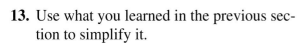

### REVIEW MINUS PUZZLE

20. a. Using the Lab Gear, show $-4$ in five different ways.
    b. What numbers of blocks can and cannot be used to show $-4$?

# 2.3 Multiplying

the Lab Gear

## THREE DIMENSIONS

Just as we used the area of a rectangle to help us model multiplication of two factors, we can use the volume of a box to help us model multiplication of three factors.

For example, $5 \cdot x \cdot y$ can be shown like this.

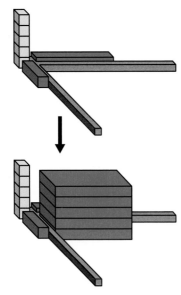

But another way to show it could be:

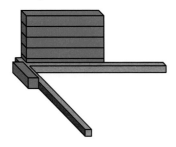

1. 🔑 Use the Lab Gear to show how $x^2y$ can be seen as a product of:
   a. three factors;
   b. two factors;
   c. two factors in another way.

## ASSOCIATIVE AND COMMUTATIVE LAWS

In a multiplication the factors can be grouped in any way. For example, $(-2 \cdot 3) \cdot 4 = -2 \cdot (3 \cdot 4)$. This is called *the associative law for multiplication.*

In a multiplication the factors can be multiplied in any order. For example, $5 \cdot (-6) = (-6) \cdot 5$. This is called *the commutative law for multiplication.*

2. Using six $xy$-blocks, it is possible to make a rectangle in four different ways. Find all four rectangles, and write a multiplication equation for each.

3. Using six $xy$-blocks, it is also possible to make a three-dimensional box. There are many such boxes. Find five, and write at least two multiplications for each one.

4. **Summary** Explain how problems 2-3 about $6xy$ provide examples of the associative and commutative laws for multiplication.

## HOW MANY TERMS?

5. **Exploration** After combining like terms, how many terms does the product have for each of the following multiplications? Is there a pattern? You may use the Lab Gear.
   a. $2x \cdot 3x$
   b. $2(x + 3)$
   c. $2x(x + 3x)$
   d. $(3 + x)(x + 2)$

The figure shows $(x + 3)(x + 5)$.

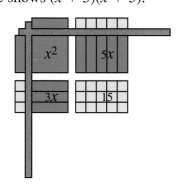

The resulting rectangle is made up of four smaller rectangles. The area of each one is shown in the figure.

6. a. Which two rectangles are made up of the same kind of block?

   b. What is the answer to the multiplication $(x + 3)(x + 5)$? Combine like terms in your answer. How many terms are in your final answer?

7. a. Use the corner piece to model the multiplication $3x(x + 5)$. Sketch it, showing the resulting rectangle.

   b. On your sketch, write the area of each of the smaller rectangles that make up the larger rectangle.

   c. Write the result of the multiplication $3x(x + 5)$. Combine like terms.

   d. How many terms are in your final answer?

8. Repeat problem 7 for
$$(x + 3)(x + y + 5).$$

9. Repeat problem 7 for
$$(x + y + 3)(x + y + 5).$$

10. ☞ Use the Lab Gear to model a multiplication problem that has four terms in the final answer. Sketch the blocks and write the multiplication.

### MAKE A RECTANGLE

Take blocks for each expression.
   a. Arrange them into a rectangle.
   b. Write a multiplication equation of the form *length times width equals area*.

11. $xy + 5y$            12. $xy + 7x$

13. $7y + 7x$            14. $x^2 + 7x$

15. $x^2 + 7x + xy$

16. ☞ Do not use the Lab Gear for this problem. Write the addition
$$y^2 + 2xy + 3y$$
as a multiplication. Explain how you solved the problem.

In problems 17 and 18, take blocks for each expression.
   a. Arrange them into a rectangle.
   b. Write a multiplication equation of the form *length times width equals area*.

17. 💡 $x^2 + 7x + 6$

18. 💡 $x^2 + 7x + 10$

# The Distributive Law

## LINEAR ADDITION AND SUBTRACTION

In the case of *x*, *y*, and constant blocks — in other words quantities of degree 1 or 0 — you can think of adding as putting together blocks end-to-end *in a line*. For example, $2x + 5$ is shown by connecting the two *x*-blocks and the 5-block on their 1-by-1 faces.

Similarly, subtraction of quantities of degree 0 and 1 can be shown linearly, by making sure that the uncovered area models a single line segment. The figure shows $y - 5$.

This representation is based on a *length* model of addition and subtraction.

**1.** Sketch these sums, showing length.
  a. $y + 2$     b. $3x + 1$

**2.** Sketch these differences, showing length.
  a. $y - 2$     b. $3x - 1$

## THE UNCOVERED RECTANGLE

It is possible to use the corner piece for multiplication when minus signs are involved. For example, this figure shows the multiplication $5(5 - 2)$.

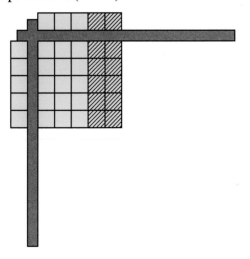

Remember that the shaded blocks are upstairs. Look at the part of the downstairs blocks that are not covered by upstairs blocks. The answer to the multiplication is represented by the **uncovered rectangle** with dimensions 5 and $5 - 2$. Of course, the product is 5 times 3, or 15, which is the answer you get when you simplify upstairs and downstairs blocks.

## THE DISTRIBUTIVE LAW

Find these products, using the Lab Gear. Remember to use upstairs for minus.

**3.** $x(5 + y)$        **4.** $(5 - x)y$

**5.** $5(x + y)$        **6.** $(y - 5)x$

**7.** $y(5 + x)$        **8.** $(y - x)5$

**9.** | Summary | Explain how you can correctly remove parentheses from an algebraic expression when they are preceded or followed by a multiplication, and when there is more than one term in the parentheses. ∎

**10.** ☞ Remove the parentheses.
  a. $a(b + c)$      b. $(a - b)c$

The rule you have discovered in this section is called *the distributive law of multiplication over addition and subtraction*.

Use the distributive law to multiply. You may use the Lab Gear to check your work.

**11.** a. $2x(x + 1)$      b. $2x(x - 1)$

**12.** a. $2x(x + y + 5)$
  b. $2x(x + y - 5)$
  c. $2x(-x + y + 5)$
  d. $2x(x - y + 5)$

For problems 13-18:
   a. Show the quantity with the Lab Gear, using upstairs to show minus.
   b. Arrange the blocks so the uncovered part is a rectangle.
   c. Write a multiplication of the type, *length times width = area* for the uncovered rectangle.

**13.** $xy - 2y$          **14.** $xy - 2x$

**15.** $xy - x^2$          **16.** $xy + x - x^2$

**17.** $y^2 + xy - 5y$     **18.** $y^2 - xy - y$

**19.** 💡 Explain how someone might have done problem 18 without the Lab Gear.

**20.** 💡 Write $x^2 - xy - x$ as a multiplication of the type, *length times width = area,* for the uncovered rectangle.

═══ **RELATED PRODUCTS** ═══

**21.** Use the corner piece to show
$$(3x + 1)(2x - 1).$$
This figure shows the product $(3x + 1)(2x - 1)$.

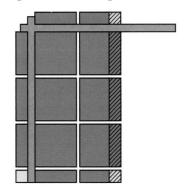

Notice that, inside the corner piece, the uncovered rectangle has dimensions $3x + 1$ and $2x - 1$. These are the original factors. This tells you that we did the multiplication correctly. But the product can be simplified, as shown below.

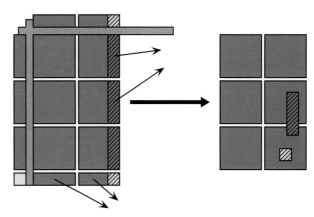

**22.** a. Explain what was done to the blocks in problem 21 after using the corner piece. Which blocks were removed, and why?
   b. Write the final answer, combining like terms.

**23.** Use the Lab Gear to find the product: $(3x - 1)(2x + 1)$. Sketch the process as was done for problem 21.

**24.** a. Show the multiplication $(3x + 2)(2x + 5)$ with the Lab Gear. Write the product.
   b. Write two more multiplications, both involving minus, that use the same blocks as $(3x + 2)(2x + 5)$. In each case write the product.

**25.** Summary You can use the same blocks to show all three of these products with the Lab Gear. Explain why the products are different, even though the same blocks are used. Include sketches as part of your explanation.

a. $(2x + 3)(3x + 5)$

b. $(2x + 3)(3x - 5)$

c. $(2x - 3)(3x + 5)$

**26.** You will learn how to model
$$(2x - 3)(3x - 5)$$
with the Lab Gear in a later chapter. Try to find a way to do this without looking ahead in the book.

REVIEW UNLIKE TERMS

**27.** Al *still* doesn't like terms. For each problem, give the correct answer, if possible, and explain what Al did wrong. Use Lab Gear sketches or substitute numbers.

a. $x^2 - x = x$

b. $3x - x = 3$

c. $9x - 4y = 5(x - y)$

# 2.A Operations

The teacher had just returned the math test, and no one was looking very happy. Martin had missed *all* the problems.

Test                    Name: *Martin P.*

## Operations

1. $2^3 = 6$

2. $3x + x = 3x^2$

3. $2x^3 - x^2 = x$

4. $5 - 2x = 3x$

5. $4 - 2 \cdot 6x = 12x$

6. $(2x - 3) - (x - 2) = x + 5$

7. $6x - (x^2 - 4x) = 2x - x^2$

8. $-(y^2 - x^2) = -y^2 - x^2$

9. $(2x + 1)(3x - 5) = 6x^2 - 5$

10. $2x(-y + 5) = 2x - y + 5$

11. $2y + 3x = 5xy$

12. $6 - 2(x + 3) = 4x + 12$

"I hate math tests," Martin groaned. "I'd rather have my teeth pulled out." Mary would not show her test to anyone, but she looked miserable, too. "I'll need a brain transplant to pass this course," she moaned. Lew, the math whiz, grimaced at his test score and glared at his crutches. He was used to getting everything right, but he had just had an operation on his knee after an injury on the playing field. Math had been the last thing on his mind when he took the test.

Then the teacher did an unusual thing. He handed out these instructions:

### Free Points!

You can get extra points on the **Operations** test if you can correct your mistakes. This is what you need to do:

a. For each problem, explain your mistake. Try to figure out what you were thinking. Most of your mistakes have to do with operations.

b. Show me you now know how to do the problem correctly. Use sketches of the Lab Gear or explain a rule you have learned. Don't just give me the answer.

c. Finally, write the correct answer to the problem.

What should Martin write to get his free points? Write out the corrections for him.

LESSON 2.5

# Powers

## DOING DISHES

Abe agreed to do the dishes daily in exchange for one cent on April 1st, two cents on April 2nd, four cents on April 3rd, and so on, doubling the amount every day.

**1.** To find out how much money Abe was earning, make a table like this one, for at least the first ten days.

| Day # | Cents | Total |
|---|---|---|
| 1 | 1 | 1 |
| 2 | 2 | 3 |
| 3 | 4 | 7 |
| 4 | ... | ... |

**2.** How are the numbers in the *Cents* column calculated?

**3.** How much money did Abe get paid on April 30? Explain how you figured out the answer. Do you think you could talk your parents into an arrangement like this?

**4.** a. Study the table, looking for a pattern in the *Total* column. Describe the pattern.

b. How much money did Abe make altogether during the month of April?

**Definitions: Exponents**

*Exponentiation,* or *raising to a power,* is the operation of multiplying a number by itself repeatedly. The number that is multiplied is called the *base.* The number of factors is called the *exponent.*

**Examples:**

- The expression $2 \cdot 2 \cdot 2 \cdot 2 \cdot 2$ is written $2^5$, where 2 is the base and 5 is the exponent.
- You are already familiar with squaring and cubing, which are special cases of exponentiation in the case of raising to the second and third powers.
- The numbers in the Cents column in the above table are called the *powers of 2,* because they can be obtained by raising 2 to different powers.

**Notation:**

- On calculators, it is not possible to use this notation. Instead, $2^5$ is entered as 2 [$y^x$] 5, 2 [$x^y$] 5, or 2 [^] 5.
- On computers, most word processors allow the user to type exponents (called *superscripts*).
- Computer programming languages use 2^5, 2**5, or `POWER 2 5`.

**5.** Generalization

a. How much money did Abe make on the $n^{th}$ day of April? (Watch out.)

b. What is the number in the *Total* column on day $n$? Explain.

## EXPONENTIAL NOTATION

The number 64 can be written in exponential notation as $2^6$ or $8^2$. (Check this with your calculator or by mental multiplication.)

**6.** Find another way to write 64 in exponential notation.

**7.** Write each of these numbers in exponential notation. Do not use 1 as an exponent. If possible, find more than one way. It may help to use your calculator.

a. 81 b. 1

c. 1024 d. 625

e. 6561 f. -512

## CHAIN LETTER

Lara received this letter.

> Dear Lara,
>
> Send copies of this letter to five people, or the most terrible bad luck will afflict you. One man broke the chain, and a flower-pot fell on his head, giving him a terrible headache which continues to this day.
>
> Don't look a gift-horse in the eye. Rome was not built in a pond. Don't cry over spilt tears.
>
> Please do not break the chain! It was started in 1919 by a psychic.
>
> Bea

Assume that the chain is not broken, and that each person who receives it takes a week to send out five copies.

8. After one week, five people receive Lara's letter. After another week, how many people receive the letter? Make a table like the following for the first ten weeks.

| Week # | Letters received this week | Total number received so far |
|--------|--------|--------|
| 1 | 5 | 5 |
| 2 | 25 | 30 |
| 3 | ... | ... |

9. How many weeks until the number of letters received that week is greater than the population of the United States?

10. How many letters were received in the $n^{th}$ week?

11. If each person made six copies of the letter instead of five, how would your answer to problem 10 change?

12. Do you think that the chain was started in 1919? Explain why or why not.

13. How do the assumptions we made to solve this problem compare with what happens in the real world with chain letters?

## GETTING HELP

Assume Lara gave a copy of the letter to Lea and they each sent five copies in the first week.

14. If everything continues as in the previous section, how many people receive the letter? Make a table like the following for the first five weeks.

| Week # | Letters received this week | Total number received so far |
|--------|--------|--------|
| 1 | 10 | 10 |
| 2 | 50 | 60 |
| 3 | ... | ... |

15. ♡ Write the number of letters received in the $10^{th}$ week as an expression *using exponents*.

16. ♡ How many letters were received in the $n^{th}$ week?

17. ♡ If each person asked a friend to help in the same way, how would your answers to problems 14-16 change?

# 2.6 Finding Patterns

**You will need:**

graph paper

## PARKING RATES

Two downtown parking garages charge differ-ent amounts, as shown by the following signs.

| Ball Garage | | | Bear Garage | |
|---|---|---|---|---|
| up to: | 'U' pay: | | up to: | fee: |
| 1/2 hour | 35 cents | | 1 hour | $1.05 |
| 1 hour | 70 cents | | 2 hours | $2.10 |
| 1 1/2 hr | $1.05 | | 3 hours | $3.15 |
| 2 hours | $1.40 | | 4 hours | $4.20 |
| 3 hours | $2.65 | | 5 hours | $5.25 |
| 4 hours | $3.90 | | 6 hours | $6.30 |
| 5 hours | $5.15 | | all day | $7.25 |
| 6 hours | $6.40 | | | |
| 7 hours | $7.65 | | | |
| all day | $8.90 | | | |

1. If you park for two hours and five minutes, you have to pay the three-hour fee. How much is that at each garage?

2. People who work downtown tend to use one of the garages, and people who shop there tend to use the other. Explain why, with examples.

3. Lara notices that for the amount of time she is planning to park, the cost difference between the two garages is less than a quarter. How long is she planning to park?

4. The parking fees at the Bear Garage mostly fit a pattern. Describe the pattern in words. Where does it break down?

5. The parking fees at the Ball Garage fit a more complicated pattern. Describe the pattern in words. Why might the owner of Ball Garage have chosen a complicated pattern?

Analyzing numbers can be useful in making intelligent decisions. Here is an example.

6. Zalman owns an empty lot. He decides to convert it to a parking garage. He wants to charge a fee that is not too expensive. He decides on these rules:

   • The fee should increase by a constant amount for each half-hour.

   • For parking times from a half-hour to nine hours, the fee should never be more than 25 cents higher than either Ball's or Bear's fee.

   • The fee should be the highest possible fee that satisfies these rules.

   a. Explain why Zalman might have cho-sen each rule.

   b. What rate should he choose? (For con-venience in making change, it should be a multiple of 5 cents.) Explain.

7. Graph the parking fees for all three garages. Put *time* on the horizontal axis, and *cost* on the vertical axis.

*Chapter 2 Operations and Functions*

## FIBONACCI SEQUENCES

The following numbers are called *Fibonacci numbers* after the Italian mathematician who first studied them:

1, 1, 2, 3, 5, 8, 13, 21...

8.  Describe the pattern. Then give the next five Fibonacci numbers. (As a hint, if you have not yet discovered the pattern, look at the *Lucas numbers* — named after another mathematician — which follow the same principle: 1, 3, 4, 7, 11, 18, 29, 47, 76, 123...)

9.  **Exploration** Look for patterns in the Fibonacci numbers. You may use addition, subtraction, or multiplication.

| **Definition:** A *sequence* is an ordered list of numbers or expressions.

10.  You can create your own Fibonacci-like sequence. Choose any two numbers, and use them as the starting values for a sequence like the ones described in problem 8. Name the sequence after yourself. Have a classmate check that your sequence is correct.

11.  a.  Find the first ten terms in a new sequence by adding the Fibonacci and the Lucas numbers. (The sequence should start: 2, 4, 6, 10, 16...) Is the resulting sequence a Fibonacci-like sequence? (Does it follow the same rule?)

   b.  Find the first ten terms in a new sequence by subtracting the Fibonacci numbers from the Lucas numbers. Compare your answer to the one in (a).

   c.  Find the first ten terms in a new sequence by dividing the sequence in (b) by 2. The result should be familiar.

12.  Look for odd/even patterns in Fibonacci-like sequences including the original one, the Lucas sequence, and three named after students in your class. Explain.

13.  Extend the Fibonacci and Lucas sequences to the left. In other words, what number should come before the first number? What number should come before that, and so on? Describe the resulting patterns.

## MISSING NUMBERS

The following Fibonacci-like sequence fragments have numbers missing. Copy the sequences and fill in the blanks.

14.  a.  0.5, 1.1, ___, ___, ___
    b.  5, -4, ___, ___, ___
    c.  -6, -7, ___, ___, ___

15.  a.  ___, ___, ___, 11, 20
    b.  2, ___, 7, ___, ___
    c.  ___, 3, ___, 9, ___

You may need to use trial and error for these.

16.  a.  1, ___, ___, 11, ___
    b.  12, ___, ___, 13, ___
    c.  ___, 8, ___, ___, 10

17.  a.  1, ___, ___, ___, 11
    b.  1, ___, ___, ___, 20
    c.  2, ___, ___, ___, 19

18.  a.  3, ___, ___, ___, ___, 29
    b.  5, ___, ___, ___, ___, ___, 17

**USING VARIABLES**

**19.** Look at problem 17. Describe the relationship between the middle number and the outer numbers.

**20.** Create a five-term Fibonacci-like sequence in which the first two terms are $x$ and $y$.

**21.** Check whether the pattern you noticed in problem 19 works for the sequence you just created. Explain.

**22.** Fill in the blanks for this Fibonacci-like sequence. -123, ___, ___, ___, 456

**23.** Extend the sequence you started in problem 20. Look for patterns.

**FIBONACCI PUZZLE**

**24.** How many Fibonacci-like sequences can you find that involve only positive whole numbers and include your age *in fourth place or later?* How about your teacher's age, or the age of a parent or adult friend?

**DISCOVERY** *PERIMETER ARRANGEMENTS*

**25.** **Exploration** Make sketches of some different ways that you could put together an $x$-block and an $x^2$-block in two dimensions. (They have to touch each other, but they don't have to make a rectangle.) Use your imagination. There are more than two arrangements possible. Is it possible to sketch all the arrangements you think up?

**26.** Find the perimeters of the arrangements you sketched in problem 19. Write each perimeter next to the sketch. Make sure you have found the largest and smallest perimeters possible.

**27.** 💡 Find two arrangements that have the same perimeter, but look as different from each other as possible.

**REVIEW** *MISSING TERMS*

**28.** What terms are missing? More than one term may be missing in each problem.
   a. $3x^2 - 4x + $ ___ $ = -9x^2 + 8x + 7$
   b. $-x^2y + 6xy + $ ___ $ = 9x^2y + 8y$
   c. $3x^2 - 4x - ($ ___ $) = -9x^2 + 8x + 7$
   d. $-x^2y + 6xy - ($ ___ $) = 9x^2y + 8y$

**PUZZLE** *MAGIC TRIANGLE*

**29.** Put an integer from -4 to 4 in each circle to get equal sums along each side of the triangle. Find as many different sums as you can.

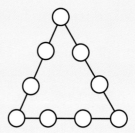

*Chapter 2 Operations and Functions*

# LESSON 2.7

## Functions and Function Diagrams

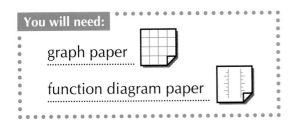

**You will need:**

graph paper

function diagram paper

---

### FUNCTIONS FROM IN-OUT TABLES

**Definition:** The following tables are called input-output tables, or *in-out tables.*

The number that is put in is *x*, and *y* is the number that comes out. Each table has a rule that allows you to get *y* from *x*. For example, the rule for the table in problem 1 is *to get y, add three to x.* We say that *y* can be written *as a function of x:* $y = x + 3$.

**Definition:** A *function* is a rule that assigns a single output to each input.

For each of the following problems:

a. Copy the table.

b. Describe the rule that allows you to get *y* from *x*.

c. Use the rule to find the missing numbers. (In some cases, the missing numbers may be difficult to find; use trial and error and a calculator to make it easier.)

d. Write *y* as a function of *x*.

**1.**

| x | y |
|---|---|
| -5 | -2 |
| 7 | 10 |
| 5 | |
| | -7 |

**2.**

| x | y |
|---|---|
| 7 | 3.8 |
| 10 | 6.8 |
| 0 | |
| | 10 |

**3.**

| x | y |
|---|---|
| 5 | 20 |
| 3 | 12 |
| 1 | |
| | -1 |

**4.**

| x | y |
|---|---|
| 7 | 40 |
| 1 | 16 |
| -2 | 4 |
| -5 | |
| | -12 |

**5.**

| x | y |
|---|---|
| 3 | 8 |
| 4 | 13 |
| 1 | -2 |
| 7 | |
| | 20 |

**6.**

| x | y |
|---|---|
| 5 | 15 |
| 2 | -6 |
| -1 | -9 |
| 6 | |
| | 54 |

**7.** **Exploration** Find as many functions as possible that assign the *y* value 4 to the *x* value 1.

---

### FUNCTION DIAGRAMS

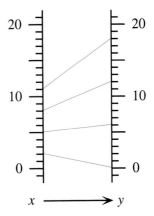

The figure above shows a function diagram for this table.

| x | y |
|---|---|
| 2 | 0 |
| 5 | 6 |
| 8 | 12 |
| 11 | 18 |

**8.** What is the function illustrated in the previous function diagram?

For each function in problems 9-12:
   a. Make a table, using at least five in-out pairs.
   b. Make a function diagram, using the scale shown below.

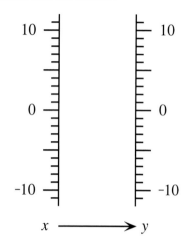

**9.** $y = x + 2$     **10.** $y = x - 2$

**11.** $y = 2x$     **12.** $y = x/2$

**13.** Make a function diagram for each of the tables in problems 1, 2, and 3. You will have to decide what scale to use on the $x$- and $y$-number lines. (For each problem, use the same scale on both number lines.)

Function diagrams are an important way of understanding functions. We will use them throughout this course.

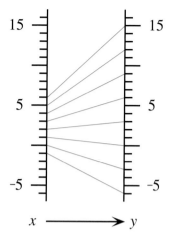

The following problems are about the above function diagram. Assume that more in-out lines could be added, following the same pattern.

**14.** Find the output when the input is:
   a. 0          b. 5          c. –5

**15.** Find the output when the input is:
   a. 99          b. –100          c. 1000

**16.** Find the output when the input is:
   a. 1/2          b. 1/3          c. 1/6

For the following problem, you may need to use trial and error.

**17.** Find the input when the output is:
   a. 0          b. 5          c. –5
   d. 99          e. –100          f. 1000

## UPS AND DOWNS

Each line in a function diagram connects an input point on the *x*-number line to its output point on the *y*-number line. We use the notation (*x*, *y*) to refer to such a line. Notice that in the previous diagram some of the lines go up, and some go down. For example: (5, 12) goes up, and (0, –3) goes down.

**18.** If you were to draw additional lines in the function diagram, could you correctly draw one that goes neither up nor down? Where would it start?

**19.** In describing the diagram, one might say 5 goes to 12, "moving" up 7 units. Which point "moves" down 5 units?

**20.** Find a point that moves
  a. up 3 units;    b. down 3 units;
  c. up 6 units;    d. down 4 units.

**21.** 🔆 Use trial and error to find a point that moves
  a. up 99 units;
  b. down 100 units.

**22.** 🔆 Generalization If you know of a point that moves up *n* units in the previous diagram, how would you find a point that moves down *n* units? Write a full explanation.

### DISCOVERY  SURFACE AREA OF A BOX

The volume of a box is given by the formula
$$volume = length \cdot width \cdot height.$$

**23.** Write the surface area of a box as a function of length, width, and height. Compare your function with the ones found by some of your classmates.

# Time, Distance, Speed

## MOTION PICTURES

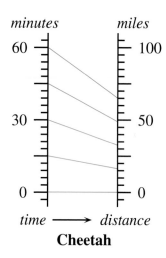

**Roller Skater**

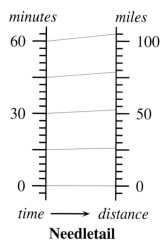

**Cheetah**

minutes          miles

60                    100

30                    50

0                      0

time ⟶ distance
**Needletail**

The above function diagrams represent the motion of three living creatures: a fast roller skater; a cheetah (one of the world's fastest mammals, it's a large, wild cat that lives in Africa); and a white-throated needletail (one of the world's fastest birds, it lives in Australia).

The diagrams assume that the three creatures ran a one-hour race, and were able to maintain their top speed for the full hour. (This is not realistic, but then neither is the idea of a roller skater racing with a cheetah and a bird.)

Each diagram shows minutes on the *x*-number line, and miles on the *y*-number line.

1. Use the diagrams to estimate how far each went in an hour.

2. After thirty minutes, approximately
   a. how far is the needletail ahead of the cheetah?
   b. how far is the cheetah ahead of the skater?

3. Estimate each speed
   a. in miles per hour;
   b. in miles per minute.

4. ⚷ Explain how time-distance function diagrams allow you to compare speeds. Time is on the *x*-number line, distance is on the *y*-number line. Where is speed?

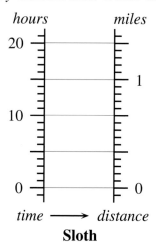

**Sloth**

*Chapter 2  Operations and Functions*

5. The preceding diagram shows the hypothetical progress of a sloth. The *x*-number line represents time in hours, and the *y*-number line represents distance in miles. Compare the sloth's motion to the motion of the skater, cheetah, and needletail. How fast is it going per hour? Per minute?

6. Explain why someone comparing the sloth's speed to the needletail's might make a mistake and take the diagrams to mean the sloth is almost as fast as the needletail.

### THE BALL

In a physics experiment, a ball is launched straight up by some device, and its height above the ground is recorded at one-second intervals. The resulting information is displayed in the function diagram below, where the *x*-number line represents time in seconds, and the *y*-number line represents distance from the ground at that time in meters.

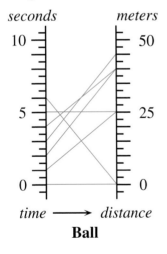

**Ball**

On the function diagram, follow the motion of the ball with your finger on the *y*-number line, second by second.

7. During which one-second interval(s) did the ball move the fastest? The slowest?

8. At what time did the ball change direction?

9. Make a table like this one, showing the height of the ball at one-second intervals. Extend the table until you have included all the information given on the function diagram.

| Time (seconds) | Height (meters) |
|----------------|-----------------|
| 0 | 0 |
| 1 | 25 |
| 2 | ... |

10. Estimate the times when the ball was at the following heights. (Give two times for each part, one on the way up, and one on the way down.)
   a. 40 m       b. 30 m
   c. 20 m       d. 10 m

A family is traveling by car from City A, in Cool County, towards City E. On this diagram, the *x*-number line represents the time of day, with 9 A.M. near the bottom, and 7 P.M. near the top; the *y*-number line represents distance from City A in miles.

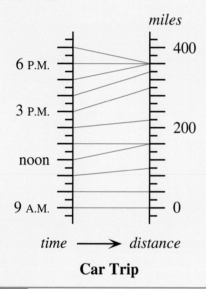

*miles*

**Car Trip**

1. Report Describe the trip as best you can from the information on the function diagram. In your paragraph, make clear what you get from the diagram and where you are making guesses to interpret the information. Your paragraph should include answers to the following questions, but should not be limited to them.

- What time did the trip start?
- What happened from 12 to 1? Where did it happen?
- When did the family drive faster than the speed limit? How fast were they going then?
- How could you explain the changes in speed that are evident from the diagram?
- What time did they arrive at their destination?
- How far is City E from City A?

2. Project

a. Using real towns and distances (perhaps taken from a road map), draw a map and a function diagram for another car trip.

b. Get the map and function diagram that one of your classmates made in part (a). Write a paragraph describing the trip shown. Discuss your description with the person who made the map and diagram. Do you agree on what the figures convey? If you disagree, is one of you misinterpreting the figures? Or are both interpretations correct?

# Operations and Function Diagrams

**You will need:**

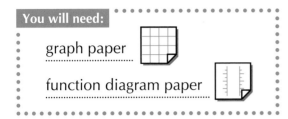

graph paper

function diagram paper

### ADDITION

1. Draw a function diagram to represent each of these functions.
   a. $y = x + 6$  b. $y = x + 3$
   c. Compare the two diagrams. How are they alike? How are they different?

The two function diagrams you just drew both represented functions of the form $y = x + b$, where $b$ is a constant. In the first case, $b$ was 6. In the second case, $b$ was 3.

2. Draw three other function diagrams of the form $y = x + b$. Be sure to try at least one negative value of $b$.

3. a. Draw a function diagram for the function $y = x$.
   b. The function $y = x$ is also of the form $y = x + b$. What is $b$?

4. ◄━ The function diagrams you drew in problems 1-3 represent addition. In each case, to get the value of $y$, you added the number $b$ to $x$. How are all of these diagrams alike? How are they different? How does the value of $b$ affect the diagram?

### MULTIPLICATION

5. Draw a function diagram to represent each of these functions.
   a. $y = 2x$       b. $y = 3x$
   c. Compare the two diagrams. How are they alike? How are they different?

The two function diagrams you just drew both represented functions of the form $y = mx$, where $m$ is a constant. In the first case, $m$ was 2. In the second case, $m$ was 3.

6. Draw three other function diagrams of the form $y = mx$. Be sure to try at least one negative value of $m$ and one value of $m$ between 0 and 1.

7. The function $y = x$, for which you already have a diagram, is also of the form $y = mx$. What is $m$?

8. The function diagrams you just drew represent multiplication. In each case, to get the value of $y$ you multiplied $x$ by a number. How are all of these diagrams the same? How are they different?

9. ◄━ Look at your multiplication diagrams. For each one, as the value of $x$ increases from the bottom of its number line, follow the value of $y$ on its number line with your finger.
   a. For what values of $m$ does the value of $y$ go up? Down?
   b. Is there a value of $m$ for which $y$ goes neither up nor down, but remains unchanged?
   c. For what values of $m$ does the value of $y$ change faster than $x$? More slowly?
   d. Is there a value of $m$ for which $y$ changes at the same rate as $x$?

MIRROR IMAGE DIAGRAMS

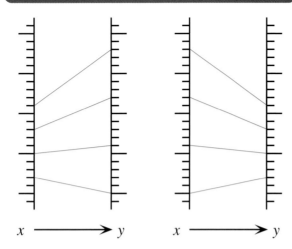

$$x \longrightarrow y \qquad x \longrightarrow y$$

The two function diagrams above are mirror images of each other.

**10.** Explain how to draw the mirror image of a function diagram.

For each of the following functions:

    a. Draw the function diagram, using the same scale on the $x$- and $y$-number lines.

    b. Draw the mirror image diagram.

    c. Find the function corresponding to the mirror image.

**11.** $y = x + 3$     **12.** $y = 4x$

**13.** $y = x - 4$     **14.** $y = x/3$

**15.** ⚷ Explain the relationship between the function corresponding to the mirror image and the original function.

**16.** Report Write a report summarizing what you learned in this lesson. Illustrate your report with examples of function diagrams. Your report should include, but not be limited to, answers to the following questions:

• Addition can be represented by functions of the form $y = x + b$. What do their function diagrams look like if $b = 0$? What if $b$ is greater than 0? Less than 0?

• Subtraction can be represented by functions of the form $y = x - b$. How do their function diagrams compare with those of addition?

• Multiplication can be represented by functions of the form $y = mx$. What do their function diagrams look like if $m$ is negative? If $m$ is positive? What if $m$ is a number between 0 and 1?

• Division can be represented by functions of the form $y = x/m$. How do their function diagrams compare with those of multiplication? What if $m$ is positive? Negative? What if $m$ is a number between 0 and 1?

**17.** 💡 Compare function diagrams of the form $y = b - x$ with those of the form $y = x - b$.

*Chapter 2  Operations and Functions*

# 2.10

# Perimeter and Surface Area Functions

**You will need:**

the Lab Gear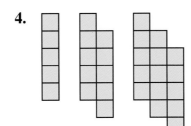

## PERIMETER

1. Look at this sequence of block figures. Think about how it would continue, following the pattern. Then:

   a. Sketch the next figure in the sequence.

   b. Copy and complete the table below.

   c. Describe the pattern in words.

| Figure # | Perimeter |
|:--------:|:---------:|
| 1 | 4 |
| 2 | 6 |
| 3 | 8 |
| 4 | ... |
| 10 | ... |
| 100 | ... |
| $n$ | ... |

Repeat problem 1 for each of these sequences.

2.
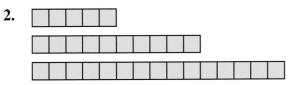

3.
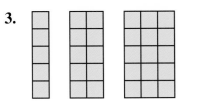

4.
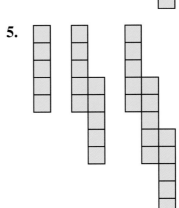

5.
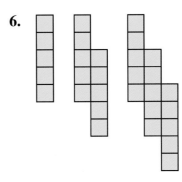

6.

If you have trouble answering questions 7-8 by trial and error, try making graphs from the data in your tables, with the figure number ($n$) on the horizontal axis and the perimeter on the vertical axis.

7. In problem 1, which figure would have perimeter 50?

8. Is it possible to have perimeter 50 for any of the patterns in problems 2-6?

9.  Look at the *x*-block.
    a.  What is the perimeter of its top face?
    b.  What is its perimeter if $x = 1, 2, 3, 4, 10$? Make a table like the ones above.
    c.  Compare your table with those in problems 1-6. It should be the same as one of them. Which one? Explain why you think this works.

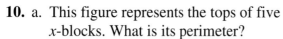

10. a.  This figure represents the tops of five *x*-blocks. What is its perimeter?
    b.  What is its perimeter if $x = 1, 2, 3, 4, 10$? Make a table like the ones above.
    c.  This figure is related to one of problems 2-6. Which one? Explain.

Note that in problems 9 and 10, just one figure represents a whole infinite sequence of figures, because of the use of variables.

11. Find the blue block that is related to problem 3. Explain.

12. 💡 For each of problems 4-6, build a related figure made of blue blocks. Check your answer by making a table.

### SURFACE AREA

13. Look at the sequence of cube figures. Think about how it would continue, following the pattern. Then:
    a.  Sketch the next figure in the sequence.
    b.  Copy and complete the following table.
    c.  Describe the pattern in words.

| Figure # | Surface Area |
|----------|--------------|
| 1 | 6 |
| 2 | 10 |
| 3 | 14 |
| 4 | ... |
| 10 | ... |
| 100 | ... |
| $n$ | ... |

Repeat problem 13 for each of these sequences.

14.

15. 💡 

16. 💡

17. 💡 For each of problems 13-16, build a related figure made of blue blocks. Check your answers by making a table.

### MORE SURFACE AREA

18. Look at the sequence. Think about how it continues, following the pattern. Then:
    a.  Sketch the next figure.
    b.  Make a table like the following one.

*Chapter 2 Operations and Functions*

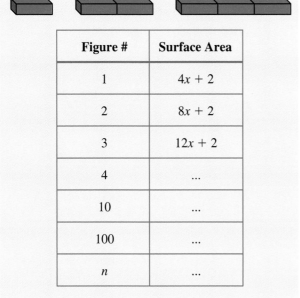

| Figure # | Surface Area |
|----------|--------------|
| 1 | $4x + 2$ |
| 2 | $8x + 2$ |
| 3 | $12x + 2$ |
| 4 | ... |
| 10 | ... |
| 100 | ... |
| $n$ | ... |

c. Describe the pattern in words.

Repeat problem 18 for each of these sequences.

**19.**

**20.**

**21.**

**22.** Make a figure out of blue blocks such that by substituting 1, 2, 3, ... for $y$ in its surface area you get the same sequence as you did in problem 19. Check your work by making a table.

**GAME** *SPROUTS*

This is a game for two players. Start with three dots on a piece of paper. These represent towns. Players take turns. To make a move:

- Join a town to itself or to another town with a *road* (a line).
- Place another town somewhere on the road you just created.

**Rules:**

- A road cannot cross itself, another road, or an existing town.
- No town can have more than three roads coming out of it.

The winner is the last person able to make a legal move.

**23.** Play the game with a classmate.

**24.** What is the maximum number of moves possible in a game?

# Polyomino Functions

**You will need:**

graph paper

## POLYOMINO EYES

**Definition:** The points of intersection of the grid lines inside a polyomino are called *eyes*.

1. **Exploration** Any polyomino has an area, a perimeter, and a number of eyes. Is there a relationship between the three numbers? Can you express the perimeter as a function of the area and the number of eyes? (Hint: To find out, draw several polyominoes *that have the same area,* but different perimeters. For each one, write the number of eyes and the perimeter. As the number of eyes increases, does the perimeter get longer or shorter? Repeat the process for a different area.) Write a paragraph telling what you discover.

2. Complete the table shown at the top of the next column. Use data from these figures.

3. Write a formula for the perimeter of a polyomino having area 12 and *e* eyes.

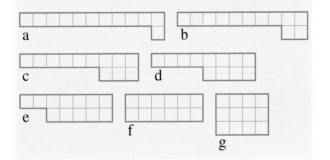

| Figure | Eyes | Area | Perimeter |
|--------|------|------|-----------|
| a | 0 | 12 | ... |
| b | ... | ... | ... |

4. Fill out a similar table for another area. Write a formula for the perimeter as a function of the number of eyes for your area.

5. If you know that a polyomino has 0 eyes, and area 100, how could you get its perimeter?

6. Answer question 5 using area 100 and 10 eyes.

7. **Generalization** Write a formula for the perimeter *p* of a polyomino having area *a* and *e* eyes. (This formula is a function of two variables, *a* and *e*.)

8. 💡 For a given area, what is the maximum number of eyes? Find a pattern by experimenting with areas 4 and greater.

## A GRAPH PAPER SPIRAL

9. Make a polyomino spiral on your graph paper by shading in one square at a time. See the figure below.

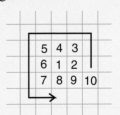

Every time you shade a square, write the perimeter of the figure in a table like the following. Continue until you see a pattern.

| Area | Perimeter |
|------|-----------|
| 1 | 4 |
| 2 | 6 |
| 3 | 8 |
| ... | ... |

10. Describe the pattern you see.

11. Now make a new spiral the same way. This time record *only* the areas of squares and rectangles that you get along the way, in two tables like those below, continuing until you see a pattern in all the columns.

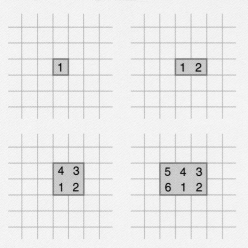

| Square # | Area | Perimeter |
|----------|------|-----------|
| 1 | 1 | 4 |
| 2 | 4 | 8 |
| 3 | ... | ... |

| Rectangle # | Area | Perimeter |
|-------------|------|-----------|
| 1 | 2 | 6 |
| 2 | 6 | 10 |
| 3 | ... | ... |

12. Describe the patterns you see in each column.

13. What will the area and perimeter be for square #100?

14. Write a function for:
    a. the area of square #x;
    b. the perimeter of square #x.

15. What will the area and perimeter be for rectangle #100?

16. Write a function for:
    a. the area of rectangle #x;
    b. the perimeter of rectangle #x.

17. **Report**  What do you know about the relationship between area and perimeter of polyominoes? You may draw information from this lesson, as well as from Chapter 1, Lessons 1 and 2. Use graphs and illustrations.

# Geoboard Triangles

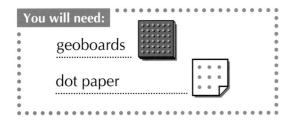
1. **Exploration** If many triangles have one vertical side in common, how is their area related to the position of the third vertex? To find out, make many triangles having vertices at (0, 0) and (0, 8). For each one, keep a record of the coordinates of the third vertex and the area. Look for patterns. Write a paragraph explaining what you found out. Use sketches.

## HORIZONTAL *AND* VERTICAL SIDES

2. Make a triangle having a horizontal side of length 6 and a vertical side of length 4. What is its area?

3. In this problem, use triangles having a horizontal side of 6.

   a. Make a table like the following. All triangles should have a horizontal side of length 6, but the length of the vertical side will vary. Extend the table all the way to vertical side of length 10.

| Vertical Side | Area |
|:---:|:---:|
| 0 | ... |
| 1 | ... |
| 2 | 6 |
| ... | ... |

   b. Explain how you could find the area of a triangle having horizontal side 6 and vertical side 100.

   c. Express the area as a function of the vertical side.

4. Repeat problem 3 for a horizontal side of length 9.

## ONE HORIZONTAL *OR* VERTICAL SIDE

5. Make a triangle having vertices at (0, 0) and (0, 7) and the third vertex at (1, 4). What is its area?

6. Make a table like the following for triangles having vertices at (0, 0) and (0, 7) and the third vertex as indicated. Extend the table all the way to vertex (7, 4).

| 3ʳᵈ Vertex | Area |
|:---:|:---:|
| (0, 4) | ... |
| (1, 4) | ... |
| (2, 4) | ... |
| ... | ... |

7. Write the area as a function of the $x$-coordinate of the third vertex.

8. a. Make the triangle having vertices (0, 0), (0, 7), and (9, 4). Guess its area.

   b. With another rubber band, make the smallest rectangle that covers the triangle. If you did it correctly, you should now see two new triangles. Find the area of the rectangle and the area of the two new triangles.

   c. Find the area of the original triangle. This should match your guess from part (a).

9. ◆━━ How would you find the area of the triangle having vertices at (1, 0), (6, 0), and (9, 9)? Find it and explain what you did, using a sketch and a paragraph.

### Generalizations

10. a. Make triangles having vertices at (0, 0) and (0, 6) and the third vertex at $(x, 9)$, where $x$ takes each of the whole number values from 0 to 10. Make a table of values to show the area as a function of $x$.

b. Make triangles having vertices at (0, 0) and (0, 6) and the third vertex at $(9, y)$, where $y$ takes each of the whole number values from 0 to 10. Make a table of values to show the area as a function of $y$.

c. How do the answers to (a) and (b) differ?

11. a. Make at least three triangles having vertices at (0, 1) and (0, 6) and the third vertex at $(x, y)$, where $x$ and $y$ take whole number values from 1 to 8. Sketch each one and find its area.

b. Explain how you would find the area of a triangle having vertices at (0, 1), (0, 6), and (99, 99) without drawing a picture.

12. 💡 Explain how you would find the area of a triangle having vertices at (0, 0), $(b, 0)$, and $(x, h)$, where $b$ and $h$ are nonnegative.

### NO HORIZONTAL OR VERTICAL SIDES

13. Exploration What is the area of the triangle having vertices (0, 6), (7, 8), and (6, 1)? Explain how you arrive at the answer. Use sketches on dot paper.

14. What is the area of the four-sided shape having vertices at (0, 7), (2, 10), (10, 5), (5, 0)? Hint: First find the area of the whole geoboard, then use subtraction.

15. Make a triangle having no horizontal or vertical sides and having vertices on the outside edges of the geoboard. Use subtraction to find its area.

16. Repeat problem 15 on another triangle.

17. What is the area of the triangle having vertices at (1, 8), (2, 4), and (9, 3)? Hint: You may use the triangles having these vertices.

$$(1, 8), (1, 3), (9, 3)$$
$$(2, 4), (1, 3), (9, 3)$$
$$(1, 8), (2, 4), (1, 3)$$

18. Report Write an illustrated report on how to find the area of any geoboard triangle. Give examples of the different techniques. Make sure you include examples of using division by two, addition, and subtraction.

# 2.C Towns, Roads, and Zones

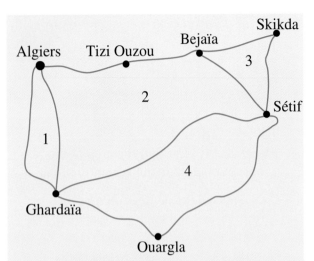

This is a simplified road map of part of Algeria. It shows 7 towns and 10 roads. For the purposes of this lesson we will call any area completely surrounded by roads, (and not crossed by any road,) a *zone*. As you can see, there are 4 zones on this map.

**Rules:** Each town is connected to all the others by roads (not necessarily a direct connection); all roads begin and end at a town. It is possible for a road to connect a town to itself. It is possible for more than one road to connect two towns.

In maps like this one there is a relationship between the number of towns, roads, and zones. Your goal in this lesson is to find it. The relationship was discovered by the Swiss mathematician and astronomer Leonhard Euler. It is part of a branch of geometry called *topology*, which he created.

1. **Exploration** Make many different "maps" like the ones above. Keep track of the number of roads, towns, and zones in a table. Try to find a pattern in the relationship of the three numbers. (If you cannot find a relationship between all three numbers, keep one of the numbers constant and look for a relationship between the other two.)

2. Make at least six different three-town maps. What is the relationship between the number of roads and the number of zones? Express it in words, and write $r$ (the number of roads) as a function of $z$ (the number of zones).

3. Make at least six different four-town maps. What is the relationship between the number of roads and the number of zones? Express it in words and write a function.

4. Make at least six different five-road maps. What is the relationship between the number of towns and the number of zones? Express it in words and write a function.

5. Make at least six different six-road maps. What is the relationship between the number of towns and the number of zones? Express it in words and write a function.

6. Make at least six different four-zone maps. What is the relationship between the number of roads and the number of towns? Express it in words and write a function.

7. **Report** Write an illustrated report describing what you have learned about towns, roads, and zones. Give examples. Your report should answer the following questions, but not be limited to them:

- If there are $t$ towns and $r$ roads, how many zones are there?
- If there are $t$ towns and $z$ zones, how many roads are there?
- If there are $r$ roads and $z$ zones, how many towns are there?

8. **Project** **Euler**

Find out about Leonhard Euler and/or the Koenigsberg Bridge Problem. Prepare an oral presentation or a bulletin board display.

# Essential Ideas

### THREE MEANINGS OF MINUS

**1.** For each of the following, write an explanation of what the minus sign means.

a. $-2$    b. $-(2 + 2x)$

c. $x - 2$    d. $-y$

### OPPOSITES

**2.** Find the opposite of each quantity. Remember: A quantity and its opposite add up to zero.

a. $x$    b. $2$

c. $-2$    d. $-x$

e. $x + 2$    f. $x - 2$

### ADDING AND SUBTRACTING

In problems 3-4 you may want to make sketches or use the Lab Gear.

**3.** Simplify. (Add and combine like terms.)

a. $(y^2 + x^2 - 3y) + (y + 3x^2 - x^2)$

b. $x + (25 - yx - y^2) + (xy - y - x)$

**4.** Simplify. (Subtract; combine like terms.)

a. $(4 - x^2 - 5x) - 3x - 2$

b. $(4 - x^2 + 5x) - (3x - 2)$

c. $(4 + x^2 - 5x) - (3x + 2)$

d. $(-4 - x^2 - 5x) - (-3x + 2)$

### MULTIPLYING

In problems 5-8 you may want to make sketches or use the Lab Gear.

**5.** Multiply.

a. $2x \cdot 4x$    b. $5x \cdot 6y$

c. $3xy \cdot 10$

**6.** The quantity $36xy$ can be written as the product $9x \cdot 4y$. Write $36xy$ as a product in at least four other ways.

**7.** Multiply.

a. $2(x + y - 5)$    b. $x(x + y + 5)$

c. $x(-x + y + 5)$

**8.** Choose two of the three multiplications in problem 7. Make a sketch of what they look like when modeled with the Lab Gear.

### EXPONENTIAL NOTATION

**9.** Write each of these numbers in exponential notation. If possible, find more than one way. It may help to use your calculator.

a. 32    b. 64    c. 256

d. 4096    e. 1    f. 6561

### FUNCTIONS AND FUNCTION DIAGRAMS

For each of the following problems:

a. Copy the table.

b. Describe the rule that allows you to get $y$ from $x$.

c. Use the rule to find the missing numbers. (In some cases, the missing numbers may be difficult to find; use trial and error and a calculator to make it easier.)

d. Write $y$ as a function of $x$.

**10.**　　　　**11.**　　　　**12.**

| $x$ | $y$ |
|---|---|
| -1 | -7 |
| 4 | 28 |
| 0 |  |
|  | 7 |

| $x$ | $y$ |
|---|---|
| 3 | 4 |
| 12 | 1 |
| 6 | 2 |
|  | 5 |

| $x$ | $y$ |
|---|---|
| 5 | 2 |
|  | 4 |
| 1 |  |
|  | -1 |

**13.** a. Make a function diagram in which the output ($y$) is always 4 more than the input ($x$).

b. Write a rule (function) for your function diagram.

*Chapter 2 Operations and Functions*

**14. a.** Make a function diagram in which the output ($y$) is always 4 times the input ($x$).

  **b.** Write a rule (function) for your function diagram.

**15.** Make a function diagram with *time* on the $x$-number line (show one hour from the bottom to the top), and *distance* on the $y$-number line, to represent the motion of a cyclist riding at a constant speed of 15 miles per hour. Your diagram should have five in-out lines.

PATTERNS AND FUNCTIONS

**16.** Look at the sequence of figures. Think about how it would continue, following the pattern. Then:

  **a.** Sketch the next figure in the sequence.

  **b.** Copy and complete a table like the one below.

  **c.** Describe the pattern in words.

| Figure # | Perimeter |
|----------|-----------|
| 1 | ... |
| 2 | ... |
| 3 | ... |
| 4 | ... |
| 10 | ... |
| 100 | ... |
| $n$ | ... |

Repeat problem 16 for these sequences.

**17.**

**18.**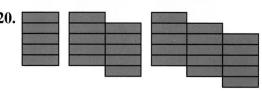

**19.**

**20.**

**21.** In problem 16, what figure would have a perimeter of $88x + 2$? Use trial and error if necessary.

**22.** Which sequence in problems 17-20, if any, contains a perimeter of

  **a.** $2x + 100$?

  **b.** $100x + 2$?

  **c.** $100x + 100$?

**23.** 💡 Look at the $xy$-block.

  **a.** What is the perimeter of its top face?

  **b.** What is its perimeter if $y = 1, 2, 3, 4, 10$? (Do not substitute a number for $x$.) Arrange your answers in a table.

  **c.** Compare your table with those in problems 16-20. It should be the same as one of them. Which one? Explain.

**24.** 💡 Use blue blocks to make a figure. Substitute $1, 2, 3, \ldots$ for $y$ in its perimeter to get the same sequence as problem 18. Check your work; make a table.

GEOBOARD TRIANGLES

**25.** On dot paper, sketch triangles having area 18, and having

  **a.** one horizontal and one vertical side;

  **b.** one horizontal side, no vertical side;

  **c.** no horizontal or vertical side.

# CHAPTER 3

The double helix of a DNA molecule

## *Coming in this chapter:*

**Exploration** Algebank offers to double your money every month, in exchange for a monthly fee. Is this a good deal? Does the answer depend on the fee, on the amount of money you have to invest, or on both?

# WORKING BACKWARDS

# Instant Riches

The following ad appeared in the school paper.

> Amazing investment opportunity at Algebank! Double your money instantly! Invest any amount! No amount is too small. Our bank will *double* the amount of money in your account every month. Watch your money grow!
>
> A service charge of $100 will be deducted from your account at the end of every month.

1. **Exploration** Do you think this is a good deal? Why or why not? Use some calculations to back up your opinion.

2. Reg was interested in this investment. After calling to make sure that the $100 fee would be deducted *after* his money was doubled, he decided to join. However, after his service charge was deducted at the end of the fourth month, he discovered that his bank balance was exactly $0! How much money did he start out with? Explain your answer.

Three other students invested their money. Gabe started with $45, Earl with $60, and Lara with $200. The figure shows a way to keep track of what happened to Lara's investment.

Month:

$$\underset{0}{\textcircled{200}} \xrightarrow{\cdot 2} 400 \xrightarrow{-100} \underset{1}{\textcircled{300}} \xrightarrow{\cdot 2} 600\ldots$$

3. a. Use arrows in this way to show what happened to Lara's, Gabe's, and Earl's investments for the first five months.
   b. Give advice to each of these students.

RUNNING OUT OF MONEY

4. Bea joined the plan, but discovered after one month that she had an account balance of exactly $0. How much money had she invested?

5. Lea discovered that she had an account balance of exactly $0 after two months. What was her initial investment?

6. Rea had an account balance of exactly $0 after three months. How much money did she start out with?

7. Summarize your answers to problems 4-6 by making a table like the one below. Then extend the table to show up to at least ten months.

**Months to Reach a Zero-Dollar Balance**

| Months | Amount Invested |
|--------|-----------------|
| 1      |                 |
| 2      |                 |
| ...    |                 |

8. Describe the pattern in your table.

GAINING AND LOSING

9. Mr. Lear joined the plan, but discovered that at the end of every month he had exactly the same amount of money as when he started. How much money is it? Explain how that happened.

**10.** Algebank sends its customers statements quarterly (every three months). Several students were comparing their statements at the end of the first quarter. One had $50, another had $100, and a third had $150 in the account.

    **a.** What will happen to each student? Will all of them eventually gain money? What will their next quarterly statements look like? Explain.

    **b.** Explain how you can figure out how much money each of them started with.

**11.** ◯ Find two initial investment amounts that differ by $1, such that one of them will make money in this plan, and the other will lose money. How far apart will the amounts be in six months? Explain.

**12.** `Report` You have been asked to write an article on Algebank's investment plan for the Consumers' Guide column in the school paper. Write an article giving general advice to people wanting to join this plan. Describe the plan clearly and explain the pros and cons of joining it. Who will benefit from the plan? Who will lose in the long run? Explain, giving some examples. Make your article interesting, eye-catching, and readable.

**13.** `Generalization` Use what you have learned in this lesson to answer the following questions about plans with similar policies, but different numbers.

    **a.** Give advice to people wanting to join a plan, if their money is *tripled* every month and the service charge is $100.

    **b.** Give advice to people wanting to join a plan if their money is doubled every month but the service charge is $200.

**14.** ◯ Suppose Algebank were to deduct the service charge *before* doubling the money. How would this change your answers to problems 12 and 13b?

**15.** Describe another possible investment scheme and give advice to people about who should join and who should not.

# Two Negatives

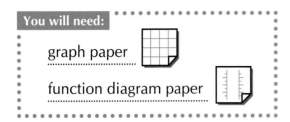

graph paper

function diagram paper

1. **Exploration** Many people have heard the rule that *two negatives make a positive.* Investigate to decide whether this rule is always, sometimes, or never true when you *add* two negative numbers. Explain, giving examples. Then repeat your investigation for *subtracting, multiplying,* and *dividing* two negative numbers. Write a brief summary explaining your conclusions.

2. What does *not unilliterate* mean? What about *not uninteresting*? Look up *irregardless* in a dictionary.

## SUBTRACTION

3. This function diagram represents a function of the type $y = b - x$. What is the value of $b$?

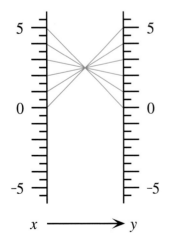

4. Make an in-out table for the in-out lines shown on the function diagram.

5. Copy the function diagram. Extend the table and the function diagram for negative values of $x$.

6. 🔑 If you know the values of $b$ and $x$, how can you calculate $b - x$ *by using addition?* Explain, using examples.

## THE CARTESIAN COORDINATE SYSTEM

When you draw horizontal and vertical axes and plot points you are using a *Cartesian coordinate system*. It is named after the French mathematician and philosopher René Descartes. He is credited with bringing together algebra and geometry by using graphs to make geometric representations of algebraic equations.

An important skill in algebra is predicting what the graph will look like from the equation, or what the equation will be from the graph.

You should know the vocabulary of the Cartesian coordinate system.

- The horizontal number line is the *x-axis*.
- The vertical number line is the *y-axis*.
- The numbers $(x, y)$ associated with a point are the *coordinates* of the point.
- The axes divide the coordinate system into four parts, called *quadrants*.
- The quadrants are numbered counterclockwise, as shown. In the first quadrant, the coordinates of every point are both positive.
- The point where the axes cross is called the *origin*. The coordinates of the origin are (0, 0).

*Chapter 3 Working Backwards*

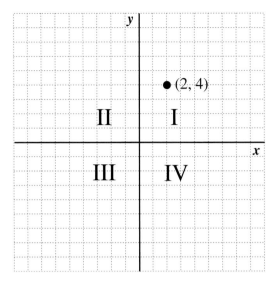

**7.** In which two quadrants does a graph lie if
  a. the second coordinate is always positive?
  b. the first coordinate is always positive?
  c. the two coordinates always have the same sign (both positive or both negative)?

**8.** What can you say about the signs of $x$ and/or $y$ if you know that $(x, y)$ is in either
  a. the third or the fourth quadrant?
  b. the second or the fourth quadrant?
  c. the second or the third quadrant?

**9.** If a point is on the $x$-axis, what is its $y$-coordinate? If a point is on the $y$-axis, what is its $x$-coordinate?

**Important:** Zero, 0, is neither positive nor negative.

**10.** Make a Cartesian graph for the function from problem 3, using the in-out table you made in problems 4 and 5.

**11.** ⚷ Look at the part of the graph where the $y$-values are greater than 5. What are the $x$-values there? Explain what this says about *two negatives*.

The graph below shows the function $y = 3x$. The $y$-coordinate is always three times the $x$-coordinate. Three points are labeled.

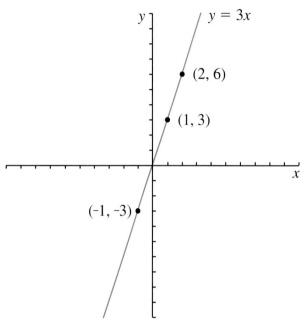

**12.** a. List three more $(x, y)$ pairs that would be on the graph above, including at least one negative and one fractional value for $x$.
  b. In which two quadrants does the graph lie?
  c. In each $(x, y)$ pair, how are the signs of the $x$-coordinate and the $y$-coordinate related?

**13.** This problem is about the function $y = -3x$.
  a. Make a table of at least six $(x, y)$ values for this function. Use negative numbers and fractions as well as positive whole numbers.
  b. Write the multiplication fact that is represented by each $(x, y)$ pair in your table.
  c. Use your table to make a graph of the function $y = -3x$.

d. In which two quadrants does the graph lie?

e. In each (x, y) pair in your table, how are the signs of the x-coordinate and the y-coordinate related?

**14.** a. Make a function diagram for the function $y = -3x$.

b. On the diagram, see how the signs of $x$ and $-3x$ are related. When $x$ is negative, what can you say about $-3x$?

**15.** ⚷— What is the sign of the answer (positive or negative) when you

a. multiply a negative number and a positive number?

b. multiply two negative numbers?

c. multiply three negative numbers?

**16.** What is the sign of the answer? (You do not need to find the answer.)

a. $(-5)(-4)(-3)(-2)(-1)(0)(1)(2)(3)(4)(5)$

b. $(-9)(-87)(-7.65)(-43210)$

c. $(-9)^9$      d. $(-99)^{99}$

---

### MULTIPLYING BY -1

Match each function diagram 17-19 with one or more functions from this list.

a. $y = 0$          b. $y = x$

c. $y = x + 0$      d. $y = 1 \cdot x$

e. $y = -x$         f. $y = -1 \cdot x$

g. $y = 0 \cdot x$  h. $y = 0 \cdot x^2$

**17.**

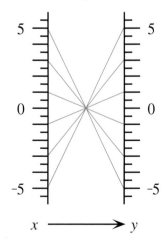

**18.**

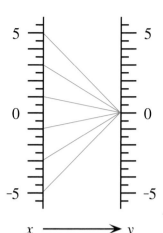

**19.**

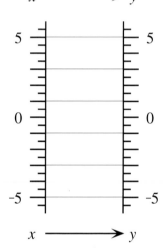

**20.** *Multiplying x by -1 is the same as taking the opposite of x. Explain.*

**21.** Generalization Explain each step of this calculation.

a. $(-x)(-y) = (-1)(x)(-1)(y)$

b. $\qquad\quad = (-1)(-1)(x)(y)$

c. $\qquad\quad = (1)(x)(y) = xy$

**22.** ⚷— Simplify $(-a)(b)(-c)(-d)$ by the same method.

**23.** Find each product.

a. $-3 \cdot 5y(-x)$

b. $(-2y)(-3x)(-4)(12xy)$

c. $(-1.3x)(-7x^2)$

d. $(-3x)^2$

e. $(-3x)^3$

*Chapter 3  Working Backwards*

# More on Minus

**You will need:**

the Lab Gear

1. **Exploration** Choose several numbers and investigate the following questions. Write an explanation, using variables, of what you discover. What is the result when you

   a. add a number to its opposite?

   b. subtract a number from its opposite?

   c. multiply a number by its opposite?

   d. divide a number by its opposite?

## MINUS AND THE DISTRIBUTIVE LAW

For each problem below:

- Use the Lab Gear to model the first expression on the left side of the workmat.
- If possible, simplify the expression by adding zero and removing matching blocks. Get all blocks downstairs.
- Then decide which of the expressions a, b, c, or d is equal to the given expression. Setting up each one in turn on the right side of the workmat may help. Explain your answers.

2. $x - (5 + 2x)$

   a. $x - 5 + 2x$  b. $x - 5 - 2x$

   c. $x + 5 + 2x$  d. $x + 5 - 2x$

3. $2x - (-4 + 3x)$

   a. $2x - 4 + 3x$  b. $2x - 4 - 3x$

   c. $2x + 4 + 3x$  d. $2x + 4 - 3x$

4. $3y + (5 - 2y)$

   a. $3y - 5 + 2y$  b. $3y - 5 - 2y$

   c. $3y + 5 + 2y$  d. $3y + 5 - 2y$

5. $x - (7 - 2y)$

   a. $x - 7 + 2y$  b. $x - 7 - 2y$

   c. $x + 7 + 2y$  d. $x + 7 - 2y$

6. $6x - (-3 - x)$

   a. $6x - 3 + x$  b. $6x + 3 + x$

   c. $6x - 3 - x$  d. $6x + 3 - x$

7. Write an equivalent expression without parentheses.

   a. $2x^2 - (4 - x - x^2)$

   b. $(2x^2 - 4) - (x - x^2)$

   c. $(y - 5) - 3x - 2$

   d. $y - 5 - (3x - 2)$

8. Write an expression containing at least one pair of parentheses that is equivalent to the given expression. (Do not put parentheses around the whole expression, or around a single term.)

   $$3x^3 - 6x + 2 - 5y$$

9. Compare your answers to problem 8 with your classmates. Try to find several different correct answers.

A minus sign preceding parentheses tells you to subtract or take the opposite of everything in the parentheses. Writing an equivalent expression without parentheses is called *distributing the minus sign.*

10. **Summary** Explain how to distribute a minus sign. Use examples.

11. Write an equivalent expression without parentheses.

    a. $-(r + s)$      b. $-(-r + s)$

    c. $-(r - s)$      d. $-(-r - s)$

12. Write an equivalent expression without parentheses.

    a. $-1(r + s)$      b. $-1(-r + s)$

    c. $-1(r - s)$      d. $-1(-r - s)$

You can see from these problems that distributing a minus sign is really just distributing $-1$.

### ADDING THE OPPOSITE

Find the expression that must be added or subtracted. It may help to use the Lab Gear.

**13.** a. $3x^2 + (-5x) + \underline{\quad} = -(5x + x^2)$
b. $3x^2 + (-5x) - (\underline{\quad}) = -(5x + x^2)$

**14.** a. $-2xy + x + \underline{\quad} = 6xy - 2x$
b. $-2xy + x - (\underline{\quad}) = 6xy - 2x$

**15.** a. $-12 + 4yx + \underline{\quad} = 7xy - 15$
b. $-12 + 4yx - (\underline{\quad}) = 7xy - 15$

**16.** 🔑 Compare your answers to parts (a) and (b) in problems 13-15. How are they related? Explain.

**17.** Generalization Problems 13-15 illustrated the following fact: *Subtracting is the same as adding the opposite.* For each subtraction, write an equivalent addition.
a. $y - (-x)$
b. $y - x$
c. $-y - x$

**18.** Find the sign of the answer. (You do not need to find the answer.)
a. $1646 - (-2459)$
b. $-2459 - 1646$
c. $-1646 - (-2459)$
d. $2459 - (-1646)$
e. $-1646 - (2459)$

**19.** Simplify each expression.
a. $6 - (-5)$
b. $-5 - (-7)$
c. $-21 - (-3x) + 15$
d. $-2x - (-12x) - 5xy$

**20.** Find each difference.
a. $2y - 7y$    b. $3xy - (-2xy)$
c. $-x^2 - 4x^2$    d. $2xy - 2x$

### REVIEW AREA AND MULTIPLICATION

**21.** What is the other side of a rectangle, if one side is $x$ and the area is
a. $5x$?
b. $x^2$?
c. $x^2 + 2xy$?
d. $x^2 + 2xy + 5x$?

The following equations are of the form *length times width = area of the rectangle*. Fill in the blanks. You may use the Lab Gear to help you. If you do, remember to use *upstairs* for minus and to build a figure with an *uncovered rectangle* of the required dimensions in the corner piece.

**22.** $x \cdot \underline{\quad} = xy - x^2$
**23.** $(y - 2) \cdot \underline{\quad} = 5y - 10$
**24.** $(\underline{\quad} - 3) \cdot x = 2xy - 3x$
**25.** $2x \cdot \underline{\quad} = 2xy + 4x^2 - 10x$

Use the Lab Gear for these.

**26.** $(x + \underline{\quad})(y - 5) = xy + 5y - 5x - 25$
**27.** $(y - 1) \cdot \underline{\quad} = xy + 5y - x - 5$
**28.** $(y + 2)(y - 1) = \underline{\quad}$ (Simplify.)
**29.** 💡 $(y - 1) \cdot \underline{\quad} = y^2 + 4y - 5$ (Hint: Study problem 28.)

*A SUBSTITUTION CODE*

This message has been coded by a *simple substitution code*.

**Rules:**
- Each letter is always replaced by the same letter throughout the message.
- No letter is ever replaced by itself.

QEB NRIB CLN QEFP GFKA LC TLAB FP
QEHQ BHTE IBQQBN FP HISHUP NBMI-
HTBA OU QEB PHJB IBQQBN
QENLRDELRQ QEB JBPPHDB.

30. Try to break the code. (Copy the message carefully, leaving blank space between the lines. If you have a guess for a letter, enter it every place that letter appears. For clarity, use lower-case letters for your solution, and capitals for the coded message. Use a pencil and an eraser. Hint: The first word is a very common three-letter word.)

**PREVIEW** *MAKE A RECTANGLE*

31. For each problem make a Lab Gear rectangle having the given area. Write a multiplication equation.
   a. $x^2 + 9x + 8$
   b. $x^2 + 6x + 8$

# Algebra Magic

**You will need:**

the Lab Gear

## MAGIC TRICKS

1. **Exploration** A magician asked everyone in the audience to think of a number. "Don't tell your number to anyone," she said. "Now do the following things to your number.

   Step 1: Add the number to one more than the number.
   Step 2: Add 7 to the result.
   Step 3: Divide by 2.
   Step 4: Subtract the original number.
   Step 5: Divide by 4.

   When you are finished, you should all have the same number"

   What was the number, and how did the magician know it would be the same for everyone?

2. Try the following algebra magic problem. Record your result and compare it with others in your group. Do you all get the same answer, or does your answer depend on the number you started with?

   1) Think of a number.
   2) Multiply the number by 3.
   3) Add 8 more than the original number.
   4) Divide by 4.
   5) Subtract the original number.

3. Do the same trick, but change the final step to *subtract* 2. Compare answers with your group members again. Are they the same or different? Explain.

## LAB GEAR MAGIC

The following trick has been modeled with the Lab Gear.

1) Think of a number.

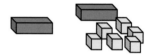

2) Add 6 more than the original number to the number.

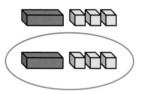

3) Divide by 2.
4) Subtract 2.

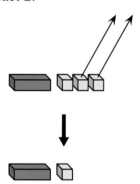

4. a. In this magic trick, do you think everyone should end up with the same or different answers? Explain.

   b. How will a person's answer be related to his or her original number? Explain.

*Chapter 3 Working Backwards*

5. Do the following magic trick with the Lab Gear. Start with an *x*-block, which represents the number a person chose. Sketch each step and write it algebraically.

1) Start with any number.
2) Multiply the number by 4.
3) Add 5.
4) Subtract 1.
5) Divide by 4.
6) Subtract one more than the original number.

Should everyone have the same result? If yes, what is it?

## REVISING MAGIC TRICKS

6. Change the magic trick in problem 5 by reversing the order of Steps (3) and (4). Do you get the same answer as you did before? Explain.

7. Change the magic trick in problem 5 by reversing the order of Steps (2) and (3). Was this harder or easier than reversing Steps (3) and (4)? Explain.

8. Change the last step in problem 5 so that everyone ends up with the number they started out with.

9. Do the following algebraic magic trick. Which steps can you reverse without changing the result? Why?

1) Think of a number.
2) Subtract 7.
3) Add 3 more than the number.
4) Add 4.
5) Multiply by 3.
6) Divide by 6.

You should end up with the original number.

## INVENTING MAGIC TRICKS

The following trick has one step missing.

1) Think of a number.
2) Take its opposite.
3) Multiply by 2.
4) Subtract 2.
5) Divide by 2.
6) ?????

10. Use the Lab Gear to model the first five steps of this trick. Use *y* to represent the original number. Then translate each step into an algebraic expression. Compare your result after step (5) with your classmates' answers.

11. Decide what step (6) should be, so that the given condition is satisfied.
a. The final result is one more than the original number.
b. The final result is the opposite of the original number.
c. The final result is always zero.
d. The final result is always -1.

12. For each of these conditions, (a-d), make up an algebra magic trick with at least five steps.
a. The final result is the original number.
b. The final result is 2, regardless of what the original number was.
c. The final result is the same, whether you do the steps backward or forward.
d. The trick uses all four operations (multiplication, division, addition, subtraction).

13. **Summary** Choose one of the tricks you wrote in problem 12. Test your trick with three numbers, including a negative number and a fraction. Show your work. Use algebra to explain the trick.

First we will use functions to create codes. Later we will use functions to break codes. Assign a number to each letter of the alphabet. A is 1, B is 2, and so on.

| A | 1 | H | 8 | O | 15 | V | 22 |
|---|---|---|---|---|----|---|----|
| B | 2 | I | 9 | P | 16 | W | 23 |
| C | 3 | J | 10 | Q | 17 | X | 24 |
| D | 4 | K | 11 | R | 18 | Y | 25 |
| E | 5 | L | 12 | S | 19 | Z | 26 |
| F | 6 | M | 13 | T | 20 | | |
| G | 7 | N | 14 | U | 21 | | |

**Definition:** The text of a message, before it is encoded, is called the *plaintext*.

The easiest code works by replacing each letter by one that follows it at a certain distance in the alphabet. For example, A (letter 1) is replaced with H (letter 8), B (2) is replaced with I (9), and so on. The function used in this example is $y = 7 + x$, where $x$ is the number of the plaintext letter, and $y$ is the number of the coded letter.

If the number of the coded letter is greater than 26, subtract 26 from it. For example, V's number is 22, $22 + 7 = 29$, $29 - 26 = 3$, so the code letter for V is C.

1. Copy and complete this table to show the $y = 7 + x$ code.

| Plaintext | Code |
|-----------|------|
| A | H |
| B | I |
| C | ... |

2. Use $y = 7 + x$ to encode the words `smile, juggle, dance, puzzle.`

3. Choose a number, $b$, and use $y = b + x$ to encode a message for a classmate. (Let the classmate know the value of $b$ so he or she will be able to decode the message quickly.)

4. Decode the following message, which has been encoded with $y = 10 + x$.
   `DRSC COXDOXMO ECOC RKVP DRO VODDOBC SX DRO KVZRKLOD.`

5. Find the function that would decode the message in problem 4. Check your answer by actually using it on `DRSC`, and making sure it gives the expected plaintext.

6. a. Use the function $y = 27 - x$ to encode these names.
      `Bernard, Carol, Ellen, Peter`
   b. Describe in words the code obtained from this function.

7. a. Encode your name with $y = 30 - x$.
   b. Now take the answer to (a) and encode it with $y = 30 - x$ again.
   c. Comment on the result in (b).

8. a. Encode the word `bilingual` with $y = 8 - x$ and then with $y = x - 8$. Do you get the same answer? Explain.
   b. Find a decoding function for each function in part (a).

9. **Report** In this lesson you learned about two kinds of coding functions. Some look like $y = 7 + x$, and others look like $y = 8 - x$. Write a report on how to decode messages coded by each kind of function and also by functions like $y = x - 8$. Give examples using other numbers for each of the three kinds of functions. Mention any special numbers. (For example, what happens when $y = x + 26$?)

# Introduction to Inequalities

## WHICH IS GREATER?

You can tell which of two numbers is greater by their positions on the number line.

-7 -6 -5 -4 -3 -2 -1 0 1 2 3 4 5 6 7

The number that is greater is farther to the right. The number that is less is farther to the left.

**Notation:** The symbol for *less than* is <. For example, -5 < 3, 0 < 7, and -6 < -2. The symbol for *greater than* is >. For example, 6 > 3, 0 > -2, and -5 > -9.

1. Use the correct symbol.
   a. -5 ? -7          b. -5 ? -1

This workmat shows two expressions.
$x + 4 - 5 - (x + 5)$ and $10 + 2x - 1 - (2x - 1)$

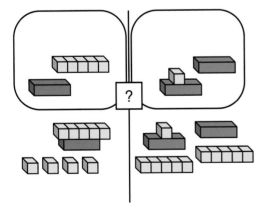

Which is greater? The question mark shows that this is unknown.

2. Put out blocks to match the figure. Simplify both sides. Write an expression for the blocks that remain on the left side. Write an expression for the blocks on the right side. Which side is greater? Show your answer by writing the correct *inequality sign* between the two expressions.

For each problem, put out blocks to match the figure, and
   a. write the two expressions;
   b. simplify both sides on the workmat;
   c. decide which side is greater or whether they are equal, and write the correct sign between the expressions.

3.
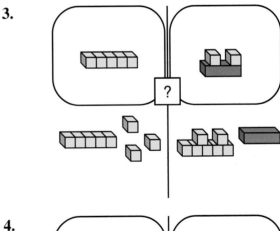

4.
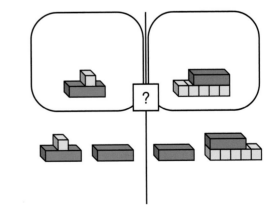

**5.**

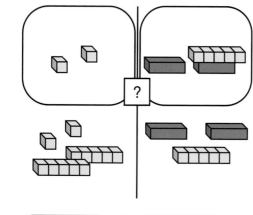

**6.**

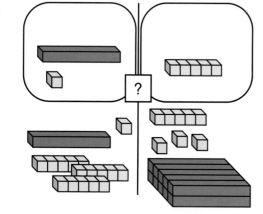

---

**CAN YOU TELL?**

To compare $2x - x + 5 - (5 - x)$ with $5 + 3x - 1 - (x - 3)$, first show the two expressions with the Lab Gear.

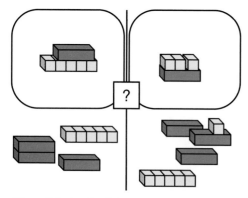

**7.** Simplify both sides, then arrange the blocks in a logical manner to determine which side is greater.

---

Your workmat should look like this.

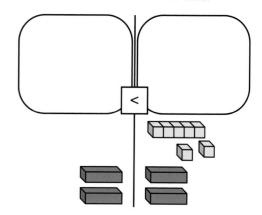

Both sides include $2x$, but the right side is greater, as it also includes 7 more units. So we can write

$$2x < 2x + 7.$$

Now compare these expressions.

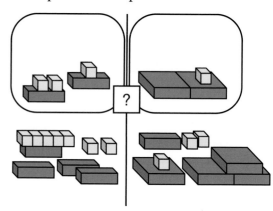

**8.** Write both expressions as they are shown in this figure.

**9.** Simplify both sides, then arrange the blocks in a logical manner to determine which side is greater.

Your workmat should look like this.

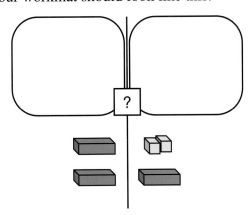

In this case, it is impossible to tell which side is greater, because we do not know whether $x$ is greater or less than 2.

For problems 10-13, write both expressions as they are given. Then simplify, using your blocks, and write the expressions in simplified form. Decide which side is greater, whether they are equal, or whether it is impossible to tell. Write the correct symbol or ?.

**10.**

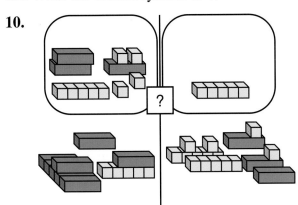

**11.**

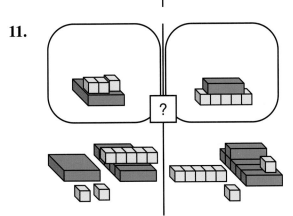

**12.**

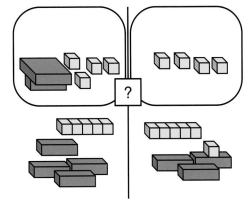

**13.**

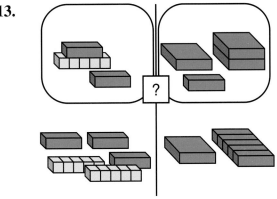

TESTING VALUES OF $X$

Look at these two expressions.

$$2x - 5 \qquad -3x + 6$$

Which is greater? The answer depends on the value of $x$.

**14.** a. Substitute ⁻1 for $x$ in both expressions and tell which is greater.

b. Substitute 3 for $x$ in both expressions and tell which is greater.

c. Find another value for $x$ which makes $2x - 5$ greater.

d. Find another value for $x$ which makes $-3x + 6$ greater.

**15.** For each of the following pairs of expressions, find two values of $x$, one that makes the first expression greater and one that makes the second expression greater. Show all your calculations.

a. $7x - 4$          $3x - 2$

b. $-2x + 6$       $8x - 4$

c. $x$                 ⁻$x$

For each pair of expressions, write

  **A** if the expression in column A is greater;
  **B** if the expression in column B is greater;
  **?** if you would have to know the value of
  $x$ in order to know which is greater.

Remember that $x$ can have negative and fractional values. It may help to think about the Lab Gear. In each case *explain your answer*, giving test values of $x$ if it helps your explanation.

|  | **A** | **B** |
|---|---|---|
| **16.** | $7x$ | $7x - 1$ |
| **17.** | $7x + 1$ | $-7x + 1$ |
| **18.** | $7x + 1$ | $7x - 1$ |
| **19.** | $7x - 1$ | $-7x - 1$ |
| **20.** | $7x + 1$ | $-7x - 1$ |
| **21.** | $7x^2 - 1$ | $7x - 1$ |

**22.** Compare your answers to problems 16-21 with other students' answers. Discuss your disagreements. If you disagree with another student, try to find an example to show which answer is not correct.

**23.** Write an expression containing $x$, that is less than 4 when $x$ is less than 9.

**24.** Write an expression containing $x$, that is less than 4 when $x$ is more than 9.

**25.** ⚲ Write an expression containing $x$, that is less than 4 for all values of $x$.

────────────────────────────────

**DISCOVERY** **MORE CODES**

If the coding function is of the form $y = mx$, it is more difficult to encode and decode. (For the letter values, see **Thinking/Writing 3.A.**)

**26.** a. Encode the word `extra` using $y = 3x$.
  b. What did you do when $3x$ was larger than 26?

**27.** Decode the following sentence which was encoded with $y = 3x$. It may help to make a table showing the matching of the plaintext and coded alphabet.
  `APIBOCEO HXO VOCIO.`

**28.** Encode the word `multiplication` with:
  a. $y = x;$     b. $y = 2x;$
  c. $y = 13x;$    d. $y = 26x.$

**29.** ⚲
  a. Decode the following message, which was encoded with $y = 2x$. It may help to make a table showing the matching

of the plaintext and coded alphabet.
  `HD NPJ JRNPN NPRBN. DPN PDT`
  `FBB XDP NJXX TPBN'L JRNPN?`
  b. What makes $y = 2x$ a difficult code to crack?

**DISCOVERY** **SUMMING UP**

Say that the sum of a word is the sum of the numbers corresponding to its letters. (For the letter values, see **Thinking/Writing 3.A.**) For example, the word `topic` has value
$$20 + 15 + 16 + 9 + 3 = 63.$$

**30.** What is the sum of the word `algebra`?

**31.** Find as many words as possible having sum 100.

# Multiplication and Division

**You will need:**

the Lab Gear

**Notation:** In algebra, the symbol ÷ is not used, perhaps because it looks too much like a + sign. To show division, use the format of a fraction.

$$\frac{6}{2} = 3$$

Or, if you're using a typewriter or computer, write it with a slash, 6/2 = 3.

In this book we will write division both ways.

## ONE MULTIPLICATION, TWO DIVISIONS

For most multiplication equations, there are two division equations. For example, corresponding to 7 · 3 = 21, we have

$$21/7 = 3 \quad \text{and} \quad 21/3 = 7.$$

With the Lab Gear, you can use a rectangle to model multiplication and division.

Arrange your corner piece and blocks to match this figure.

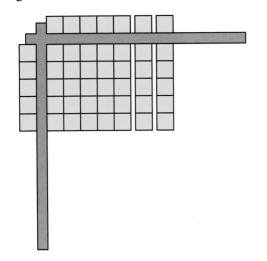

1. Write the multiplication equation that is shown by the figure.

2. Write the two division equations that are shown by the figure.

3. You could use the corner piece to set up several different divisions having numerator 12. For each, write the division equation and the corresponding multiplication equation.

4. Explain why it is impossible to set up the division 12/0 with the Lab Gear.

5. ⚷ Some algebra students believe that 12/0 = 0. Explain why they are *wrong* by discussing the multiplication that would correspond to this division.

6. a. Using the corner piece, multiply $(x + 4)(x + 3)$.

   b. Write two division equations related to the multiplication.

## DIVISION IN THE CORNER PIECE

Here is an example of dividing in the corner piece.

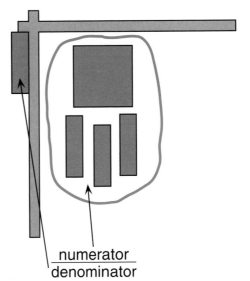

numerator
denominator

- Put the denominator to the left of the corner piece.
- Make a rectangle out of the numerator and place it inside the corner piece so that one side of the rectangle matches the denominator.

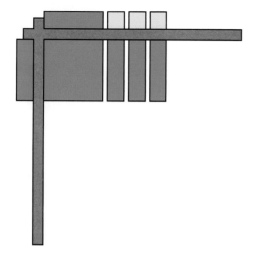

- Finally, to get the answer, figure out what blocks go along the top of the corner piece.

**7.** Write the division equation shown by the figure.

The denominator was a factor of the numerator, and a rectangle was formed with no pieces left over. However, in some cases, there will be a remainder. Here is an example.

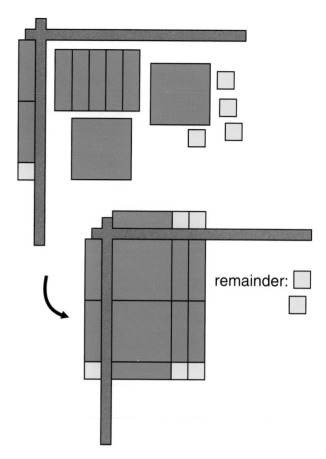

remainder:

**8.** What are the numerator, denominator, quotient, and remainder in the above division?

**9.** Divide.

a. $\dfrac{6x^2 + 3x}{3x}$   b. $\dfrac{9x + 3}{3}$

c. $\dfrac{x^2 + x + xy + y}{x + y}$   d. $\dfrac{xy + 2x + x^2}{x + y}$

e. $\dfrac{2x^2 + 6x + 4}{x + 2}$   f. $\dfrac{3x^2 + 10x + 5}{x + 3}$

**10.** For each division in problem 9, write the related multiplication equation.

**11.** 〇

a. Divide. $\dfrac{y^2x + x^2y + 2xy + x^2 + y^2 + x + y}{x + 1}$

b. Write four multiplications having the product
$y^2x + x^2y + 2xy + x^2 + y^2 + x + y.$

### MULTIPLICATION WITHOUT THE LAB GEAR

Here is a method for multiplying polynomials without the Lab Gear. To perform the multiplication $(x + 2)(3y - 4x + 5)$, write the terms along the side and the top of a table.

|   | $3y$ | $-4x$ | $5$ |
|---|---|---|---|
| $x$ |  |  |  |
| $2$ |  |  |  |

Then enter the products of the terms in the corresponding boxes.

|   | $3y$ | $-4x$ | $5$ |
|---|---|---|---|
| $x$ | $3xy$ | $-4x^2$ | $5x$ |
| $2$ | $6y$ | $-8x$ | $10$ |

Then combine like terms, and you are done.

$(x + 2)(3y - 4x + 5) =$
$\quad 3xy - 4x^2 - 3x + 6y + 10$

Use this method for the following products.

**12.** $x(2x + 3xy + y^2)$

**13.** $(2x - y)(x + 3y)$

**14.** $(2x - y)(x - 3y)$

**15.** $(2x + y)(x - 3y)$

**16.** $(2x + y)(x + 3y)$

**17.** $(x + xy + 2yx)(y + 2 + x)$

This method for multiplication is a way to apply the distributive law to the multiplication of polynomials. *Every term must be multiplied by every term.*

### MULTIPLICATION PUZZLES

Fill in the tables, including the polynomial factors along the side and the top. All coefficients are whole numbers. Is more than one solution possible for either table?

**18.**

|   |   |   |
|---|---|---|
| $2x^3$ |  | $-6x$ |
|  | $-x$ | $-3$ |

**19.**

|   |   |   |
|---|---|---|
| $12xy$ | $15x^2y$ |  |
|  |  | $x^2y^2$ |

**20.** 〇 Create a puzzle of this type that has a unique solution. Give the solver as few terms as possible.

**21.** Solve a classmate's puzzle.

〰〰〰〰〰〰〰〰〰〰〰〰〰〰〰〰〰〰

### REVIEW  *WHAT'S YOUR SIGN?*

**22.** What is the sign of the missing factor?

a. $-123.4 \cdot \_\_\_\_ = 567.89$

b. $98.76 \cdot (-54.3) \cdot \_\_\_\_ = -21$

c. $98.76 \cdot (-54.3) \cdot \_\_\_\_ = 0$

# Reciprocals

## A MODEL FOR MULTIPLICATION

You cannot easily show multiplication by fractions with the Lab Gear, but the Lab Gear can help you think about it. For example, $(1/5) \cdot 50$ is read *one-fifth of fifty*. This means that we divide 50 into five parts and take one of them.

The diagram shows that $(1/5) \cdot 50 = 10$.

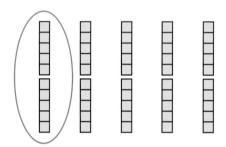

(2/5) is two of five parts, so $2/5 \cdot 50 = 20$.

1. Find a number you could multiply by 8 to get a number less than 8.

2. Without finding its value, decide whether $x$ would be more or less than 1. Explain how you know.
   a. $8 \cdot x = 50$    b. $8 \cdot x = 5$
   c. $8 \cdot x = 0.05$

3. Find the value of $x$ for each equation in problem 2. (Hint: Remember that for any multiplication, there are two related divisions. You may use a calculator.)

## A MULTIPLICATION SHORTCUT

4. Take 8, 3, and 2. They are three numbers whose product is 48. Another multiplication possibility is $6 \cdot 4 \cdot 2$. Find as many ways of writing 48 as a product of three different numbers as you can. Do not use 1 as a factor.

5. **Exploration** *Do not use 1 as a factor.*
   a. Write 2 as a product of two different numbers.
   b. Write 4 as a product of four different numbers.
   c. Write 6 as a product of six different numbers.
   d. Write 12 as a product of twelve different numbers.

> **Definition:** The product of a number and its *reciprocal* is 1. Another way of saying this is, *the reciprocal of a number is the result of dividing 1 by the number.*

> **Examples:**  $3 \cdot 1/3 = 1$
> $2/3 \cdot 3/2 = 1$
> $0.31 \cdot 100/31 = 1$

6. ⚷ Explain how the reciprocals of 3, 2/3, and 0.31 may have been found for the examples above. (No calculator was used.)

Guess the value of $x$, *without using your calculator.* If you think about reciprocals you will have to do very little arithmetic.

7. a. $5 \cdot \frac{1}{5} \cdot x = 6$
   b. $4 \cdot x \cdot 9 \cdot \frac{1}{4} = 45$
   c. $x \cdot 8 \cdot 7 = 8$
   d. $x \cdot 8 \cdot 3 = 3$
   e. $\frac{2}{3} \cdot x \cdot 3 \cdot \frac{1}{2} = 15$

8. a. $2 \cdot x \cdot 3 = 2$
   b. $x \cdot 2 \cdot 2 \cdot 9 \cdot 3 = 6$
   c. $\frac{1}{5} \cdot (5x) \cdot 3 = 1$
   d. $\frac{1}{5} \cdot (5x) = \frac{3}{5}$

9. Make up two more equations like problems 7 and 8 and solve them.

*Chapter 3 Working Backwards*

**10.** 💡 Find two numbers *a* and *b* that will satisfy each equation. *Don't use your calculator.* Instead, think about reciprocals. Do not use 1 for *a* or *b*.

a. $a \cdot b \cdot 14 = 28$    b. $a \cdot b \cdot 28 = 14$

c. $\frac{2}{3} \cdot a \cdot b = 10$    d. $a \cdot b \cdot 10 = \frac{2}{3}$

---
**RECIPROCALS ON THE CALCULATOR**
---

Most scientific calculators have a key for reciprocals: $\boxed{1/x}$, or $\boxed{x^{-1}}$ . (On calculators that do not have such a key, you can divide 1 by a number to find the number's reciprocal.)

**11.** Find the reciprocal of:

a. 1/23;    b. 0.456;    c. 7.89.

**12.** Report  What is the result when you

a. multiply a number by its reciprocal?

b. divide a number by its reciprocal?

Be sure your results work for all numbers. Explain how you reached your conclusions.

**13.** $1/82 < 0.0123 < 1/81$. Explain.

**14.** Find two consecutive whole numbers such that 0.00123 is between their reciprocals.

**15.** Repeat problem 14 for 0.000123

**16.** 🔑 Explain your method for solving problems 14 and 15.

---
**A MODEL FOR DIVISION**
---

**17.** Exploration  Find a positive number such that when you divide that number by 5, your answer is

a. a number less than 1;

b. a number between 10 and 20;

c. a number greater than 100.

**18.** Find a positive number such that when you divide 5 by it, your answer is

a. a number less than 1;

b. a number between 10 and 20;

c. a number greater than 100.

Division by numbers between 0 and 1 is hard to show with the Lab Gear.

These diagrams show 10/5, 10/2, and 10/1.

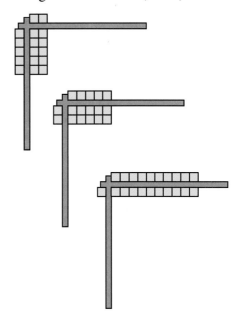

What would 10/(1/2) look like? We cannot actually build this with the Lab Gear, but we could imagine what it would look like if we sliced each block in half.

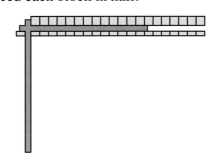

**19.** a. What is the answer to the division shown in the figure?

  b. Dividing by 1/2 is equivalent to multiplying by what number?

**20.** a. Will the result of the division 8/(1/4) be more or less than 8?

  b. Use a sketch to show the division 8/(1/4).

  c. What is the answer to the division?

  d. Dividing by 1/4 is equivalent to multiplying by what number?

**21.** 🔑

  a. What is the result of the division of 8 by 0.1, 0.01, 0.001?

  b. What would happen if you divided 8 by a number that is much smaller than 0.001, almost equal to zero?

  c. How about dividing 8 by 0?

A DIVISION SHORTCUT

**22.** a. If you multiplied 5 by a number and got 30, what was the number?

  b. If you divided 5 by a number and got 30, what was the number?

  c. Compare your answers to parts (a) and (b). How are these numbers related?

**23.** 🔑 *Dividing by a number is the same as multiplying by its reciprocal.* Explain, using examples.

Use this fact to perform each of the following divisions without your calculator.

**24.** 12/(1/4)  **25.** 12/(2/3)

**26.** 10/0.4  **27.** $x^2/(1/x)$

SMALL NUMBERS

**28.** Find two numbers such that you get a result between 0 and 1 whether you add them, multiply them, subtract one from the other, or divide one by the other.

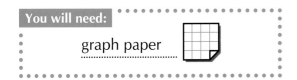
# A Hot Day

**You will need:**

graph paper

The sign at Algebank near Abe's house gives the time and temperature. The temperature is given two ways, using both the Celsius and Fahrenheit temperature scales. One hot day Abe made a record of the time and temperature at several times during the day. He tried to look at the bank sign exactly on the hour, but usually he was off by a few minutes. His data appear below.

| Time | Temp (C) | Temp (F) |
|------|----------|----------|
| 11:03 | 31 | 87 |
| 12:00 | 32 | 90 |
| 2:00 | 35 | 95 |
| 3:04 | 35 | 95 |
| 4:08 | 34 | 93 |
| 8:03 | 27 | 81 |

1. **Exploration** Abe heard on the radio that the low for the night had been 74 degrees (Fahrenheit) at 4:30 A.M. and the high for the day had been 97 degrees at 3:30 P.M. Using the information in the table, estimate what you think the Celsius readings on the bank sign would have been at those two times. Explain how you got your answers. ■

## TEMPERATURE VARIATION

2. a. Draw a pair of axes on graph paper. Label the horizontal axis *Time* and the vertical axis *Temp*.

   b. Plot the points that show how the Celsius temperature changes with time. Your first point will be (11:03, 31).

3. a. Draw another pair of axes like the first one.

   b. Plot the points that show how the Fahrenheit temperature changes with time. Your first point will be (11:03, 87).

4. Write a short description of what your graphs show. Compare the two graphs.

## COMPARING TEMPERATURE SCALES

A graph will help to show how the two temperature scales are related.

5. Draw a pair of axes. Put the Fahrenheit temperature on the vertical axis (label it *F*) and the Celsius temperature on the horizontal axis (label it *C*). Put the axes in the middle of your graph paper and leave plenty of room to extend your graph in all directions. Plot the points in Abe's table. Your first point will be (31, 87).

6. The points of your graph should fall approximately in a straight line. Draw a straight line that seems to go through most of the points.

Use your graph to estimate the answers to these questions. If necessary, extend your graph.

7. Approximately what is the
   a. Fahrenheit temperature when the Celsius temperature is 25°?
   b. Celsius temperature when the Fahrenheit temperature is 50°?
   c. Celsius temperature when the Fahrenheit temperature is -30°?

**8.** 💡 Is there a temperature where a Fahrenheit and Celsius thermometer show the same number? If so, what is it?

Abe's sister Bea wanted to estimate the Fahrenheit temperature for 17° Celsius. Someone had told her that the best way to remember the Celsius-Fahrenheit relationship was to memorize the fact that 16° Celsius is 61° Fahrenheit. Abe joked, "So 17° Celsius must be 71° Fahrenheit!" Bea replied, "I'll just add one degree. That means 17° Celsius must be 62° Fahrenheit."

**9.** Explain what Bea did wrong. Use your graph. Give examples explaining to Bea how to make the conversion correctly.

**10.** ☞ Judging from your graph, if you increase the Celsius temperature by one degree, by about how much does the temperature increase on the Fahrenheit scale?

### CONVERTING CELSIUS TO FAHRENHEIT

Bea and Abe's parents, Mr. and Mrs. Gral, were planning a trip to Europe, where temperatures are given in Celsius. They asked their children to help them figure out how to convert from Celsius to Fahrenheit.

Abe asked his science teacher, who gave him the following rule: To get the Fahrenheit temperature, multiply the Celsius temperature by 1.8, then add 32.

**11.** ☞
   a. Write a formula for this rule. Use $F$ for the Fahrenheit temperature and $C$ for the Celsius temperature.
   b. Check your formula by using it to convert one of the Celsius temperatures in Abe's table.

Bea looked up the subject in an almanac, which gave these instructions: To get the Fahrenheit temperature, multiply the Celsius temperature by 9, divide by 5, then add 32.

**12.** ☞
   a. Write a formula for this rule.
   b. Check your formula by using it to convert one of the Celsius temperatures in Abe's table.

**13.** Compare the two formulas you wrote. Do you think they always give the same results? Explain, giving examples.

**14.** Use either method to convert these two Celsius temperatures to Fahrenheit.
   a. 20° Celsius = ___ Fahrenheit
   b. 21° Celsius = ___ Fahrenheit

**15.** ☞ According to your calculation in problem 14, when you increase the Celsius temperature by one degree, by about how much does the temperature increase on the Fahrenheit scale? Where does this number appear in the formula? Explain.

### CONVERTING FAHRENHEIT TO CELSIUS

A journalist from Spain, G. Balear, is staying with the Grals. She is writing an article for a Spanish newspaper about her experiences in the United States. She wants to convert Fahrenheit temperatures to Celsius for her article.

**16.** The Fahrenheit temperature dropped to 41°. Bea is trying to help Ms. Balear convert it to Celsius. She has the idea of working backwards using the rule from the almanac. Use this method, or another method you think might work, to convert 41° F to Celsius.

**17.** ☞ Describe the method you devised in problem 16 for converting Fahrenheit to Celsius. Explain why it works. Show that it works for other temperatures by using it to convert some of the temperatures in Abe's table.

# 3.B Opposites and Reciprocals

### OPPOSITES

The function $y = -x$ can be thought of as the *opposite function,* since $y$ and $x$ are opposites.

1.  a. Make a function diagram for the function $y = -x$.
    b. Describe the in-out lines. (Are they parallel? Do they meet in a single point? If so, where is that point?)

2.  To answer these questions, look at the diagram you made for problem 1.
    a. As $x$ increases, what happens to $y$?
    b. Are $x$ and $y$ ever equal? Explain.
    c. When $x$ increases by 3, what happens to $y$?

3.  Find the number and its opposite that are described. Use trial and error. Look for patterns. Try to develop a shortcut strategy.
    a. a number 16 more than its opposite
    b. a number 0.5 more than its opposite
    c. a number 21 less than its opposite
    d. 💡 a number $A$ less than its opposite
    e. 💡 a number 8 more than twice its opposite.

4.  Report In a few paragraphs, summarize what you learned about opposites and their function diagrams. Include examples.

### RECIPROCALS

The function $y = 1/x$ can be thought of as the *reciprocal function,* since $y$ and $x$ are reciprocals.

5.  a. Make an in-out table for the function $y = 1/x$, using the following values for $x$: -5, -4, -3, -2, -1, -0.8, -0.6, -0.4, -0.2, and the opposites of these numbers (0.2, 0.4, etc.)
    b. Make a whole-page function diagram for the function.

6.  Use the function diagram you made in problem 5. Follow $y$ with your finger as $x$ goes up its number line. Answer these questions.
    a. As $x$ increases, what happens to $y$?
    b. Are $x$ and $y$ ever equal?

7.  🔑 On your function diagram of $y = 1/x$, as $x$ moves up the number line, answer questions (a-h), describing what happens to $y$. (Does it move up or down? Fast or slowly? From what to what?)
    a. when $x$ is a negative number far from 0
    b. when $x$ approaches -1
    c. when $x$ passes -1
    d. when $x$ approaches 0
    e. when $x$ passes 0
    f. when $x$ approaches 1
    g. when $x$ passes 1
    h. when $x$ is a large positive number

8.  Use your calculator to look for a number and its reciprocal that satisfy these requirements. If you cannot find an exact number, get as close as you can by trial and error. One is impossible.
    a. The number is 9 times its reciprocal.
    b. The number is 1/9 of its reciprocal.
    c. The number equals the opposite of its reciprocal.
    d. 💡 The number is 3 times its reciprocal.
    e. 💡 The number is one more than its reciprocal.

9.  Report Summarize what you learned about reciprocals and their function diagrams. Include examples. (Do not forget to discuss what happens when $x = 0$.)

# Equations and the Cover-Up Method

## WRITING EQUATIONS

A seamstress makes dresses for a living. After an illness, she has only $100 in her business bank account. She takes out a $1000 loan at Algebank. The interest on the loan is $15 per month if it gets paid back in the first year. She spends $720 on dress-making materials, and keeps the rest in her bank account to cover additional costs, such as sewing machine repairs or whatever else may come up. Materials for one dress come to $20. She makes two dresses a day, four days a week, and spends one day a week selling the dresses and dealing with other matters related to her business.

She sells as many dresses as she can to private customers for $160 each, and the rest of the dresses to stores, for $100 each. She needs $750 a week for living expenses and puts any income over that in her bank account. She hopes to pay back her loan, and to make enough money so that when she needs to buy more materials, she does not have to take out another loan. Can the seamstress meet her goals? How could she improve her financial situation?

One way to think about a problem like this one is to break it down into smaller problems, and to write and solve equations for those. For example, let's write an expression that would tell us how much money the seamstress puts in her bank account every week.

1. **Exploration** Assume the seamstress has $x$ private customers a week. Answer the following questions for one week, in terms of $x$.
   a. How many dresses does she sell to stores?
   b. How much money does she receive from private customers?
   c. How much money does she receive from stores?
   d. What is the total amount of money she receives every week?
   e. How much of it is she able to put in her bank account? Simplify your answer.

If you answered the questions correctly, you should have ended up with the expression $60x + 50$ for the amount she deposits every week as a function of $x$. Let's say that she would like this amount to be $300. This gives us the equation $60x + 50 = 300$. Remember that $x$ is the number of private customers per week. We can now find out how many private customers she would need to deposit $300 per week. All we need to do is solve the equation.

## SOLVING EQUATIONS

**Definition:** Finding all the values of a variable that make an equation true is called *solving the equation.*

You have already solved equations by trial and error. The *cover-up method* is another technique for solving equations. It is based on the idea of working backwards.

**Example 1:** $60x + 50 = 300$

With your finger, cover up the term that has the $x$ in it. The equation looks like

$$\square + 50 = 300.$$

Clearly, what's in the box is 250. So

$$60x = 250.$$

Think of a division that is related to this multiplication, and you will see that

$$x = 250/60$$

or $\qquad x = \mathbf{4.1666\ldots.}$

So in order to deposit $300 a week, the seamstress needs to have more than four private customers a week.

*Chapter 3 Working Backwards*

**Example 2:** This one is about a more complicated equation.

$$5 + \frac{3x - 1}{4} = 7$$

Cover up the expression $\frac{3x - 1}{4}$. You get

$$5 + \square = 7.$$

Whatever is hidden must be equal to 2. So

$$\frac{3x - 1}{4} = 2$$

Now cover up $3x - 1$ with your finger.

$$\frac{\square}{4} = 2$$

What is under your finger must be 8. So

$$3x - 1 = 8.$$

Cover up the term containing $x$.

$$\square - 1 = 8$$

What's under your finger must equal 9. So

$$3x = 9$$

and

$$x = 3.$$

2. Check the solutions to examples 1 and 2 by substituting them in the original equations.

Solve each equation. Use the cover-up method, then check each answer by substituting.

3. a. $3(x - 10) = 15$
   b. $3(x + 10) = 15$
   c. $3 + \frac{x}{10} = 15$
   d. $\frac{18}{x} + 12 = 15$

4. a. $34 - \frac{2x + 6}{2} = 4$
   b. $34 - \frac{2x + 6}{2} = -4$

5. a. $21 = 12 + \frac{3x}{8}$    b. $12 = 21 + \frac{3x}{8}$

6. a. $5 + \frac{x}{6} = 17$    b. $5 + \frac{6}{x} = 17$
   c. $5 - \frac{x}{6} = 17$    d. $5 - \frac{6}{x} = 17$

7. a. $3 = \frac{12}{x + 1}$    b. $3 = \frac{x + 1}{12}$
   c. $3 = \frac{12}{x + 7}$    d. $3 = \frac{x + 7}{12}$

8. ⊶ Make up an equation like the ones above that has as its solution
   a. 4;    b. -4;    c. $\frac{1}{4}$ .

Since the cover-up method is based on covering up the part of the equation that includes an $x$, it can be used only in equations like the ones above, where $x$ appears only once. In other equations, for example

$$160x + 100(8 - x) - 750 = 300,$$

you cannot use the cover-up method, unless you simplify first.

9. 💡 Find out how many private customers the seamstress needs every week so that, at the end of four weeks, she has enough money in her bank account to pay back her loan and buy dress-making materials for the next four weeks. Use equations and the cover-up method if you can. Otherwise, use any other method. In either case, explain how you arrive at your answers.

## 3.9

**REVIEW** *DIVIDING BY ZERO*

**10.** Explain, using multiplication, why
$20/5 = 4$.

**11.** Explain, using multiplication, why 20/0 is
not defined. (Hint: Start by writing
$20/0 = q$. Write a related multiplication.
What must $q$ be?)

**12.** Explain, using multiplication, why 0/0 is
not defined. (Hint: Start by writing
$0/0 = q$. Write a related multiplication.
What must $q$ be? Could it be something
else?)

**DISCOVERY** *BE PRODUCTIVE*

Say that the product of a word is the product of
the numbers corresponding to its letters. (For
the letter values, see **Thinking/Writing 3.A.**)
For example, the word `optic` has value
$$15 \cdot 16 \cdot 20 \cdot 9 \cdot 3 = 129{,}600$$

**13.** What is the product of the word **ALGEBRA**?

**14.** Find words whose product is as close to
one million as possible.

**15.** ♡ Find words having these products.
(Hint: It would help to find the prime factors of the numbers.)

a. 6          b. 8

c. 12         d. 14

e. 15         f. 16

g. 20         h. 24

i. 35         j. 455

k. 715        l. 2185

m. 106,029    n. ♡ 4,410,000

# Combining Functions

**LESSON 3.10**

**You will need:**

graph paper

## DIAGRAMS OF COMBINED FUNCTIONS

Function diagrams can be used to show the result of combining functions. Here are two simple functions. One function doubles $x$. The other function adds 1 to $x$.

$$y_1 = 2x \qquad y_2 = x + 1$$

> **Notation:** The 2 in the name $y_2$ is called a *subscript*. It is written lower and smaller than the $y$. It does *not* mean *multiply by 2* or *square*. It is just a way to distinguish two variables that would otherwise have the same name.

**1.** Draw function diagrams for $y_1$ and $y_2$.

This two-step function diagram shows one way of combining $y_1$ and $y_2$. First, double $x$. Then add 1 to the result. The $y$ value of $y_1$ becomes the new $x$ value for $y_2$.

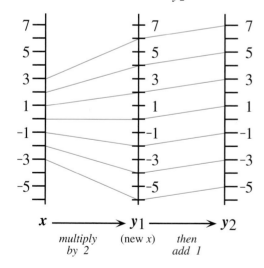

These two steps can be combined as shown in this one-step function diagram.

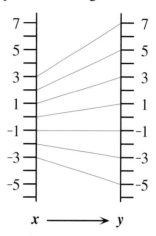

**2.** Write a rule for this function diagram.

The functions $y_1$ and $y_2$ can also be combined in the other order: First, add 1 to $x$. Then double the result. The $y$ value of $y_2$ becomes the new $x$ value for $y_1$.

**3.** Draw a two-step function diagram showing the combination of the functions in this order.

**4.** Summarize your two-step function diagram in a one-step function diagram.

**5.** Write a rule for the one-step function diagram you drew.

**6.** ⚷ Does the order in which we combine the functions matter? Explain.

These problems are about the following two functions.

$$y_1 = -3x \qquad y_2 = x + 2$$

**7.** Show a two-step function diagram, combining the functions by performing $y_1$ first and then $y_2$.

8. Summarize your two-step diagram in a one-step diagram and write the function that corresponds to your one-step function diagram.

9. Repeat problems 7 and 8, but this time combine the two functions by performing $y_2$ first, followed by $y_1$.

10. Did the resulting function change, when you changed the order in which you combined the two functions? Explain.

11. **Exploration** Sometimes you can combine two functions in either order and the resulting function is the same. Find pairs of functions that have this property. You may use function diagrams to verify your answer. Discuss any patterns you notice.

### INVERSE ACTIONS

The inverse of an action is the action that undoes it. For example, suppose you were leaving home in the car. You would perform these four actions.

ACTION 1: Open the car door.
ACTION 2: Get into the car.
ACTION 3: Close the door.
ACTION 4: Start the car.

If, before driving away, you suddenly realized that you forgot something, you would have to undo all these actions. You would undo the actions in the reverse order:

First, UNDO ACTION 4: Stop the car.
Second, UNDO ACTION 3: Open the door.
Next, UNDO ACTION 2: Get out of the car.
Last, UNDO ACTION 1: Close the car door.

12. Describe how to undo these actions.

   a. In the morning, you put on your socks, then put on your shoes. What do you do in the evening?

   b. To take a break from this homework, you close your math book, stand up from your desk, turn on the television, and sit down on the sofa. What do you do to get back to work?

13. Al believes that the way to undo the actions *open the car window; stick your head out* is *close the car window; pull your head in.* Comment on this idea.

14. Create your own example of inverse actions.

### INVERSE FUNCTIONS

15. **Exploration** Choose any function and make a function diagram for it. Then draw the mirror image of this function diagram. What is the function associated with the mirror image? How is it related to the original function? Try this with several functions. Write about any patterns you notice.

The inverse of a function is a function that undoes it. For example, look at these two input-output tables.

| $x$ | $y$ |
|-----|-----|
| 2   | 6   |
| -1  | -3  |
| 4   | 12  |

| $x$ | $y$ |
|-----|-----|
| 6   | 2   |
| -3  | -1  |
| 12  | 4   |

16. a. What happens when you use an output from the first table as the input for the second table?

   b. What two functions do you think are represented by these two tables? How are the functions related?

*Chapter 3 Working Backwards*

If $y_1 = 2x$ and $y_2 = (1/2)x$, a two-step function diagram shows that $y_2$ undoes $y_1$.

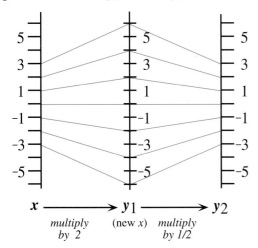

This is shown dramatically when the two-step diagram is summarized in a one-step diagram.

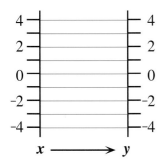

A function $y_1$ performs the following operations on a number.

Multiply the number by 3, subtract 1.

17. Write in words what the inverse function does. (Call it $y_2$.)

18. a. Write a rule in the form $y_1 =$ for the original function.
    b. Write a rule in the form $y_2 =$ for the inverse function.

19. a. Make separate function diagrams for $y_1$ and $y_2$.
    b. Describe how the diagrams you made are related.

20. Make a two-step function diagram for the combination of $y_1$ and $y_2$.

21. Make a one-step function diagram summarizing your two-step diagram. Would it matter if you combined $y_1$ and $y_2$ in the other order?

22. **Summary** Write a summary of what you have learned in this lesson about combining function diagrams, especially those of inverse functions. Use examples.

23. ◯ Find functions that are their own inverses. What do you notice about their function diagrams? Explain.

# Math on Another Planet

## SMALL POCKETS

On the treeless planet of Glosia, the currency consists of florins, ecus, and ducats. *One florin is worth two ecus, and one ecu is worth two ducats.* Since there is no paper, there is no paper money, and the people of Glosia have to carry coins everywhere. King Evariste VII, being immensely rich, must wear bloomers with enormous reinforced pockets to hold his money.

One day the King realizes that there is a new trend in Glosian fashion. Elegant men and women wear only small pockets. Evariste VII, not one to be left behind by the great movements of style, decides to institute a drastic economic reform by enacting a strange law: *One ducat is worth two florins!* (The old rules are not changed.) When you realize trades can be made in either direction, you can see how the King's brilliant legislation will abolish poverty forever.

The people of Glosia are ecstatic. With the new system, one may have a fortune in one's pockets, and yet never carry more than three coins! One can be rich and fashionable at the same time. For example, if you own eight ecus, you can go to the bank, and trade them in for four florins. These can be traded again, for two ducats, which equal one ecu, which will certainly fit in your pocket.

1. **Exploration**

   a. The King trades his coins at the bank, according to their official value, with the object of having as few coins as possible in the tiny pocket of his slinky new pants. He starts with 1000 florins. What does he end up with?

   b. Prince Enbel has one ducat. He buys a toastereo (a popular appliance which, unfortunately, does not make coffee), costing 50 ecus. If he is given the fewest coins possible, how much change does he get?

   c. Princess Lisa has one ecu. She wins the first prize in a contest in *Names* Magazine. The prize is one ducat, one ecu, and one florin. She now has four coins, but they won't fit into her pocket. What does she have after trading them in to get as few coins as possible? (The second prize would have been a T-shirt with the *Names* logo and no pockets at all.)

   d. Sol Grundy has no money. He gets a job at the toastereo store, earning one florin per day, seven days a week. Since his pockets are fashionably small, he trades his money as often as possible in order to have as few coins as possible. If he starts his new job on Monday, how much does he have each day of the week? The next week? (Assume he doesn't spend any money.)

2. Make a list of the amounts of money one can have that cannot be reduced to a smaller number of coins. (Hint: There are seven possible amounts.) One of the amounts is $(d + e)$.

3. Make an addition table for Glosian money. It should be a seven-by-seven table, with a row and column for each of the amounts you found in problem 2. For example, your table should show that $(d + e) + d = f$.

4. One of the seven amounts you found in problem 3 can be considered to be the "zero" of Glosian money, since adding it to a collection of coins does not change the collection's value (after trading to get the smallest possible number of coins). Which amount is the zero for Glosian money?

5. The opposite of an amount is the amount you add to it to get the zero. Find the opposite of each of the seven amounts in problem 3.

### A LONG MONTH

The King can never remember which month it is and how many days the month has. He decides to start a new calendar, with a single infinite month, the month of *Evary,* named after himself. This is what the calendar looks like.

| | | | Evary | | | |
|---|---|---|---|---|---|---|
| Mo | Tu | We | Th | Fr | Sa | Su |
| | | | 1 | 2 | 3 | 4 |
| 5 | 6 | 7 | 8 | 9 | 10 | 11 |
| 12 | 13 | 14 | 15 | 16 | 17 | 18 |
| 19 | 20 | 21 | 22 | 23 | 24 | 25 |
| 26 | 27 | 28 | 29 | 30 | 31 | 32 |
| 33 | 34 | 35 | 36 | 37 | 38 | ... |

6. What day of the week will it be on Evary 100th? Explain how you figured it out.

The King is so pleased with the new calendar that he decides to invent a new kind of math. He calls it *Calendar Math.* In Calendar Math, Monday + Tuesday →

$$5 + 6 = 11 \rightarrow \text{Sunday,}$$
or, more briefly, Mo + Tu = Su.

7. Check whether, if you picked different numbers for Monday (such as 12, 19, etc.) and Tuesday (13, 20, etc.), you would still get Sunday for the sum.

8. Make an addition table for Calendar Math. It should be a seven-by-seven table, with the days of the week along the left side and across the top and their sums inside the table.

9. *Calendar Zero* is a day of the week such that, when you add it to any other day, you get that other day for the answer. What day is Calendar Zero?

10. Find the *Calendar Opposite* for each day of the week. That is the day you add to a given day to get Calendar Zero. If a day does not have an opposite, or is its own opposite, explain.

11. Calculate.
    a. Mo + Mo
    b. Mo + Mo + Mo
    c. Mo + Mo + Mo + Mo, etc.

12. How many times do you add Mo to itself to get back Mo?

13. Make a multiplication table for Calendar Math. Here is an example of a result that would appear in it.
    Mo · Tu → 5 · 6 = 30 → Fr,
    so,    Mo · Tu = Fr.

14. What is special about Calendar Zero in multiplication?

15. *Calendar One* is a day of the week such that when you multiply it by any other day, you get that other day for the answer. What day is Calendar One?

16. The *Calendar Reciprocal* of a day is the day you multiply it by to get Calendar One. Find the Calendar Reciprocal for each day. If a day does not have a reciprocal, or is its own reciprocal, explain.

17. Calculate $Su^2$, $Su^3$, etc. What power of Su is equal to Su?

18. **Summary** Summarize Calendar Math.

# Similar Figures

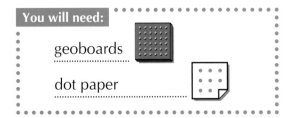

## EQUIVALENT FRACTIONS

1. Using a rubber band, connect the origin and (6, 9). The line misses most geoboard pegs, but it goes *exactly* over two of them (in addition to the pegs it connects). What are their coordinates?

Problem 1 provides a way to find equivalent fractions on the geoboard. If you think of (6, 9) as representing 6/9, you have found two other fractions equivalent to it, making this a set of three equivalent geoboard fractions.

2. **Exploration** Find as many sets of equivalent geoboard fractions as possible. Do not use zero in the numerator or denominator. There are 56 fractions distributed in 19 sets. Do not include sets that consist of just one fraction.

## ENLARGING WITHOUT DISTORTION

3. a. Make the face of an alien with rubber bands on your geoboard. The whole face needs to fit in the bottom left quarter of the board. In other words, none of the coordinates can be greater than 5. Don't make it too complicated.

   b. Make a record of the coordinates you used. You will need those in the next problems.

   c. Copy the face on dot paper.

4. Doubling the *x*-coordinates and leaving the *y*-coordinates the same, make a copy of your alien's face on dot paper. This is called the (2*x*, *y*) copy.

5. Repeat problem 4, but this time leave the *x*-coordinates as in the original and double the *y*-coordinates only. This is called the (*x*, 2*y*) copy.

6. Repeat problem 4 again, with both *x*- and *y*-coordinates doubled. This is called the (2*x*, 2*y*) copy.

7. **Summary** Write a paragraph answering these questions: Which of the copies looks most like an enlarged version of the original? How are the other copies distorted?

8. Write a story about the alien's adventures, explaining why its face went through these changes.

9. Enlarge the following figures without distortion. Explain how you did it.

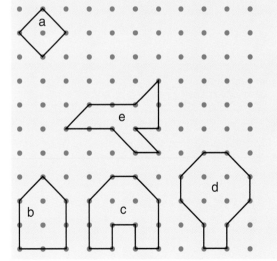

## SIMILAR RECTANGLES

**Definition:** When one figure can be obtained from another by enlarging it or shrinking it without distortion, the figures are said to be *similar.*

10. Make a rectangle having vertices at (0, 0), (4, 0), (4, 6), and (0, 6). Find a smaller rectangle that is similar to it by finding a number you can multiply the given coordinates by to get whole number coordinates that will fit on the geoboard. Sketch both on the same figure.

11. Repeat problem 10, but find a larger rectangle that is similar to the given one. Sketch it on the same figure as in problem 10.

The following questions are about the three rectangles from problems 10 and 11.

12. Connect the origin with the opposite vertex in the largest rectangle. Does your rubber band pass through vertices of the other two rectangles?

13. What are the length and width of each rectangle? How are they related to each other?

14. Can you think of a *single number* that tells what all three rectangles have in common?

Here are two ways to tell whether two rectangles are similar.

**Geoboard diagonal method:** Make both rectangles in the bottom left of a geoboard, with one vertex on the origin, and sides along the *x*- and *y*-axes. Then connect the origin to the opposite vertex of the larger rectangle. If the diagonal you created passes exactly over the vertex of the smaller rectangle, they are similar.

**Calculator division method:** Check whether the ratio of the dimensions is the same in both the rectangles.

**Example:**
a. a 2-by-6 rectangle and a 3-by-8 rectangle
b. a 2-by-6 rectangle and a 3-by-9 rectangle

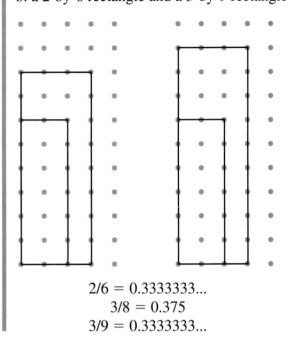

$$2/6 = 0.3333333...$$
$$3/8 = 0.375$$
$$3/9 = 0.3333333...$$

15. Explain the results of the two methods in this example.

You may know other methods for recognizing whether fractions are equivalent. You can use those also, to determine whether rectangles are similar.

16. **Summary** Explain how the ideas of *similar rectangles* and *equivalent fractions* are related.

17. 💡 Are these two rectangles similar? The first one has vertices: (0, 1), (2, 0), (4, 4), and (2, 5). The other one has vertices (7, 3), (9, 6), (3, 10), and (1, 7). Since the methods outlined above will probably not work, explain how you arrive at your answer.

**18.** Write an expression using
- the numbers 1, 2, and -3, in any order,
- two subtractions,

in as many ways as possible.

In each case, calculate the value of the expression.

**Examples:** $2 - 1 - -3 = 4$
$2 - (1 - -3) = -2$
$(-3 - 1) - 2 = -6$

**19.** Do the commutative and associative laws apply to subtraction? Explain.

Clock Math can be defined by saying that only the numbers on the face of a clock (1, 2, ..., 12) are used. In Clock Math, $5 + 9 = 2$, and $5 \times 9 = 9$. This is because when you pass 12, you keep counting around the clock.

**20.** **Report** Write a report on Clock Math. You may start with a science fiction or fantasy story to explain an imaginary origin for Clock Math. Your report should include, but not be limited to, answers to the following questions: Is there a *Clock Zero*? What is it? Does every number have a *Clock Opposite*? What is it? Is there a *Clock One*? Does every number have a *Clock Reciprocal*? What is it? Don't forget to make addition and multiplication tables.

Reg works for Algebank. He was trying to analyze the investment plan described in the first lesson of this chapter. He decided to use $x$'s and $y$'s in his analysis. He wrote:

$x$ = amount of money the person invests
$y$ = amount of money the person has after one month

Since the bank doubles the investor's money and deducts the $100 fee, the function relating $x$ and $y$ is $y = 2x - 100$.

1. Make a function diagram for this function.

2. Use your function diagram to find out
   a. how much an investor, who had $300 after one month, started with;
   b. how much an investor, who started with $300, had after one month.

3. Use your function diagram to find the amount of money the investor started with, who ended up with the same amount of money after one month. (This is called the *fixed point* of the function.)

4. What happens to an investor who starts out with an amount of money less than the fixed point? With an amount of money greater than the fixed point?

To analyze what happens to an investment over a period of more than one month, Reg connected function diagrams. Since the amount at the end of the first month is the amount at the beginning of the second month, he used the $y$-number line from the first diagram as the $x$-number line of the next, doing this many times.

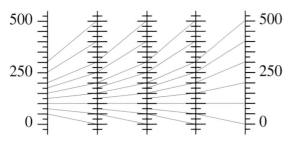

5. Describe what the linked function diagrams show.

6. How could one use a single-function diagram to follow what would happen to an investment over a period of more than one month?

7. 🔑 Use Reg's method to analyze a plan where the investment is multiplied by 1.5 and the service charge is $50. Describe what your linked diagrams show.

8. Compare the plan in problem 7 with the first plan for someone who invests
   a. $90;    b. $100;    c. $110.

9. Which do you think has a bigger influence on the amount of money the investor makes, the service charge, or the number by which the investment is multiplied? Write an explanation supporting your opinion. Use several examples.

10. Explain why Al thought it was important to know whether the service charge was deducted before or after the money was doubled. Use some examples. Express each policy with a function.

11. **Report** Write a report on investment plans of the type studied in this assignment and in Lesson 1, plus, optionally, other plans of your design. Use variables. Your report should include, but not be limited to, answers to problems 9 and 10.

12. **Project** Find out what the service charge and interest rate are at three real banks. Figure out what would happen to $100 invested at each service charge and interest rate over a period of three years. Write up what you discover as if it were an article for the school newspaper, and you were giving advice to students.

# ◆ Essential Ideas

## WORKING BACKWARDS

Abe and Bea had baked a batch of cookies. They told Reg, Al, and Lara that they could each have one-third of the cookies. Later, Reg went into the kitchen and took one-third of the cookies. An hour after that, not knowing that Reg had already taken his share, Lara claimed one-third of the remaining cookies. A few minutes later Al, thinking he was the first to find the cookies, devoured one-third of what was left.

**1.** If 8 cookies are left, how many must Abe and Bea have baked?

## TWO NEGATIVES

**2.** Find the sign of the result.
   a. $3 - 5$      b. $3 - (-5)$
   c. $-5 - (3)$      d. $-5 - (-3)$

**3.** Find the sign of the result.
   a. $-(5)(-3)$      b. $-(5 - 3)$
   c. $-[-3 - (-5)]$      d. $-(-5)(-3)$

## POSITIVE, NEGATIVE, OR ZERO?

**4.** For each expression, write $P$, $N$, and/or $0$, depending on whether it can possibly be positive, negative, or 0. (Try various values for the variables to help you decide. For example, -2, 0, and 2.) Explain your answers.
   a. $5x$      b. $-2x^2$
   c. $-9y$      d. $5y^2$
   e. $z^3$      f. $-a^4$

## SIMPLIFYING EXPRESSIONS

Simplify each expression.

**5.** $12x - 6xy - (-3x) - (-2y)$

**6.** $-3x^2 - (3)2 + x^2 - (2 - x^2)$

**7.** $x - (x - 5) - (5 - x)$

## FROM WORDS TO ALGEBRA

**8.** a. Translate each step into algebra.
      1) Think of a number.
      2) Add 4.
      3) Multiply the result by 2.
   b. If I got 46, what was my original number?

**9.** a. Translate each step into algebra.
      1) Think of a number.
      2) Multiply by 2.
      3) Add 4.
   b. If I got 46, what was my original number?
   c. Compare your answer to part (b) with your answer to part (b) in problem 8. Were your answers the same or different? Explain.

## COMPARING EXPRESSIONS

**10.** Find a value of $x$ for which
   a. $-8x - 1$ is less than $8x + 3$;
   b. $-8x - 1$ is greater than $8x + 3$;
   c. 💡 $-8x - 1$ is equal to $8x + 3$.

## MULTIPLICATION TABLES

Find these products. Combine like terms.

**11.** $(x + 3)(2x + 4)$

**12.** $(x + 3)(2x + 4y)$

**13.** $(x + 3 + y)(2x + 4y)$

Fill in the blanks.

**14.**

| ___ | $x$ | $-3$ | $5y$ |
|---|---|---|---|
| | $2x^2$ | $-6x$ | $10xy$ |

**15.**

| | ___ | ___ | ___ |
|---|---|---|---|
| $3y$ | $-6x^2y$ | $15y^3$ | $-3y$ |

**16.** _____ $(x - 2) = 2 - x$

## OPPOSITES AND RECIPROCALS

**17.** Simplify each expression. Look for short-cuts.

a. $9 \cdot \frac{1}{3} \cdot \frac{2}{3} \cdot 5 \cdot \frac{3}{2}$

b. $[5x - (-5x)] - [5x - (-5x)] - 16x$

c. $0.5 \cdot 25 \cdot 0.02 \cdot 2$

**18.** Gabe and Abe were arguing about $xy$. Gabe said that the opposite of $xy$ is $yx$. Abe said that the opposite of $xy$ is $-xy$. Lara overheard them, and said she thought that the opposite of $xy$ is $-yx$. Write an explanation that will settle their argument.

**19.** What numbers are

a. greater than their reciprocal?

b. less than their reciprocal?

c. equal to their reciprocal?

d. less than their opposite?

e. equal to their opposite?

**20.** a. Which of the following is the reciprocal of $3x$?

$$\frac{1}{3x}, \ \frac{3}{x}, \ \text{or} \ \frac{1}{3}$$

b. Check your answer by substituting two different numbers for $x$ and showing that the product of $3x$ and its reciprocal is 1 in both cases.

## INVERSE FUNCTIONS

Write the inverse of each of the following functions.

**21.** a. The function adds 2 to $x$ and multiplies the result by 4.

b. The function multiplies $x$ by 4 and adds 2 to the result.

c. 💡 $y = 7x - 4$

**22.** a. The function takes the opposite of $x$.

b. The function takes the opposite of $x$, adds 5, and divides the result by 2.

c. 💡 $y = \frac{3 - x}{6}$

Scientists sometimes use the Kelvin temperature scale. To convert Kelvin temperatures to Celsius, you subtract 273. For example, the melting temperature of iron is 1808° Kelvin, or 1535° Celsius.

**23.** Lead melts at 600° Kelvin. What temperature is that in Fahrenheit? (Use the information from Lesson 8.)

**24.** Explain how to convert Kelvin temperatures to Fahrenheit, and how to convert Fahrenheit to Kelvin. (Hint: Use arrows to show each step of the conversion.)

**25.** a. Make a function diagram for the function $y_1 = (x/2) + 1$.

b. Make the function diagram of its inverse and find the rule.

c. Find the function that results from combining $y_1$ and its inverse. Does the order in which you combine the functions matter? Explain.

## SOLVING EQUATIONS

Use the cover-up method to solve these equations.

**26.** $\frac{24}{x - 5} + 3 = 9$    **27.** $\frac{x - 5}{24} + 3 = 9$

**28.** $\frac{5 - x}{24} + 3 = 9$    **29.** $\frac{24}{5 - x} + 3 = 9$

**30.** Compare the solutions to each pair of equations. (Use related multiplication equations.)

a. $\frac{2}{M} = 6$ and $\frac{6}{M} = 2$

b. $\frac{8}{M} = 4$ and $\frac{4}{M} = 8$

c. $\frac{20}{M} = 5$ and $\frac{5}{M} = 20$

d. Make up another example like this.

**31.** Describe the pattern you found in problem 30. Explain why it works.

# PRACTICE

1. $x + 0.2x$    2. $x - 0.2x$

3. $x + 0.8x$    4. $x + (1/4)x$

5. $x - (1/4)x$

## PREVIEW    EQUAL RATIOS

The equations below all involve two equal ratios. Find the value of $x$ that will make the ratios equal. You may want to use trial and error with your calculator.

6. $\frac{x}{4} = \frac{6}{1}$    7. $\frac{3}{x} = \frac{5}{7}$

8. $\frac{x}{3} = \frac{5}{7}$    9. $\frac{3}{1} = \frac{6}{x + 7}$

10. $\frac{4}{5} = \frac{6}{x + 7}$

11. For each equation, use trial and error to find a value of $n$ that makes it true.
    a. $3n + 10 = 5n$
    b. $5n + 10 = 3n$
    c. $7n + 10 = 8n$
    d. $8n + 10 = 7n$

12. Use trial and error or the cover-up method to solve these equations.
    a. $2(x + 5) = 8$
    b. $5 + 2(x + 4) = 19$
    c. $3(2x + 4) - 7 = 11$
    d. $-4(10x - 3) - 6 = -14$

13. Find a positive integer that satisfies each equation.
    a. $3n - 1 = 47$
    b. $n^2 - 5 = 59$

14. Find a negative integer and a positive integer that satisfy the equation
$$n^2 - n = 20.$$

# CHAPTER 4

The spiral curve of a West African chameleon's tail

## *Coming in this chapter:*

### Exploration

- Find as many functions as possible whose graphs go through the origin.

- Find as many functions as possible whose output is 5 when the input is 2.

# INTERPRETING GRAPHS

# 4.1 A 100-Mile Trip

**You will need:**
graph paper

1. By which of these methods do you think a person could travel 100 miles in one day? Explain how you arrive at your guess.

   walking                running

   bicycling              ice skating

   riding a scooter       riding in a car

   riding in a helicopter

2. Ophelia and Xavier are traveling along a road. If you could view the road from above and make a sketch of what you saw every ten minutes, your sketches might look something like the figure below.

   a. Which person (O or X) is traveling faster?

   b. If the entire length of the road is six miles, can you figure out approximately how fast each person is traveling? Explain.

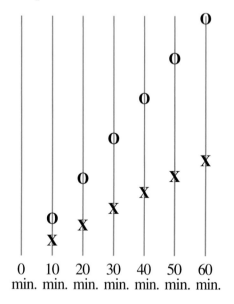

**TIME VS. SPEED**

3. Copy and complete this table showing how many hours it would take each person to travel 100 miles.

| Person | Mode of Travel | Speed (mph) | Time (hours) |
|--------|---------------|-------------|--------------|
| Abe | walking | 4 | 25 |
| Al | van | 50 | |
| Bea | skating | 10 | |
| Gabe | scooter | 30 | |
| Lara | helicopter | 100 | |
| Lea | bike | 25 | |
| Reg | running | 8 | |

4. Copy and complete the graph that shows how long it would take for each person to make the 100-mile trip.

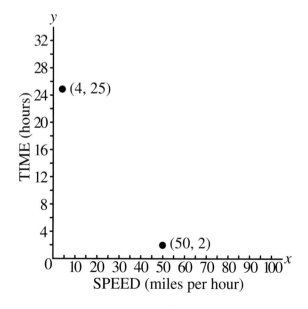

*Chapter 4  Interpreting Graphs*

**5.** Generalization

   a. What pattern do you notice in the table?

   b. How long would it take for someone who travels at a constant speed of $S$ miles per hour to cover 100 miles?

**DISTANCE VS. TIME**

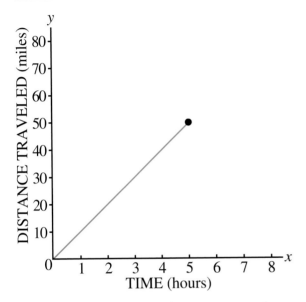

**6.** The graph shows Bea's progress on the trip. It shows that after 5 hours of roller-skating she had traveled 50 miles.

   a. Copy the graph onto graph paper. Use a whole piece of graph paper. You will be adding more to this graph.

   b. One of the points on the graph is (5, 50). Mark and label three more points on the graph of Bea's progress.

**7.** In this lesson we are assuming everyone travels at a constant speed. How valid is this assumption? For each mode of travel what might make it impossible to travel at a constant speed? Explain.

The table shows how long it took for Abe to go certain distances.

**Abe's Progress**

| Time (hours) | Distance (miles) |
| --- | --- |
| 1 | 4 |
| 2 | 8 |

**8.** a. Copy and complete the table up to 20 miles.

   b. For this problem, use the same axes you used for Bea. Plot and label the points from the table in part (a).

   c. Connect the points with a straight line. Then find and label a point that is on the line but not in your table. Interpret the coordinates of the point in terms of this problem.

**9.** Make a table like the one you made for Abe showing Gabe's progress on his scooter and Al's progress in the van. Make graphs of their progress on the same axes you used to show Abe's and Bea's progress. Label the four different lines.

**10.** Use your graphs to help you answer these questions. If Bea and Abe start out at the same time,

   a. how far apart will they be after one hour?

   b. how far apart will they be after two hours?

**11.** Generalization Look for a pattern. How far apart will Abe and Bea be after $H$ hours? Explain.

12. Mrs. Gral was traveling at a constant speed. She started at the same time as Abe, and was two miles ahead of him after one hour.
    a. Add a graph of Mrs. Gral's progress to your axes.
    b. How far ahead was Mrs. Gral after two hours?
    c. After three hours, how far was Mrs. Gral behind Bea?
    d. How fast was Mrs. Gral going? What mode of travel do you think she was using?

13. **Summary**
    a. How does the mode of travel affect the steepness of the line? Explain.
    b. What is the meaning of points on two of the graphs that have the same $x$-coordinate but different $y$-coordinates?
    c. What is the meaning of the vertical distance between two lines for a given value of $x$?

**DISTANCE VS. SPEED**

14. Using the same speed data, figure out how far each person could travel in two-and-a-half hours. Make a table and a graph showing speed on the horizontal axis and distance on the vertical axis.

15. ⚷ How would the graph be changed if the travel time was greater? Less? Explain.

**SPEED BY GRAPHS AND FORMULAS**

16. **Summary** Each graph in this lesson gives information on how fast people travel, but it does it in a different way. Explain.

17. **Generalization** If someone is traveling at a constant speed of $S$ miles per hour, for a distance of $D$ miles, and takes $T$ hours, what is the relationship between $S$, $D$, and $T$? Write this relationship in more than one way.

**DISCOVERY** *FRAMING PHOTOGRAPHS*

A photograph is mounted on a background which sticks out one inch on each side. The width of the photo is two inches and the height is three inches.

18. a. Sketch the photo and its frame.
    b. What are the dimensions of the frame?
    c. Are the photo and frame similar rectangles? Explain.

19. The photo needs to be enlarged so it will fit in a frame having a height of 12 inches. Again, the width of the frame is to be one inch. Find the dimensions of the enlarged photo and its frame. Of course the photo cannot be distorted!

20. Is the frame for the enlarged picture similar to the picture? Is it similar to the original frame? Explain.

# Points, Graphs, and Equations

## PATTERNS FROM POINTS

1.  a. Draw a pair of axes and plot these
       points.

| x | y |
|---|---|
| 0 | -1 |
| -2 | -3 |
| -5 | -6 |
| 5 | 4 |

   b. Study the table and your graph.
      Describe the relationship between the
      x-value and y-value of each pair.

   c. Use the pattern you found to add more
      points to your table and graph.

   d. Write an equation that tells how to get
      the y-value from the x-value.

2.  Repeat problem 1 for each of these tables.

   a.

| x | y |
|---|---|
| 4 | -8 |
| 1 | -2 |
| -3 | 6 |
| 0 | 0 |

   b.

| x | y |
|---|---|
| -3 | -3 |
| 5 | -3 |
| -6 | -3 |
| -1 | -3 |

   c.

| x | y |
|---|---|
| 6 | 4 |
| 12 | -2 |
| -1 | 11 |
| 3 | 7 |

## GRAPHS FROM PATTERNS

3.  For each description below, make a table
    of at least five (x, y) pairs that fit it. Then
    graph the (x, y) pairs. Use a separate coor-
    dinate system for each graph.

    a. The y-coordinate is always equal to the
       x-coordinate.

    b. The y-coordinate is always four less
       than the x-coordinate.

    c. The y-coordinate is always one-half of
       the x-coordinate.

    d. The y-coordinate is always the opposite
       of the x-coordinate.

    e. The y-coordinate is always the square
       of the x-coordinate.

## EQUATIONS FROM PATTERNS

4.  For each description in problem 3, find an
    equation that describes the relationship
    between x and y. Write the equations on
    your graphs.

5.  a. Make a table of four number pairs (x, y)
       that have this property: The sum of x
       and y is always 6.

    b. Graph these (x, y) pairs.

    c. Connect the points with a straight line.

    d. Write the relationship between x and y
       as an equation.

6.  a. Using fractions and negative numbers,
       write two more (x, y) pairs having the
       property that the sum of x and y is 6.
       Do these points lie on the line?

    b. Choose a point that is not on the line.
       Do its (x, y) coordinates add up to 6?

    c. Write any number pair (x, y) whose sum
       is not 6. Find this point. Is it on the line
       you drew?

On each graph below, four points are labeled. For each graph:

   a. Make a table of the (*x*, *y*) pairs and look for a relationship between *x* and *y*.

   b. Add three more points to the table, making sure each one does belong on the graph.

   c. Write an equation describing the relationship between *x* and *y*.

**7.**

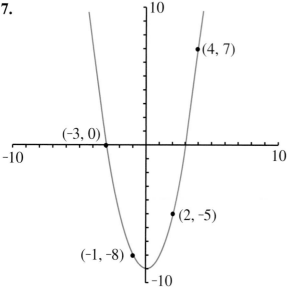

**8.**

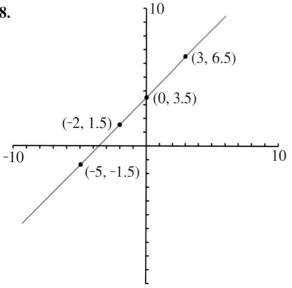

**9.**

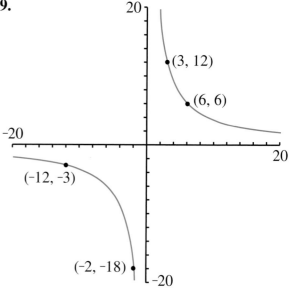

**10.**

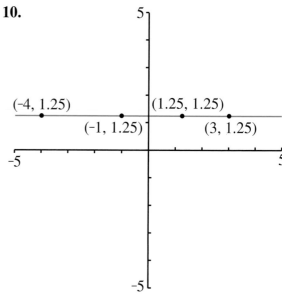

The following questions are about the graph of the function $y = 4x + 5$. Try to answer the questions without graphing.

**11.** Is the point (7, 32) on it? Explain.

**12.** The point (3, *y*) is on it. What is *y*? Explain.

**13.** The point (*x*, 6) is on it. What is *x*? Explain.

# Polynomial Functions

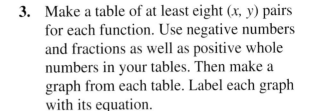

**You will need:**

graph paper

**Definition:** A *polynomial function* is a function of the form $y$ = a polynomial.

1. **Exploration** Which of these polynomial functions do you think have graphs that are straight lines? Which have curved graphs? Explain why you think so.
   a. $y = x^2$       b. $y = 2x - 1$
   c. $y = 2x^2$       d. $y = x^3$

## ORDER OF OPERATIONS

2. Make a table of at least eight $(x, y)$ pairs for each function. Use negative numbers and fractions as well as positive whole numbers in your tables. Then make a graph from each table. Label each graph with its equation. You will need to refer to these graphs later.
   a. $y = x^2$       b. $y = x^3$

To make a table of values for graphing $y = -x^2$, we have to know what the expression $-x^2$ means. Does it mean *square x, then take its opposite* or *take the opposite of x, then square it*? Which operation should be done first?

To avoid this kind of confusion, mathematicians have agreed on the following rule.

**Rule:** *Exponentiation should be performed before other operations.* To change this order, we have to use parentheses.

**Examples:**
• $-x^2$ means *square x, then take the opposite.*
• $(-x)^2$ means *take the opposite of x, then square the result.*

3. Make a table of at least eight $(x, y)$ pairs for each function. Use negative numbers and fractions as well as positive whole numbers in your tables. Then make a graph from each table. Label each graph with its equation.
   a. $y = (-x)^2$       b. $y = -x^2$

4. ⌛ Compare your graphs in problem 3 with the graph of $y = x^2$. Explain what you observe.

5. Graph these polynomial functions.
   a. $y = -x^3$       b. $y = (-x)^3$

6. ⌛ Compare your graphs in problem 5 with the graph of $y = x^3$. Explain what you observe.

## DEGREE

**Definition:** The degree of a polynomial function in one variable is the highest power of the variable that appears in the polynomial.

**Examples:** $y = x^3$ and $y = x^2 + 2x^3$ are both third-degree polynomial functions. The equation $y = 2x$ is first-degree, and the equation $y = 1$ is zero-degree.

7. What is the degree of each of these polynomial functions?
   a. $y = 5 + x^2 - x$
   b. $y = 4x^3 - 3x^2 + 5$
   c. $y = 45$

8. Make a table of at least eight values for each third-degree function. Use negative numbers and fractions as well as positive whole numbers in your tables. Then make a graph from each table.
   a. $y = 2x^3$       b. $y = x^3 + 1$
   c. $y = -x^3 - 2$

**9.** Repeat problem 8 for these second-degree functions.

a. $y = x^2 - 1$    b. $y = -3x^2$

c. $y = -x^2 + 2$

**10.** Graph these first-degree functions.

a. $y = 5x$    b. $y = x$

c. $y = -2x + 1$

**11.** Graph these zero-degree functions.

a. $y = 4$    b. $y = -3$

c. $y = 0$

THE EFFECT OF DEGREE

**12.** ⚷ Tell whether each sentence (a-b) could describe the graph of a zero-degree, first-degree, second-degree, or third-degree polynomial function. More than one answer may be possible for each description.

a. The graph is a straight line.

b. The graph is a curve.

**13.** ⚷ Repeat problem 12 for these descriptions.

a. The graph goes through the origin.

b. The graph never crosses the $x$-axis.

c. The graph never crosses the $y$-axis.

**14.** ⚷ Repeat problem 12 for these descriptions.

a. The graph passes through quadrants I and III only.

b. The graph passes through quadrants II and IV only.

c. The graph passes through quadrants I and II only.

**15.** Summary  How does the degree of the equation affect its graph? Write a summary explaining everything you know about this.

**16.** 💡

a. Make a table of values and graph the function $y = 24/x$.

b. Is this a polynomial function? Explain.

---

**REVIEW**  *POSSIBLE OR IMPOSSIBLE?*

**17.** Decide whether each of the following situations is possible or impossible. If it is possible, give an example. If it is impossible, explain *why* it is impossible. Can you subtract

a. a negative number from a negative number to get a positive number?

b. a negative number from a negative number to get a negative number?

c. a negative number from a positive number to get a positive number?

d. a negative number from a positive number to get a negative number?

e. a positive number from a negative number to get a negative number?

f. a positive number from a negative number to get a positive number?

# Graphs Through Points

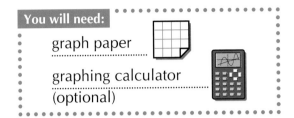

**You will need:**

graph paper

graphing calculator
(optional)

## INTERCEPTS

**Definitions:** The *y-intercept* of a graph is the point where the graph crosses the *y*-axis. The *x-intercept* of a graph is the point where the graph crosses the *x*-axis.

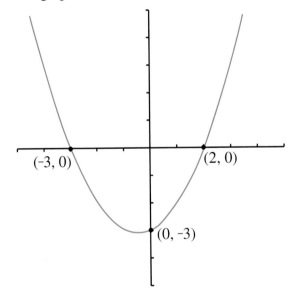

(−3, 0)  (2, 0)  (0, −3)

**Example:** The curve in the figure above has *y*-intercept (0, −3), and *x*-intercepts (−3, 0) and (2, 0).

For problems 1-5:

a. Guess the coordinates of the *x*- and *y*-intercepts (if you think they exist).

b. *On graph paper* draw the graph described.

c. Check the correctness of your guess.

**1.** A line is parallel to the *y*-axis and passes through the point (2, −3).

**2.** A line passes through the origin and the point (2, −3).

**3.** The sum of every $(x, y)$ pair on the line is 8.

**4.** The line passes through the points (2, −3) and (3, −2).

**5.** To get the *y*-coordinate, square the *x*-coordinate and add 1.

## POINTS ON AND OFF GRAPHS

**6.** Bea thinks that $8 - 2x$ means *multiply x by 2 and subtract the result from 8.* Lea thinks it means *subtract 2 from 8 and multiply the result by x.* Who is right? Explain.

**7.** Which of these points do you think will lie on the graph of $y = 8 - 2x$? Explain.
a. (2, 4)          b. (2, −4)
c. (0.5, 6)        d. (0.5, −6)
e. (−1, −10)       f. (−1, 10)

For the remaining problems in this lesson (8-23), use a graphing calculator if you have one. Otherwise, use graph paper.

**8.** a. Graph $y = 8 - 2x$.
b. Use your graph to check your answers to problem (a).
c. Write both coordinates of the *x*-intercept of $y = 8 - 2x$.
d. Write both coordinates of the *y*-intercept of $y = 8 - 2x$.

**Definition:** If two graphs share a point, they are said to *intersect* at that point.

**9.** a. On the same coordinate system, graph $y = 2x - 8$.
b. Do your two graphs intersect at any point? If so, where?

Follow these instructions for problems 10 through 12 below.

   a. Make tables of values for the two functions given. Then graph them on the same pair of axes. Label at least three points on each graph.

   b. Find and label a point that is not on either graph.

   c. Find and label a point that is on both graphs (if there is one).

   d. Find and label a point that is in the region between the two graphs.

   e. Find and label a point that is neither on nor between the graphs.

**10.** $y = 2x$ and $y = 0.5x$

**11.** $y = x$ and $y = x + 2$

**12.** $y = x^2$ and $y = x^2 - 3$

**13.** For problems 10-12, find an equation whose graph is entirely contained between the two given graphs.

### FIND AN EQUATION

In problems 14-17, find the equation of any graph that satisfies the characteristics given.

**14.** A second-degree function whose graph passes through the point $(0, 0)$

**15.** A second-degree function whose graph passes through the point $(0, 1)$

**16.** A third-degree function whose graph passes through the point $(0, -1)$

**17.** A first-degree function whose graph passes through the point $(-1, -1)$

**18.** a. Write any equation whose graph contains the point $(1, 2)$.

   b. Write any other equation whose graph passes through the point $(1, 2)$.

   c. Graph the two equations. Where do they intersect?

**19.** Report  Write a report explaining the answers to these questions. Use examples in your explanations.

   a. Given an equation, how can you figure out which points lie on its graph?

   b. Given a point and an equation, how can you tell whether or not the point lies on the graph of the equation?

### GRAPHS THROUGH THE ORIGIN

**20.** Which of the following equations have graphs that go through the origin? How could one tell without actually graphing them?

   a. $y = 2x - 6$    b. $y = x^2 - x$
   c. $y = -x^3 - 4$

**21.** Give three equations (one each of first, second, and third degree) that satisfy each of these two given conditions.

   a. The graph will pass through the origin.

   b. The graph will not pass through the origin.

**22.** Write the equation of a graph that lies in quadrants I and III *only* and

   a. passes through the origin;

   b. ⚪ does not pass through the origin.

**23.** Summary  Explain how you can tell from an equation whether or not its graph goes through the origin. Give some examples.

# 4.A The Bicycle Trip

Sally is riding her bike on a trip with her bicycle club. She left the staging area in Chapley at 10 A.M. and took a break at a rest area located about halfway to the final destination of Berkhill, 70 miles away. Neil is driving the sweep vehicle, a van with food, water, first aid, and a bicycle rack. The distance-time graph below shows their progress. There are train tracks along the road. The progress of a train is also shown on the graph.

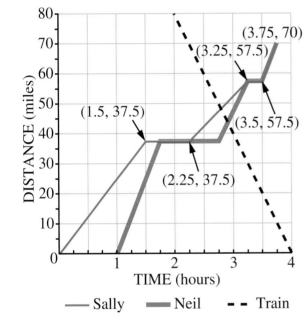

TIME (hours)

—— Sally    ▬▬ Neil    – – Train

1.  Compare Sally's and Neil's progress. Who left first? Where did she or he stop? What happened at the end? What was the total distance covered?

2.  Including the origin, the coordinates of six points on Sally's graph are given. Describe her ride between consecutive points.
    a.  At what time did each leg of her trip start and end? How far did she ride each time? How long did it take? How long were her breaks?
    b.  How fast was she going during each leg of the trip?

3.  a.  If you were to guess about which part of the trip was downhill or uphill, what would you guess? Why?

    b.  How else might one account for the different speeds?

4.  How fast did Neil drive in each leg of his trip?

5.  Describe the train's progress. Which way was it going? Where and when did it pass Sally and Neil?

6.  Where were Sally, Neil, and the train at 12:30 P.M.?

7.  At what times were Sally, Neil, and the train 20 miles from the staging area?

8.  The equation of the train's motion is $D = 160 - 40t$.
    a.  Choose three points on the train's graph and check that their coordinates satisfy the equation.
    b.  Do any points in Sally's and Neil's graphs satisfy the train's equation? If so, which ones?

9.  **Summary**
    a.  In a distance-time graph, what does it mean if two points are on the same horizontal line? On the same vertical line?
    b.  As you go from left to right on the graph, what is the meaning of a part that goes up? Down? What is the meaning of a horizontal segment? Why is a vertical segment impossible?
    c.  What is the significance of a point that belongs to the motion graphs of two different people?

10. **Report** Tell the story of the bicycle trip. Use information you gathered from the graph. Make guesses about the trip. Include a graph for Irva, another member of the bicycle club. She too left at 10 A.M. and stopped at the rest area.

4.5

# Lines Through the Origin

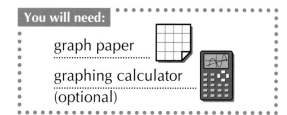

**You will need:**

graph paper

graphing calculator
(optional)

**Definition:** Since the graphs of first-degree equations are straight lines, these equations are also called *linear* equations.

1. Predict whether or not the graph of each linear equation will pass through the origin. Explain how you know, using graphs or calculations.

   a. $y = 4 - 2x$      b. $y = -2x$

   c. $y = 2x$          d. $y = 2x - 4$

2. Write two linear equations which you think will have graphs through the origin. Explain your reasoning.

---
**RATIO**
---

Lara and Lea were arguing about points and graphs. Lea said, "If the point (1, 4) lies on the line, then the point (2, 8) must also lie on the line." Lara showed her that she was wrong by drawing three lines.

3. On graph paper, draw a line that goes

   a. through both points;

   b. through (1, 4) but not through (2, 8);

   c. through (2, 8) but not through (1, 4).

4. Of the three lines you drew in problem 3, which goes through the origin?

5. a. Plot and label at least three more points that are on the line through (1, 4) and (2, 8).

   b. Find the equation of the line through (1, 4) and (2, 8).

6. ⟜ Plot these eight points on the same axes. Label them with their coordinates.

   (1, 2)        (-1, -2)       (1, -2)

   (-1, 2)       (3, 6)         (-3, -6)

   (6, 3)        (6, -3)

   a. Draw a line connecting each point with the origin. Which points lie on the same line through the origin?

   b. Explain how to find the equations of the lines you drew.

**Definition:** The *ratio* of a to b is the result of the division a/b.

**Example:** The ratio of 6 to 3 is 6/3 or 2, while the ratio of 3 to 6 is 3/6, or 1/2, or 0.5.

7. a. Write two $(x, y)$ pairs for which the ratio of $y$ to $x$ is 1/3.

   b. Plot these two points and graph the straight line through them. Find the equation of the line.

   c. Write two $(x, y)$ pairs for which the ratio of $y$ to $x$ is 3.

   d. Plot these two points and graph the straight line through them. Find the equation of the line.

**8.** For each line in the graph below, find three points on the line. Then find an equation for the line.

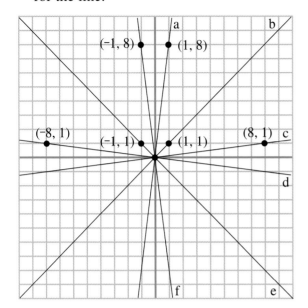

**9.** Explain how you can find more points on the same line through the origin as (4, 5) without drawing a graph. Then check by graphing the line. Find the equation of the line.

Lea noticed that for the points (1, 4) and (2, 8) the ratio of the *y*-value to the *x*-value was the same. That is, 4/1 = 8/2. She guessed that (100, 400) will lie on the same line through the origin because the ratio of the *y*-value to the *x*-value is also 4.

**10.** 🗝 Tell whether or not you agree with Lea, and why.

**11.** Find a point whose coordinates have the same ratio of *y* to *x* as the point (4, 12). Does this point lie on the same line through the origin as (4, 12)? If so, find the equation of this line.

**12.** a. Graph the line through (-1, 2) and (3, 4).
   b. Is the ratio of 5 to -10 equal to the ratio of -1 to 2?
   c. Is the point (5, -10) on the line? Explain why or why not.

**13.** Generalization
   a. What would be the ratio of the coordinates of points on the line through the origin and the point (*a*, *b*)? Explain.
   b. If *b*/*a* = *d*/*c*, what can you say about the line joining (*a*, *b*) to (*c*, *d*)? Explain.

**14.** Summary Explain what ratio has to do with lines through the origin.

SPEED

The table shows the amount of time it took several people to travel the distances given.

| Person | Time (hours) | Distance (kilometers) |
|---|---|---|
| A | 3 | 80 |
| B | 7 | 140 |
| C | 12 | 320 |
| D | 1 | 30 |
| E | 2 | 30 |
| F | 1 | 20 |
| G | 5 | 150 |

**15.** a. Draw a pair of axes and label the vertical axis *distance* and the horizontal axis *time*. Plot and label the points in the table. Draw lines connecting each point with the origin.
   b. Which points lie on the same line through the origin?

**16.** Use the table and your graph to answer these questions.
   a. Which people are traveling at the same speed?
   b. Who is traveling faster, *A* or *B*?
   c. How far will *A* have traveled in four hours?

**17. a.** *H* has been traveling two hours at the same speed as *G*. Add *H* to your graph.

   **b.** I have been traveling four hours at the same speed as *A*. Add me to your graph.

**18.** *J* is traveling faster than *B* but more slowly than *D*. Draw one possible distance-time graph showing *J's* progress.

**19.** Each line you drew has an equation that relates distance to time. Find these equations and add them to your graph.

**20.** Summary

   **a.** Explain how one can think of speed as a ratio.

   **b.** If you are given time and distance for two travelers, explain how to use calculations or graphs to compare their speeds.

---

**DISCOVERY** *HAPPY NUMBERS*

Take the number 23.
Square each digit and add.
$$2^2 + 3^2 = 13$$
Repeat this process.
$$1^2 + 3^2 = 10$$
$$1^2 + 0^2 = 1$$
$$1^2 = 1$$
The final result is 1.

Whenever the final result of this procedure is 1, the original number is called a *happy* number. So 23 is a happy number.

**21.** There are 17 two-digit happy numbers. Try to find all of them. It will save you time and help you look for patterns if you keep a neat record of the above process for each number.

**22.** Describe any patterns you notice.

*Chapter 4  Interpreting Graphs*

## 4.6

# In the Lab

**You will need:**

graph paper

### A MYSTERY LIQUID

Reg, Bea, and Gabe were doing an experiment in science class. They had an unknown liquid whose volume they measured in a graduated cylinder. A graduated cylinder is a tall, narrow container that is used for measuring liquid volume accurately. They used a cylinder that weighed 50 grams and measured volume in milliliters. They used a balance to find the weight of the liquid to the nearest gram.

### Reg's Data

| Volume | Weight |
|--------|--------|
| 10 ml  | 16 g   |
| 20 ml  | 32 g   |
| 50 ml  | 80 g   |
| 80 ml  | 128 g  |

1.  Plot Reg's data, with *weight* on the vertical axis and *volume* on the horizontal axis.

2.  Does it make sense to connect the points on your graph? Explain.

3.  Find an equation relating weight to volume.

4.  Estimate the weight of:
    a.  60 ml of liquid;
    b.  1 ml of liquid.

5.  If you add 30 ml to the volume, how much are you adding to the weight? See if you get the same answer in two different cases.

6.  If you double the volume, do you double the weight?

### Bea's Data

| Weight | Volume |
|--------|--------|
| 16 g   | 10 ml  |
| 32 g   | 20 ml  |
| 48 g   | 30 ml  |
| 64 g   | 40 ml  |

7.  Plot Bea's data with *volume* on the vertical axis and *weight* on the horizontal axis.

8.  Connect the points on your graph with a line and write an equation for the line.

9.  Estimate the volume of:
    a.  100 g of liquid;   b.  1 g of liquid.

10. Compare Bea's graph with Reg's graph. Explain the similarities and differences.

We say that Reg graphed weight versus volume, while Bea graphed volume versus weight.

11. If you add 10 ml to the volume, how much are you adding to the weight? See if you get the same answer in three different cases. Is the answer consistent with what you found in Reg's data?

**Definition:** *Density* equals weight per unit of volume. This means that to find the density of the mystery liquid, you would find the weight of 1 ml of the liquid. (Actually, scientists use *mass* rather than *weight,* but we will use weight which is equivalent for our purposes.)

12. Find the density of the mystery liquid, using three different pairs of weight/volume values from Reg's and Bea's data. Do all your answers agree? Explain.

13. In problems 4b and 9b, you have found the weight in grams of one ml of liquid, and the volume in ml of one gram. Multiply the two numbers. Explain the result.

### THE MYSTERY GROWS

### Gabe's Data:

| Volume | Weight |
|--------|--------|
| 10 ml | 66 g |
| 20 ml | 82 g |
| 40 ml | 114 g |
| 60 ml | 146 g |

14. Draw a pair of axes and label the vertical axis *weight* and the horizontal axis *volume*. Plot Gabe's data.

15. If you double the volume, does the weight double? Check this in two cases.

16. If you add 20 ml, how much weight are you adding? Is this consistent with what you learned from Reg's and Bea's data?

17. *According to Gabe's graph,* what is the weight of 0 ml of the liquid? Does this make sense?

18. What might be the real meaning of the y-intercept on Gabe's graph? Did Gabe make a mistake? Explain.

19. Find the density of the mystery liquid by dividing weight by volume for three different pairs of values from Gabe's data. Do all your answers agree? Explain.

20. ◯ Write an equation that expresses weight as a function of volume for Gabe's data.

### DIRECT VARIATION

**Definition:** If the relationship between two variables $x$ and $y$ can be expressed in the form $y = mx$, we call this a *direct variation*, or say that $y$ *varies directly with x.*

21. Which of Reg's, Bea's, and Gabe's data are an example of a direct variation? Explain.

22. Compare Gabe's graph to Reg's. How are they the same and how are they different?

23. ☞ There are number patterns in all the data.
    a. What pattern is there in all of Reg's, Bea's, and Gabe's data?
    b. What patterns are true only of Reg's and Bea's data?

24. **Summary** What do you know about direct variation? Be sure to discuss equation, graph, and number patterns. You may get ideas from this lesson and Lesson 5.

**OTHER SUBSTANCES**

**25.** The graph shows the relationship between weight and volume for some familiar substances. The substances are aluminum, cork, gold, ice, iron, and oak. Which substance do you think is represented by each line? Explain why you think so.

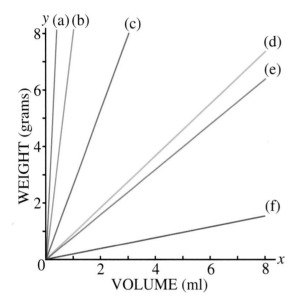

**26.** Using the graph, estimate the densities of the substances in problem 25.

**27.** Project

a. Look up the densities of those substances in a science book, almanac, or other reference book. How close were your estimates?

b. Based on your research, what do you think the mystery liquid is? Could it be water? Explain.

# LESSON
## 4.7

# *Real* Numbers and Estimation

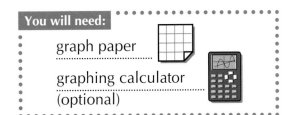

You will need:

graph paper

graphing calculator
(optional)

### MEASUREMENT ERROR

The three tables in Lesson 6 contained data that were invented. You can tell because all the points lie exactly on a line. In real experiments measurements can never be exact. This table contains more realistic data.

| Volume | Weight |
|--------|--------|
| 10 ml | 32 g |
| 20 ml | 63 g |
| 50 ml | 146 g |
| 80 ml | 245 g |

1. Draw and label a pair of axes and plot these points.

2. You cannot draw a straight line through all the points, but draw one that passes as closely as possible to all of them. Be sure your line goes through the origin. (Explain why it must pass through the origin.)

3. What is the equation of the line you drew? (Hint: Choose a point on the line to help you figure this out.)

4. Based on your answer to problem 3, what would you estimate the density of the substance to be?

5. Find the ratio of weight to volume for each data point in the table.

6. Based on your calculations in problem 5, what do you estimate the density of the substance to be?

7. **Summary** You estimated the density of this substance in two different ways. If you did not get the same answer using both methods, explain any differences. Which method do you like better, and why?

### ESTIMATING TEMPERATURE

In Chapter 3, Lesson 8, you learned this rule for converting Celsius to Fahrenheit: *Multiply the Celsius temperature by 1.8. Add 32 to the result.*
If

$F$ = the Fahrenheit temperature and
$C$ = the Celsius temperature,

then this statement can be written as a function:

$$F = 1.8 C + 32.$$

8. Draw and label a pair of axes with $F$ on the $y$-axis and $C$ on the $x$-axis. Make a table of values, using values of $C$ from -10 to 30. Use your table to graph the function $F = 1.8 C + 32$. Label a few points on your graph.

Abe doesn't like to multiply by 1.8. Since 1.8 is a little less than 2, and 32 is a little more than 30, he made up this rule for estimating: *To estimate the Fahrenheit temperature, multiply the Celsius temperature by 2 and add 30.*

9. Using the letters $C$ and $F$ as was done in problem 8, write a function for Abe's rule.

10. Make a table using values of $C$ from -10 to 30 for the function you wrote for Abe's rule. Use your table to graph the function on the same pair of axes as you used in problem 8.

*Chapter 4 Interpreting Graphs*

**11.** Compare the two graphs.

a. How far off would Abe's estimate be if the Celsius temperature were 0?

b. Compare the result from Abe's estimation method with the exact values for several other temperatures. Be sure to try some negative Celsius temperatures. Do you think Abe's method is a good one? Why or why not?

c. There is one temperature for which Abe's estimation method gives the exact value. What is it?

**12.** ☛ For what range of temperatures would you judge Abe's method to be acceptable? Explain.

Sometimes exact answers are important. In everyday life, estimates or *rules of thumb* are often just as good. For example, Mr. and Mrs. Gral, who are planning a trip to Europe, are not really interested in knowing how to make exact temperature conversions. They just want some advice about what to wear.

**13.** Bea and Abe are making a chart for their parents' reference. Complete it.

| Celsius temperature between __ and __ | You should wear: |
| --- | --- |
| | your coolest clothes |
| | a sweater |
| | a coat |
| | heavy coat, gloves, hat, and scarf |
| | a space suit |

Here is a method to figure out how much tip to leave for the server at a restaurant. Say the bill was for $20.73.

• Round up to the next even whole number of dollars, in this case 22.

• Add half of the number you got to the number, in this case $22 + 11 = 33$.

• Round up to the next multiple of five, in this case 35.

• Divide by ten to get the tip, in this case $3.50.

**14.** What percentage of $20.73 is $3.50? (Round off your answer.)

**15.** Does this method always give the same percentage of the bill? Try it for several amounts to see whether the percentage varies. If it does, what seem to be the lowest and the highest value it will give?

Here is another method to figure out the tip.

• Divide the amount of the bill by ten. (In this case you would get $2.07.)

• Multiply the result by two. (In this case you would get $4.14.)

• Take the average of the two numbers, rounded to the nearest nickel.

**16.** a. What is the tip by this calculation?

b. What percentage of the bill is it?

**17.** Does the second method always give the same percentage of the bill? Explain.

**18.** Summary Compare the two methods. Explain which one you prefer and why.

**19.** 💡 What percentage of the bill do you think is an appropriate tip? Create your own method to figure it without a calculator.

# Jarring Discoveries

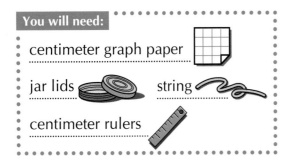

**You will need:**

centimeter graph paper

jar lids       string

centimeter rulers

## FLAT SCIENCE

Doctor Dimension is a flat scientist. He stores two-dimensional liquids in two-dimensional jars, like the ones shown in this figure.

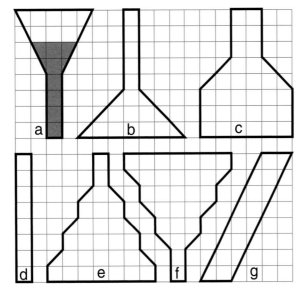

One day, as part of his scientific research, he decides to graph the amount of liquid in a jar as a function of the height of liquid. Since he lives in a two-dimensional world, liquid is measured in square units. For example, jar (a) is filled to a height of six units and contains eight square units of liquid.

The following graph represents jar (a).

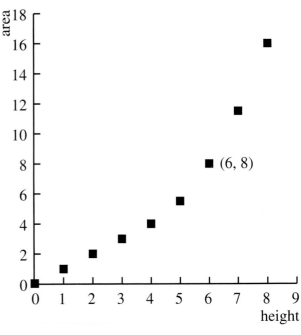

1. Some of the dots lie on one straight line. In which part of the graph does this happen? Explain why this is so.

2. Make a graph for each of the remaining jars.

3. For which jars is the area of liquid a direct variation function of the height? Explain.

**4.** Draw two different jars for each graph below.

**a**

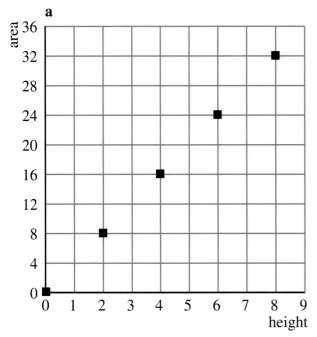

**b**

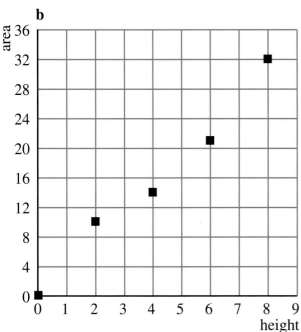

**5.** Draw a jar for part (a) of problem 4 for which the area of liquid is *not* a direct variation function of the height.

**6.** Predict the shape of the graph for this jar. Then test your prediction.

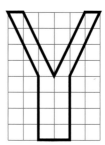

**7.** Summary Explain how the shape of the jar affects the shape of the graph. Explain what it takes for a jar to have a graph that is a straight line through the origin. ▪

**8.** Generalization How do you think the shape of a three-dimensional jar affects the shape of the graph of the volume of liquid as a function of height? What jar shapes correspond to a direct variation function? ▪

A dipstick can be used to measure the amount of liquid in a jar, but the dipstick must be specially designed for the jar. For example, the following dipstick would work for jar (a).

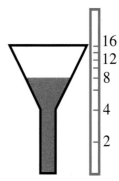

On it, area is marked off with a tick for every two square units.

**9.** 🔑 Note that the dipstick ticks are not evenly spaced. Explain why.

10. 🔑 Which jars would have a dipstick whose ticks are evenly spaced? Explain.

11. **Project** Draw an accurate dipstick for each of several different jars. Write a report showing sketches of the jars and their dipsticks, and explain your method.

**JAR LIDS: CIRCUMFERENCE**

For this section, use jar lids of at least five different sizes, including one very small one and one very large one.

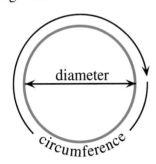

12. Measure the diameter and circumference of each of the jar lids in centimeters, as accurately as possible. (Use the string to help find the circumference.) Make a table showing your data.

13. Make a graph of your data, putting diameter on the *x*-axis and circumference on the *y*-axis. Don't forget to include a point for a lid having diameter 0.

14. 🔑 What is the relationship of circumference to diameter for each jar lid? Describe it in words and with an equation. Explain how you figured it out.

15. Is the relationship between diameter and circumference an example of direct variation? Explain.

16. According to your data, what is the approximate value of the ratio of circumference to diameter?

**JAR LIDS: AREA**

17. Estimate the area of the top of each jar lid by tracing around it on centimeter graph paper and estimating the number of square centimeters it covers. Make a table and a graph of the relationship between diameter and area, including a point for a lid having diameter 0.

18. Is the relationship between diameter and area an example of direct variation? Explain.

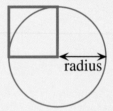

The figure shows a square whose side equals the radius of the circle.

19. For each jar lid, calculate the area of a square like the one shown in the figure. Add a column for these data in your jar-lid area table.

20. Graph the area of the circles as a function of the area of the squares.

*Chapter 4 Interpreting Graphs*

**21.** 🔑 What is the relationship between the area of the circles and the area of the squares? Describe it in words and with an equation. Explain how you figured it out.

**22.** Is the relationship between the area of the circles and the area of the squares an example of direct variation? Explain.

**23.** According to your data, what is the approximate value of the ratio of the area of the circle to the area of the square?

**24.** Summary According to your data, what is the relationship between the area of a circle and its radius? The area of a circle and its diameter? Explain.

---

### REVIEW DIVIDING ON A CALCULATOR

Phil used his calculator to find the reciprocal of 7, and got the number 0.1428571429. Lyn's calculator, on the other hand, gave the number 0.1428571428.

**25.** Explain how two calculators can give different results, even though neither is defective.

Phil's grandfather does not believe in calculators. He said, "Do you really believe either number is the reciprocal of 7? I have news for you. Multiply each one by 7 without a calculator, and you'll see why you should not trust these machines."

**26.** Work with a classmate. Do the two multiplications on paper to see who was right, Phil, Lyn, or their grandfather. Explain your results.

The grandfather added, "To find the real reciprocal of 7, you have to use good old-fashioned long division."

**27.** Find the real reciprocal of 7.

**28.** Report Write a letter to Lyn and Phil's grandfather, explaining why students are allowed to use calculators nowadays. Your letter should include, but not be limited to:
- Answers to the grandfather's probable objections;
- A table showing the real reciprocals of the whole numbers from 0 to 10, and the

reciprocals as given by Lyn's and Phil's calculators;
- An explanation of how you can find the real reciprocal by using a calculator;
- An argument explaining why Lyn's or Phil's calculator is the better one for the purpose of finding reciprocals.

**29.** Make a *division table* like this one. Extend it to show whole-number numerators and denominators from 0 to 10. You may use a calculator, but enter only exact answers. Look for patterns and work with a partner. Some answers were entered for you.

Numerators

| | 0 | 1 | 2 | 3 | ... |
|---|---|---|---|---|---|
| 0 | | | | | |
| 1 | | | | | |
| 2 | 0 | 0.5 | 1 | 1.5 | ... |
| 3 | | | | | |
| ... | | | | | ... |

Denominators

**30.** What patterns do you notice about the row of your table for denominator 7?

**31.** Learn how to use the FIX mode on your calculator.

# 4.B **Direct Variation**

### POINTS ON LINES

1. Choose a number *m,* and draw the graph of the equation $y = mx$. Choose any point $(a, b)$ on the line.
   a. Is the point $(2a, 2b)$ on the line?
   b. Is the point $(3a, 3b)$ on the line?
   c. Is the point $(ka, kb)$ on the line for any value of $k$?

2. Refer to the line you drew in problem 1.
   a. Is the point $(a + 1, b + 1)$ on it?
   b. Is the point $(a + k, b + k)$ on the line for any value of $k$?

3. **Report** Repeat problems 1 and 2 for several graphs of the form $y = mx$, $y = x + b$, and $y = mx + b$. If a point $(a, b)$ is on the line, in what case is $(ka, kb)$ on the line? What about $(a + k, b + k)$?

### AREA FUNCTIONS

4. The graph shows $y = 2x$. The region between the line and the $x$-axis from $x = 0$ to $x = 6$ is shaded.
   a. What is the area of the shaded region?
   b. What is the area of the region between the line and the $x$-axis from $x = 0$ to $x = 4$?

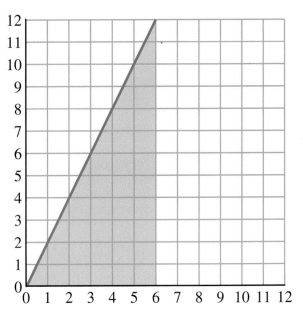

| Endpoint | Area |
|----------|------|
| $x = 1$ | |
| $x = 2$ | |
| $x = 3$ | |
| $x = 5$ | |
| $x = a$ | |

5. Copy and complete the table giving the area between the line and the $x$-axis from $x = 0$ to the given endpoint value of $x$.

6. Find a function relating the area to the endpoint value of $x$.

**7.** Is the area function you wrote an example of direct variation? Explain.

| Endpoint | Area |
|----------|------|
| $x = 1$ | |
| $x = 2$ | |
| $x = 3$ | |
| $x = 5$ | |
| $x = a$ | |

**8.** The graph shows the line $y = 3$. Copy and complete the table giving the area between the line and the $x$-axis from $x = 0$ to the given endpoint value of $x$.

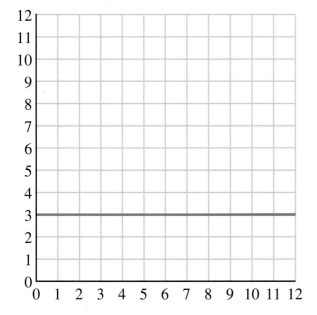

**9.** Find a function relating the area to the endpoint value of $x$.

**10.** Is the area function you wrote an example of direct variation? Explain.

**11.** Report Repeat problems 4 through 7 for several other lines. For which lines did you find area functions that are examples of direct variation? What generalizations can you make? Write an illustrated report about your results.

▽ **4.9** ▽

# Rules of the Road

## UNIT CONVERSION

When you talk about the speed you are traveling, you usually give the speed in *miles per hour*. In this lesson it will be useful to give speed in *feet per second*. Use the fact that 100 miles per hour (mph) is about 147 feet per second (fps).

**1.** How many fps is 50 mph?

**2.** Complete the table to show the relationship of miles per hour to feet per second. Extend the table up to 80 miles per hour.

| mph | fps |
|-----|------|
| 10  | 14.7 |
| 20  |      |

**3.** If you made a graph from your table with *mph* on the *x*-axis and *fps* on the *y*-axis, what would the graph look like? (If you are not sure, draw it.)

**4.** If you were traveling at 1 mph, how fast would you be going in fps?

## STOPPING DISTANCE

To stop a car in an emergency, you first react and then put on the brakes.

stopping distance =
reaction distance + braking distance

**5.** What kinds of things do you think would affect reaction time and distance? Braking time and distance?

Reaction time is often considered to be about 3/4 of a second, but how far you travel during this time depends on how fast you are going.

**6.** Reaction distance:
   a. Figure out how many feet you would travel in 3/4 of a second if you were going at various speeds (10 mph, 20 mph, etc.). Make a table to display your data.

   b. Graph your data. Put *reaction distance in feet* on the *y*-axis and *speed in miles per hour* on the *x*-axis.

   c. Describe the relationship between the two variables on your graph.

**7.** Braking distance: A formula for finding braking distance in feet is to take the speed in miles per hour, square it, and divide the result by 20. For example, if the speed were 10 mph, the braking distance would be $(10)^2/20 = 100/20 = 5$ feet.

   a. The graph on the next page shows the relationship between the braking distance (in feet) and the speed (in miles per hour). All the points on the graph were found by using the formula. Make a table showing the coordinates of at least five points on the graph.

   b. According to the table and graph, if you double your speed, will you double your braking distance? Explain, giving examples.

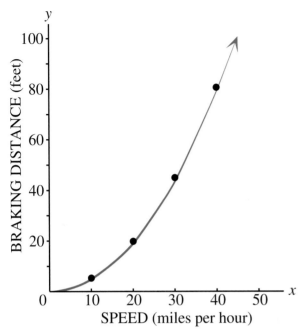

**8.** Total stopping distance: Use your tables and graphs from problems 6 and 7 to make a table with the headings shown. Use at least five different speeds.

| Speed (mph) | Reaction distance (feet) | Braking distance (feet) | Total stopping distance (feet) |
|---|---|---|---|
| | | | |

---

### SAFE DISTANCE

It is estimated that about 30 percent of all automobile accidents are caused by following too closely. Two rules of thumb for avoiding accidents follow.

**Rule 1: The 3-Second Rule.** Notice when the vehicle in front of you passes some object, such as a road sign. Then time approximately three seconds by counting, "One-thousand-one, one-thousand-two, one-thousand-three." If you pass the same object before you get to one-thousand-three, you are following too closely.

**Rule 2: The 1-for-10 Rule.** Leave one car length between you and the car in front of you for every 10 mph of driving speed.

**9.** Exploration Which rule do you think is safer? Taking into account what you found out about stopping distance, what do you think would make a good rule of thumb?

To compare the two rules, it helps to convert miles per hour to feet per second, so that all units are in feet and seconds.

**10. a.** Copy and complete the table to show the distance traveled in three seconds at the speeds given. Extend the table up to 100 miles per hour.

| Speed (mph) | Speed (fps) | Distance (ft) |
|---|---|---|
| 10 | 14.7 | 44.1 |
| 20 | | |

**b.** According to the table, how many feet would a car traveling at 50 mph cover in three seconds?

**c.** If you were instructed to stay three seconds behind the car in front of you, how many feet would that be, if you were traveling at 70 mph?

**d.** If you slowed down to 35 mph, could you cut your following distance in half? Explain.

**e.** If you drew a graph with speed on the *y*-axis and *distance traveled in three seconds* on the *x*-axis, what would it look like? Explain. If you are not sure, sketch the graph.

**11.** Most cars are about 14 to 18 feet in length. Choose a car length in this interval and make a table showing safe following distances at certain speeds according to Rule 2.

| Speed (mph) | Speed (fps) | Safe distance (car lengths) | Safe distance (feet) |
|---|---|---|---|
| 10 | 14.7 | 1 | |
| 20 | | 2 | |

**12.** ⛏ Use your tables to compare Rule 1 and Rule 2. How are they different? Which one suggests greater caution? Explain.

**13.** ⛏ Should one evaluate Rule 2 based on its implementation using a small-car length or a large-car length? Explain.

**14.** Report  Use the information about total stopping distance to decide whether you agree with the advice given by Rule 1 or by Rule 2, or whether you would suggest a different rule. Write a paragraph explaining your opinion.

**DISCOVERY  ROUNDING**

Because of measurement error, it is meaningless to say that someone weighs 157.2490368 pounds. No scale is that accurate, and even if it were, one does not need that level of accuracy. For most purposes, it is satisfactory to talk of someone's weight to the nearest pound, so this number should be rounded off to 157.

When dealing with amounts of money, one usually rounds off to the nearest cent. In some cases, one rounds up, or down. When doing work with *real* numbers, make sure you do not copy answers from your calculator without thinking of whether you should round off, round up, or round down.

**15.** If you buy one 95-cent pastry at the Columbia Street Bakery, you will be charged $1.00 even. But if you buy two pastries, you will be charged $2.01.

  a. What is the sales tax in this town?

  b. Does the cash register round off to the nearest cent, or does it round up or down? Explain.

**16.** In the same town, if you buy a 94-cent soda at Eddie's, you will be charged $1.00. If you buy two sodas, you will be charged $1.99. Does this cash register round off to the nearest cent? Does it round up or down? Explain.

# Up in the Air

**You will need:**

graph paper

People rarely travel at constant speeds. Almost all travel involves speeding up and slowing down. However, sometimes to simplify a problem it is useful to use the average speed over a given period of time. In this lesson we will use the average speed.

## MULTIPLE MEANINGS

The graph below shows the relationship between the altitude of the airplane and the time after take-off.

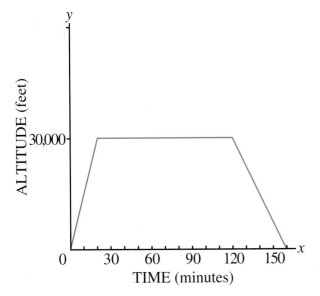

1. How high was the airplane 20 minutes after take-off?

2. How long after take-off did the airplane reach its cruising altitude?

3. How long did the plane cruise at a constant altitude before descending?

4. Can you figure out the speed of the airplane from this graph? Explain.

The graph below shows that Flight 101 left its home airport at 8 A.M. and flew to the town of Alaberg. It stayed in Alaberg for several hours and then returned to its home airport.

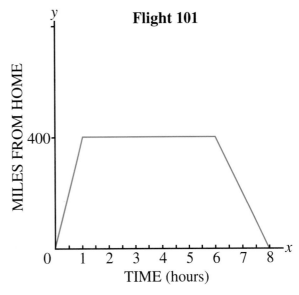

5. According to the graph, how far away is Alaberg?

6. How long did it take Flight 101 to get to Alaberg?

7. How long did the plane stay in Alaberg?

8. Can you figure out the speed of the airplane from this graph? Explain.

Someone made this graph about Flight 202, but accidentally left off the labels and the scale for the axes.

**Flight 202**

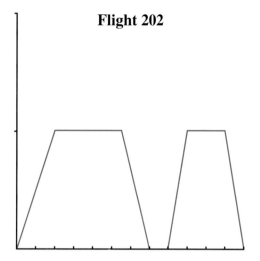

**9.** Copy the graph and label the axes like those in the figure just before problem 1. Write a description of what the graph conveys.

**10.** Make another copy of the graph and label the axes like those in the figure preceding problem 5. Write a description of what that graph conveys.

**11.** What else might the axes and scale be for the graph about Flight 202? Make up another possibility and write a description of what your graph shows.

### DISCRETE AND CONTINUOUS GRAPHS

Alaberg has a large airport with several terminals. A small train runs through the airport, carrying passengers between the terminals. Passengers use this train when they have to transfer from one plane to another. The graph shows the relationship between the location of the train between the terminals and the number of passengers in the train.

**12.** Write a description of what is conveyed by this graph.

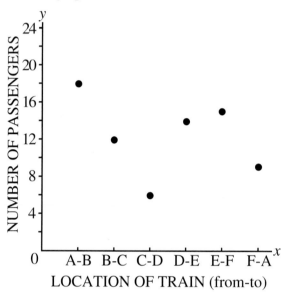

**13.** Can you tell how many passengers got on and off at each terminal? Explain.

**14.** Can you tell if the train was ever empty?

**15.** Can you tell from this graph how fast the train was traveling?

The Alaberg Airport Express is a van service that carries passengers between the city and Alaberg Airport. A group of math teachers is holding a convention in Alaberg, and 1024 people have arrived at the airport. They all need to get into the city.

**16.** If the Alaberg Airport Express van holds 20 people, how many trips will be needed to take all the people into the city?

**17.** If more vans were available, fewer trips would be needed per van. If 15 vans were available, and the trips were divided as evenly as possible among the vans, what would be the maximum number of trips that any van would need to take?

**18.** Copy and complete the table to show the relationship between vans available and maximum number of trips per van necessary. (Once again, assume that the trips would be divided as evenly as possible among the vans.)

| Number of vans | Max number of trips per van necessary |
|---|---|
| 1 ⋮ 15 | |

**19.** a. Make a graph from your table.

   b. What is the rule for finding the maximum number of trips per van necessary, given the number of vans?

**20.** ⚷ The graphs you used in problems 12 and 19 involved points instead of lines. Explain why it does not make sense to connect these points.

**Definition:** If the points are not connected on a graph, it is called *discrete*. If the points are connected, it is called *continuous*.

### YOUR OWN GRAPHS

**21.** ⚷ The meaning of this graph is still up in the air until you add some things to it. Copy the graph, label the axes, and show the scale. If it makes sense, connect the points. Tell what the graph conveys.

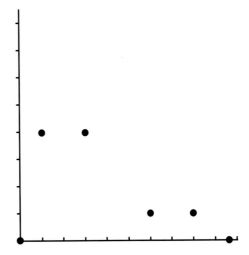

**22.** ⚷ Make up a discrete graph. Label the axes and indicate the scale. Write a description of what the graph conveys.

**23.** ⚷ Repeat problem 22 for a continuous graph.

# Horizontal and Vertical Lines

**You will need:**

graph paper

### STEP FUNCTIONS

1.  This graph shows how the number of passengers in the Alaberg Airport Express van changes over time. The graph shows a trip between the city and the airport.

    a.  Write a description of what is shown by this graph.

    b.  Why is there a long horizontal line on the graph?

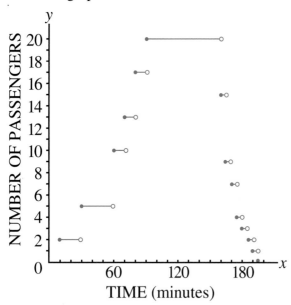

**Definitions:** This graph is an example of a *step function*. Note that the endpoints of the steps are either filled-in (this is called a *closed circle*), or hollow (this is called an *open circle*).

For a given value of $x$, the value of $y$ can be found by looking for the corresponding point on the graph. Only points on the steps and closed circles are considered to be on the graph. The open circles are there to show where the step ends, but that point is not considered to be on the graph. This way a given $x$-value has only one corresponding $y$-value.

2.  After 60 minutes, how many people were in the van?

### HORIZONTAL AND VERTICAL LINES

3.  a.  Graph the vertical line through the point (1, –2).

    b.  Label four more points on this line.

    c.  Which coordinate is the same for all the points on the line, the $x$-coordinate or the $y$-coordinate?

4.  a.  Graph the horizontal line through the point (1, –2).

    b.  Label four more points on this line.

    c.  Which coordinate is the same for all the points on the line, the $x$-coordinate or the $y$-coordinate?

5.  a.  The equation of a line is $y = -3$. There is no $x$ in the equation because the value of $y$ does not depend on the value of $x$. Graph this equation.

    b.  Did you graph a horizontal or a vertical line?

*Chapter 4 Interpreting Graphs*

**6.**  a.  The equation of a line is $x = 6$. There is no $y$ in the equation because the value of $x$ does not depend on the value of $y$. Graph this equation.

   b.  Did you graph a horizontal or a vertical line?

**7.**  a.  Graph the vertical line through $(2, -5)$. Write its equation.

   b.  Find the coordinates of any point on the line.

   c.  Find the coordinates of any point to the right of the line.

   d.  Find the coordinates of any point to the left of the line.

   e.  For each part (b), (c), and (d), answer this question: What do you think all the points chosen by students in your class have in common?

**8.**  The equation of a line is $y = 5$. If possible, answer these questions without graphing the line.

   a.  Is the line vertical or horizontal?

   b.  Where does the point $(4, -2)$ lie in relation to the line? Explain.

   c.  Write the coordinates of one point on the line and one point not on the line.

   d.  What can you say about the $y$-coordinate of any point that lies on the line? Below the line? Above the line?

---

### INEQUALITIES

The $x$-coordinate of any point that lies to the left of the vertical line $x = 6$ must be a number less than 6. For example $(2, 7)$ is such a point, since $2 < 6$. The expressions $2 < 6$ and $x < 4$ are examples of *inequalities*.

**9.**  The mathematical shorthand for *less than* is $<$. What are the mathematical symbols for *greater than, less than or equal to,* and *greater than or equal to*?

Inequalities can be used to describe sets of points on a graph. For example, all the points that lie on or to the right of the line $x = 7$ can be described by the inequality $x \geq 7$.

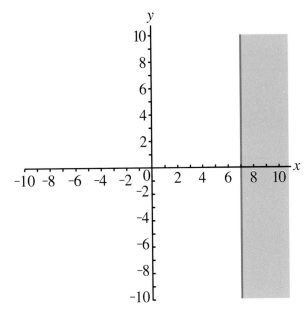

**10.**  Graph each set of points given. Use one or more inequalities to describe it.

   a.  All points that lie on or below the line $y = -1$

   b.  All points that lie on or above the $x$-axis

   c.  All points that lie on or between the vertical lines $x = 3$ and $x = 6$

**11.**  **Report**  Write an illustrated report on horizontal lines, vertical lines, and inequalities.

### DISTANCE VS. TIME, AGAIN

These graphs represent the motion of Paul's car. The vertical axis shows distance from his house, and the horizontal axis shows time.

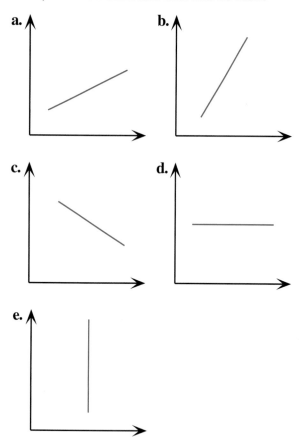

a.

b.

c.

d.

e.

**12.** 🔑 Describe the trips shown in each graph. Are all of them possible?

### COST OF MAILING A LETTER

In January of 1991 the United States Postal Service raised its rates for first-class mail. It printed the following table in a flyer for postal customers.

**13.** Answer questions (a-c) using the information in the following table.

| Single-Piece Letter Rates: | | | |
|---|---|---|---|
| Pieces not exceeding (oz) | The rate is | Pieces not exceeding (oz) | The rate is |
| 1 | $0.29 | 7 | $1.67 |
| 2 | $0.52 | 8 | $1.90 |
| 3 | $0.75 | 9 | $2.13 |
| 4 | $0.98 | 10 | $2.36 |
| 5 | $1.21 | 11 | $2.59 |
| 6 | $1.44 | | |

a. How much does it cost to mail a letter weighing 7 and 1/2 ounces?

b. How much does it cost to mail a letter weighing exactly 3 ounces?

c. Would it be possible for a letter to cost 45 cents to mail? If so, how much would it weigh? If not, explain why not.

**14.** Use the data in the table to graph the relationship of cost to weight. It is a step function. Copy and complete this graph.

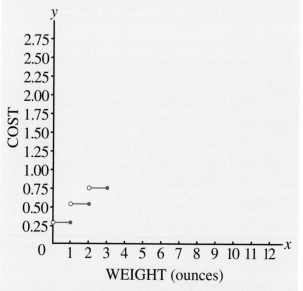

**15.** Study the table. What is the rule being used to determine these rates?

L E S S O N

# 4.12 Complicated Areas

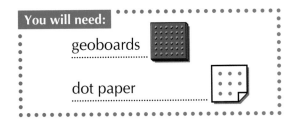

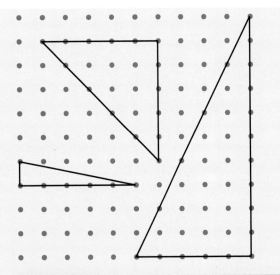

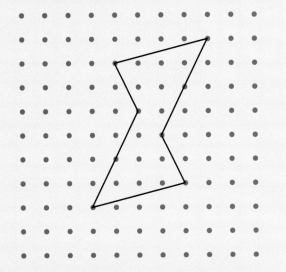

**You will need:**

geoboards ......................

dot paper ......................

### DISCOVERING AN AREA FORMULA

1. a. Find the area of this figure.
   b. Explain how you did it, with the help of illustrations on dot paper.
   c. Compare your approach with other students' work.

In the figure above, the rubber band is in contact with 8 geoboard pegs (which we will call *boundary dots*). The figure encloses 12 inside pegs, which we will call *inside dots*.

2. For each figure, give the number of boundary dots, the number of inside dots, and the area.

3. **Exploration** Try to figure out the relationship between boundary dots, inside dots, and area. (Hints: Sketch many simple figures, count their dots, and find their areas. Keep detailed and clear records. Start by working on the problem for figures having zero inside dots, then one inside dot, and so on.) Keep records of your work in a table like this one.

| Boundary Dots | Inside Dots | Area |
|---|---|---|
| ... | ... | ... |

4. Make three figures having 3 boundary dots and 0 inside dots. Find the area of each figure.

**5.** Make three figures having 4 boundary dots and 0 inside dots. Find the area of each figure.

**6.** Make three figures having 5 boundary dots and 0 inside dots. Find the area of each figure.

**7.** 🔑

   a. If two figures have no inside dots and the same number of boundary dots, what can you say about their areas?

   b. What happens to the area if the number of boundary dots increases by 1?

**8.** a. Predict the area of a figure having 10 boundary dots and 0 inside dots.

   b. Check your prediction by making three such shapes and finding their areas.

   c. What would the area of a figure having 99 boundary dots and 0 inside dots be?

**9.** | Generalization | Explain how one could find the area of a figure having $b$ boundary dots and 0 inside dots, without making or drawing the figure.

**10.** Make figures having 10 boundary dots and 1, 2, 3, etc. inside dots. For each one, find its area. Keep your work organized in a table.

**11.** 🔑 What happens to the area when the number of inside dots increases by 1?

**12.** a. Predict the area of a figure having 10 boundary dots and 10 inside dots.

   b. Check your prediction by making three such shapes and finding their areas.

   c. What would the area of a figure having 99 boundary dots and 101 inside dots be?

**13.** | Generalization | Explain how one could find the area of a shape having $b$ boundary dots and $i$ inside dots, without making or drawing the figure. You have discovered *Pick's Formula*.

**14.** Use the result from problem 13 to check your answers to problems 1 and 2.

---

**DISCOVERY** *PATTERNS AND FUNCTIONS*

**15.** Find as many functions of $x$ as possible whose value is 5 when $x$ is 2.

**16.** Multiply.

$$\left(1 - \tfrac{1}{7}\right) \cdot \left(1 - \tfrac{2}{7}\right) \cdot \left(1 - \tfrac{3}{7}\right) \cdot \ldots \cdot \left(1 - \tfrac{9}{7}\right)$$

**17.** 1
1+2+1
1+2+3+2+1
1+2+3+4+3+2+1

What do you notice about these sums? Explain the pattern, using a figure if you can.

# 4.C Letter Strings

In abstract algebra, letters do not stand for numbers. Abstract algebra has many applications, for example, to particle physics or to the analysis of the Rubik's cube. Here is a simple example.

## THE YZ GAME

In this game, starting with a string of Y's and Z's, the object is to simplify the string by following strict rules. The rules are:

> YYY can be erased.
> ZZ can be erased.
> the commutative law: YZ = ZY.
> E is the empty string (a string with no Y's or Z's).

**Examples:**

a. $\underline{\text{YZZ}}$YYZYZYYZ (erase ZZ)
   Y $\underline{\text{YYZ}}$YZYYZ (erase YYY)
   $\quad\quad$ Z$\underline{\text{YZ}}$ZYYZ (commute YZ)
   $\quad\quad$ Z$\underline{\text{ZZ}}$$\underline{\text{YYY}}$Z (erase ZZ and YYY)
   $\quad\quad\quad$ Z $\quad\quad$ (can't be simplified)

b. Z$\underline{\text{YYY}}$Z $\quad\quad$ (erase YYY)
   $\underline{\text{Z} \quad\quad \text{Z}}$ $\quad\quad\quad$ (erase ZZ)
   $\quad$ E $\quad\quad\quad$ (the empty string is left)

1. Simplify the strings.
   a. YZYZZYYZ $\quad$ b. YYYYZZYZY
   c. YZYZYZYZYZYZYZZZYZYZYYZY

Including the empty string E, there are six essentially different strings that cannot be simplified. They are called the *elements of the YZ group.*

2. Find all the elements of the YZ group.

The symbol ↔ represents the operation *put together and simplify.* For example:

$\quad$ Y ↔ YY = E
$\quad$ YZ ↔ YZ = YY
$\quad$ Y ↔ E = Y

3. Compute.
   a. E ↔ YZ $\quad\quad$ b. YZ ↔ YY
   c. Z ↔ YZ

4. Find the missing term.
   a. YZ ↔ ___ = E
   b. Z ↔ ___ = YZ
   c. YY ↔ ___ = Z

For the YZ group, ↔ works a little bit like multiplication. Another way to write the first two rules is
$$Y^3 = E \text{ and } Z^2 = E.$$

5. The only powers of Y are: Y, $Y^2$, and E. Explain.

6. Find *all* the powers of each element of the YZ group.

7. Simplify. (Show your work.)
   a. $Y^{1000}$ $\quad\quad\quad$ b. $(YZ)^{1001}$

8. Make a ↔ table.

9. What element of the group works like 1 for multiplication?

10. What is the reciprocal of each element? (In other words, for each element, what element can be put together with it to get the 1?)

## THE yz GAME

For this group, the rules are:

> yyy can be erased.
> zz can be erased.
> yzy = z.
> The empty string is called e.
> *There is no commutative law.*

11. 💡 Do problems 1-10 for the yz group. (Hint: zyy and yyz *can* be simplified.)

12. **Report** Write a report on the yz group.

# ◆ Essential Ideas

## FUEL VS. DISTANCE

Gabe's scooter gets good mileage, but it has a small tank. The graph below shows how much gas was in his tank during one trip he took.

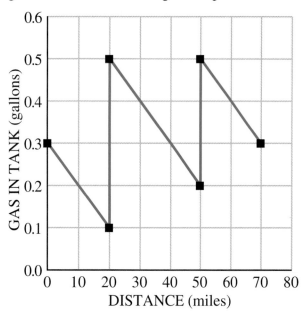

1. Write a paragraph describing Gabe's trip. Include the answers to these questions: How much gas did Gabe start with? How much did he end with? How many times did he stop for gas? How much gas did he use for the whole trip? How far did he travel before stopping each time? What is probably the capacity of his gas tank? How many miles did he get per gallon?

2. The gas station stops took ten minutes each. Gabe left home at 9 A.M. and arrived at his destination at 11:05 A.M. How fast does the scooter go?

3. In what ways might this graph be unrealistic?

## EQUATIONS AND GRAPHS

4. Make a graph of several $(x, y)$ pairs having the property that the sum of $x$ and $y$ is 16. Connect the points on your graph. Write the equation of your graph.

5. Write the equation of:
   a. a line through the origin containing the point $(2, 5)$;
   b. another first-degree polynomial containing the point $(2, 5)$;
   c. a second-degree polynomial containing the point $(2, 5)$.

These questions are about the graph of the equation $y = -x^2 + 2$.

6. Which of these points are on it?
   $(3, -11)$   $(-3, 11)$   $(3, -7)$   $(-3, -7)$

7. The point $(-6, y)$ is on it. What is $y$?

8. The point $(x, -14)$ is on it. What are the two possible values of $x$?

For each of the equations below, if possible, find an $(x, y)$ pair for which
   a. $x$ is negative and $y$ is positive;
   b. $x$ is positive and $y$ is negative;
   c. $x$ and $y$ are both negative.

9. $y = 4x$          10. $y = x^2 - 2$

11. $y = x(x - 1)$     12. $y = -2x + 6$

13. Which of the above four equations' graphs
   a. are straight lines?
   b. pass through the origin?

14. If possible, sketch the graph of a zero-degree, first-degree, second-degree, and third-degree polynomial function which passes through all quadrants but the first.

For problems 15 through 17:

    a. Plot the points given in the table.

    b. Study the table and your graph. Describe the relationship between the x-value and y-value of each pair.

    c. Use the pattern you found to add more points to your table and graph.

    d. Write an equation that tells how to get the y-value from the x-value.

**15.**

| x | y |
|---|---|
| 0 | 1 |
| 1 | 3 |
| -1 | -1 |
| 3 | 7 |

**16.**

| x | y |
|---|---|
| 2 | 9 |
| 3 | 6 |
| -3 | -6 |
| 4.5 | 4 |
| 4 | 4.5 |

**17.**

| x | y |
|---|---|
| 3 | 8 |
| -2 | 3 |
| -1 | 0 |
| 0 | -1 |
| 1/2 | -3/4 |
| 2 | 3 |

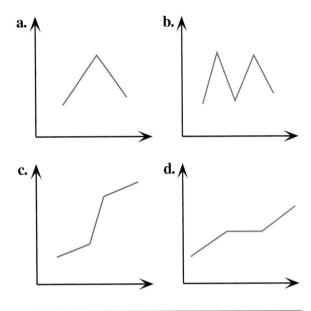

**DISTANCE VS. TIME**

**18.** These graphs represent the motion of Paul's car. The vertical axis shows distance from his house, and the horizontal axis shows time. Write a short paragraph describing the trip summarized by each graph.

**POSTAL PROBLEM**

The post office puts size restrictions on first-class mail. Standard letters that are 1/4 inch thick or less must meet these requirements for width and height.

    • The height is at least 3 and 1/2 in. and cannot exceed 6 and 1/8 in.

    • The width is at least 5 in. and not more than 11 and 1/2 in.

**19.** The first condition can be written $3.5 \leq \text{height} \leq 6.125$. (This is called a *compound inequality*.) How would you write the second condition?

**20.** Sketch (to scale) and give the width, height, and area of each of these letters.

   a. The letter having the least possible area
   b. The letter having the greatest possible area
   c. The tallest, thinnest letter
   d. The shortest, widest letter

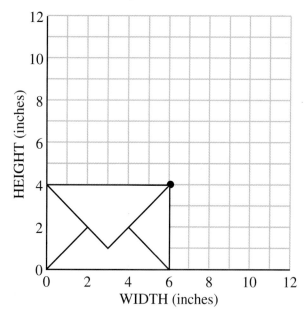

You can use a graph to show allowable dimensions of a letter. In the graph above, the point (6, 4) represents the dimensions of a letter that is 4 in. high and 6 in. wide.

**21.** Plot four points for the four envelopes you listed in problem 20. (Don't draw the envelopes!)

**22.** Write the equations of two horizontal and two vertical lines through those points.

**23.** The four points should form a rectangle. Find some points inside the rectangle, outside the rectangle, and on the rectangle. Which points represent allowable dimensions of letters? Explain, using examples.

In order to avoid extra fees, your letter must satisfy the following restriction.

• The width divided by the height must be between 1.3 and 2.5, inclusive.

**24.** Write a compound inequality for this restriction.

**25.** Find the ratio of the width to the height of each letter you listed in problem 20. Which ones meet the new requirement?

**26.** a. Experiment with your calculator until you find an allowable width and height that have a ratio of 1.3. On your graph, plot these dimensions. Draw a line through this point and the origin.

   b. Find other points on the line. What is the ratio for each one? Explain.

   c. Repeat (a) and (b) for the ratio 2.5.

**27.** Check the ratio for points between the two lines, above the upper line, and below the lower line.

**28.** Explain how to use the graph to find

   a. dimensions that satisfy all the rules;
   b. dimensions that satisfy the first two rules, but not the ratio rule;
   c. dimensions that satisfy the ratio rule, but not the first two rules.

**29.** If the ratio of the width to the height is 1.3, what is the ratio of the height to the width?

**30.** Find the equation of the lines through the origin in your graph. Explain how they are examples of direct variation.

# PRACTICE

**REVIEW**

### DIRECT VARIATION

1. Without graphing, tell which of the following lines pass through the origin. Explain. The line containing points
   a. (2, 6) and (4, 12);
   b. (3, 8) and (4, 9);
   c. (6, 5) and (18, 15).

2. A line contains the points (0, 1) and (2, 4). Does it also contain the point (4, 8)? Explain.

3. A line contains the points (2, 5) and (4, 10). Does it also contain the point (200, 500)? Explain.

### CREATE AN EQUATION

4. Create an equation that has $x = 3$ as a solution.

5. Create an equation that has $y = -3$ as a solution.

6. Create an equation where $x$ appears on both sides of the equation and
   a. the solution is $x = 0$;
   b. the solution is $x = -1/2$.

# CHAPTER

**5**

The colorful spiral of a lollipop

## Coming in this chapter:

**Exploration** Build as many rectangles as you can with one $x^2$, ten $x$-blocks, and any number of yellow blocks.

Build as many rectangles as you can with $x^2$, 18, and any number of $x$-blocks.

# SUMS AND PRODUCTS

# LESSON 5.1

## Constant Sums

**You will need:**

graph paper

### AT THE GAS STATION

When Oliver and Alice pulled up to the self-serve island at Jacob's gas station, they noticed a new sign:

> **Buy Gas Card in Office**

They went into the office, which was decorated with photographs and cartoons. The attendant Harold explained to them that he could sell them a gas card for any amount from 5 to 100 dollars. They would put it in the special slot in the pump, and pump gas as usual. The value of the card would automatically go down, and a display on the pump would indicate the value left in the card. After getting gas, there would be no need to go back to the office, unless they wanted to trade the card back for cash. (This could be done only if the card had less than $5 left on it.) Or they could use the remaining money left on the card the next time they stopped at Jacob's.

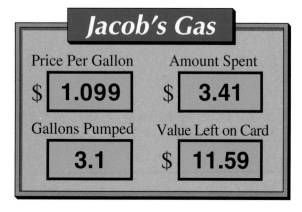

### Jacob's Gas

| Price Per Gallon | Amount Spent |
|---|---|
| $ **1.099** | $ **3.41** |
| Gallons Pumped | Value Left on Card |
| **3.1** | $ **11.59** |

1. Look at the dials in the figure. How much did Oliver and Alice pay for their gas card?

2. Oliver and Alice plan to buy about $10.00 worth of gas. List at least five other pairs of numbers that will appear on the last two dials while they are pumping gas.

3. When exactly 11 gallons have been pumped, what numbers will appear on the four dials?

4. **Generalization** When $D$ dollars have been spent, what is the value left on the card?

5. When $G$ gallons have been pumped,
   a. how many dollars have been spent?
   b. what is the value left on the card?

### FUNCTION DIAGRAMS FROM RULERS

Alice wanted to know how long her ruler was. Oliver suggested she measure it with a longer ruler, as in this figure.

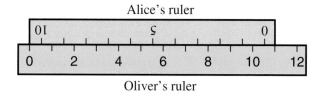

Alice's ruler

Oliver's ruler

6. How long is her ruler?

Oliver had to write about function diagrams for algebra. (His class was using this textbook, and in a curious coincidence, they were doing exactly this page!) He decided to use the rulers as a way to get tables of $x$- and $y$-values and build a function diagram from them. He used the rulers setup to create a table that started this way.

| $x$ | $y$ |
|-----|-----|
| 1 | 9.5 |
| 2 | 8.5 |
| 3 | 7.5 |

**7.** Describe the pattern for the numbers in the table. Does it matter which ruler you use for $x$ and which for $y$? Explain.

**8.** Write a function of the type $y = $ *an expression in terms of $x$* for Oliver's table.

**9.** Make a function diagram for Oliver's table. (Use at least five in-out lines.)

**10.** Use rulers to create two more tables, and for each, write a function and make a function diagram. At least one of them should match 0 with a number other than a whole number.

**11.** How could you set up rulers to get this function diagram? Explain.

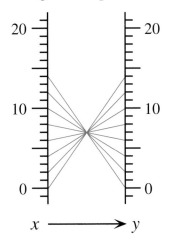

All the function diagrams you just drew have something in common. For each one, the sum of all the $(x, y)$ pairs is a constant. We could call them *constant sum* functions.

**12.** **Summary** Write an illustrated summary describing what you noticed about diagrams of constant sum functions. It should include, but not be limited to, examples and answers to the following questions:
- Do the in-out lines meet in one point?
- If they do, could you predict the position of this point if you knew the value of the constant sum?

**GRAPHS OF CONSTANT SUMS**

**13. a.** On a pair of axes, plot these $(x, y)$ pairs.
$(2, 4)$ $(4, 2)$ $(-1, 7)$ $(8, -2)$
**b.** In words, we could describe the pattern of the $(x, y)$ pairs by saying that the sum of $x$ and $y$ is always six. How would you write this using algebra?
**c.** Find three more $(x, y)$ pairs that fit this pattern, and add the points to your graph.
**d.** Connect all the points with a line or curve. Describe the graph.

**14. a.** Find points such that $x + y < 6$. Where are they in relation to the graph in problem 13?
**b.** Repeat for $x + y = 6$.
**c.** Repeat for $x + y > 6$.

**15.** Find a point $(x, y)$ such that $x = y$ and $x + y = 6$. Label it on the graph.

**16.** Choose a positive value for $S$ and make a table of $(x, y)$ pairs that satisfy the equation $x + y = S$. Use your table to make a graph.

17. 🔑 Experiment with some other constant sum graphs. Try several different positive values for S. For each one, make a table of at least five (x, y) pairs having the sum S. Then draw a graph. Draw all your graphs on the same pair of axes.

18. 🔑 Do any of the lines go through the origin? If not, do you think you could pick a number for your sum so that the line would go through the origin? Explain.

19. 🔑 Repeat your investigations for equations of the form $x + y = S$, where S is negative. Keep a record of what you try, using tables and graphs.

20. **Report** Write an illustrated report summarizing your findings about constant sum graphs. Your report should include neatly labeled graphs with accompanying explanations. Include answers to the following questions:

- Were the graphs straight lines or curved, or were there some of each?
- Without drawing the graph, could you now predict which quadrants the graph would be in, if you knew the value of S? Explain.
- Without drawing the graph, could you predict the x-intercepts and y-intercepts of the graph, if you knew the value of S? Explain.
- What determines whether the graph slopes up or down as it goes from left to right? Could you predict this without graphing if you knew the value of S? Explain.
- Do any of your graphs intersect each other? If so, which ones? If not, why not?

# Constant Products

If you plan to take a trip of 100 miles, the amount of gas you need depends on how many miles per gallon your vehicle gets. Some very large recreational vehicles get only about 5 miles per gallon, while a scooter can get 100 miles per gallon.

1.  Copy and complete the table to show how many gallons of gasoline you should buy if your vehicle gets the mileage indicated. Continue the table up to 100 miles per gallon.

| Mileage (miles per gallon) | Gasoline needed (gallons) | Total trip distance (miles) |
| --- | --- | --- |
| 5 | —— | 100 |
| 10.5 | —— | 100 |
| 20 | —— | 100 |

2.  Graph the $(x, y)$ pairs in the first two columns of the table.

3.  Describe your graph in words. If you were to extend your graph, would it go through the origin? Would it touch or cross the axes? Explain.

4.  Make a table containing these points and plot the $(x, y)$ pairs on a Cartesian graph.
    (2, 12) (3, 8) (4, 6) (8, 3)

5.  Describe the pattern of the $(x, y)$ pairs in problem 4
    a. in words;       b. using algebra.

6.  a. Find five more $(x, y)$ pairs that fit this pattern and add the points to your table and graph. Use positive values for $x$. Include some fractional values.
    b. Add five more $(x, y)$ pairs to your table and graph. This time use negative values for $x$, including some fractional values.

7.  Study the points on your graph. If necessary, add more points so that you can answer the following questions.
    a. Which quadrants do your points lie in? Why?
    b. Can you find a point on the $y$-axis that fits the pattern? Can you find a point on the $x$-axis? Explain.
    c. If you were to connect the points with a smooth curve, would the curve go through the origin? Explain.

8.  Add to your graph a point that fits the pattern and
    a. has an $x$-value less than 1/2;
    b. has a $y$-value less than 1/2;
    c. has an $x$-value greater than 24;
    d. has a $y$-value less than -24.

9.  Study your answers to problems 4-8. Then very carefully connect the points with a curve. Your curve should have two parts *that are not connected* to one another.
    a. Describe the graph.
    b. Explain why the two parts are not connected.

**10.** For (a-d), find several pairs of numbers (*x, y*) that satisfy the description. Plot these points on your graph.

  a. *x* is positive and *xy* is more than 24.

  b. *x* is positive and *xy* is less than 24.

  c. *x* is negative and *xy* is more than 24.

  d. *x* is negative and *xy* is less than 24.

**11.** ○ Plot a point (*x, y*) such that *xy* = 24 and *x* = *y.*

We could call the curve you drew in problem 9 a *constant product* graph, since the product of the coordinates of every point is the same number. We could graph many other *constant product* graphs of the form *xy* = *P*, where *P* could be any number we choose.

**12.** ⚷ Experiment with the graphs of some equations of the form *xy* = *P*. Try several different positive values for *P*. Then try several different negative values for *P*. For each one, make a table of at least eight (*x, y*) pairs having the same product. Then draw a graph. Draw all your graphs on the same pair of axes.

**13.** Report Write a report summarizing your findings about constant product graphs. Your report should include neatly labeled graphs with accompanying explanations. Include answers to the following questions:

- What is the shape of the graph?

- Without drawing the graph, could you now predict which quadrants the graph would be in, if you knew the value of *P*? Explain.

- Do any of the graphs go through the origin? If not, do you think you could find a value of *P* so that the graph would go through the origin? Explain.

- Where can you find points whose product is not *P*?

- Comment on anything you notice about the *x*-intercepts and *y*-intercepts.

- Do any of your graphs intersect? Explain why or why not.

## OTHER GRAPHS

In order to graph some functions, Tomas made tables of values, plotted the points, and connected the dots. (For one of the equations, he tried two different ways.) He asked his teacher if he had done it right. Mr. Stephens answered that the individual points had been plotted correctly, but he asked Tomas to think about how he had connected them. He said, *"Every point on the graph, even the ones obtained by connecting the dots, must satisfy the equation."* Tomas didn't understand. Mr. Stephens added, "Check whether you connected the dots correctly, by substituting a few more values of *x* into the equation. Use your calculator to see if the *y*-value you get is on the graph you drew." Tomas still didn't understand.

Name: Tomas

$y = x - 2$         $y = x^2$         $y = -6/x$

| x | y |
|---|---|
| -2 | -4 |
| -1 | -3 |
| 0 | -2 |
| 1 | -1 |
| 2 | 0 |

| x | y |
|---|---|
| -2 | 4 |
| -1 | 1 |
| 0 | 0 |
| 1 | 1 |
| 2 | 4 |

| x | y |
|---|---|
| -2 | 3 |
| -1 | 6 |
| 0 | imp. |
| 1 | -6 |
| 2 | -3 |

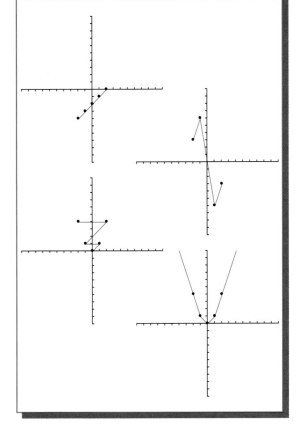

**14.** Report  Explain how Tomas can improve his graphs. Show your calculations. Give Tomas advice he can understand, on:
- how to label axes, points, and graphs;
- how to connect the dots correctly;
- how to extend the graph to the left and right;
- how a calculator can help.

# 5.3 ▽ The Distributive Law

**You will need:**

the Lab Gear

## HOW MANY TERMS?

For each multiplication, write an equation of the form *length · width equals area.* (You may use the Lab Gear and the corner piece to model the multiplication by making a rectangle.) In your expression for the area, combine like terms.

1. $x(2x + 5)$

2. $2x(y - 2)$

3. $y(2y + 2 - x)$

4. $(2x + 2)(3x - 5)$

5. $(x + 2)(3y + 1)$

6. $(x + 2)(y - 3x + 1)$

For each multiplication, write an equation of the form *length · width · height equals volume.* (You may want to use the Lab Gear and the corner piece to model the multiplication by making a box.) In your expression for the volume, combine like terms.

7. $x(x + 2)(x + 5)$

8. $y(x + 2)(y + 1)$

9. $x(x + 5)(x + y + 1)$

**Definitions:** A polynomial having two terms is called a *binomial;* one having three terms is called a *trinomial.* A polynomial having one term is called a *monomial.*

10. **Report** In problems 1-9, you multiplied two or three polynomials of degree 1. In each case, the product was also a polynomial. Write a report describing the patterns you saw in the products. You should use the words *monomial, binomial,* and *trinomial.* Give examples and illustrate your work with drawings of the Lab Gear. Your report should address the points listed below, but should also include any other observations you made.

- What determines the degree of the product?
- What determines the number of terms in the product?
- Compare problems having one variable to problems having two variables.

## DIVISION AND THE DISTRIBUTIVE LAW

As you probably remember, you can use the corner piece to model division.

**Example:** Simplify $\dfrac{4x + 6 + 2y}{2}$

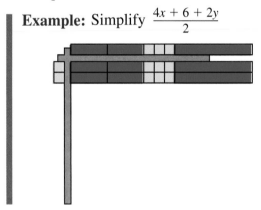

In some cases, you can use the Lab Gear in another way to show that a division like this one can be thought of as three divisions.

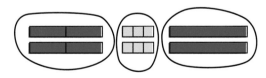

11. What is the result of the division?

Simplify these expressions, using the Lab Gear if you wish.

12. $\dfrac{10x + 5y + 15}{5}$

13. $\dfrac{2x + 4}{x + 2}$

**14.** $\dfrac{x^2 + 4x + 4}{x + 2}$

**15.** 💡 $\dfrac{3(y - x) + 6(x - 2)}{3}$

Another way to simplify some fractions is to rewrite the division into a multiplication and use the distributive law.

> **Example:** To simplify $\dfrac{6x + 4 + 2y}{2}$ :
> - Rewrite the problem as a multiplication.
> $$\tfrac{1}{2}(6x + 4 + 2y)$$
> - Apply the distributive law.
> $$\tfrac{1}{2} \cdot 6x + \tfrac{1}{2} \cdot 4 + \tfrac{1}{2} \cdot 2y$$
> - Simplify.
> $$3x + 2 + y$$

You can see that we could have divided every term in the numerator by 2. That is:
$$\dfrac{6x + 4 + 2y}{2} = \dfrac{6x}{2} + \dfrac{4}{2} + \dfrac{2y}{2}.$$

The single division problem was equivalent to three divisions. This example illustrates *the distributive law of division over addition and subtraction.*

Divide.

**16.** $\dfrac{9x + 6y + 6}{3}$

**17.** $\dfrac{3x^2 + 2x}{2x}$

**18.** $\dfrac{6x^2 + 4x}{2x}$

**19.** 💡 $\dfrac{2(x + 3) + 5(x + 3)}{x + 3}$

### DISTRIBUTIVE LAW PRACTICE

Find these products, using the Lab Gear or any other method.

**20.** $2x(x - 1)$   **21.** $y(y + 4)$

**22.** $3x(x + y - 5)$   **23.** $(x + 5)(3x - 2)$

**24.** $(2x + 4)(x + y + 2)$

**25.** $(2y - x - 3)(y + x)$

Write equivalent expressions without the parentheses. Combine like terms.

**26.** $z(x + y) + z(x - y)$

**27.** $z(x + y) + z(x + y)$

**28.** $z(x + y) + x(z + y)$

**29.** $z(x + y) - x(z + y)$

### MULTIPLYING BINOMIALS

The following problems involve multiplying two binomials of the form $ax + b$ or $ax - b$. Multiplications like this arise often in math. As you do them, look for patterns and shortcuts.

**30.** $(3x + 2)(5x + 6)$

**31.** $(3x - 2)(5x + 6)$

**32.** $(3x + 2)(5x - 6)$

**33.** $(ax + 2)(3x + d)$

**34.** $(2x + b)(cx - 3)$

**35.** ⚷ When you multiply two binomials of the form $ax + b$ or $ax - b$,
a. what is the degree of the product?
b. how many terms are in the product?

**36.** ⚷ When multiplying two binomials of the form $ax + b$ or $ax - b$, how do you find
a. the coefficient of $x^2$?
b. the coefficient of $x$?
c. the constant term?

# Factoring Trinomials

**You will need:**

........ the Lab Gear ........

## LAB GEAR RECTANGLES

**1.** **Exploration**

   a. Use the Lab Gear to make as many different rectangles as you can with one $x^2$-block, ten $x$-blocks, and any number of yellow blocks. For each one, write a multiplication equation to show that *area = length times width*. Look for patterns.

   b. Use the Lab Gear to make as many different rectangles as you can with one $x^2$-block, 18 yellow blocks, and any number of $x$-blocks. For each one, write a multiplication equation to show that *area = length times width*. Look for patterns.

**2.** Use the Lab Gear to help you find the other side of the rectangle having the given area. Look for patterns. One is impossible.

| Side | Area |
|------|------|
| a. $x + 4$ | $x^2 + 9x + 20$ |
| b. $x + 3$ | $x^2 + 4x + 3$ |
| c. $x + 6$ | $x^2 + 6x + 8$ |
| d. $x + 1$ | $x^2 + 3x + 2$ |
| e. $x + 4$ | $x^2 + 7x + 12$ |

## FACTORS AND PRODUCTS

**Definition:** To *factor* means to write as a product.

For example, two ways of factoring 12 are to write it as $6 \cdot 2$ or as $4 \cdot 3$. Some polynomials can be factored. With the Lab Gear we model this by making a rectangle or a box.

**3.** By making a Lab Gear rectangle and writing a related multiplication equation, show that $5y + y^2$ can be written as the product of a monomial and a binomial.

You have factored the polynomial $5y + y^2$.

**4.** By making a rectangle with the Lab Gear and writing a related multiplication equation, show that the trinomial $x^2 + 3x + 2$ can be written as a product of two binomials.

As this problem showed, some trinomials of the form $x^2 + bx + c$ can be factored.

**5.** Factor each trinomial into the product of two binomials. It may help to use the Lab Gear to make rectangles.

   a. $x^2 + 8x + 7$
   b. $x^2 + 8x + 12$
   c. $x^2 + 8x + 15$

**6.** ⚷ Are there any more trinomials of the form $x^2 + 8x +$ ___ that can be factored into two binomials? If so, write and factor them. If not, explain.

**7.** Factor each trinomial into the product of two binomials. It may help to use the Lab Gear to make rectangles.

   a. $x^2 + 13x + 12$
   b. $x^2 + 8x + 12$
   c. $x^2 + 7x + 12$

**8.** ⚷ Are there any more trinomials of the form $x^2 +$ __$x + 12$ that can be factored into two binomials? If so, write and factor them. If not, explain.

9. Factor these third-degree polynomials into a product of three first-degree polynomials. Making a box with the Lab Gear may help.
   a. $x^2y + 5xy + 6y$
   b. $x^3 + 5x^2 + 6x$
   c. $y^3 + 5y^2 + 6y$
   d. $xy^2 + 5xy + 6x$

10. 🔑 Describe a strategy to factor the polynomials above without the Lab Gear.

11. 💡 Factor, using the Lab Gear if you need to, $x^2y + x^2 + 5xy + 5x + 6y + 6$.

12. a. Use the corner piece and the Lab Gear to show the multiplication
       $$(y + 4)(y + 3).$$
       Write the product.
    b. How many blocks of each type were needed to show the product?

13. a. Use the corner piece and the Lab Gear to show the multiplication
       $$(y - 4)(y + 3).$$
       Write the product.
    b. Compare the number of blocks of each type used to show this product with the number of blocks used in problem 12.

14. Write another multiplication that requires one $y^2$-block, seven $y$-blocks, and twelve 1-blocks to show the product. Model it with the blocks and write the product. Compare work with your classmates. Is there more than one possibility?

Supply the missing terms. Then compare your answers with your classmates' answers.

15. $x^2 + 15x + \underline{\phantom{xx}} = (x + \underline{\phantom{x}})(x + \underline{\phantom{x}})$

16. $x^2 - 7x + \underline{\phantom{xx}} = (x - \underline{\phantom{x}})(x - \underline{\phantom{x}})$

17. $x^2 + \underline{\phantom{xx}}x + 15 = (x + \underline{\phantom{x}})(x + \underline{\phantom{x}})$

18. $x^2 - \underline{\phantom{xx}}x + 7 = (x - \underline{\phantom{x}})(x - \underline{\phantom{x}})$

19. 🔑 Which problems, 15-18, have more than one answer? Explain.

20. If possible, factor each trinomial into a product of binomials. Try to do it without using the Lab Gear.
    a. $x^2 + 5x + 6$
    b. $a^2 + 11a + 30$
    c. $m^2 + 20m + 100$
    d. $p^2 + 2p + 1$

21. Factor.
    a. $x^2 - 5x + 6$
    b. $x^2 - 13x + 12$
    c. $x^2 - 8x + 15$
    d. $x^2 - 9$

22. 💡 Factor.
    a. $6x^2 + 5x + 1$
    c. $6x^2 + x - 1$
    d. $6x^2 - x - 1$

23. 💡 Factor.
    a. $x^4 - 8x^2 + 15$
    b. $x^4 - 8x^2 + 16$

24. Make up six trinomials of the form $x^2 + bx + c$. Four should be factorable, and two should be impossible to factor. Exchange with another student, and try to factor each other's trinomials.

# 5.A Analyzing Graphs

**You will need:**

graph paper

## CONSTANT PRODUCTS

**1.** a. On the same pair of axes, graph the constant product function $xy = 24$ and the constant sum function $x + y = 10$.

b. Find and label the points where these two graphs intersect.

c. Add the graph of $x + y = 4$ to the same pair of axes. Does it intersect either graph?

**2.** If possible, factor each trinomial.

a. $x^2 + 10x + 24$

b. $x^2 + 4x + 24$

**3.** ⌐━ Explain the relationship between problem 1 and problem 2.

**4.** Make a large graph of the constant product equation. $xy = 36$. Show both branches on your graph.

**5.** On the graph of $xy = 36$, find two $(x, y)$ pairs whose sum is 13. Plot and label these points, and connect them with a straight line. What is the equation of the line connecting these two points?

**6.** Add to your graph several lines of the form $x + y = S$, where $S$ is an integer, as described below. Draw at least three lines

a. that intersect the graph of $xy = 36$ in the first quadrant. (Label the graphs and the points of intersection.)

b. that intersect the graph of $xy = 36$ in the third quadrant. (Label the graphs and the points of intersection.)

c. that never intersect the graph of $xy = 36$.

**7.** ⌐━ Consider the expression $x^2 + \underline{\phantom{xx}}x + 36$. What numbers could you put in the blank to get a trinomial that can be factored? Explain your answer, giving examples.

## CONSTANT SUMS

**8.** Make a large graph of the constant sum $x + y = 12$.

**9.** a. Find many $(x, y)$ pairs whose product is 20.

b. Plot these points and connect them with a smooth curve.

c. What is the equation of the curve?

d. Where does it meet the graph of $x + y = 12$?

**10.** Add to your graph several curves with equations of the form $x \cdot y = P$, where $P$ is an integer, as described below. Draw at least three curves

a. that intersect the graph of $x + y = 12$ in the first quadrant;

b. that intersect the graph of $x + y = 12$ in the second and fourth quadrants;

c. that never intersect the graph of $x + y = 12$.

**11.** ⌐━ Consider the expression $x^2 + 12x + \underline{\phantom{xx}}$. What numbers could you put in the blank to get a trinomial that can be factored? Explain your answer, giving examples.

**12.** **Report** Summarize what you discovered in this lesson. Concentrate on the question: *How are the points of intersection of constant sum and constant product graphs related to factoring trinomials?* Use examples and illustrate your report with graphs. (The examples given in this lesson involved only positive whole numbers for the sums and products. In your report, you may use negative numbers or zero.)

# 5.5 Graphing Parabolas

**You will need:**

graph paper

**Definitions:**

- Second-degree polynomial functions are also called *quadratic* functions.
- Graphs of quadratic functions have a special shape called a *parabola.*
- The lowest or highest point on a parabola is called its *vertex.*

Here are two quadratic functions and their graphs. Each one has two *x*-intercepts and one vertex.

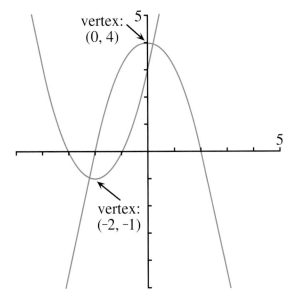

vertex:
(0, 4)

vertex:
(-2, -1)

**1.** What is the *y*-coordinate of the *x*-intercepts? What is the *x*-coordinate of the *y*-intercept?

**2.** For each parabola in the figure,
   a. what are the *x*- and *y*-intercepts?
   b. which *x*-intercept is the vertex closer to?

---

**FINDING INTERCEPTS AND THE VERTEX**

**3.** a. Copy and complete the table of values for the quadratic function $y = x^2 + 2x - 8$. Use at least six values from -5 to 5. Using the format shown will help you avoid making mistakes in computation.

| $x$ | $x^2 + 2x - 8$ | $y$ |
|-----|----------------|-----|
| -5 | $(-5)^2 + 2(-5) - 8$ | 7 |
| -4 | ———————— | — |
| ... | ———————— | — |
| 4 | ———————— | — |
| 5 | ———————— | — |

   b. Use your table to make a graph of the function.
   c. Label the intercepts and the vertex.

**4.** Repeat problem 3 for the function $y = (x + 4)(x - 2)$.

**5.** ⚷
   a. Compare your graphs in problems 3 and 4. Explain what you observe.
   b. How are the *x*-intercepts related to the expression $(x + 4)(x - 2)$?

**6.** The quadratic function $y = x^2 - 6x + 8$ can be written in factored form as $y = (x - 4)(x - 2)$.
   a. Make a table of values for this function, including the intercepts and the vertex.
   b. Graph the function. Label the intercepts and the vertex.
   c. How are the *x*-intercepts related to the expression $(x - 4)(x - 2)$?
   d. How is the *y*-intercept related to the expression $x^2 - 6x + 8$?

---

For each problem, 7-10:

    a. Write the function in factored form.

    b. Make a table of values, including the intercepts and the vertex.

    c. Graph the function, labeling the intercepts and the vertex.

**7.** $y = x^2 - 2x - 3$

**8.** $y = x^2 + 4x + 3$

**9.** $y = x^2 - 4x + 3$

**10.** $y = x^2 + 2x - 3$

**11.** ⌖ Write the equation of a quadratic function whose graph would cross the $x$-axis at $(2, 0)$ and $(-3, 0)$. Explain how you know it will work.

**12.** ⌖ Write the equation of a parabola having $y$-intercept -4. Explain how you know it will work.

**13.** Generalization Consider functions of the form $y = x^2 + bx + c$ that can be factored into $y = (x - p)(x - q)$.

    a. How are $b$, $c$, $p$, and $q$ related?

    b. How would you find the coordinates of the intercepts?

    c. 💡 How would you find the coordinates of the vertex?

---

### SMILES AND FROWNS

**14.** Make a table of values for the quadratic function $y = (x - 4)(x - 1)$ and graph it.

**15.** Repeat for $y = -(x - 4)(x - 1)$.

**16.** Compare your graphs from problems 14-15. What is alike about the graphs and what is different? How do their $x$-intercepts and vertices compare?

**17.** Write an equation of a quadratic function whose graph satisfies these given conditions.

    a. a *smile* parabola having $x$-intercepts $(3, 0)$ and $(-2, 0)$

    b. a *frown* parabola having $x$-intercepts $(3, 0)$ and $(-2, 0)$

    c. a *smile* parabola having $x$-intercepts $(-3, 0)$ and $(-2, 0)$

    d. a *frown* parabola having $x$-intercepts $(-3, 0)$ and $(-2, 0)$

**18.** ⌖ Explain how you know that your answers to problem 17 are correct. You may check your answers by making a table of values, and graphing.

**19.** ⌖ Write the equation of a quadratic function that passes through the origin and $(5, 0)$. Explain.

**20.** Write an equation of a quadratic function whose graph satisfies the given conditions.

    a. a parabola having one $x$-intercept at $(1, 0)$ and the vertex with $x$-coordinate 2

    b. a parabola having one $x$-intercept at $(1, 0)$ and the vertex at $(2, 1)$

    c. 💡 a parabola having one $x$-intercept at $(1, 0)$ and the vertex at $(2, 2)$

---

### HOW MANY x-INTERCEPTS?

**21.** Graph each of these four quadratic functions on the same axes.

    a. $y = x^2 + 6x + 5$

    b. $y = x^2 + 6x + 8$

    c. $y = x^2 + 6x + 9$

    d. $y = x^2 + 6x + 12$

**22.** ⟜ Write a paragraph describing and comparing the graphs you drew in problem 21. Which graph or graphs have two *x*-intercepts? Which have one? Which have none? Could you have predicted this before graphing? Explain.

**23.** 💡 Consider the quadratic function $y = x^2 + 4x +$ ___. Fill in the blank with a number that will give a function whose graph is

a. a parabola having one *x*-intercept;

b. a parabola having two *x*-intercepts;

c. a parabola having no *x*-intercepts.

**24.** 💡 Check your answers to problem 23 by graphing, or explain why you are sure you are correct.

**PUZZLES** *MAKING CHANGE*

**25.** Find the largest number of pennies, nickels, and dimes that you can have and still not be able to make change for a quarter. Explain your answer.

**26.** Find the largest number of coins you can have and still not be able to make change for a dollar. (Assume that you can have any coins except a silver dollar.) Explain this answer.

**PREVIEW** *ZEROING IN*

**27.** If $ab = 0$, $bc = 0$, and $ac = 1$, what is $b$?

**28.** ⟜ If $abc = 0$ and $bcd = 1$, what conclusion can you draw? Explain.

**PUZZLE** *SQUARE SUMS*

**29.** 💡 Arrange the whole numbers from 1 to 18 into nine pairs, so that the sum of the numbers in each pair is a perfect square.

# LESSON
## 5.6
# Factors

**You will need:**

....... the Lab Gear ·······

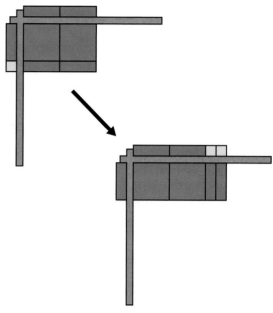

**1.** **Exploration**

a. Draw a rectangle whose sides are any two consecutive even numbers, like 4 and 6. Find its area. If the side lengths have to be whole numbers, is it possible to draw a rectangle having the *same area but different sides*? Try this with another pair of consecutive even numbers. Is it possible this time? Do you think it is always, sometimes, or never possible?

b. Does your result change if you use two consecutive odd numbers, like 3 and 5?

c. What about consecutive multiples of 3, like 6 and 9?

---

### SAME AREA, DIFFERENT PERIMETER

**Example:** Use the Lab Gear to build a rectangle having a width of $2x$ and a length of $x + 1$.

a. Sketch the rectangle. Label it with an equation of the form *length times width equals area*.

b. Find the perimeter of the rectangle.

c. Rearrange your rectangle into a rectangle having the *same area* but a *different perimeter*.

d. Write another equation of the form *length times width equals area*.

For problems 2-4 below, build a Lab Gear rectangle of the given width and length. Then follow the instructions in parts (a) through (d) in the example.

**2.** width: $2x$      length: $2x + 2$

**3.** width: $3x$      length: $3 + x$

**4.** width: $x$      length: $4 + 4x$

For problems 5-6 follow the instructions in the example, but build at least two rectangles, and three if possible.

**5.** width: $4 + 2x$      length: $2 + 4x$

**6.** width: $2 + 2x$      length: $3 + 2x$

### RECOGNIZING FACTORS

For each expression, 7-12, write as many different products equal to it as you can. Use only whole numbers. (In some cases, it may be helpful to use the Lab Gear to build rectangles and/or boxes.)

**7.** 24

**8.** $6y^2$

**9.** $(2x + 4)(3x + 6)$

**10.** $12x^3$

**11.** $12x^2 + 4x$

**12.** $2x(6x + 18)$

### COMMON FACTORS

**Example:** As you know, factoring a polynomial can sometimes be modeled by making a Lab Gear rectangle.

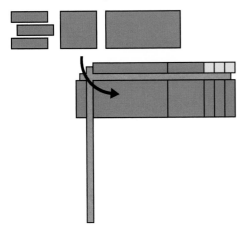

$$xy + x^2 + 3x = x(y + x + 3)$$

By multiplying the factors, you get the original polynomial back. Factoring is using the distributive law in reverse.

In this example, we say that $x$ is a *common factor* of all three terms in the original polynomial, because it divides each term evenly. In the case of $2x^3 + 8x^2 + 2x^2y$, the common factors are 2, $x$, and $x^2$. In factoring such a polynomial, it is usually best to *take out* the *greatest common factor,* which is $2x^2$.

In the following problems, factor the polynomials by taking out the greatest common factor. Not all are possible.

**13.** $2x^3 + 8x^2 + 2x^2y$

**14.** $2x^2 - 6x$

**15.** $2x^2 + 6x + 1$

**16.** $3x^2 + 2x + 4xy$

**17.** $3x^2y - 3xy + 6xy^2$

**18.** $3y^2 + 9y - 6y^3 + 3x^2y + 6xy^2 + 9xy$

### FACTORING COMPLETELY

As you have seen in this lesson, there are often many ways to factor a polynomial. However, there is only one way to factor it *completely.* For example, $(4x + 8)(3x + 9)$ is factored, but to factor it completely you would have to factor 4 out of $(4x + 8)$ and 3 out of $(3x + 9)$.

Factor completely.

**19.** $(2x + 6)(3x + 6)$

**20.** $4(x^2 + 5x + 6)$

**21.** $4x^2 + 40x + 64$

**22.** $2x^2 + 8x + 8$

**23.** $3x^2 + 21x + 30$

**24.** $2x^2 + 26x + 72$

**25.** $x^3 + 5x^2 + 6x$

5.7 **Minus and the Distributive Law**

**REVIEW** *ORDER OF OPERATIONS*

1. Compare these two expressions, and these two figures.

$$(5 - 3)(x - 2)$$
$$5 - 3(x - 2)$$

**(i)**

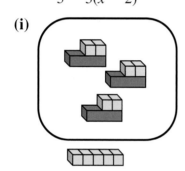

**(ii)**

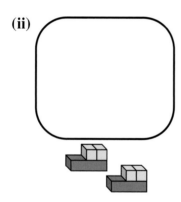

a. Which expression means *multiply (x − 2) by 3 and subtract the result from 5*? (Remember order of operations.)

b. Which figure shows that expression with the Lab Gear?

c. Which expression means *subtract 3 from 5 and multiply the result by (x − 2)*?

d. Which figure shows that expression with the Lab Gear?

e. Here are the same expressions, rewritten without parentheses. Which is which?

$$11 - 3x \qquad 2x - 4$$

Write without parentheses.

2. $7 - 3(y - 4)$    3. $(7 - 3)(y - 4)$

4. $(4 - 2)x + 1$    5. $(4 - 2)(x + 1)$

6. $x - 2(x + 1)$    7. $(x - 2)(x + 1)$

8. $(x - 2)x - 1$

If you added another set of parentheses to the expression in problem 8, you would get $(x - 2)(x - 1)$. One way to multiply these binomials is to use the multiplication table format.

| | $x$ | $-2$ |
|---|---|---|
| $x$ | _____ | _____ |
| $-1$ | _____ | _____ |

9. What is the product?

**USING THE CORNER PIECE**

In this lesson, you will learn how to model a product like this with the Lab Gear. You will practice it with numbers before using variables.

**Example:** In the case of $(6 - 2)(5 - 3)$ set up the problem as shown in the figure. The method you will follow is to *multiply all the blocks on the left side by all the blocks across the top.*

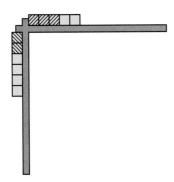

Put the upstairs blocks at the corner of the corner piece.

First, multiply the downstairs blocks. Then multiply the upstairs blocks by each other. Since -2(-3) = 6, a positive number, these blocks must appear *downstairs* somewhere. They will be arranged in a 2-by-3 rectangle. It would be nice to line up the rectangle with its factors, but then it would have to be upstairs, making it -6, which would be wrong. So we can *line it up with only one of the two factors.* Let's choose the -3.

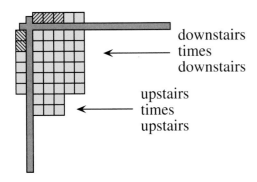

downstairs
times
downstairs

upstairs
times
upstairs

Finally, multiply upstairs blocks on the left with downstairs blocks at the top, and vice versa, placing them as shown.

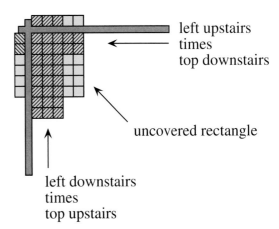

left upstairs
times
top downstairs

uncovered rectangle

left downstairs
times
top upstairs

You can now see that the answer (4 times 2 = 8) is shown by *the uncovered rectangle.*

10. Use the corner piece to show the product (5 − 2)(7 − 4).

**USING VARIABLES**

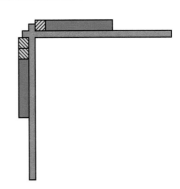

11. Write the polynomials being multiplied.

12. ⚬━ Follow the process shown in the following figures with your blocks. Write a brief explanation of each step.

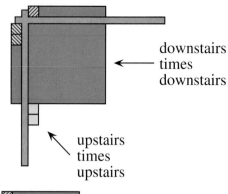

downstairs
times
downstairs

upstairs
times
upstairs

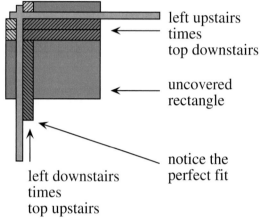

left upstairs
times
top downstairs

uncovered
rectangle

notice the
perfect fit

left downstairs
times
top upstairs

**13.** Write the dimensions of the uncovered rectangle and the product.

**14.** Use the Lab Gear to multiply.
   a. $(x - 1)(2x - 3)$
   b. $(y - 5)(2y - 1)$

**15.** Use the Lab Gear to multiply.
   a. $(y + 1)(y + 5)$
   b. $(y - 1)(y + 5)$
   c. $(y + 1)(y - 5)$
   d. $(y - 1)(y - 5)$

**16.** Use the Lab Gear to multiply.
   a. $(2x + 3)^2$      b. $(2x - 3)^2$
   c. $(2x + 3)(2x - 3)$

**17.** 💡 This figure shows four ways to set up the multiplication $(y - 2)(y - 5)$. Of those, three will work. Experiment to find out which three. Sketch your solutions.

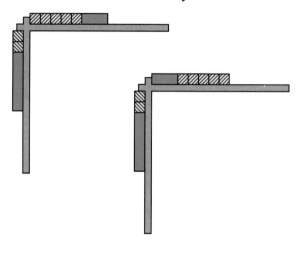

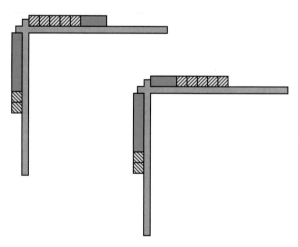

**MAKE A SQUARE**

For each problem, arrange the blocks into a square. Not all are possible. Write an equation relating the side length and area of the square.

**18.** $x^2 + 6x + 9$

**19.** $4x^2 + 4x + 1$

**20.** $x^2 + 8x + 4$

**21.** $x^2 + 4x + 16$

**22.** $9x^2 + 12x + 4$

**23.** $x^2 + 2xy + y^2$

**REVIEW** **SOLVING EQUATIONS**

**24.** Use the cover-up method to solve these equations.
   a. $30 - 3(2x + 1) = 9$
   b. $19 - 2(x + 5) = 1$
   c. $(5 - 3x) - 2 = -3$
   d. $5 - 3(x - 2) = 20$
   e. $(5 - 3)(x - 2) = 10$

**REVIEW** **FUNCTION DIAGRAMS FOR CONSTANT PRODUCTS**

For each equation, 25-27:
   a. Make a large function diagram (with number lines ranging from at least $-12$ to 12), using your calculator to help you find values if needed.
   b. Do all the in-out lines meet in a single point?
   c. Are there any horizontal in-out lines? (In other words, in-out lines where $x = y$.) For what values of $x$ and $y$?
   d. Follow the $y$-value with your finger as $x$ changes from $-12$ to 12. Describe $y$'s motion. (Does it move up or down? Does it ever *jump*? For what values of $x$ does it move fast? Slowly?)

**25.** $xy = 9$

**26.** $xy = 8$

**27.** $xy = -9$

**28.** 💡 $x$ is greater than 1, and $6/x$ is a whole number. What could $x$ be? (Hint: There are more than three solutions.)

# Building-Block Numbers

In this lesson, use just whole numbers.

## FOOD FOR THOUGHT

**1.** **Exploration** Eric tried to order 13 chicken nuggets at the fast food store. The employee informed him that he could order only 6, 9, or 20 nuggets. Eric realized he had to decide between ordering $6 + 6 = 12$, or $6 + 9 = 15$. What numbers of nuggets can be ordered by combining 6, 9, and 20? What numbers cannot be ordered? What is the greatest number that cannot be ordered? Explain.

## TWO BUILDING BLOCKS

**2.** You have an unlimited supply of coins. What amounts can be obtained, and what amounts cannot be obtained using only dimes and quarters? Explain.

**3.** At Albert's Kitchen Supply, cabinets are available in two lengths: 3 feet and 5 feet. By putting cabinets end to end, walls of different lengths can be accommodated. Imagine that kitchens can be any size. What length walls are possible to line exactly with cabinets? What lengths are impossible?

**4.** In 1958 it cost 4 cents to mail a letter. In 1963 it cost 5 cents. Imagine you have an unlimited supply of 4- and 5-cent stamps. What amounts can you make? What is the largest amount you cannot make?

For each problem, 5-10, using only addition and the building-block numbers given, what numbers can you reach? What numbers can't you reach? If there is one, what is the greatest number you cannot reach?

**5.** 2, 5    **6.** 7, 11    **7.** 4, 6

**8.** 5, 12    **9.** 5, 15    **10.** 8, 1

Given the two numbers 7 and 11 and the operation of addition, it is possible to build every number beyond 59. However, with the numbers 4 and 6 there is no limit to the size of numbers that cannot be built.

**11.** **Generalizations** Suppose you find that for two numbers, $a$ and $b$, and the operation of addition, you can build every number beyond a certain number. What can you say about $a$ and $b$? Explain, using examples. (Hint: You may need to use the idea of common factors. For example: 4 and 6 have the common factor 2; 5 and 15 have the common factor 5.)

**12.** Given two numbers, $a$ and $b$, such that their greatest common factor is 1, how can you calculate the greatest number that *cannot* be written as a sum of multiples of $a$ and $b$? Explain, using examples.

## A STRATEGY

In problems 13 and 14 you will investigate the numbers 5 and 6 as building blocks.

**13.** Write the numbers from 1 to 40 in an array like this.

| 0 | 1 | 2 | 3 | 4 |
|---|---|---|---|---|
| 5 | 6 | 7 | 8 | 9 |
| 10 | 11 | 12 | 13 | 14... |

a. Circle the multiples of 5. (0 is a multiple of 5.)

b. Circle the numbers that are equal to 6 plus a multiple of 5.

c. Circle the numbers that are equal to 12 plus a multiple of 5.

*Chapter 5 Sums and Products*

d. Circle the numbers that are equal to 18 plus a multiple of 5.

e. Circle the numbers that are equal to 24 plus a multiple of 5.

**14.** What is the largest number that **cannot** be built from 5 and 7? Explain how you know for sure that every number greater than this number can be built.

**15.** Repeat the same strategy to analyze 5 and 6 as building blocks.

**16.** Repeat the same strategy to analyze 4 and 7 as building blocks. (This time set up your array with only four columns.)

**17.** Generalization If you were to use the same strategy for numbers $a$ and $b$, with $a < b$:

a. How many columns should you have in your array?

b. What numbers should you circle first?

c. What numbers should you circle next?

d. What is the smallest number in the last column you circled? (Write this number in terms of $a$ and $b$.)

e. If you were not able to solve problem 12, try again with the help of this strategy.

---

**DISCOVERY** *HOLIDAY MATH*

**18.** Candles are lit every night for the eight nights of Hanukah. Two candles are lit on the first night, three on the second night, and so on, adding one candle each night. How many candles should be in the boxes of candles sold especially for Hanukah? Explain.

**19.** Find the words to the song "The Twelve Days of Christmas."

a. Make a sketch or drawing to show what is happening in the song. How many gifts did the singer receive on the twelfth day of Christmas? Explain.

b. The singer received six gifts on the 3rd day. How many gifts did the singer receive on the 4th day? The 5th day? The $n$th day? Explain.

c. The singer received 22 turtledoves. Find the total number of each other kind of gift that the singer received.

d. Suppose there were $n$ days of Christmas. How many gifts would the singer receive in all? Explain.

**PREVIEW** *COIN PROBLEMS*

**20.** You have ten coins. Their total value is $1.10. How many of each coin do you have? The problem has several solutions. Find as many as you can.

**21.** Add extra information that makes problem 20 have a unique solution. Explain how you know the solution is unique.

**22.** Create your own coin problem that has several solutions. Solve your problem.

**23.** Solve someone else's coin problem.

**24.** Add extra information to your problem so it will have a unique solution.

**25.** You want to mail a letter. It needs 52 cents postage, but all you have are 29-cent stamps: $29 + 29 = 58$. What would be convenient would be to have negative stamps. Then you could put two 29-cent stamps and a minus 6-cent stamp on your envelope, and it would solve your problem. Write a paragraph about this idea. How would the post office "sell" negative stamps? Why do you think they don't do it?

**26.** How many *digits* are used in numbering the pages of this book? Explain how you figured it out.

**27.** It took 1992 digits to number the pages of a book. Every page was numbered, starting with page 1. How many pages does the book have?

**28.** ◌ Explain how to find out how many digits are needed to number the pages of a book that has *n* pages, if *n* is

   a. more than 9, but less than 100;

   b. more than 99, but less than 1000.

# 5.B Distributing

Look at this sequence of consecutive integers.

$$8, 9, 10, 11$$

- The product of the outside pair is 88.
- The product of the inside pair is 90.
- The difference between the inside product and the outside product is 2.

1. Find the difference between the inside and outside product for each of these sequences.
   a. 4, 5, 6, 7
   b. 10, 11, 12, 13
   c. 10, 10 + 1, 10 + 2, 10 + 3
   d. $y, y + 1, y + 2, y + 3$

2. What pattern did you notice in problem 1?

3. Look at some sequences of four integers that differ by three. For example, you could try 4, 7, 10, 13. What pattern do you notice in the difference between their inside and outside products?

4. What pattern would you expect to see in the difference of inside and outside products for sequences of numbers that differ by two? What about sequences of numbers that differ by four? Experiment.

5. Find the difference between the inside and outside product for each of these sequences.
   a. $y, y + 2, y + 4, y + 6$
   b. $y, y + 3, y + 6, y + 9$
   c. $y, y + 5, y + 10, y + 15$
   d. $y, y + 5, y + 2 \cdot 5, y + 3 \cdot 5$
   e. $y, y + x, y + 2x, y + 3x$

6. **Report** Write a detailed report describing the patterns you discovered in this lesson. Give examples and show all your calculations. Your report should include, but not be limited to, the answers to the following questions:

- How is the difference between the inside and outside products related to the difference between numbers in the sequence?
- How can you use algebra (and/or the Lab Gear) to show that your answer is correct?
- Does your generalization work for all kinds of numbers? For example, could you choose a sequence made up entirely of negative numbers? What about fractions?

You might wonder if there are more distributive laws.

7. Is there a distributive law of exponentiation over addition? If there were, it would mean that $(x + y)^2$ would always be equal to $x^2 + y^2$. It would also mean that $(x + y)^3$ would equal $x^3 + y^3$. Do you think such a law exists? Explain why or why not.

8. Is there a distributive law of multiplication over multiplication? If there were, it would mean that $a(xy)$ would always be equal to $ax \cdot ay$. For example, $2(xy)$ would have to equal $2x \cdot 2y$. Do you think such a law exists? Explain why or why not.

9. **Report** Write a report about distributive laws. Use numerical examples and/or sketches of the Lab Gear. Your report should include a discussion of which of the following laws exist, and why.

The distributive law of:
- multiplication over addition and subtraction
- division over addition and subtraction
- exponentiation over addition and subtraction
- multiplication over multiplication

# 5.9 Staircase Sums

## ONE STEP AT A TIME

Here is an example of a kind of arrangement that we'll call a *staircase*. It has 4 steps and the first step is of height 2.

**Definition:** For this lesson, we will define a *staircase* as a sequence of stacks of tiles in which each stack is one tile higher than the previous stack. *There must be two or more steps in the staircase,* and the first step can be of any height.

1. How many tiles would you need to build each of these staircases?

    a. First step: 7   Number of steps: 8

    b. First step: 8   Number of steps: 7

    c. First step: 6   Number of steps: 9

2. There are two different nine-tile staircases: $2 + 3 + 4$ and $4 + 5$.

    a. Find three different 15-tile staircases.

    b. 💡 Find four different 105-tile staircases.

3. **Exploration** Find every possible staircase with each number of tiles from 2 to 34. Hints:

    • Work with other students.

    • Keep organized records of your work.

    • It is not necessary to draw the staircases.

    • Look for strategies: What numbers can be made into two-step staircases? Three-step?

    • Look for patterns: What numbers are easiest? What numbers are impossible?

4. The number 10 can be written as the sum of four consecutive numbers.

    a. What are these four numbers?

    b. If negative integers and zero are allowed, can the number 10 be written as the sum of consecutive numbers in any other way? If so, show how.

5. Show how the number 4 can be written as a sum of consecutive integers if negative numbers and zero can be used.

6. **Generalization** What is the maximum number of consecutive integers that can be used to write the number 17 as a sum? What is the maximum number of consecutive integers that can be used to write the number $N$ as a sum? (Assume $N$ is an integer.) Explain your answer, giving examples.

## SUMS FROM RECTANGLES

7. a. On graph paper, sketch the staircase illustrated at the beginning of the lesson. Then make a rectangle by sketching a copy of the staircase *upside down* on the first staircase. (You can also do this by building the staircases with tiles.)

    b. What are the length, width, and area of the rectangle?

8. Imagine a staircase having 100 steps, and a first step of height 17.

    a. It would be half of what rectangle? (Give the length and width.)

    b. How many tiles would you need to build the staircase? Explain how you know.

**9.** Show how you could find the sum of:

    a. the integers from 5 to 55, inclusive;

    b. the integers from 0 to 100, inclusive.

**GAUSS'S METHOD**

Math teachers like to tell a story about Carl Friedrich Gauss. One day in elementary school he was punished by his teacher who asked him to add up all the whole numbers from 0 to 100. Carl immediately gave the answer, to his teacher's amazement. He grew up to be one of the greatest mathematicians of all time.

Gauss's method was to imagine all the numbers from 0 to 100 written from left to right, and directly beneath that, all the numbers written from right to left. It would look like this:

```
  0   1   2   3   4   5   6   7   8   9...
100  99  98  97  96  95  94  93  92  91...
```

He mentally added each column, getting 100 each time. He multiplied 100 by the number of columns, and did one more thing to get the correct answer.

**10.** Finish Gauss's calculation. Be sure to use the correct number of columns, and to carry out the final step. Did you get the same answer as in problem 9b?

**11.** ☞ What would happen if the numbers to be added started at 1 instead of 0? Obviously, the sum should be the same. Would Gauss's method still give the same answer? Explain.

**12.** <u>Summary</u> You now know two methods for calculating staircase sums: one involves making a rectangle; the other is Gauss's method. Both methods work well, but it is easy to make mistakes when using them. Write a paragraph explaining how you would use each method to calculate the sum, $5 + 6 + 7 + ... + 89$. Use sketches as part of your explanation. Both methods should give the same answer.

**VARIABLE STAIRCASES**

You can build staircases with the Lab Gear. This diagram shows $(x) + (x + 1) + (x + 2) + (x + 3)$.

**13.** In terms of $x$, what is the sum of $(x) + (x + 1) + (x + 2) + (x + 3)$?

**14.** Find the sum of $(x) + (x + 1) + (x + 2) + (x + 3)$ if:

    a. $x = 4$;        b. $x = 99$.

**15.** Find each sum. Explain how you got your answer.

    a. $(x) + (x + 1) + (x + 2) + ... + (x + 26)$

    b. $(x + 1) + (x + 5) + ... + (x + 84)$

**16.** <u>Generalization</u> What is the sum of each staircase?

    a. $1 + 2 + 3 + ... + n$

    b. $(x) + (x + 1) + ... + (x + n)$

    c. $(x + 1) + ... + (x + n)$

# Sequences

**Definitions:** A *sequence* is an ordered list of numbers, called *terms*. (Notice that this is a new use of the word *term.*) Terms are often indicated with subscripted variables, such as $t_1$, $t_2$, or $t_n$.

## GRAPHS OF SEQUENCES

**Definition:** The *natural numbers* are the numbers we count with: 1, 2, 3, 4, ...

The natural numbers are the easiest sequence of numbers to write using a variable. The first natural number is 1, the second natural number is 2, and so on; $t_1 = 1$, $t_2 = 2$, ... The $n^{\text{th}}$ natural number is $n$, so $t_n = n$. The graph shows the sequence of natural numbers.

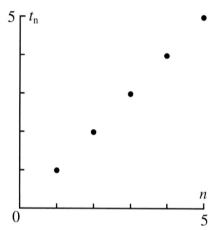

1. Graph the first few terms of the sequence below. Does it make sense to connect the dots? Explain.

| $n$ | 1 | 2 | 3 | 4 | ... | $n$ |
|---|---|---|---|---|---|---|
| $t_n$ | 2 | 5 | 8 | 11 | ... | $3n - 1$ |

2. Make a table, and graph the first few terms of the sequence whose $n^{\text{th}}$ term is $t_n = 3n + 1$. Compare your graph with the one you drew in problem 1. How are they the same? How are they different?

3. You may remember this sequence.

| $n$ | 1 | 2 | 3 | 4 | ... | $n$ |
|---|---|---|---|---|---|---|
| $t_n$ | 1 | 3 | 6 | 10 | ... | ? |

   a. What is the 6th term?
   b. 💡 What is the $n^{\text{th}}$ term?
   c. Graph the first few terms. Is your graph a straight line?

## GETTING EVEN

4. If 2 is the first even number, 4 the second, and so on, what is the millionth even number? In terms of $n$, what is the $n^{\text{th}}$ even number?

5. Graph the first few terms of the sequence of even numbers. Is your graph a straight line?

| $n$ | 1 | 2 | 3 | ... | ? | $n$ |
|---|---|---|---|---|---|---|
| $t_n$ | 2 | 6 | ? | ... | 42 | ? |

6. The $n^{\text{th}}$ term in the above sequence is the *sum of the first n even numbers.*
   a. What is $t_5$?
   b. Which term has a value of 42?
   c. Graph the first few terms. Is your graph a straight line?
   d. 💡 In terms of $n$, what is the $n^{\text{th}}$ term of this sequence?

## THAT'S ODD!

7. If 1 is the first odd number, 3 the second, 5 the third, what is the one-hundredth odd number?

**8.** a. In terms of $n$, what is the $n^{th}$ odd number?

b. Graph the first few terms in the sequence of odd numbers.

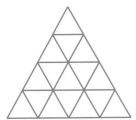

**9.** a. Look at the figure. How many unit triangles are in the first row? The second? The third? (Count triangles whether they point up or down.)

b. If the triangle were extended indefinitely, how many unit triangles would there be in the $n^{th}$ row?

**10.** a. How many unit triangles are there altogether in the first two rows? The first three rows?

b. How many unit triangles are in the first $n$ rows?

**11.** What is the sum of the first two odd numbers? The first three?

**12.** a. What is the sum of the first $n$ odd numbers?

b. Graph the first few terms in the sequence of sums of odd numbers.

## ARITHMETIC SEQUENCES

**Definition:** In an *arithmetic sequence,* the difference between consecutive terms is always the same. It is called the *common difference.*

**Examples:** These are arithmetic sequences.
2, 7, 12, 17, 22 (The common difference is 5.)
5, 8, 11, 14, 17, 20, 23, 26, 29, 32 (The common difference is 3.)

These are not arithmetic sequences.
3, 9, 27, 81
1, -1, 1, -1, 1, -1
4, 9, 16, 25, 49

**13.** Which of these are arithmetic sequences? For those that are, what is the common difference?

a. 2, 6, 8, 12, 16, 20

b. 3, 6, 3, 7, 3, 8

c. 19, 13, 7, 1, -5, ...

d. the sequence of even numbers

e. the sequence of odd numbers

f. $2, 2 + 9, 2 + 2 \cdot 9, 2 + 3 \cdot 9, 2 + 4 \cdot 9$

**14.** Make up an arithmetic sequence for another student.

**15.** Answer these questions about a classmate's sequence.

a. Is it really an arithmetic sequence?

b. What is the common difference?

c. 💡 In terms of $n$, what is the $n^{th}$ term?

**16.** 💡 For each arithmetic sequence, find the common difference, and write the $n^{th}$ term in terms of $n$.

a. 2, 7, 12, 22, ...

b. $2 + 1 \cdot 5, 2 + 2 \cdot 5, 2 + 3 \cdot 5, ...$

c. $2, 2 + 1 \cdot 5, 2 + 2 \cdot 5, 2 + 3 \cdot 5, ...$

**17.** 💡 Answer the same questions as in problem 15 for:

a. $y, y + 1 \cdot 5, y + 2 \cdot 5, y + 3 \cdot 5, ...$

b. $2 + 1 \cdot x, 2 + 2 \cdot x, 2 + 3 \cdot x, ...$

c. $y + 1 \cdot x, y + 2 \cdot x, y + 3 \cdot x, ...$

d. $y, y + 1 \cdot x, y + 2 \cdot x, y + 3 \cdot x, ...$

**18.** **Summary** Explain how to calculate the $n^{th}$ term of an arithmetic sequence, if you know the first term and the common difference. Test your method on several arithmetic sequences.

**19.** For each equation, find values of $x_1$, $x_2$, and $x_3$, that make it true.

    a. $(x_1 + x_2 + x_3)/3 = 100$

    b. $(x_1 + x_2 + x_3)/3 = 50$

    c. $(x_1 + x_2 + x_3)/3 = 20$

    d. $(x_1 + x_2 + x_3)/3 = 10$

**20.** For each equation in problem 19, find another set of values for $x_1$, $x_2$, and $x_3$ that will work.

**21.** If possible, find a value of $x_3$ to satisfy each equation.

    a. $(15 + 20 + x_3)/3 = 100$

    b. $(15 + 20 + x_3)/3 = 50$

    c. $(15 + 20 + x_3)/3 = 20$

    d. $(15 + 20 + x_3)/3 = 10$

```
            1
           3 5
          7 9 11
        13 15 17 19
      21 23 25 27 29
```

**22.** Look at the array of numbers above.

    a. Write the next two rows.

    b. Describe how the array is made.

**23.** a. Look at the middle number in rows that have a middle number. What is the pattern?

    b. In rows that do not have a middle number, think of the number between the middle two numbers. What is the pattern?

    c. Find the sum of the numbers in each row. What is the pattern?

**24.** 

    a. What is the first number in the $n^{th}$ row?

    b. What is the last number in the $n^{th}$ row?

    c. What is the sum of all the numbers in the first $n$ rows?

# Averages and Sums

## MEANS AND MEDIANS

You probably know how to find the average of a set of numbers. For example, the ages of the people in Tina's family are 10, 48, 20, 22, and 57. You would find the average age by adding the numbers and dividing by 5.

$$\frac{10 + 48 + 20 + 22 + 57}{5} = 31.4$$

We call this average the *mean*. Another kind of average is the *median*.

> **Definition:** The *median* is the middle of a set of numbers that are in order from least to greatest. To find the median of an even number of numbers, find the two middle numbers and find their mean.

> **Examples:** To find the median age in Tina's family, first write the numbers in ascending or descending order.
>
> 10  20  **22**  48  57
>
> The median is **22.**

These are the ages of people in Lana's family: 52, 20, 15, and 53. To find the median, first write the numbers in ascending or descending order.

53  **52  20**  15

Compute the mean of the middle two numbers: $\frac{52 + 20}{2} = $ **36**, so the median is 36.

1. Find the mean of the ages in Lana's family. Compare it with the median.

2. Make up a sequence of seven numbers in which
   a. the mean is less than the median;
   b. the median is less than the mean;
   c. the mean and the median are equal.

3. Repeat problem 2 for a sequence of eight numbers.

4. **Exploration** Find some sequences of numbers in which the mean and the median are equal. Work with your classmates and compare your answers. What can you conclude about these sequences? Write a summary of your conclusions, including examples. (At least one example should be an arithmetic sequence, and at least one should not be.)

5. For each example below, make up two sequences that fit the given description.
   a. The greatest term is 19, and both mean and median equal 10.
   b. There are six terms. The greatest is 25, the mean is 10, and the median is less than 10.
   c. There are seven terms. The least is -60, the median is 18, and the mean is less than 18.
   d. The mean and the median are both -4. There are nine terms.

6. ⚿ If possible, make up an arithmetic sequence that fits each description in problem 5. If it's not possible, explain why not.

## MEANS AND SUMS

7. Find the mean and the sum of each arithmetic sequence.
   a. -2, -14, -26, -38, -50, -62, -74
   b. -5, -1.8, 1.4, 4.6, 7.8, 11, 14.2, 17.4
   c. 31, 29, 27, 25, 23, 21
   d. 17, 20, 23, 26, 29, 32

8. ⚿ Study your answers to problem 7.
   a. In which cases was the mean one of the terms in the sequence?
   b. When the mean was not one of the terms in the sequence, how was it related to those terms?

c. How are the number of terms, the mean, and the sum related?

Suppose we wanted to find the sum and the mean of this arithmetic sequence:

3, 9, 15, 21, 27, 33, 39, 45, 51.

Using Gauss's method, write the sequence twice, once from left to right, and then from right to left.

| 3 | 9 | 15 | 21 | 27 | 33 | 39 | 45 | 51 |
|---|---|----|----|----|----|----|----|----|
| 51 | 45 | 39 | 33 | 27 | 21 | 15 | 9 | 3 |

9. ⚿

   a. Add each column above.

   b. Find the mean and the sum of the sequence.

   c. How are your answers to (b) related to the sum of each column?

10. Using your results from problem 9, find a shortcut for calculating the sum and the mean of an arithmetic sequence. Try it on the examples in problem 7, comparing your results with your previous answers.

11. Find the sum and the mean of each arithmetic sequence described.

   a. The sequence has 15 terms. The first term is 12, and the last term is 110.

   b. The first term is –11, and the last term is –33. Each term is obtained by adding –2 to the previous term.

   c. The first term is –14, and the difference between consecutive terms is 5. There are 41 terms in the sequence.

   d. The first term is 7, and each term is obtained by adding –1.4 to the previous term. There are eight terms in the sequence.

12. Generalization Find the sum and the mean of each arithmetic sequence.

   a. The first term is $b$, and the final term is 5. There are six terms in the sequence.

   b. The first term is $b$, and the final term is $f$. There are 10 terms in the sequence.

   c. The first term is $b$, and the final term is $f$. There are $n$ terms in the sequence.

   d. 💡 The first term is $b$, and each successive term is obtained by adding $d$. There are $n$ terms in the sequence.

### THEATER SEATS

Seats in a theater are arranged so that there are 35 seats in the front (first) row, 38 in the next row, 41 in the row behind that, and so on, adding three seats each time.

13. How many seats are in the
   a. $10^{th}$ row?       b. the $n^{th}$ row?

14. How many total seats are needed if the theater has
   a. 26 rows?       b. $n$ rows?

15. How would your answers to questions 13-14 be different if there were 34 seats in the first row?

16. Suppose there were 35 seats in the first row, 37 in the next, and so on, adding two seats each time. How would your answers to questions 13-14 be different?

# Smooth Moves

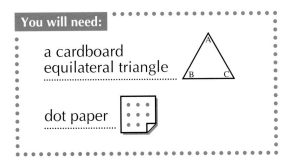

## FLIPS AND TURNS

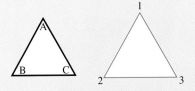

1. a. Write the letters A, B, and C on your triangle, near the vertices. Make sure the same letter appears on both sides of the cardboard at each vertex.

   b. Outline the triangle on a piece of paper, and write the numbers 1, 2, and 3 outside the outline, as in the figure.

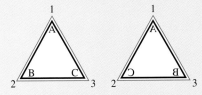

There are several different ways you can place the triangle on its outline. The two ways shown in the figure can be written ABC and ACB. ABC is called the *home position*.

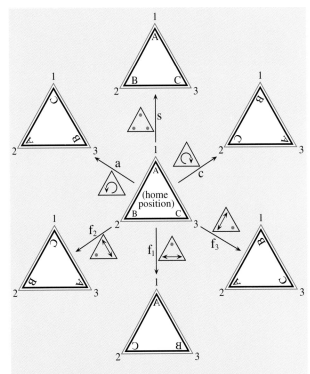

• means *this corner does not move*.

As you can see on the figure, you can get from the home position to each other position by using one of the following moves.

**Turns:**

• the clockwise turn (abbreviation: *c*)
• the counterclockwise turn (abbreviation: *a* — short for *anticlockwise*)

To do the turns (also called *rotations*), you do not lift the triangle off the page. You turn it until the triangle fits into the outline again.

**Flips:**

There are three flips. To do a flip you keep one corner in place and have the other two switch positions. For example, for flip 2 ($f_2$), you keep corner 2 fixed, and corners 1 and 3 switch positions. (Flips are also called *reflections.*)

**Stay:**

the *move* that does not move (abbreviation: $s$)

2. Which corner stays fixed and which changes position
   a. for flip 3 ($f_3$)?
   b. for flip 1 ($f_1$)?

Practice the turns and flips, making sure you know what each one does. In this lesson, you will have to execute turns and flips in succession, without going back to the home position in between.

> **Example:** Do $f_1$, then $a$. (Such a sequence is simply written $f_1a$.) If you start at the home position, and do these moves in order, you will end up in the position BAC. (Try it.) But since you could have ended up there *in one move* ($f_3$), you can write: $f_1a = f_3$.

3. Find out whether $af_1 = f_3$

4. Simplify. That is, give the one move that has the same result as the given sequence of moves.
   a. $aa$    b. $f_1f_3$    c. $f_3f_1$
   d. $sf_2$    e. $ac$    f. $ca$

5. Simplify.
   a. $f_1f_2f_3$    b. $af_1af_2af_3$
   c. $f_1af_2af_3a$    d. $cf_1cf_2cf_3$

6. Figure out a way to write each of the six moves in terms of only $f_1$ and $c$.

7. Fill in the blanks.
   a. $a$___$= f_1$    b. ___$a = f_1$
   c. $f_1$___$= f_2$    d. ___$f_1 = c$

### THE ALGEBRA OF MOVES

Executing moves in order is an *operation* on triangle moves, just as multiplication is an operation on numbers. The set of six moves, together with this operation, is called the *symmetry group* for the triangle.

8. 🔑 Make a *multiplication table* for triangle moves. That is, figure out the one move that has the same result as doing the two given moves. Describe any interesting patterns you find in the finished table.

Then...

| First... | s | a | c | $f_1$ | $f_2$ | $f_3$ |
|---|---|---|---|---|---|---|
| s | — | — | — | — | — | — |
| a | — | — | — | $f_3$ | — | — |
| c | — | — | — | — | — | — |
| $f_1$ | — | — | — | — | — | — |
| $f_2$ | — | — | — | — | — | — |
| $f_3$ | — | — | — | — | — | — |

9. 🔑 For each of the six moves, what move *undoes* it?

Executing one move (or sequence) repeatedly can be written with *power notation*. For example, $f_2^7$ means *execute $f_2$ seven times.*

10. Simplify.
    a. $a^{999}$    b. $c^{1000}$
    c. $f_2^{1000}$    d. $(af_2)^{1001}$

11. **Project** What flips and turns are possible for another figure, like a rectangle or a square? Write a report on the symmetry group for that figure.

## DISCOVERY MAGIC CARPETS

Imagine that you can travel from dot to dot on dot paper, using magic carpets such as the ones illustrated in this figure. Carpets cost only $1, plus $1000 per arrow.

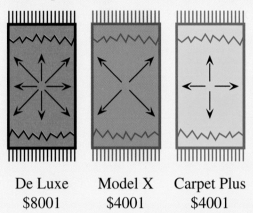

| De Luxe | Model X | Carpet Plus |
|---|---|---|
| $8001 | $4001 | $4001 |

Magic carpets move in carpet steps. Each step takes the carpet and its riders to the next dot in the direction of one of the carpet's arrows. Each step takes one second. Carpets do not turn, so that the Carpet Plus cannot move diagonally, and the Model X cannot move horizontally or vertically.

Say you want to go from the origin to (6, 4). Here is a way to get there on each of the three carpets shown.

De Luxe: →→↗↗↗↗

Model X: ↗↗↗↗↗↘

Carpet Plus: →→→→→→↑↑↑↑

**12.** Find another way to get to (6, 4) on each of the three carpets.

**13.** Compare the advantages and shortcomings of the three carpets. Keep in mind cost, speed, and ability to reach any dot.

**14.** Project

a. Experiment with various $3001 carpets. What are the advantages and shortcomings of each design? Again, keep in mind cost, speed, and ability to reach any dot. Give a full explanation of your findings.

b. Repeat part (a) for $5001 carpets.

Using the directions North, East, West, and South instead of the arrows, the three examples given above could be written:

De Luxe — E E (NE) (NE) (NE) (NE)
Model X — (NE) (NE) (NE) (NE) (NE) (SE)
Carpet Plus — E E E E E E N N N N,

or even:

De Luxe — $E^2 (NE)^4$
Model X — $(NE)^5 (SE)$
Carpet Plus — $E^6 N^4$.

Since all three paths lead to the same place, we can write:

$$E^2 (NE)^4 = (NE)^5 (SE) = E^6 N^4.$$

In a sense, the last expression is the simplest.

**15.** What are the rules that allow you to simplify expressions using the N, E, W, S notation? Explain.

# 5.C Sequences as Functions

A sequence can be thought of as a function. The input numbers are the natural numbers, and the output numbers are the terms. In this assignment, we will study sequences as functions.

> **Definition:** In a *geometric sequence,* each term is obtained from the previous term by multiplying by a constant amount, the *common ratio.*

> **Examples:** These are geometric sequences.
> 2, 10, 50, 250, 1250
> 3, 1, 1/3, 1/9, 1/27

For each of the following:
   a. Tell whether the sequence is geometric, arithmetic, or neither.
   b. If it is arithmetic, find the common difference. If it is geometric, find the common ratio.

**1.** 5, 1, -3, -7, -11     **2.** -7, 2, 11, 20, 29

**3.** 1, 1, 2, 3, 5, 8     **4.** 6, 3, 3/2, 3/4, 3/8

**5.** 25, 5, 1, 1/5, 1/25

**6.** 1/2, 3/4, 7/8, 5/16, 31/32, 63/64

**7.** Find the final term of each sequence.
   a. a geometric sequence having five terms, common ratio 2, and first term 6
   b. an arithmetic sequence having six terms, common difference 9, and first term -4

**8.** Find the first term of each sequence.
   a. an arithmetic sequence having 10 terms, common difference 7, and last term -3
   b. a geometric sequence having eight terms, common ratio 1/2, and last term 1/4

**9.** Graph these arithmetic sequences by graphing the term number ($n$) on the horizontal axis and the term ($t_n$) on the vertical axis.
   a. 2, -4, -10, -16, -22
   b. 2, 8, 14, 20, 26
   c. -5, -11, -17, -23, -29

**10.** Graph these geometric sequences.
   a. 2, 6, 12, 24, 48
   b. 3, 3/2, 3/4, 3/8, 3/16
   c. 1/8, 1/4, 1/2, 1, 2

**11.** These *mystery sequences* are neither geometric nor arithmetic. Graph them.
   a. 5, 8, 13, 20, 29, 40, 53, 68
   b. 7, 13, 23, 37, 55
   c. -2, 7, 22, 43, 70

**12.** By looking at the graphs in problem 11, one might think that the sequences are geometric, but it is clear from looking at the numbers that there is no common ratio. However, the numbers do have a special pattern. Find the pattern and describe it.

**13.** Report   Write a report about what you discovered about graphs of arithmetic sequences, geometric sequences, and the mystery sequences in problem 11. Illustrate your report with examples. Your report should include, but not be limited to, answers to the following questions:
- Which sequences have graphs that are straight lines? Which have graphs that are curved? How are the two kinds of curved graphs different?
- For arithmetic sequences, how does the common difference show up in each graph?
- For geometric sequences, what difference does it make in the graph if the common ratio is greater or less than 1?
- What are the graphs of the mystery sequences called?

# Essential Ideas

**CONSTANT SUMS AND PRODUCTS**

1. If possible, write an equation of the form $x + y = S$ such that the graph of the equation
   a. lies in the 2nd, 3rd, and 4th quadrants;
   b. lies in the 1st, 2nd, and 3rd quadrants;
   c. passes through the origin;
   d. intersects the $x$-axis at $(-7, 0)$;
   e. contains the point $(12, -3.25)$.

2. A graph has an equation of the form $x + y = S$. Find two more points on the graph if:
   a. the point $(-3, -5.8)$ is on the graph;
   b. the graph has $x$-intercept $(1/2, 0)$;
   c. the graph has $y$-intercept $(0, -6.5)$.

3. If possible, write an equation of the form $x \cdot y = P$ such that the graph of the equation
   a. lies in the 2nd and 4th quadrants;
   b. contains the point $(-9, 1/2)$;
   c. passes through $(-2.5, -3.5)$;
   d. intersects the graph of $x + y = 16$ at the point $(10, 6)$;
   e. passes through the origin.

4. Write one equation of the form $x + y = S$ and one of the form $x \cdot y = P$ such that
   a. neither graph passes through the first quadrant;
   b. the two graphs intersect at $(8, 4)$ and $(4, 8)$.

**THE DISTRIBUTIVE LAW**

5. Write an equivalent expression without parentheses. Combine like terms.
   a. $2 \cdot (3 + x)$
   b. $2 \cdot (3x)$
   c. $(6x + 3)(2x - 4)$
   d. $(6x \cdot 3)(2x - 4)$
   e. $(6x \cdot 3)(2x \cdot 4)$

6. In which part of problem 5 did you use the distributive law to remove parentheses? Explain.

7. Write equivalent expressions without the parentheses. Combine like terms.
   a. $-2(9 + x) - x(2 - x)$
   b. $-2(9) + x - x(2 - x)$
   c. $-2(9 + x) - 2x - x$
   d. $-2(9) + x(-2x) - x$

8. In which parts of problem 7 did you use the distributive law to remove parentheses? Explain.

9. Write without parentheses. Combine like terms.
   a. $(x + 3)(x + 5)$
   b. $(x + 3)(x - 5)$
   c. $(x - 3)(x - 5)$
   d. $(x - 3)(x + 5)$

10. Divide.
   a. $\dfrac{6y^2 + 4xy}{2y}$
   b. $\dfrac{4x + 4}{4}$

**FACTORING**

11. Multiply $(2x - 7)(3x + 5)$.

12. Factor $6x^2 - 11x - 35$.

13. a. Fill in the blank with a whole number so that the trinomial $x^2 + 9x + \underline{\phantom{xx}}$ can be factored as a product of binomials. Write the factored form.
    b. How many different integer answers are there for part (a)? Find all of them. (Don't forget negative integers.)

14. a. Fill in the blank with an integer so that the trinomial $x^2 + \underline{\phantom{xx}} x + 18$ can be factored as a product of binomials. Write the factored form.

b. How many different integer answers are there for part (a)? Find all of them. (Don't forget negative integers.)

15. Factor completely.
    a. $(2x + 8)(x^2 + 2x)$
    b. $2yx^2 + 12yx + 16y$
    c. $x^3 + 6x^2 + 8x$

16. How many $x$-intercepts does each parabola have? Explain.
    a. $y = x^2 + 12x + 20$
    b. $y = x^2 + 12x + 36$
    c. $y = x^2 + 12x + 49$
    d. $y = x^2 - 12x + 36$

17. In problem 16, find the coordinates of:
    a. the $y$-intercept;
    b. the $x$-intercept(s), if any;
    c. 💡 the vertex.

---
### SEQUENCES
---

18. If you were to plot these sequences (with $n$ on one axis and $t_n$ on the other axis), for which one(s) would the points lie in a straight line? Explain how you know.
    a. 3, 3.5, 4.5, 5.5, 6.5
    b. -1, -10, -19, -28, -37, -46
    c. 1/2, 1/4, 1/8, 1/16, 1/32
    d. 4, 7, 11, 16, 22, 29

---
### PYRAMIDS
---

A pyramid is made by stacking rows of blue, red, and yellow blocks. There are 100 blocks in the bottom (first) row, 98 in the next row, and so on, with 2 fewer blocks in each successive row. The bottom row is blue, the next row is red, the third row is yellow, and so on, continuing the pattern.

19. Make a sketch or schematic drawing of what you think the pyramid might look like. Write about any patterns you notice.

20. How many rows of blocks are there?

21. How many rows of each color are there?

22. How many blocks are in the $10^{th}$ row? $11^{th}$ row? $n^{th}$ row? Top row?

23. What color is the $10^{th}$ row? What color is the top row?

24. There are 30 blocks in a row. Which row is it?

25. Given the number of a row ($5^{th}$, $10^{th}$, $20^{th}$, etc.) can you give its color? Explain the pattern.

26. Given the number of blocks in a row, can you give its color? Explain the pattern.

27. How many blocks in all are needed to build the pyramid?

28. How would your answers to questions 19-27 be different if there were 50 blocks in the bottom row?

29. Suppose four colors were used instead of three. Would any of your answers to problems 19-27 be different? Explain.

30. Report Summarize and explain the patterns you noticed in the above problems. What generalizations can you make?

### THE DISTRIBUTIVE LAW

Simplify each pair of expressions.

1.  a. $4 + 2[s - 6s - 1)]$
    b. $(4 + 2)[s - 6(s - 1)]$

2.  a. $4x - 2x[x - 6(x + 1)]$
    b. $4x - x[x - 6(x + 2)]$

### EQUATIONS

3.  The solution to this equation is 6:
    $$5x - 1 = 29.$$

    a. Change one number in the equation so that the solution will be 5.

    b. Change the coefficient of $x$ so that the solution to the equation will be 15.

### PARENTHESES

4.  Simplify. Compare your answers for (a) and (b).
    a. $10 - 5 - 3 + 2$
    b. $10 - (5 - 3 + 2)$

5.  What is the smallest number you can get by inserting parentheses in the first expression? The largest number? Explain, showing your work.

6.  a. Make up an expression containing three terms whose value depends upon where the parentheses are placed. Find all the possible values.

    b. Make up an expression containing three terms whose value does not depend upon where the parentheses are placed.

# CHAPTER 6

The outward spiral path of a spider web

## *Coming in this chapter:*

Exploration A movie discount card, valid for three months, costs $T. With the card, it costs only $D to attend a movie, instead of $5. How many movies would you have to see in three months in order to save money with the discount card? Does your answer depend on $T$, $D$, or on both?

# MAKING COMPARISONS

# Comparing Car Rentals

LESSON 6.1

**You will need:**

graph paper

This table gives the results of a phone survey of the cost of renting a mid-size car in a large city.

| Company | Daily rate | "Free" miles | Cost per additional mile |
|---------|-----------|------------|------------------------|
| A | $34.99 | 150 miles | 24 cents |
| B | $26.95 | 100 miles | 30 cents |
| C | $39.95 | 100 miles | 30 cents |
| D | $41.95 | unlimited mileage | — |
| E | $27.99 | unlimited mileage | — |

1. **Exploration** Suppose you wanted to rent a car for a short trip and you had the information in the table. There is one car that is clearly the "best deal" in most cases. Which car is this? If this car were not available, how would you decide which car to rent? Write a paragraph explaining how you would decide. Include the following:

   • What things would you consider?

   • Show any calculations you would need to do to make your decision.

   • Is there any additional information not included in the table that you think you would need to know?

**USING TABLES**

2. Which car do you think would be the best deal if you planned to drive a short distance? Which car would you rent to drive several hundred miles? Explain.

This table gives the cost of renting each car for one day to drive the indicated number of miles.

3. Copy and complete the table, indicating how much it would cost to rent each car for the given miles.

**Total Cost of Car Rental**

| Company | Miles driven | | | | |
|---------|------|------|------|------|------|
| | **50** | **100** | **150** | **200** | **250** |
| A | 34.99 | 34.99 | 34.99 | 46.99 | 58.99 |
| B | 26.95 | 26.95 | 41.95 | 56.95 | — |
| C | — | — | — | — | — |
| D | — | — | — | — | — |
| E | — | — | — | — | — |

4. Copy and complete the next table. It ranks each car according to the amount it would cost to rent it to drive the given number of miles. The code is **1** for least expensive and **5** for most expensive.

*Chapter 6  Making Comparisons*

**Company Rankings**

| Company | Miles driven | | | | |
|---|---|---|---|---|---|
| | **50** | **100** | **150** | **200** | **250** |
| **A** | 3 | — | — | — | — |
| **B** | 1 | — | — | — | — |
| **C** | 4 | — | — | — | — |
| **D** | 5 | — | — | — | — |
| **E** | 2 | — | — | — | — |

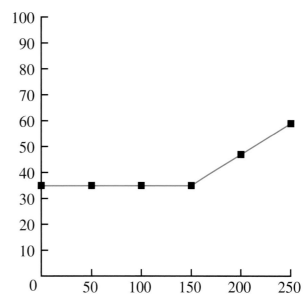

**5.** In the table you just completed, you can see that B is less expensive than A for 50 miles and 100 miles of travel, but this is reversed for 150 miles of travel.

a. Which is less expensive for 125 miles of travel?

b. Show that the costs of A and B are almost exactly the same for 130 miles of travel.

**USING GRAPHS**

**6.** The graph above problem 7 shows, for a single day of rental, how the cost of renting a car from Company A varies as a function of the number of miles driven.

a. Make an enlarged copy of the graph on your own paper.

b. Add to the same grid a similar graph for each of the other four companies. Your graphs must be accurate.

**7.** 🔑 Two of the graphs should be horizontal lines. Which ones, and why?

**8.** According to your graphs, if you plan to drive 100 miles or less,

a. which company is the most expensive?

b. which company is the least expensive?

**9.** Company A has a higher daily rate and lower mileage costs than Company B.

a. Which of the two is more expensive for someone who travels 100 miles?

b. Which is more expensive for someone who travels 150 miles?

c. For what length trip is the cost of the two the same?

**10.** Company D has a slightly higher daily rate than Company C, but its mileage costs are zero.

a. For what length trip is D cheaper?

b. For what length trip are they the same?

11. ☞ The graphs for B and D intersect at the point (150, 41.95).

    a. Label this point of intersection on your graph.

    b. Label other points of intersection on any of the other graphs.

    c. How would you interpret these points of intersection in terms of cost comparisons?

12. ☞ In what ways are tables better than graphs in helping you make a decision of this type? In what ways are graphs better?

### USING EQUATIONS

Equations are useful if you want to use a computer or a programmable calculator to help you analyze a problem like this one. You can write an equation for the cost of renting a car from Company A for one day as a function of the number of miles traveled. Notice that the graph has two parts: a horizontal part, and a part that slopes upward. The equation also has two parts.

If $y$ is the cost in dollars and $x$ is the number of miles driven, then:

$y = 34.99$                 if $x \leq 150$

$y = 34.99 + 0.24(x - 150)$   if $x > 150$

13. Which part of the equation represents the horizontal part of the graph?

14. ☞ Explain every part of the second equation. (Why is 150 subtracted from $x$? Why are parentheses necessary? What is the meaning of the quantity in the parentheses? Why is it multiplied by 0.24? Why is the result added to 34.99? What is the meaning of the sum?)

15. 💡 Write equations for the costs of renting the other cars as a function of miles driven.

---

### DISCOVERY   GRADE AVERAGES

Mrs. Washman gives a quiz every Thursday. A student's current average at the end of any week can be computed by finding the ratio of *total correct points* to *total possible points* to date. The table shows Caden's scores.

|  | Q1 | Q2 | Q3 | Q4 | Q5 |
|---|---|---|---|---|---|
| **Correct** | 8 | 9 | 10 | 13 | — |
| **Possible** | 12 | 20 | 10 | 15 | — |

16. Find Caden's current average at the end of week 1, week 2, week 3, and week 4.

17. Caden found his current average by doing this computation:

$$\frac{8}{12} + \frac{9}{20} + \frac{10}{10} + \frac{13}{15} = \frac{40}{57}$$

Amiko said this was wrong because you don't add fractions by adding the numerators and adding the denominators. Who was right? Were they both right? Were they both wrong? Explain.

18. What would Caden's average be at the end of week 5 if Quiz 5 had

    a. 20 points, and he got 12 correct?

    b. 40 points, and he got 80% correct?

    c. 25 points, and he got $N$ correct?

# Which is Greater?

**You will need:**

the Lab Gear

**Exploration** For each problem, if possible, give one value of $x$ that

    a. makes the right side greater;

    b. makes the left side greater;

    c. makes the two sides equal.

Describe the method you used for each problem.

**1.** $x$ ? $2x + 3$

**2** $y - 2$ ? $-y - 2$

**3.** $6x$ ? $7x^2 + 6x - 7$

### USING THE LAB GEAR

For each problem:

    a. Simplify each expression.

    b. Compare the two expressions. It may help to build them with the Lab Gear, one on each side of the workmat.

    c. Is one side greater, or are they equal? Write the correct symbol: $>$, $<$, or $=$. If it is impossible to tell, write **?**. Remember that $x$ is not necessarily a positive integer.

**4.** $x(x + 2) - 4$          $(x + 1)(x + 1)$

**5.** $(x + 1)(x + 2)$        $2 + 3x - x^2$

**6.** $3x^2 + 9 - (x^2 + 2)$     $3x^2 + 9 - x^2 + 2$

**7.** $3x^2 + 9 - (x^2 + 2x)$    $3x^2 + 9 - x^2 + 2x$

**8.** If you did not get at least one **?** as an answer in problems 4-7, check your work.

### USING TABLES

For which values of $x$ is $14x - [4x - (2 - 3x)]$ greater than $5x - 2[x - (3x + 2)]$ ?

These two expressions are too complicated to build with the Lab Gear. It is easier to compare them if they are simplified first. Both expressions have two sets of grouping symbols, *parentheses* and *brackets*. Brackets mean exactly the same thing as parentheses.

| **Rule:** Simplify from the inside out, removing the parentheses first.

**9.** Removing parentheses, the first expression is $14x - [4x - 2 + 3x]$. Continue simplifying.

**10.** Removing parentheses, the second expression is $5x - 2[x - 3x - 2]$. Continue simplifying.

The table below compares the expressions $9x + 4$ and $7x + 2$ for some values of $x$.

| $x$ | $9x + 4$ | $7x + 2$ |
|-----|----------|----------|
| 10  | 94       | 72       |
| 5   | 49       | 37       |
| 0.1 | 4.9      | 2.7      |

**11.** Copy and extend the table.

    a. Find some values of $x$ for which $9x + 4$ is less than $7x + 2$.

    b. Try to find a value of $x$ for which the two expressions are equal.

    c. Describe any patterns you see in your table.

Lea and Earl were trying to compare these expressions:

Expression A: $5 - [x - (3x + 1)]$

Expression B: $5 - 3[x - (3x + 1)]$

They got different results when they simplified Expression B.

### Simplifying Expression B

|         | Lea's work          | Earl's work         |
|---------|---------------------|---------------------|
| Step 1  | $5 - 3[x - 3x - 1]$ | $5 - 3[x - 3x - 1]$ |
| Step 2  | $5 - 3[-2x - 1]$    | $5 - 3[-2x - 1]$    |
| Step 3  | $5 + 6x - 3$        | $2[-2x - 1]$        |
| Step 4  | $2 + 6x$            | $-4x - 2$           |

Lea and Earl wanted to know which one of them had made a mistake. They asked their teacher, Mr. Martin. "You can't both be right," he said, "but you could both be wrong."

**12.** Are Lea and Earl both wrong, or is only one of them wrong? Is Mr. Martin wrong? Look for mistakes in their work. When you find a mistake, explain what the student did wrong.

**13.** Look at Expressions A and B again. Simplify both expressions correctly.

**14.** Using the simplified form of each expression, compare Expressions A and B by making a table of values.

**15.** ⚷ Summarize the information in your table by telling when Expression A is greater, when Expression B is greater, and when the two expressions are equal.

**16.** Simplify each pair of expressions.
   a. $4x - 2x[3 - 6(x + 1)]$
   $4 - x[x - 6(2x + 1)]$
   b. $4 - 2[y - 6(y + 1)]$
   $4 - [y - 6(y + 1)]$

**17.** Compare each pair of expressions in problem 16. Make a table of values and summarize your findings in each case, telling when the first expression is greater, when the second expression is greater, and when they are equal.

SOLVING INEQUALITIES

**18.** Use a table of values to show that $2x + 6 > 8$ for all values of $x$ greater than 1.

We say that the *solution* to the inequality $2x + 6 > 8$ is "all numbers greater than 1" because this describes *all* the values for which the inequality is true. Using mathematical symbols, we say that the solution is $x > 1$.

Find the solution of each inequality. That is, describe all the numbers for which the inequality is true.

**19.** $x + 5 > 1$     **20.** $n - 5 > 1$

**21.** $y + 5 > 0$     **22.** $r - 5 > 0$

**23.** $x - 5 > -1$     **24.** $x + 5 > -1$

**25.** $-x > 6$     **26.** $-x > -6$

**27.** ⚷ Many students get problems 25 and 26 wrong. Check your answers to them by substituting specific values of $x$. What makes them more difficult than the other ones?

---

**DISCOVERY**   *SQUARES ON A CHESSBOARD*

**28.** 💡 How many squares of any size are there on an 8-by-8 chessboard? Explain how you get your answer. (Hint: First analyze smaller boards.)

# 6.3

# Solving Linear Equations

**You will need:**

the Lab Gear

1. **Exploration** Find a value of $x$ that makes each equation true. Describe the method you used.

   a. $3(x + 2) = x + 5$

   b. $3x + 2 = x + 5$

   c. $3x + 2 = x - 5$

   d. $3(x + 2) = x - 5$

## USING THE LAB GEAR

The easiest equations to solve are linear, or first-degree equations in one variable. All four of the equations above are linear. The equation $x^2 = 2x - 1$ is not linear, because it contains an $x^2$ term.

You have already learned to solve equations by trial and error and the cover-up method. Some kinds of equations can also be solved using the Lab Gear.

This figure represents an equation. We want to find out what value of $x$ will make the quantity on the left side of the workmat equal to the quantity on the right side.

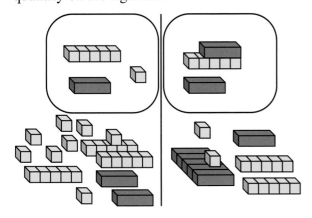

2. Copy the figure with your Lab Gear.

3. Simplify each side. If you did it correctly, your blocks should match this figure.

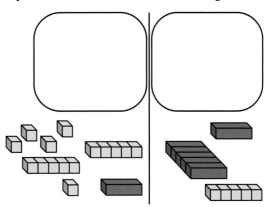

4. Rearrange the blocks to match this figure. Which blocks on the right side can be matched with identical blocks on the left side?

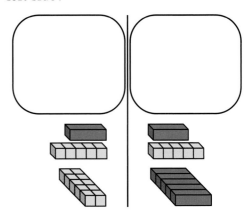

There are some blocks that cannot be matched with blocks on the other side. The figure shows a two-dimensional view of these blocks.

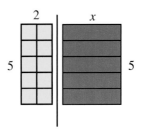

Look at these remaining blocks. Remember that the two sides are equal. This is true even though they don't *look* equal. Remember $x$ can have any value.

**5.** What must $x$ be in order for the two sides to be equal?

This figure shows how you would set out the blocks to solve the equation $2x + 1 = 4x - 5$.

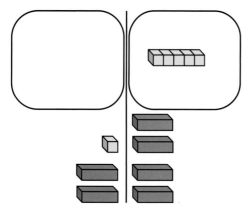

Each side is simplified. The blocks have been arranged to show which blocks can be matched with blocks on the other side. Even so, it is not easy to tell what the solution is.

It helps to add zero.

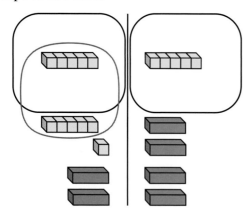

Notice that the blocks on one side are rearranged to show which ones can be matched with blocks on the other side.

The remaining blocks (those that cannot be matched with blocks on the other side) can then be rearranged to make it easy to see the solution to the equation.

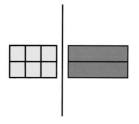

**6.** What is the solution to this equation?

For problems 7-11:
  a. Write the original equation.
  b. Use the Lab Gear to find the solution. Write equations to show some of the steps as you move your blocks.
  c. Write the solution.

**7.**

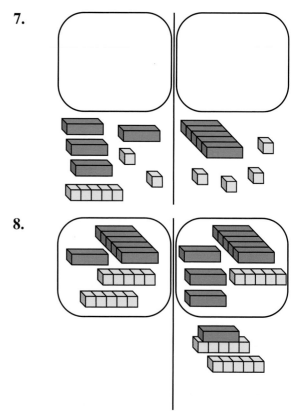

**8.**

*Chapter 6 Making Comparisons*

**9.**

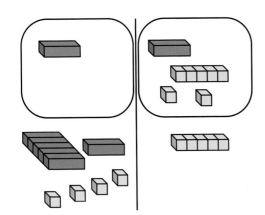

**10.**

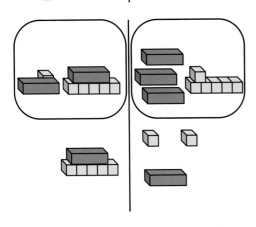

**11.**

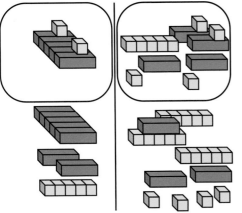

You have learned to solve equations using tables, trial and error, the cover-up method, and the Lab Gear. Solve these equations in whatever way you want, but *show your work.*

**12.** $3x + 5 = 6$

**13.** $3x + 5 = -2x - 10$

**14.** $2y - 6 = 5y + 3$

**15.** $\frac{6x - 6}{4} = 3$

**16.** $\frac{6x - 6}{4} + 15 = 3$

Make up an equation satisfying each of the following descriptions. Try to make up one that would be challenging for another student to solve, but not so challenging that you can't solve it.

**17.** An equation whose solution is $x = 4$

**18.** An equation whose solution is $y = -1/2$

**19.** An equation that has variables on both sides of the equation and the solution $m = 2$

**20.** 💡 An equation that has more than one solution

**DISCOVERY** *USING VARIABLES*

21. A student is *x* years old. How many months old is he? (Are you sure?)

22. Another student is *y* years old.
    a. How many years until she can vote?
    b. How many months?

23. I start with 99 peanuts. It takes me *x* seconds to eat one.
    a. How long will it take to eat them all?
    b. After eating *n* peanuts, how many are left?
    c. After *z* seconds, how many peanuts are left?

**PUZZLES** *MAGIC SQUARES*

These puzzles will be easier to solve if you make yourself little squares of paper with numbers written on them. To solve the puzzles, move the papers around, until you find a satisfactory arrangement.

24. Arrange all the numbers from 1 to 9 into a 3-by-3 square, so that the sum of all the numbers in any row or column is always the same.

25. Repeat problem 24, but make sure the *diagonals* also add up to the same amount.

26. ◯ Arrange all the numbers from 1 to 16 into a 4-by-4 square, so that the sum of the numbers in any row or column is always the same.

**DISCOVERY** *GRADING POLICIES*

At the Shell School, math teachers give a six weeks grade based on six quizzes and two writing assignments. The math department policy requires that quizzes and writing assignments be counted equally.

For each student in her class, Mrs. Washman averages the quizzes, averages the writing assignments, and then adds those two numbers and divides by two.

For each student in his class, Mr. Pitcher adds all the grades together and divides by eight.

27. Make up a list of grades of a student who would have a higher grade with Mrs. Washman's method.

28. Make up a list of grades of a student who would have a higher grade with Mr. Pitcher's method.

29. Is it possible for a student to have the same grade using either method? Explain.

# Equations and Identities

**You will need:**

the Lab Gear

**Definition:** An *identity* is an equation that is true for all values of the variables.

**1.** Which of these equations are identities? Explain your answers.
   a. $3x + 9 - 2(x + 2) = 3x + 9 - 2x + 2$
   b. $3x + 9 - 2(x + 2) = 3x + 7(x + 2)$
   c. $3x + 9 - 2(x + 2) = x + 5$
   d. $3x + 9 - 2(x + 2) = x + 7$

### USING THE LAB GEAR

To solve the equation $5(x + 1) = 25$ you can model both the left side and the right side as rectangles. In this case, you can match the rectangles, and it is easy to see what the value of $x$ must be.

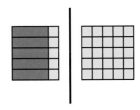

**2.** What is the value of $x$ that makes both sides equal?

Use the Lab Gear to solve these equations. If the equation is an identity, explain how you know, using sketches if necessary.

**3.** $3(x + 2) = 15$

**4.** $3(x + 2) = 3x + 6$

**5.** $4(2x + 1) = 4(x + 5)$

**6.** $4(2x - 1) = 4(x - 1)$

**7.** $4(2x - 1) = 4(2x + 1)$

**8.** $2(2x + 2) = 4(x + 1)$

**9.** $4(2x - 2) = 2(4x - 4)$

### USING GRAPHS AND TABLES

**10.** Make a table of $(x, y)$ pairs and graph each linear function.
   a. $y = -2(x - 1) + 2$
   b. $y = -2x + 4$

**11.** By simplifying the left side, show that $-2(x - 1) + 2 = -2x + 4$ is an identity.

**12.** For each pair of functions, decide whether or not both members of the pair would have the same graph. Explain.
   a. $y = 3 - 4x$ and $y = 4x - 3$
   b. $y = -6 - 8x$ and $y = 8x - 6$
   c. $y = 2x^2$ and $y = 2x(x + 2) - 4x$
   d. $y = 5 - x$ and $y = -x - 5$
   e. $y = -x + 5$ and $y = 5 - x$

**13.** Look at your answers to problem 12. For each pair that would not have the same graph, graph both functions on the same axes. Find the point where the two graphs intersect and label it on the graph.

**14.** ◆━ Which of the pairs of graphs that you drew in problem 13 do not have a point of intersection? Can you explain why this is so?

**15.** ◆━ When graphing two linear functions, there are three possibilities: You may get the same line, two parallel lines, or two lines that intersect. Explain what the tables of $(x, y)$ values look like in each case.

### ALWAYS, SOMETIMES, NEVER

While an identity is true for all values of $x$, an equation may be true for only some values of $x$, or for no values of $x$.

**Examples:** $2x + 6 = 4$ is true when $x = -1$, but not when $x = 0$. The equation $x + 5 = x$ is never true, because a number is never equal to five more than itself. We say this equation has *no solution*.

16. For each equation, state whether it is *always, sometimes,* or *never* true. If it is always or never true, explain how you know. It may help to simplify and to use tables, graphs, or sketches of the Lab Gear.
    a. $2x + 5 = 2x + 1$
    b. $3(x - 4) - 4(x - 3) = 0$
    c. $(x + 5)^2 = x^2 + 25$
    d. $6x - (7 - x) + 8 = 7x + 1$

17. Look at the equations in problem 16 that you decided were *sometimes* true. For each one, find a value of $x$ that makes it true and one that makes it false. Show your work.

For each equation 18-21:

State whether the equation is always, sometimes, or never true. Explain.

18. $0.5x - 2 = 0.5(x - 2)$

19. $0.5x - 2 = 0.5(x - 4)$

20. $0.5x - 2 = x - 4$

21. $0.5(x - 2) = x - 4$

22. `Report` Write a report about equations that are always, sometimes, or never true. Use one example of each type. Illustrate each example with a graph and a Lab Gear sketch. Be sure to include the definition of *identity* and full explanations.

---

### REVIEW WHICH IS GREATER?

23. Which is greater, or does it depend on the value of $x$? Explain.
    a. $-2x$       $-2x + 7$
    b. $6x - 4$      $6x + 4$
    c. $-x^2$        $x^2$
    d. $(-x)^2$      $-x^2$

### REVIEW/PREVIEW MAKE A SQUARE

Make a square with these blocks, adding as many yellow blocks as you want, but nothing else. For each square, write an equation relating the side length to the area.

24. $x^2 + 10x + \underline{\phantom{xx}}$     25. $4x^2 + 8x + \underline{\phantom{xx}}$

26. $9x^2 + 6x + \underline{\phantom{xx}}$      27. $x^2 + 2x + \underline{\phantom{xx}}$

28. $4x^2 + 12 + \underline{\phantom{xx}}$

29. ⚷ Is it possible to get a different square by adding a different number of yellow blocks? Explain your answer.

Make a square with these blocks, adding as many x-blocks as you want, but nothing else. For each square, write an equation relating the side length to the area.

30. $x^2 + \underline{\phantom{xx}} + 25$     31. $4x^2 + \underline{\phantom{xx}} + 25$

32. $x^2 + \underline{\phantom{xx}} + 36$     33. $9x^2 + \underline{\phantom{xx}} + 1$

34. $x^2 + \underline{\phantom{xx}} + 9$

35. ⚷ Is it possible to get a different square by adding a different number of x-blocks? Explain your answer.

36. `Summary` Describe the pattern for the square of a binomial, in terms of the Lab Gear, and in terms of the algebraic symbols.

# 6.A Money Matters

## DISCOUNTS

A discount card at a movie theater costs $10. With that card, it costs only $3 to attend a movie, instead of $5. The card is valid for three months.

1.  Use the same pair of axes for both of the graphs in this problem. Make a graph of the *total cost* (including the cost of the discount card if you got one) as a function of the *number of movies* you see
    a.  if you have the discount card;
    b.  if you do not have the discount card.

2.  What is the total cost of seeing $n$ movies in three months
    a.  with the discount card?
    b.  without the discount card?

3.  a.  If you saw 12 movies in three months, how much would you save by buying the discount card?
    b.  If you saw only two movies in three months, how much would you save by *not* buying the discount card?

4.  **Report**  Write a report explaining how you would decide whether or not to buy the card. Do a complete analysis of the situation, using graphs, tables, and equations. Your discussion should include, but not be limited to, answers to the following questions:
    * What is the break-even point; that is, how many movies would you have to see in order to spend exactly the same amount with and without the discount card?
    * How would your decision be affected if the cost of the discount card were raised to $12?
    * How would your decision be affected if the cost of the discount card were changed to $K$?

## PAYMENTS

Today Lara opened a bank account and deposited $700. She has just started a part-time job and will get a paycheck of $130 every two weeks, on the 1st and the 15th of the month. She plans to take $40 out of each paycheck for cash expenses and deposit the rest in her bank account. On the 15th of every month, when her car payment is due, she will write a check for $220.

5.  Make a table showing how much money Lara will have in her account on the 1st and 15th of every month over the next five months. It may help to show deposits and withdrawals. Look for a pattern.

6.  How much money will Lara have in her account on the 1st and the 15th of the month
    a.  eight months after receiving her first paycheck?
    b.  $n$ months after receiving her first paycheck?

7.  **Report**  Imagine that you are Lara's older sister or brother. Write a letter to her showing why she will run out of money, and when. Give her some suggestions for what she might do to avoid this.

# Graphical Solutions

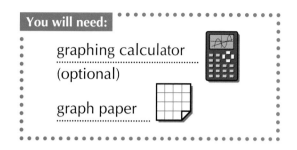

**You will need:**

graphing calculator
(optional)

graph paper

## A GRAPHICAL ANALYSIS

1. On the same axes, graph $y = x - 1$ and $y = 0.25x + 2$.

Your graph should look like the one below. The three points that are marked and labeled with their coordinates are all on the part of the graph of $y = x - 1$ that is *below* the graph of $y = 0.25x + 2$.

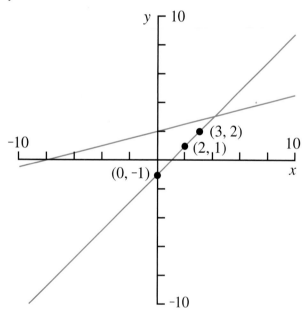

2. Find the coordinates of three points on the part of the line $y = x - 1$ that is *above* the graph of $y = 0.25x + 2$.

3. Find the coordinates of the point where the two lines cross.

4. If $x = 100$,
   a. which graph is above, $y = x - 1$ or $y = 0.25x + 2$?
   b. what is the value of $0.25x + 2$?
   c. what is the value of $x - 1$?

5. If $x = -100$,
   a. which graph is above, $y = x - 1$ or $y = 0.25x + 2$?
   b. what is the value of $0.25x + 2$?
   c. what is the value of $x - 1$?

6. Describe all the values of $x$ for which the graph of $y = x - 1$
   a. is above the graph of $y = 0.25x + 2$.
   b. is below the graph of $y = 0.25x + 2$.

7. Describe all the values of $x$ that satisfy each equation or inequality.
   a. $0.25x + 2 = x - 1$
   b. $0.25x + 2 > x - 1$
   c. $0.25x + 2 < x - 1$

## FINDING SOLUTIONS

8. Using trial and error, find three values of $x$ that satisfy each inequality.
   a. $2x < 3x + 1$
   b. $2x > 3x + 1$

It is often easy to find a few values of $x$ that satisfy an inequality. It is harder to find *all* the values, that is, to *solve* the inequality. You have solved equations and inequalities using trial and error, the cover-up method, tables, and the Lab Gear. Another method is to use graphs.

9. Graph $y = 2x$ and $y = 3x + 1$ on the same pair of axes. Use the graphs to solve the two inequalities in problem 8. Remember that even though the graph shows values of both $x$ and $y$, the original inequalities involved only the variable $x$. Your answers should involve only $x$.

10. Graph each pair of functions on graph paper. Use a separate grid for each pair.
   a. $y = 2x - 10$ and $y = 5x - 1$
   b. $y = 2x + 10$ and $y = 5x - 2$
   c. $y = 2x - 10$ and $y = 5x - 2$
   d. $y = x^2$ and $y = 4x - 4$

11. Use your graphs from problem 10 to find the values of $x$ that make these equations true.
   a. $2x - 10 = 5x - 1$
   b. $2x + 10 = 5x - 2$
   c. $2x - 10 = 5x - 2$
   d. $x^2 = 4x - 4$

12. **Summary** Write a paragraph explaining how you can use graphs to help solve equations and inequalities. Illustrate by showing how you would use your method to solve these equations and inequalities.
   a. $-2x + 1 > 3x - 4$
   b. $2x - 1 > -3x + 4$
   c. $3x + 4 = -2x - 6$
   d. $x^2 = x + 2$

▬▬▬▬▬▬ MORE EQUATIONS AND INEQUALITIES ▬▬▬▬▬▬

Use the techniques you have learned to solve these equations and inequalities. You can use trial and error, the cover-up method, tables, graphs, or the Lab Gear. Show your work.

13. $6x + 1 \leq -3x + 7$

14. $2x + 32 = 6x + 28$

15. $4(x + 5) = 4x + 20$

16. $-3 + m < -m - 3$

17. $\dfrac{5x + 3}{4} - 6 = 1$

18. $x^2 = 6 - x$

19. $\dfrac{x}{x + 1} = 1$

20. $\dfrac{x + 5}{2} + x = 19$

▬▬▬▬▬▬▬▬▬▬▬▬▬▬▬▬▬▬▬▬▬▬▬▬

**REVIEW** SUBSTITUTION

For each problem, write a simple expression that shows the relationship between $\Delta$ and $\Diamond$. (Hint: If you cannot find the relationship by using algebra, make a table of values of $\Delta$ and $\Diamond$ that make the expressions true, and find a pattern in the table.) Show your work.

21. $\Delta - \Diamond = \Delta$

22. $\Diamond + 2 = \Diamond + \Delta + \Delta$

23. $\Diamond + \Delta + \Delta + \Diamond = \Diamond$

24. $\Diamond - \Delta + \Diamond - \Delta = \Diamond$

25. $\Delta + \Delta = \Diamond + \Diamond$

26. $\Diamond + \Delta + \Delta + \Diamond = 4$

## REVIEW/PREVIEW DIVISION AND THE DISTRIBUTIVE LAW

To divide a polynomial by a monomial, you can use the multiplication table format. For example, here is the setup to divide $10x^2 - 5x$ by 5.

| | ? | ? |
|---|---|---|
| 5 | $10x^2$ | $-5x$ |

Ask yourself: *What times 5 = $10x^2$?* and *what times 5 = -5x?* Write the answers across the top of the table: $2x^2 - x$.

Divide.

**27.** $\dfrac{10x^2 - 5x}{x}$  **28.** $\dfrac{10x^2 - 5x}{5x}$

If the denominator does not divide every term of the numerator, you will still have fractions in the answer. For example:

$$\frac{10x^2 - 5x}{2} = 5x^2 - \frac{5x}{2}$$

Divide.

**29.** $\dfrac{10x^2 - 5x}{10}$  **30.** $\dfrac{10x^2 - 5x}{x^2}$

**31.** $\dfrac{10x^2 - 5x}{3}$

## DISCOVERY WEIGHTED AVERAGES

Mr. Cody counts the quiz average (Q) in his class three times as much as the test average (T). That is, he uses the formula:

$$\frac{3Q + T}{4}$$

(This is called a *weighted* average, because he weights the quizzes three times as much.)

Mr. Fletcher counts the test average twice as much as the quiz average. He uses the formula:

$$\frac{Q + 2T}{3}$$

**Oliver's grades:**
Quizzes: 75 80 85 95 70
Tests: 95 100 80
**Connie's grades:**
Quizzes: 95 98 94 88 90
Tests: 80 80 95

**32.** Which teacher would Oliver prefer to have?

**33.** Which teacher would Connie prefer to have?

**34.** Oliver and Connie are both in Mr. Dodge's class. He gives students an A who have an average of 90 or better. If possible, show how Mr. Dodge can weight the tests and quizzes so that
a. Oliver has an A average;
b. Connie has an A average;
c. both Connie and Oliver have an A average.

# Solving Techniques: Addition and Subtraction

**You will need:**

the Lab Gear

One key to solving linear equations is a technique based on this fact: If two quantities are equal, and you **add or subtract the same quantity from both**, you end up with equal quantities. This provides you with a method for simplifying equations.

## USING THE LAB GEAR

**1.** Write the equation shown by this figure.

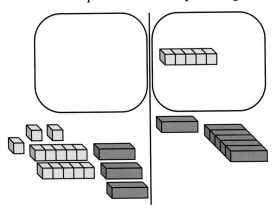

**2.** Remove three *x*-blocks from each side. Add 5 to each side and simplify. Finally, form rectangles on both sides, setting them up to show a common side.

**3.** Write the solution to the equation. Explain.

For each figure in problems 4-7, write the equation, then solve for *x*. Use the method shown in problem 2.

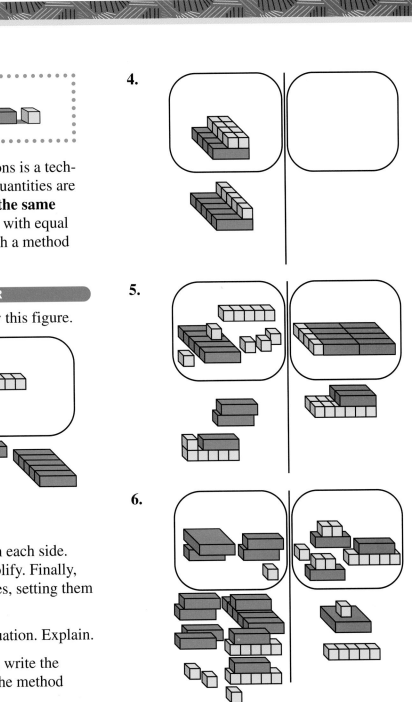

**4.**

**5.**

**6.**

**7.**

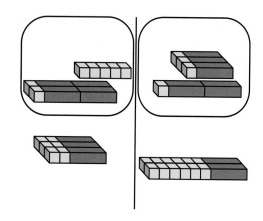

For each problem, 8-11,

    a. Model the equation with the Lab Gear.

    b. Solve it using the techniques you have learned with the blocks. Record algebraically at least two of the intermediate steps.

    c. Write the final answer.

**8.** $5x + 3(x + 3) = 25$

**9.** $5x = 25 + 3(x + 3)$

**10.** $0 = 3(6 - x) + 6x$

**11.** $15 - 4(x - 2) + 2x = 3$

**12.** Start with the equation $x = 3$.

    a. Add and/or subtract the same amount from both sides repeatedly, getting the equation to be more and more complicated. (The quantities you add and subtract may include $x$. You may use the Lab Gear. If you do, record some of the steps.) Write the final equation on paper and give it to a classmate.

    b. Solve a classmate's equation. If you both do your work correctly, the solution should be $x = 3$. (Again, you may use the Lab Gear.)

### SAVINGS PLANS

In this section, you can apply equation solving to real-life problems.

**13.** **Exploration** Tania Rhine had $123. For her birthday, she received $175 from her grandparents, and her allowance was raised to $11 a week. What is the largest amount she can spend every week, if

    a. she wants to have a total of $600 by her next birthday?

    b. she wants to have $100 left by her next birthday?

Beatrice had $321 in her savings account on September 1. She planned to save $14 a week.

**14.** Make a table or graph showing how her total savings change as a function of the number of weeks that have passed.

**15.** Look for a pattern in your table or graph. How much would Bea have at the end of:

    a. 4 weeks?    b. 52 weeks?

    c. $n$ weeks?    d. 2 years?

    e. $n$ years?

**16.** Beatrice is considering another possible savings plan. She wants to go to a movie every week, which means she would spend $5 out of the $14. She would deposit the rest in her savings account. Make a table or graph of this savings plan to compare with your first one.

**17.** With the second savings plan, how much would Beatrice have at the end of:

    a. 4 weeks?

    b. $n$ weeks?

**18.** Beatrice is saving for a stereo that costs $549. How long will it take to reach her goal under each savings plan? Try to answer this question without extending your tables or graphs. Instead, try to write and solve equations.

**19.** Abraham is also saving for the stereo. He has $235 in his savings account on October 1 and deposits $21 per week. Write an expression that gives the amount of money that Abraham has after $n$ weeks.

**20.** 🔑 Use tables, graphs, or equations to answer these questions. Show your work. Who will have enough to buy the stereo first, Abraham or Beatrice,

   a. if Beatrice has been following her first plan?

   b. if Beatrice has been following her second plan?

**21.** 🔑 On January 15, Bea and Abe see an advertisement about the stereo. For two weeks, it will be on sale for $499. Will either one of them have enough money to buy the stereo then? Do you think one of

them will already have bought the stereo? Will your answer depend on what savings plan Bea was following? Explain, showing all your work.

MORE EQUATION SOLVING

Use any of the methods you have learned to solve these equations. Show your work.

**22.** $3x + 3 - 5x + 6 = 9x - 3x + 23$

**23.** $5x - 6 = 13x - 5 - 9x$

**24.** $10x + 23 = 6x + 27$

**25.** $2 - 3x + 5 = 7x - 4 - 8x$

**26.** $4x + 5 = 4x + 7$

**27.** $3x + 4x = 8 + 7x - 8$

---

**DISCOVERY**   *HARDER FACTORING*

Factor these trinomials by making a rectangle with the Lab Gear and writing a multiplication equation relating length, width, and area.

**28.** $x^2 + xy + x + y$

**29.** $3x^2 + 5x + 2$

**30.** $6x^2 + 7x + 2$

**31.** $6x^2 + 19x + 10$

**32.** $3x^2 + 16x + 5$

**33.** $4x^2 + 20x + 25$

# LESSON 6.7
# How Much More Than?
# How Many Times as Much?

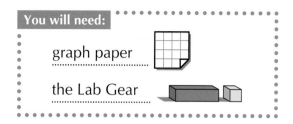

**You will need:**

graph paper

the Lab Gear

## COMPARING AGES

On Mark's 12<sup>th</sup> birthday, he said to his little brother Gordon, "You'd better do what I say. Now I'm twice as old as you are."

The six-year-old math whiz wasn't scared. "That's nothing," he laughed. "A few years ago, you were four times as old as I was. And not long after I was born, you were *thirty-seven* times as old as I was."

**1.** How old were the two brothers when
   a. Mark was four times as old as Gordon?
   b. Mark was 37 times as old?

**2.** a. As Mark and Gordon get older, does the *difference* between their ages increase, decrease, or stay the same? Explain.
   b. Does the *ratio* of their ages increase, decrease, or stay the same? Explain.

**3.** Mark was born in 1980. On the same axes, make two graphs, one showing Mark's age as a function of time and the other showing Gordon's age as a function of time. Label the *x*-axis *years after 1980* and the *y*-axis *age*. Compare the two graphs.

**4.** a. Make a graph showing the *difference* between the two boys' ages as a function of time. Label the *x*-axis *years after 1980* and the *y*-axis *difference in ages*. Describe your graph.

   b. Make a graph showing the *ratio* of Mark's age to Gordon's age as a function of time. Label the *x*-axis *years after 1980* and the *y*-axis *ratio of ages*. Describe your graph.

   c. Compare the two graphs.

**5.** ⚷
   a. Why do we usually compare people's ages using differences instead of ratios?
   b. What do you think is the smallest possible value for this ratio of Mark's age to Gordon's age? Explain.

**6.** Beau and Bea said, "The ratio of our ages will always be the same!" How could this be? Discuss.

**7.** ⚷ On Mark's 12<sup>th</sup> birthday, his mother was three times as old as Mark. Was she ever twice as old? Was she ever four times as old? Explain.

## COMPARING NUMBERS

When comparing the size of two positive numbers, for example 5 and 15, you can ask two different questions.

• 15 is *how much more than* 5?
• 15 is *how many times as much* as 5?

The question *How much more than...?* is answered using subtraction, as shown in this figure. Since $15 - 5 = 10$, you can say that 15 is 10 more than 5, (or 10 is the difference of 15 and 5).

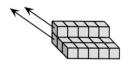

The question *How many times as much...?* is answered using division, as shown with the Lab Gear. Since 15/5 = 3, 15 is 3 times as much as 5, (or 3 is the ratio of 15 and 5).

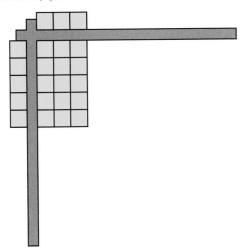

Answer both questions about these pairs of numbers in problems 8-13. Show how you got your answers. In some cases, you may want to use the Lab Gear.

    a. The first number is *how much more than* the second?

    b. The first number is *how many times as much* as the second?

**8.** 35 and 5         **9.** 10 and 10

**10.** 9 and 8        **11.** 16 and 4

**12.** 16 and $\frac{1}{4}$      **13.** 4 and 16

---

**COMPARING ALGEBRAIC EXPRESSIONS**

Sometimes you need to compare quantities given by formulas that involve variables. The same methods can be used as when comparing numbers.

To find out *how much more* $5x$ is than $x$, subtract $5x - x$, as shown.

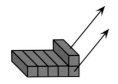

To find out *how many times as much* $5x$ is than $x$, divide as shown.

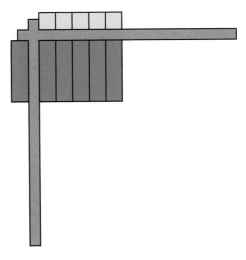

For each pair of expressions in problems 14-18:

    a. The first expression is *how much more than* the second?

    b. The first expression is *how many times as much* as the second?

**14.** $5x$ and $x$       **15.** $10x$ and 5

**16.** $10x$ and $5x$     **17.** $8xy$ and $2x$

**18.** $2x + 2y$ and $x + y$

---

**APPLICATIONS**

**19.** ⚷ The Statue of Liberty, which guards the entrance to New York harbor, was given to the United States by the people of France in honor of the centennial of American independence. The statue measures 111 feet 1 inch, from her heel to the top of her head. She was designed by Frederic Auguste Bartholdi. Suppose Mr. Bartholdi had used as a model for the statue a woman who was 5 feet 1 inch tall.

    a. How much taller is the statue than the model?

    b. How many times as tall is the statue?

    c. Which of these two numbers would have been useful to Mr. Bartholdi when designing the statue? Explain.

20. 🔑 If Reg takes the bus to work, it takes him about an hour and 15 minutes. If he drives, it takes him about 45 minutes.
    a. How much longer does it take on the bus?
    b. How many times as long does it take?
    c. Which number would be more important to Reg in deciding which method of transportation to use? Why?

21. 🔑 The A.R. Bagel Company charged 30 cents for a bagel in 1973 and 60 cents in 1983. During the same period of time, the hourly wage of a bagel deliverer increased from $2.50 per hour to $5.00 per hour. The company president said, "We try to pay our employees the highest possible wages and charge our customers the lowest possible prices. In a period of high inflation, our prices have risen only 30 cents in ten years. Yet, during the same time, we doubled hourly wages." How might the president of the Bagel Workers' Union describe this situation? Discuss.

**DISCOVERY** *TOURNAMENTS*

22. Twelve teams are playing in a tournament.
    a. Each team must be scheduled to play three games with each other team. How many games must be scheduled? (Hint: Start by thinking of a smaller tournament.)
    b. The teams play "best out of three" games. In other words, the third game of the three may not get played. What is the smallest number of games that might be played?

*Chapter 6 Making Comparisons*

# Solving Techniques: Multiplication and Division

**You will need:**

the Lab Gear

graph paper

Another key to solving equations is the fact that you can *multiply* or *divide both sides by the same number* (as long as it's not zero).

For example, if $3x = 15$, then divide both sides by 3, and you find that $x = 5$.

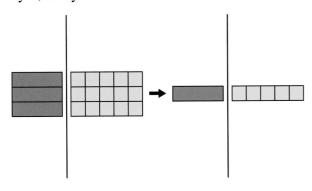

Of course, some divisions cannot be shown easily with the blocks. If you end up with $4y = 7$, then dividing both sides by 4 will reveal that $y = 7/4$. This is impossible to show with the Lab Gear.

**USING THE LAB GEAR**

Write and solve these equations.

**1.**

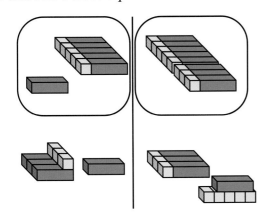

**2.**

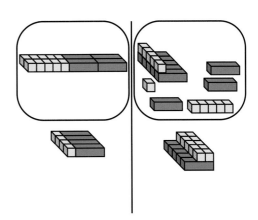

**3.**

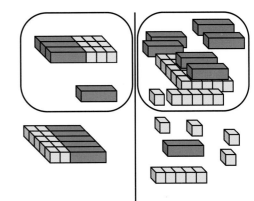

**4.**

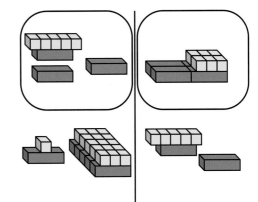

## ▼ 6.8

Solve these without the Lab Gear.

**5.** $\frac{2}{3}x = 18$  **6.** $\frac{1}{5}x = 99$

Solve these by multiplying or dividing first, and then again by first distributing the number in front of the parentheses. You should get the same answers by both methods.

**7.** $7(x - 2) = 30$  **8.** $12(x + 6) = 48$

**9.** $\frac{1}{3}(2x - 4) = 5$  **10.** $\frac{4}{5}(2 - 8x) = 16$

**11.** $\frac{1}{2}(2x - 4) = 5$  **12.** $\frac{5}{4}(2 - 8x) = 16$

**13.** Summary Use examples.

   a. Explain how to decide which of the two methods (distributing first or later) one should use in problems 7-12.

   b. Explain how to decide what number to multiply or divide both sides by when solving an equation.

**14.** Start with $x = -3$.

   a. Create an equation by adding and/or subtracting the same amount from both sides repeatedly, and by multiplying and/or dividing both sides by the same amount repeatedly. Write the final equation on paper and give it to a classmate.

   b. Solve a classmate's equation. If you both do your work correctly, the solution should be -3.

### SOLVING FOR y

You have learned to multiply or divide by a number when solving an equation containing one variable. This is also a useful technique when working with equations containing two variables, such as this one, $4y - 8x = 0$.

In a two-variable equation, it is often useful to solve for one variable *in terms of* another. This means that one variable is alone on one side of the equation.

By adding $8x$ to both sides, it is easy to rewrite this equation so that the $y$'s are on one side and the $x$'s are on the other:

$$4y = 8x.$$

Dividing both sides by 4 gives

$$y = 2x.$$

Transform each equation below so that $y$ is in terms of $x$. You may use the Lab Gear.

**15.** $3y - 6x = 9$  **16.** $6x - 3y = 12$

**17.** $x - y = 1$  **18.** $6x - 5y = 0$

### EQUIVALENT EQUATIONS

**19.** Draw axes and plot three $(x, y)$ pairs that satisfy the graph of $4y - 8x = 0$. Describe the graph.

**20.** Find three $(x, y)$ pairs that satisfy $y = 2x$ and draw the graph. Compare it with the graph in problem 19. What do you notice? Explain.

If equations in two variables have the same graph on the Cartesian coordinate system, they are called *equivalent equations*.

**21.** Explain how you could have determined *without graphing* that the equation $4y - 8x = 0$ is equivalent to $y = 2x$.

**22. a.** Write an equation that is equivalent to $6y = 12x$, but looks different.

    **b.** Describe what the graphs of both equations would look like.

For each group of equations decide which ones, if any, are equivalent equations. If you are unsure, you might want to solve the equations for $y$, make some tables, or draw some graphs.

**23.** $x + y = 2$
    $2x + 2y = 2$
    $2x + 2y = 4$

**24.** $x/y = 12$
    $y/x = 12$
    $y = 12x$

**25.** $3x - y = 6$
    $2y = 6x - 12$
    $y - 3x = 6$

**26.** $0.8x = y$
    $x - 0.2x = y$
    $y - 4/5x = 0$

**27.** $1.2\,x = y$
    $x + 0.2x - y = 0$
    $2.4x - 2y - x = 0$

---

**PUZZLES** *AGE RIDDLES*

**28.** At age 3, Henry could count to 12. How far could he count by age 21?

**29.** Augustus De Morgan lived in the nineteenth century. He said, "I was $x$ years old in the year $x^2$." In what year was he born?

**30.** 💡 Diophantus spent one-sixth of his life in childhood and one-twelfth of his life in youth. He spent one-seventh more of his life as a bachelor. Five years after he was married, his son was born. His son lived half as long as his father and died four years before his father. How many years did Diophantus live? How old was he when he got married?

**31.** Make up an age riddle.

**32.** Solve a classmate's riddle.

**RESEARCH** *FAMOUS MATHEMATICIANS*

**33.** Prepare a report about Diophantus or Augustus De Morgan. What were their contributions to mathematics?

# 6.B Constant Differences, Constant Ratios

**You will need:**

graph paper

---

### CONSTANT DIFFERENCE GRAPHS

These three $(x, y)$ pairs follow a pattern: $(6, 0)$, $(7, 1)$, $(-4, -10)$. The difference between $y$ and $x$ always equals 6. The equation $y - x = -6$ describes the relationship between $x$ and $y$.

Use the same pair of axes for all the graphs in problems 1-5.

1. Graph $y - x = -6$.

2. Choose any other integer $D$ and graph the function $y - x = D$. (For example, if you chose the integer 10, you would graph the equation $y - x = 10$.) Label the graph with its equation.

3. Graph several other functions of the form $y - x = D$. For each graph, you will need to choose a different number for $D$. Remember to try negative numbers and fractions as well as positive integers.

4. Compare your *constant difference* graphs with the *constant sum* graphs that you investigated in Chapter 5, Lesson 1.

5. Graph some constant difference graphs of the form $x - y = D$. Explain any differences or similarities with graphs of the form $y - x = D$.

---

### CONSTANT RATIO GRAPHS

These three $(x, y)$ pairs follow a pattern: $(3, 6)$, $(4, 8)$, $(-4, -8)$. The ratio of $y$ to $x$ is always equal to 2. The equation $y/x = 2$ describes the relationship between $x$ and $y$.

Use the same pair of axes for the graphs in problems 6-9.

6. Graph $y/x = 2$.

7. Choose any other number $R$ and graph the function $y/x = R$. (For example, if you chose $R$ to be 3, you would graph the equation $y/x = 3$.) Label the graph with its equation.

8. Graph several other functions of the form $y/x = R$. For each graph, you will need to choose a different number for $R$. Be sure to try some negative and fractional values as well as positive integers.

9. Now graph some *constant ratio* graphs of the form $x/y = R$. Explain any differences and similarities with graphs of the form $y/x=R$.

---

### PARAMETERS

Note: $D$ and $R$ in problems 2-9 are called *parameters*.

---

10. **Report** Write a report describing and analyzing any patterns you noticed in the graphs you just drew. Your report should be divided into two parts, one on constant differences, and the other on constant ratios. It should include, but not be limited to, answers to these questions:

   • Can you tell from the value of the parameter which quadrants the lines will pass through? Whether the lines slope up or down?

   • Do any lines go through the origin? If not, do you think you could find a value for the parameter so that the line would go through the origin? Explain.

   • For the constant ratio graphs, why is there a "hole" in the graph when $x = 0$?

   • Comment on anything you notice about the $x$-intercepts and $y$-intercepts.

   • There is one constant difference graph that is also a constant ratio graph. What are the values of $D$ and $R$?

---

# Rational Expressions

### COMPARING RATIONAL EXPRESSIONS

To add, subtract, multiply, and divide fractions involving variables, use the same rules you use for numerical fractions.

1. 🗝 Review the rules for adding, subtracting, multiplying, and dividing fractions, using an example of each kind.

2. For each expression, substitute 1, 2, and 9 for $x$ and perform the indicated operation. In which problem is the answer the same, regardless of the value of $x$?

   a. $\dfrac{5}{x} \cdot \dfrac{x}{5}$        b. $\left(\dfrac{5}{x}\right)\Big/\left(\dfrac{x}{5}\right)$

   c. $\dfrac{5}{x} + \dfrac{x}{5}$        d. $\dfrac{5}{x} - \dfrac{x}{5}$

A *rational number* is any number that can be written as a ratio of integers. A *rational expression* is an expression that involves a *ratio*. A very simple rational expression is the rational number 1/2, which is the ratio of 1 to 2. A more complicated rational expression is $(x^2 + 3x + 4)/(x^3 - 99)$, which is the ratio of two polynomials.

3. With the numbers 3 and 4, you can write the ratio 3/4 or the ratio 4/3.

   a. Which is greater, 3/4 or 4/3?

   b. Which is greater, 3/4 of 4/3 or 4/3 of 3/4? Explain.

4. 🗝 For each pair of expressions below, write:

**A** if the expression in the first column is greater

**B** if the expression in the second column is greater

**?** if the value of $x$ determines which one is greater

Explain your answers.

   a. $\dfrac{x}{5}$        $\dfrac{x-2}{5}$

   b. $x - \dfrac{2}{5}$        $\dfrac{x-2}{5}$

   c. $\dfrac{5}{x}$        $\dfrac{5}{x-2}$

### EQUIVALENT RATIONAL EXPRESSIONS

By dividing, you can show that two fractions represent the same ratio. For example, as the figure shows, 10/5 equals 2/1.

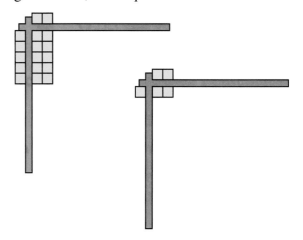

The same thing sometimes works with polynomials. As shown in the figure, the rational expression $(x^2 + 3x + 2)/(x + 1)$ is equal to $(x^2 + 5x + 6)/(x + 3)$ because the result of both divisions is the same.

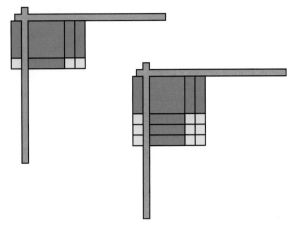

**5.** What is the result of both divisions?

(**Note:** These two rational expressions are **not** equal when $x = -1$ or $x = -3$. Can you see why? Try substituting these numbers for $x$ and see what happens.)

**6.** Are these rational expressions equal? Explain. You may use a sketch.
$(xy + 2x)/x$     $(y^2 + 2y)/y$

**7.** For each problem, find a number or expression you could put in the box that would make the two rational expressions equal. Explain each part, perhaps using a sketch.

a. $\dfrac{3x}{x}$     $\dfrac{3x + 6}{\boxed{\phantom{x}}}$

b. $\dfrac{18}{6}$     $\dfrac{15}{\boxed{\phantom{x}}}$

c. $\dfrac{\boxed{\phantom{x}}}{x + y}$     $\dfrac{2x + 2y}{2}$

d. $\dfrac{x^2 + 8x + 12}{\boxed{\phantom{x}}}$     $\dfrac{2x + 12}{2}$

**8.** | Exploration | The equation
$$\frac{x - 3}{5} = x + 1$$
cannot easily be modeled with the Lab Gear. Try to solve it using any technique you have learned. Compare your method and your answers with other students' work.

Lea and Earl both tried to solve this equation. They got different answers.

| **Lea's work** | **Earl's work** |
|---|---|
| $5\left(\dfrac{x - 3}{5}\right) = (x + 1) \cdot 5$ | $5\left(\dfrac{x - 3}{5}\right) = (x + 1) \cdot 5$ |
| $x - 3 = 5x + 5$ | $5(x - 3) = 5(x + 1)$ |
| $-3 = 4x + 5$ | $\dfrac{1}{5} \cdot 5(x - 3) = \dfrac{1}{5} \cdot 5(x + 1)$ |
| $-2 = 4x$ | $x - 3 = x + 1$ |
| $-0.5 = x$ | impossible |

**9.** Who is right, or are they both wrong? Copy each student's work and write an explanation beside each step telling what was done. If a step is incorrect, explain why and make a correction.

Solve these equations. Show your work and write a brief explanation of each step.

**10.** $\dfrac{6 - x}{8} = \dfrac{x}{2}$     **11.** $\dfrac{6 - x}{8} = \dfrac{x}{5}$

**12.** $\dfrac{x + 5}{x + 7} = 3$     **13.** $\dfrac{6 + 2x}{x + 7} = \dfrac{4}{5}$

**14.** $\dfrac{x - 3}{2} = x + 5$

**15.** | Summary | Describe a general method for solving equations like those in problems 10-14. Include the solution of an example you made up.

Write the equation shown by the blocks, then solve it. If you use the Lab Gear, write equations to show some of the steps as you move your blocks. If you don't, show all your work.

**16.**
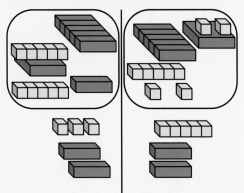

**17.**
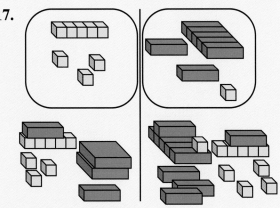

**18.**
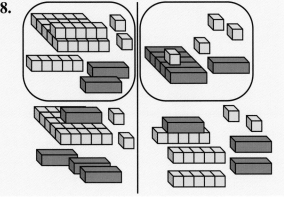

**19.**
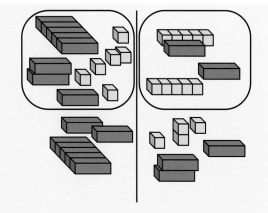

Solve.

**20.** $(x + 3)^2 = (x - 3)(x + 4)$

**21.** $(x - 1)^2 = (x + 2)(x - 6)$

Keeping in mind order of operations, insert as many pairs of parentheses as needed, to make these equations true.

**22.** $4 \cdot 2 + 3 = 20$

**23.** $\frac{1}{4} + \frac{1}{2} \cdot \frac{1}{2} = \frac{1}{2}$

**24.** $5 \cdot 3 - 2 + 6 = 35$

**25.** $3^2 + 2 \cdot 7 - 4 = 33$

**26.** $\frac{1}{3} \cdot 6 + 4 \cdot \frac{2}{6} + \frac{1}{3} = \frac{7}{3}$

**27.** $1 - 2 \cdot 2 + 5 \cdot 6 = -42$

# Improving Your Average

Alaberg High School has a girls' basketball team nicknamed "the Gals." Ms. Ball, the coach, is studying these statistics.

## Mid-Season Free-Throw Data

|  | FT-A | Average |
|---|---|---|
| Bea | 15-20 | 75% |
| Gale | 3-18 | ____ |
| Lara | ____-8 | 25% |
| Lea | 5-____ | 20% |
| Li Ann | 16-24 | ____ |

FT-A means *free throws made - free throws attempted.* The average is shown as a percent, but it could be shown as a ratio or decimal. (For example, Bea's average is 15/20 or 0.75.)

1.  Copy and complete the table. Who has the best record so far this season?

2.  **Exploration** Bea wants to have a season record of 90%. She thinks she can make every free throw that she attempts for the rest of the season. Tell how many she would have to make in a row in order for her season average to be:
    a. 80%     b. 85%     c. 90%
    d. 95%     e. 99%     f. 100%
    Discuss.

3.  If Bea has had 20 free throw attempts and has made 15 of them, her average is 15/20. If she has $x$ more attempts and makes all of them, her average is $\frac{15 + x}{20 + x}$.

a.  What is the value of this ratio when $x = 40$? (That is, what is her average if she has 40 more attempts and makes all of them?)
b.  What is her average if $x = 25$?

4.  Suppose Li Ann had $x$ free throw attempts during the rest of the season and *missed* every one.
    a.  What would her season average be, in terms of $x$? (Hint: The expression will be different from the one in problem 3.)
    b.  If she had a season average of 40%, how many more free throws after mid-season must she have attempted?
    c.  If she attempted ten more free throws, what would her season average be?

5.  Suppose Li Ann *made* every attempted free throw.
    a.  What would her season average be, in terms of $x$?
    b.  What would her season average be if she attempted eight more free throws?
    c.  If she had a season average of 0.85, how many more free throws must she have attempted?

These problems are not very realistic. Usually people do not make all their attempted free throws, but they don't miss all of them either. Lea hopes that she will make about 40% of her attempted free throws for the rest of the season.

6.  If Lea attempts $x$ more free throws, and makes 40% of them, she knows that her average for the season would be
    $$\frac{5 + 0.40x}{25 + x}.$$

a. Explain the meaning of the numerator and denominator of this expression, and how it was figured out.

b. How would the expression change if Lea made 60% of her remaining free throws?

c. How would the expression change if Lea made 20% of her remaining free throws?

7. Assume Lea makes 40% of her remaining free throws and wants to raise her season average to at least 30%. What is the minimum number of free throws she needs?

8. By the end of the season Gale had doubled both her attempts and her successes. What happened to her average?

9. **Generalization** Assume a student has made $M$ out of $T$ free throws. Assume she attempts $x$ more shots and makes $N$ of them. What will her season average be in terms of $M$, $T$, $x$, and $N$? Explain.

### GRADES

Alaberg High School has a "no pass, no play" rule for all sports. Students must have an average of 65% in all their classes in order to qualify to play any sport the following quarter.

Some members of the boys' basketball team (the Bears) are worrying about their averages for algebra. (See the table.)

Their grades in algebra are based on 12 ten-point assignments per quarter. Students who have been absent because of illness (like Hal and Zal) can complete the assignments late.

**Mid-Quarter Algebra Scores**

|  | Possible points | Points earned | Average |
|---|---|---|---|
| **Al** | 80 | 35 | — |
| **Hal** | 70 | 52 | — |
| **Cal** | 80 | 63 | — |
| **Zal** | 60 | 59 | — |
| **Sid** | 80 | 74 | — |

10. Copy and complete the table.

Use the table to answer the following questions. Assume that *passing* means having an average of 65% or better, and *failing* means having an average below 65%.

11. Who has the lowest average so far?

12. Answer the following questions for each student.

a. What is the worst conceivable average he could get by the end of the course?

b. What is the best conceivable average he could get?

c. What is the smallest number of points he needs to earn in the remaining assignments in order to pass?

REVIEW **EQUATION SOLVING**

Solve for the variable.

13. $\dfrac{y+5}{2} = \dfrac{19-y}{1}$

14. $\dfrac{y+5}{4} = \dfrac{19-y}{2}$

15. $2(y+5) = 19 - y$

16. $4(y+5) = 2(19-y)$

17. $y + 5 = 2(19-y)$

18. $\dfrac{-15+3x}{5+4x} = 7$

# Stuart Little and Alice

**You will need:**

rulers

measuring tape

and/or yardsticks

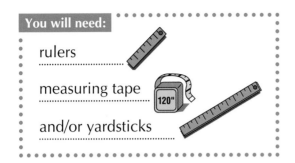

## STUART LITTLE

Here is the beginning of *Stuart Little*, a children's book by E.B. White.

> **W**hen Mrs. Frederick C. Little's second son arrived, everybody noticed that he was not much bigger than a mouse. The truth of the matter was, the baby looked very much like a mouse in every way. He was only about two inches high; and he had a mouse's sharp nose, a mouse's tail, a mouse's whiskers, and the pleasant, shy manner of a mouse. Before he was many days old he was not only looking like a mouse but acting like one, too — wearing a gray hat and carrying a small cane. Mr. and Mrs. Little named him Stuart, and Mr. Little made him a tiny bed out of four clothespins and a cigarette box.

1. Measure, in inches, the height of several boys in your class. To do the following exercises, choose someone whose height is near the average of the heights you measured.

2. Measure, in inches, the length and width of the average boy's
   a. pants;          b. shirt or coat.

3. Measure, in inches, the length and width of:
   a. a book or binder;
   b. a chair or desk.

4. 🗝 Calculate the size of each item in problems 2-3, if it were to be made for Stuart Little. Explain your work.

5. Draw each item in the size that you calculated in problem 4.

## ALICE

Here is an excerpt from *Alice in Wonderland*, a book by the English mathematician Lewis Carroll.

> ...this bottle was not marked "poison," so Alice ventured to taste it, and finding it very nice, (it had, in fact, a sort of mixed flavour of cherry-tart, custard, pine-apple, roast turkey, toffy, and hot buttered toast), she very soon finished it off.
>
> "What a curious feeling!" said Alice, "I must be shutting up like a telescope!"
>
> And so it was indeed: she was now only ten inches high, and her face brightened up at the thought that she was now the right size for going through the little door into that lovely garden.

6. Measure, in inches, the height of several girls in your class. To do the following exercises, choose someone whose height is near the average of the heights you measured.

7. Assuming that before she drank from the bottle, Alice was the size of the average girl in your class, how many times as tall was she after shrinking?

8. a. Measure a real pencil or pen.
   b. Calculate the correct size for a pencil or pen of the same kind for Alice. Explain.

c. Draw it in the size you calculated in part (b).

9. Measure a real door, and calculate the dimensions of "the little door into that lovely garden."

> "Curiouser and curiouser!" cried Alice (she was so much surprised, that for the moment she quite forgot how to speak good English). "Now I'm opening out like the largest telescope that ever was! Goodbye, feet!"...
>
> ...Just at this moment, her head struck against the roof of the hall: in fact she was now rather more than nine feet high...

10. How many times as tall as an average girl in your class is Alice now?

11. What would be the size of a pencil if it were the right size for giant Alice? Show your calculations.

### THE BIG FRIENDLY GIANT

The following are quotations about the Big Friendly Giant, a character in Roald Dahl's book *The BFG*.

 a. It was four times as tall as the tallest human.
 b. It actually had to bend down to peer into the upstairs windows. That's how tall it was.
 c. ...an arm as thick as a tree trunk...
 d. The Giant was sprinting down the High Street... Each stride he took was as long as a tennis court.

e. In the middle of the floor there was a table twelve feet high...
 f. He had truly enormous ears. Each one was as big as the wheel of a truck...

12. **Project** Estimate the height of the Giant using the information given in each quotation. Explain your work.
 • What real-world numbers did you use?
 • How did you find them?
 • What calculations did you do?
 • Did the results of your calculations agree with each other?
 • Based on all the calculations, what is your final estimate of the Giant's height?

### YOUR OWN STORY

13. **Project**
 a. Write and illustrate a story for a young child featuring little people or giants. Make sure the dimensions of all objects are sized correctly.
 b. On a separate piece of paper, explain your calculations.

### OTHER STORIES

14. **Project** Ask a librarian or an elementary school teacher to suggest a book that involves little people or giants. Make up math problems based on the book. Use specific quotations from the book as much as possible. On a separate piece of paper, solve the problems you make up.

### REVIEW SOLVING EQUATIONS

15. Solve the equation,
$$2.5x + 18 + 1.5x - 11 = 19.$$

16. If $x = 3$, calculate, $2.5x + 18 + 1.5x - 11$.

17. Explain how problems 15 and 16 are related.

# Geoboard Squares

**You will need:**

geoboards ............................

dot paper ............................................

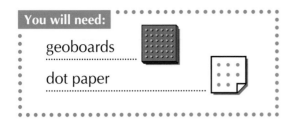

1. **Exploration** There are 33 different geoboard squares. Find as many of them as you can. (For this exercise, squares that have the same size are considered the same.) Sketch each square on dot paper.

## FIND THE AREA

2. There are 10 geoboard squares having horizontal and vertical sides. What are their areas?

3. Make a 1-by-1 square in the bottom left of your geoboard. Make a square that has this square's diagonal — (0, 1) to (1, 0) — for a side. What is the area of the new square?

4. Repeat problem 3, starting with larger and larger squares in the bottom left. What is the area of each new square?

5. Explain why only five squares can be found this way.

6. ⚷ Make a square having (0, 1) to (2, 0) as a side.
   a. Explain how you found the other vertices of the square.
   b. Find the area. Explain how you did it.

7. Make squares having (0, 1) to (x, 0) as a side. Use x = 3, 4, ... 9. Find the area of each one.

8. ⚷ Explain why you cannot find a geoboard square having (0, 1) to (10, 0) as one side.

9. Make a square having (0, 2) to (3, 0) as one side.
   a. Sketch the square.
   b. Make and sketch the smallest square having horizontal and vertical sides that entirely covers the original square. What is the area of this square?
   c. What is the total area of the four triangles that surround the original square?
   d. What is the area of the original square?

10. **Generalization** On dot paper, sketch a pair of x- and y-axes.

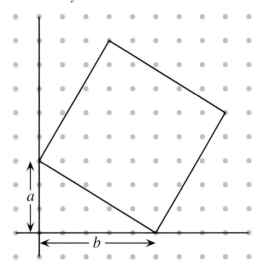

   a. Copy the above figure.
   b. Sketch the smallest square having horizontal and vertical sides that entirely covers the original square. What are its sides in terms of a and b? What is its area in terms of a and b?

c. What is the area of one of the triangles that surround the original square in terms of $a$ and $b$? What is the total area of the four triangles in terms of $a$ and $b$?

d. What is the area of the original square in terms of $a$ and $b$?

11. **Summary** How does one find the area of a geoboard square? For examples, use the squares having the following as one side.
a. (0, 3) to (4, 0)
b. 💡 (2, 4) to (7, 1)

---

**FIND THE SIDE**

12. How long is the side of a square if the area is

a. 64?  b. 81?

c. 289?  d. 0.0121?

13. How long is the side of a square if the area is 70? Give an approximate answer. (Hint: You may be able to use some of the results from problem 12.)

14. Use trial and error on a calculator to answer problem 13 to the closest one-thousandth.

15. **Summary** Use examples to explain.
a. How does one find the area of a square, if given the side?
b. How does one find the side of a square, if given the area?

---

**DISCOVERY** *CHUNKING*

16. Solve: $3(x + 3) + 5 = 4(x + 3)$

It is easier to solve this equation by first solving for $(x + 3)$, and then finding $x$, instead of distributing. This is called *chunking*, since in this method the quantity $(x + 3)$ is thought of as one chunk.

17. Solve $3y + 5 = 4y$, then use the fact that $y = x + 3$ to solve for $x$. Explain what you did, and how this problem is related to problem 16.

18. Create an equation that would be easier to solve by chunking than by distributing. Solve it.

19. Solve a classmate's chunking equation.

**DISCOVERY** *INEQUALITY RULES*

Like most students, Mary and Martin enjoy discussing inequalities during their lunch period.

20. Martin said, "I noticed something cool. If $5/x$ is less than 5, then $x/5$ is more than $1/5$." Mary said, "I don't understand. In the first place, I can't think of a value of $x$ that would make $5/x$ greater than 5."
a. Give Mary at least two values of $x$ that will make $5/x$ greater than 5.
b. Is Martin's statement correct? Give examples to explain your answer.

21. ⊸ Martin said, "If $a < b$, then by taking the reciprocals of both sides, I get $1/a > 1/b$. Notice that I changed the direction of the inequality." Mary answered, "Sorry, but you're wrong." Who is right? Explain, with examples.

22. ⊸ Martin said, "If $a < b$, then by taking the opposites of both sides, I get $-a > -b$. Notice that I changed the direction of the inequality." Mary answered, "When will you give up making up rules off the top of your head! You're wrong again!" Who is right? Explain, with examples.

*SOLVING INEQUALITIES*

*CAN TARA MAKE A B?*

Solve these inequalities. Remember that you must find *all the values* of $x$ that make the inequality true. Show your work, and check your answers.

**23.** $x - 1 > 5$

**24.** $x + 1 > 5$

**25.** $2x - 6 > 5x + 3$

**26.** $2x - 6 < 5x + 3$

**27.** $3(x + 1) > 6$

**28.** 💡 $2 - 3(x + 1) > 6$

Some auto insurance policies have a "good student" policy for high school students. If a student maintains a *B* average, he or she can qualify for a discount on insurance rates.

Tara doesn't like writing assignments because they take time outside of school, when she would rather be driving her car. However, she does well on quizzes. She needs a *B* in algebra. Her scores are:

Writing Assignments: 45 55
Quizzes: 100 50 90 85 90 95

Tara hopes that the teacher will count quizzes heavily in the average so that she can make a *B*.

**29.** Is it possible for Tara to make a *B*? If so, how much would the teacher have to weight her quizzes? If not, explain why not.

# 6.C **Group Theory**

## MOD CLOCKS

### Mod 5 Clock

The figure shows a mod clock, which is a special function machine. For any positive whole number input, it will output a number between 0 and 4. For example:

| Input | Output |
|-------|--------|
| 1 | 1 |
| 9 | 4 |
| 13 | 3 |
| 25 | 0 |
| 77 | 2 |

| Input | Output |
|-------|--------|
| 5 | 0 |
| 12 | 2 |
| 17 | 2 |
| 26 | 1 |
| 100 | 0 |

1. What would be the output of the mod clock for the following inputs? Explain.
   a. 1998    b. 1899    c. 9981

**Definition:** $a \oplus b$ is the output from the mod clock for the input $a + b$. $a \otimes b$ is the output for the input $ab$.

**Example:** $3 \oplus 2 = 0$, and $3 \otimes 2 = 1$

2. Make a table for each of $\oplus$ and $\otimes$.

3. Generalization   The clock above is a mod 5 clock. Find ways to predict the output of mod 10, mod 2, mod 9, and mod 3 clocks.

## GROUPS

**Definition:** A *group* is a set of elements, together with an operation that satisfies the following rules.

- *closure:* using the operation on two elements of the group yields an element of the group.
- *associative law:* $(ab)c = a(bc)$.
- *identity element:* one of the elements, *e*, is such that $ae = ea = a$, for any element *a* in the group.
- *inverse element:* every element *a* has an inverse $a'$ such that $a\,a' = a'a = e$

Some groups are *commutative* ($ab = ba$) and some are not.

For 4-7 assume the associative law holds.

4. a. Show that the set $\{0, 1, 2, 3, 4\}$ together with the operation $\oplus$ is a group.
   b. Show that $\{0, 1, 2, 3, 4\}$ with $\otimes$ is not a group.
   c. Show that $\{1, 2, 3, 4\}$ with $\otimes$ is a group.

5. Is the set of the integers a group with the following operations?
   a. addition    b. multiplication

6. Show that the set of rational numbers (positive and negative fractions and zero) together with multiplication is not a group. By removing one element, it can be made into a group. Which element? Explain.

7. Think about a mod 4 clock, with the numbers $\{0, 1, 2, 3\}$. Is it a group for $\oplus$? For $\otimes$? Can it be made into one by removing an element?

8. Report   Give examples of groups. For each, give the set and operation. Explain how they satisfy the rules. Include finite, infinite, commutative, and noncommutative groups.

# ◆ Essential Ideas

## EQUATIONS, IDENTITIES, INEQUALITIES

1. Always, sometimes, or never true?
   a. $2x + 6 = 2x - 6$
   b. $2x + 6 = 2(x + 6)$
   c. $2x + 6 = x + 6$
   d. $2x + 6 = 2(x + 3)$

2. For each equation above, decide which of the two expressions is greater, if they are equal, or if the answer depends on the value of $x$.

3. Solve the inequalities. You may want to use a graph.
   a. $3x < 5$        b. $x + 3 < 5$
   c. $3x + 3 < 5$    d. $2x + 6 < x + 6$

## SOLVING EQUATIONS

Solve these equations.

4.  a. $4x + 8 = 9$
    b. $-4x + 8 = 9$
    c. $4x - 8 = 9$
    d. $-4x + 8 = -9$

5.  a. $x - 6 = 2(x - 5)$
    b. $2x - 12 = 4(x - 5)$
    c. $2.5(x - 5) = 2.5x - 12$

6.  a. $\frac{1}{3}(4x - 2) = 5$
    b. $\frac{4}{5}(8 - 2x) = 16$
    c. $\frac{x - 3}{2} = x - 4.3$

7.  a. $6 - 3(m - 4) = 3m$
    b. $(6 - 3)(n - 4) = 3n$
    c. $6 - 2(p + 4) = (8 - p)(2 + 3)$
    d. $(6 - x)(x + 4) = (8 - x)(x + 2)$

8.  a. $\frac{d + 9}{5} - 3 = 15$     b. $\frac{2d + 6}{5} = \frac{3d - 7}{5}$
    c. $\frac{f - 2}{4} = f + 3$

9. Solve for $y$ in terms of $x$.
   a. $-6x + y = 4$
   b. $2y + x = 8$

## GRAPHS

10. Graph these equations on the same axes.
    $y - x = -6$        $y = 2(x - 5)$
    $y = 2x - 12$       $y = 4(x - 5)$

11. Explain how one can use this graph to check the solutions to problem 5.

12. Use your graph to solve the compound inequality, $2x - 12 < x - 6 < 2x - 10$. Explain.

## WRITING EQUATIONS

13. Write an expression telling how much money Bea will have if she
    a. starts with $321 and saves $9 a week for $n$ weeks;
    b. starts with $321 and saves $$d$ a week for $n$ weeks;
    c. starts with $$m$ and saves $$d$ a week for $n$ weeks.

14. If Bea starts with $321, how much must she save each week to reach $456 in 28 weeks? Write an equation and solve it.

## DIFFERENCES AND RATIOS

According to author Glen Rounds, Johnny Inkslinger was Paul Bunyan's accountant. He used a pencil that was "over three feet in diameter and seventy-six feet long — the first one ever used." A typical pencil is a quarter inch in diameter and seven and a half inches long. Most men in those days were probably between 5 feet 6 in. and 6 feet tall.

**15.** Compared to a normal pencil, Johnny Inkslinger's was

    a. how much wider?

    b. how many times as wide?

    c. how much longer?

    d. how many times as long?

**16.** Based on this information, how tall do you think Johnny was? Explain. (Give your answer as a range of probable heights.)

TABLES, GRAPHS, AND EQUATIONS

A telephone company offers two different billing plans. The Community Plan costs $10.77 a month and allows unlimited local calls. The Thrifty Plan costs $5.50 a month, but the cost of local calls is 5.5 cents for the first minute, plus 3.5 cents for each additional minute. Both plans cost the same for long distance calls. Which plan should different callers use?

**17.** Assume that your phone calls last an average of five minutes.

    a. How much does an average call cost under the Thrifty Plan?

    b. Write a formula for the Thrifty Plan. Use $y$ for the cost, $x$ for the number of phone calls.

    c. If you make exactly one five-minute call a day, should you use the Thrifty Plan or the Community Plan?

**18.** Write a formula for the Thrifty Plan. Use $y$ for the cost and $x$ for the number of phone calls. Assume your calls last an average of:

    a. 1 minute;    b. 3 minutes;

    c. 5 minutes;    d. 7 minutes.

**19.** Make tables to show how many calls a month make it preferable to use the Community Plan, for a customer whose calls last an average of:

    a. 1 minute;    b. 3 minutes;

    c. 5 minutes;    d. 7 minutes.

**20.** Use a graph to show the costs of both plans for each customer listed in problem 19 as a function of the number of calls made. (Your graph should include five lines.)

A consumer advocate gives advice to people about which plan to choose. In order to do that, he needs to generalize the information revealed in problems 17-20.

**21.** He would like to have a formula for the Thrifty Plan in terms of two variables: $x$ for the number of local calls, and $t$ for the average duration of each call. Find such a formula.

**22.** He would like to know the number of local calls at the "break even" point, where both plans cost roughly the same amount, in terms of $t$. To figure this out, he sets up an equation, with the formula for the Thrifty Plan on the left, and the cost of the Community Plan (10.77) on the right.

    a. Solve the equation for $x$.

    b. Check your answers to problem 17 with the formula you found in part (a).

**23.** 💡 In trying to use the formula from problem 22 he finds that people don't usually know the average duration of their phone calls. To help them figure it out, he asks them for an estimate of the numbers of local calls they make every week that last approximately: one minute, five minutes, ten minutes, and thirty minutes. Given these four numbers, how can he find the average duration of the phone calls?

**24.** Project Keep track of the duration of your phone calls for a week. Figure out which plan would be more suitable for you if you had your own phone.

# CHAPTER 7

A spiral galaxy, having arms made of gas, dust, and stars

## Coming in this chapter:

**Exploration** The expression $1^3 + 2^3 + 3^3 + 4^3 + 5^3 + \ldots + n^3$ can be modeled by building $n$ cubes out of blocks. Could you rearrange these blocks into a square? If so, what are its dimensions? Experiment with different values of $n$. Look for a pattern.

# PRODUCTS AND POWERS

# Squares and Cubes

**You will need:**

the Lab Gear

1. **Exploration** Which is greater, $2^2 + 3^2$ or $(2 + 3)^2$ ? By how much? Which is greater, $5^2 + 8^2$ or $(5 + 8)^2$ ? By how much? Is it ever true that
$$x^2 + y^2 = (x + y)^2 ?$$
How far apart are they? Experiment and write a paragraph summarizing your work and your conclusions. It may help to use the Lab Gear.

## HOW MANY SQUARES?

The square $(x + 2)^2$ can be written as the product $(x + 2)(x + 2)$. It can be represented by *a single square* with side $(x + 2)$, as shown in the figure.

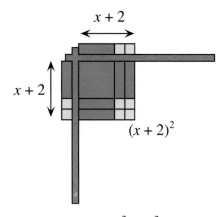

$(x + 2)^2$

The sum of the squares $x^2 + 2^2$ cannot be written as a product or represented with a single square. It must be represented by *two individual squares*.

$x^2 + 2^2$

Compare these two expressions.
(i) $2 \cdot 3^2$
(ii) $(2 \cdot 3)^2$

Because the rules for order of operations tell us to perform exponentiation first, expression (i) means *square 3 and then multiply by 2*. This can be modeled by building two squares with the Lab Gear.

$2 \cdot 3^2$

Expression (ii) means *multiply 2 by 3 and square the result*. Since $2 \cdot 3 = 6$, this can be written more simply as $6^2$. This can be modeled by building *one* square with the Lab Gear.

$6^2$

Make a rough sketch representing each expression, 2-6, with as few squares as possible. Which of these expressions can be modeled as a single square? Which require more than one square? (Be careful!)

2. a. $(x + 1)^2$    b. $x^2 + 1$

3. a. $4x^2 + 4$    b. $(2x + 2)^2$

4. a. $5^2 + 3 \cdot 5^2$    b. $2^2 + 5 \cdot 2^2$

5. a. $3^2 + 4^2$    b. $(3 + 4)^2$

6. a. $(3 \cdot 4)^2$    b. $3^2 \cdot 4^2$

7. Give the value of each expression.
a. $3^2 + 4^2$    b. $(3 \cdot 4)^2$
c. $(3 + 4)^2$    d. $3^2 \cdot 4^2$
e. $5^2 + 3 \cdot 5^2$    f. $2^2 + 5 \cdot 2^2$

The cube $(x + 2)^3$ can be written as the product $(x + 2)(x + 2)(x + 2)$. It can be represented by *a single cube* with sides $(x + 2)$, as shown.

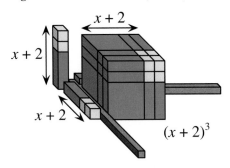

$x + 2$

$x + 2$

$x + 2$

$(x + 2)^3$

The sum of the cubes $x^3 + 2^3$ cannot be written as a product. It cannot be represented with a single cube. It must be represented by *two individual cubes*.

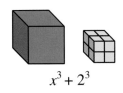

$x^3 + 2^3$

Compare these two expressions.

  (i)  $3 \cdot 2^3$
  (ii) $(3 \cdot 2)^3$

Because the order of operations tells us to perform exponentiation first, expression (i) means *cube 2 and then multiply by 3*. This can be modeled by building three cubes with the Lab Gear.

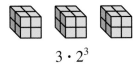

$3 \cdot 2^3$

Expression (ii) means *multiply 2 by 3 and cube the result*. Since $3 \cdot 2 = 6$, this can be written more simply as $6^3$. This can be modeled by building one cube with the Lab Gear.

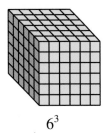

$6^3$

**8.** What number does each expression equal?
  a. $3 \cdot 2^3$    b. $(3 \cdot 2)^3$

How would you represent each expression with as few cubes as possible? It may help to use the Lab Gear. Make a sketch, giving the dimensions of each cube.

**9.** a. $(x + 1)^3$    b. $x^3 + 1$

**10.** a. $x^3 + 8$    b. $(x + 2)^3$

**11.** a. $x^3 + y^3$    b. $(x + y)^3$

Which of these expressions could be modeled using only one cube? Which require more than one cube? Tell how you would represent each expression with as few cubes as possible. Give the dimensions of each cube.

**12.** a. $6 \cdot 2^3$    b. $(6 \cdot 2)^3$

**13.** a. $6^3 + 2^3$    b. $(6 + 2)^3$

**14.** What is the value of each expression?
  a. $6 \cdot 2^3$    b. $(6 \cdot 2)^3$
  c. $6^3 + 2^3$    d. $(6 + 2)^3$

MAKING SQUARES FROM CUBES

**15.** a. Use the Lab Gear to show how the expression $1^3 + 2^3 + 3^3$ can be modeled by building three cubes.

b. What was the total number of blocks needed for part (a)?

c. Make a square by rearranging the blocks you used to make the three cubes. What are the dimensions of the square?

**16.** a. The expression $1^3 + 2^3 + 3^3 + 4^3$ could be modeled by building four cubes. What is the total number of blocks used?

b. How would one make a square by rearranging these blocks? Give the square's dimensions.

**17.** Compare your answers to problems 15 and 16. Look for a pattern. Check it for $1^3 + 2^3$. Predict the value of the sum,
$$1^3 + 2^3 + 3^3 + 4^3 + 5^3.$$
Check your prediction.

**18.** Generalization The expression
$$1^3 + 2^3 + 3^3 + 4^3 + 5^3 + \ldots + n^3$$
can be modeled by building $n$ cubes out of blocks. Could you rearrange these blocks into a square? If so, what would its dimensions be? Explain your answer.

---

_REVIEW_ _CUBING WITH A TABLE_

To find the cube of a polynomial, first find its square, then multiply the result by the polynomial. For example, to calculate $(x + 2y)^3$, first square $x + 2y$.

|     | $x$    | $2y$   |
| --- | ------ | ------ |
| $x$ | $x^2$  | $2xy$  |
| $2y$| $2xy$  | $4y^2$ |

Combine like terms in the body of the table. Multiply this result by $x + 2y$.

|      | $x^2$    | $4xy$    | $4y^2$   |
| ---- | -------- | -------- | -------- |
| $x$  | $x^3$    | $4x^2y$  | $4xy^2$  |
| $2y$ | $2x^2y$  | $8xy^2$  | $8y^3$   |

So $(x + 2y)^3 = x^3 + 6x^2y + 12xy^2 + 8y^3$.

**19.** Find the cube.

a. $(x + 1)^3$  b. $(2x + 2)^3$

c. $(x + y)^3$  d. $(2x - y)^3$

e. $(3x + 2y - 5)^3$

# Square Windows

**You will need:**

graph paper

---

**THREE TYPES OF PANES**

The A.B. Glare window store has started selling a new kind of window. These windows can be made to order by combining three types of square window panes. Each pane measures one foot on each side. The three types of panes are shown below: corner panes, edge panes, and inside panes.

A 3-foot-by-3-foot window is shown below. It was made by putting together 4 corner panes, 4 edge panes, and 1 inside pane.

1. Sketch a 4-foot-by-5-foot rectangular window. How many panes of each type were used to make it?

---

**SQUARE WINDOWS**

2. **Exploration** An architect was asked to design a recreation hall. He was going to use the A.B. Glare window panes described above. The building code imposes a limit of 72 square feet for the total area of all windows in the main part

of the hall. The architect decides to consider various combinations of square windows such that their total area is exactly 72. Find several such configurations, and for each one, find the total number of each type of pane the architect will need.

The architect is not the only one to like square windows. To save time when customers ask for them, Lara is assembling kits with the correct number of corner panes, edge panes, and inside panes to make square windows of various sizes.

3. Make a table to show how many panes of each type are needed for a 2-by-2 window, a 3-by-3 window, and so on, up to a 10-by-10 window.

4. ⚷ Study the table from problem 3. Which increases the fastest: the number of corner, edge, or inside panes? Which increases the most slowly? Why?

5. Make three graphs of the data in your table, on the same set of axes.

   a. Graph the number of corner panes as a function of the length of the side of the window. For example, since a 3-by-3 window uses four corner panes, the point (3, 4) would be on your graph.

   b. Graph the number of edge panes as a function of the side length.

   c. Graph the number of inside panes as a function of the side length.

6. ⚷ Study your graphs. Which is the steepest? Explain why.

**7.** Generalization

   a. Write a formula for the number of panes of each type in an *x*-by-*x* window. Explain each formula in reference to a sketch of such a window.

   b. How are the formulas related to the graphs in problem 5?

**8.** ⚿ Add up the algebraic expressions for the numbers of each type of pane. If you did your work correctly, the sum should be very simple.

**9.** Find the number of corner, edge, and inside panes needed for a 100-by-100 window.

### COMPARING SIZES

**10.** Lara has too many window kits of some types and not enough of other types. She has too many kits for 2-by-2 windows and not enough for 3-by-3 windows. How many panes of each type would she have to add to a 2-by-2 kit to convert it to a 3-by-3 kit?

**11.** Answer question 10 if Lara wanted to convert

   a. a 5-by-5 kit to a 6-by-6 kit;

   b. an 8-by-8 kit to a 9-by-9 kit.

**12.** Generalization How many panes of each type would Lara have to add if she wanted to convert an *N*-by-*N*-foot kit to an *N*+1-by-*N*+1-foot kit. Explain, using a sketch of an *N*+1-by-*N*+1 window.

**13.** 💡 How many panes of each type would Lara have to add if she wanted to convert an *N*-by-*N*-foot kit to an *N*+*M*-by-*N*+*M*-foot kit. Explain, using a sketch of an *N*+*M*-by-*N*+*M* window.

### MAKING THE MOST OF INVENTORY

**14.** Suppose you have 12 panes of each type in inventory.

   a. What is the largest square window you could make? Give the size of the window and tell how many panes of each type you would have left over.

   b. What is the largest square window you could make with the remaining panes? Continue until no more windows can be made. Give the size of all the windows and the number of each type of pane left at the end.

**15.** Repeat problem 14 for:

   a. 20 panes of each type;

   b. 100 panes of each type.

**16.** Now assume that instead of trying for the largest possible square window, you try to make any number of square windows, with the goal of having *as few panes as possible left over.*

   a. If you start with 100 panes of each type, what size windows should you make? What will be left over?

   b. Compare your answers with other students' answers.

### PREVIEW BIGGER WINDOWS

**17.** Suppose each pane, regardless of the type, costs $1.00.

   a. Make a table and a graph showing the cost of the window as a function of the side length.

   b. Al knows that an 8-by-8 window costs $64.00. He thinks that a 16-by-16 window should cost twice as much, but he isn't sure. What do you think? Explain your opinion.

   c. A 16-by-16 window costs how many times as much as an 8-by-8 window?

# Squares of Sums

**1.** **Exploration**

a. Model the square $(x + 1)^2$ with the Lab Gear. Then add blocks to create the square $(x + 2)^2$. What blocks did you need to add to the first square to get the second? Now add blocks to create the square $(x + 3)^2$. What blocks did you add this time? Continue to make the square grow, keeping an organized record of what blocks you add each time. Write a paragraph about any patterns you notice.

b. If $a$ and $b$ are whole numbers, what blocks would you need to add to $(x + a)^2$ to get $(x + a + 1)^2$? To get $(x + a + b)^2$?

**MISSING TERMS**

**2.** a. Use the Lab Gear to build a square using 10 $x$-blocks and any other blocks that you want (except more $x$-blocks). Sketch the square.

b. What is the area of the square?

c. What are its dimensions?

d. Is this the only such square you could build? (That is, is your answer *unique*?) If it isn't, try to find another possibility. If you can't build another square, explain why.

**3.** Repeat problem 2, using 16 one-blocks and any other blocks that you want (except more yellow blocks).

**4.** Repeat problem 2, using 8 $xy$-blocks and any other blocks that you want (except more $xy$-blocks).

**5.** Can you build a square starting with 3 $x^2$-blocks, if you can use any other blocks except more $x^2$-blocks? Explain.

**6.** Can you build a square starting with 15 one-blocks, if you can use any other blocks except more one-blocks? Explain.

**7.** Build two different squares starting with 4 $x^2$-blocks, using any other blocks except more $x^2$-blocks. Are there more solutions? Explain.

**TERMS AND COEFFICIENTS**

**8.** a. Use the Lab Gear to build three squares of the form $(x + b)^2$, using a different value of $b$ each time. Sketch the squares.

b. Write the area of the square next to each sketch, combining like terms.

c. Notice how many terms are in each expression for area. Notice the coefficient of each term. Describe what you notice.

In each expression below, a binomial is squared. Distribute and combine like terms.

**9.** $(2y + 3)^2$    **10.** $(3x + 2)^2$

**11.** $(2x + 3y)^2$    **12.** $(3x + 2y)^2$

**13.** 🔑 Refer to problems 9-12 to answer these questions.

  a. How many terms are in each product, after combining like terms?

  b. For each binomial, notice the coefficients of each of the terms. Then notice the coefficients in the related expression for area. Describe any relationships you notice.

  c. For each binomial, notice the degree of each of the terms. Then notice the degree of each term in the related expression for area. Describe any relationships you notice.

**14.** **Summary** Summarize the patterns for the square of a binomial.

**15.** **Generalization** The patterns you found can be generalized by using letters instead of numbers for coefficients. Show how you would find the area of a square having side

  a. $a + b$;　　b. $ax + b$;

  c. $a + by$;　　d. $ax + by$.

**16.** In each expression below, a binomial is squared. Distribute and combine like terms.

  a. $(m + n)^2$　　b. $(11m + 2)^2$

  c. $(5y + 6x)^2$　　d. $(1 + 9y)^2$

**RECOGNIZING PERFECT SQUARES**

$x^2 + 14x + 49$ is called a *perfect square trinomial*. It is the square of the binomial $(x + 7)$, as you can see by writing it in a multiplication table.

| | $x$ | $7$ |
|---|---|---|
| $x$ | $x^2$ | $7x$ |
| $7$ | $7x$ | $49$ |

**17.** Which of the following are perfect square trinomials? For each one, write the binomial it is the square of.

  a. $x^2 + 16x + 16$

  b. $x^2 + 4x + 4$

  c. $x^2 + 10x + 25$

  d. $x^2 + 10xy + 25y^2$

**18.** All of these are perfect square trinomials. Write each one as the square of a binomial. Sketches may help.

  a. $4x^2 + 20xy + 25y^2$

  b. $36y^2 + 12xy + x^2$

  c. $y^2 + 18y + 81$

  d. $25x^2 + 10xy + y^2$

**19.** None of these expressions is a perfect square trinomial. In each one, change just one of the terms to convert the whole expression into the square of a binomial.

  a. $4x^2 + 12x + 10$

  b. $2x^2 + 8x + 16$

  c. $36x^2 + 30x + 25$

  d. $1.44x^2 + 1.6x + 2.25$

**20.** **Summary** Explain how to recognize a perfect square trinomial. You may use sketches, but be sure to discuss *coefficients, terms,* and *degree.*

**21.** Look at each perfect square trinomial in this lesson. For each one, find the sum of the coefficients. What do you notice? Explain.

### PREVIEW HOW MANY TERMS?

**22.** Exploration Two of the following problems are impossible. Solve the other three. Find a pair of binomials such that their product has:

a. three terms

b. four terms

c. five terms

d. one term

e. two terms

### REVIEW LAB GEAR MULTIPLICATION

For each of these problems, 23-25:

a. Use the corner piece to show the multiplication.

b. Check that the resulting figure includes an *uncovered rectangle* of the required dimensions.

c. Write a *length times width equals area* equation.

**23.** $(y + 2)(y + 2)$   **24.** $(y + 2)(y - 2)$

**25.** $(y - 2)(y - 2)$

**26.** Which of the uncovered rectangles in problems 23, 24, and 25 are squares?

### DISCOVERY CONSTRAINED NUMBERS

**27.** What are $m$ and $n$ if they are whole numbers and

a. $89 = 12m + n$, with $n < 12$;

b. $123 = 45m + n$, with $n < 45$;

c. $2345 = 67m + n$, with $n < 67$.

**28.** If $N$ and $m$ are whole numbers, and $N = 7m + n$, find several values of $N$ such that $n = 2$.

# 7.4 Differences of Squares

**You will need:**

the Lab Gear

graph paper

scissors

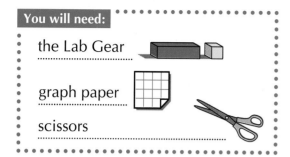

**1.** **Exploration** Which is greater, $3^2 - 2^2$ or $(3 - 2)^2$ ? Which is greater, $8^2 - 5^2$ or $(8 - 5)^2$ ? Is it ever true that
$$y^2 - x^2 = (y - x)^2 ?$$
Is it ever true that
$$y^2 - x^2 < (y - x)^2 ?$$
Experiment, and write a paragraph summarizing your work and your conclusions.

### CUTTING A SQUARE OUT OF A SQUARE

Problems 2-4 show how to model the difference of two squares geometrically.

**2.** Cut a 10-by-10 square out of graph paper. Then, out of the corner of this square, cut a 4-by-4 square. The remaining paper should look like this.

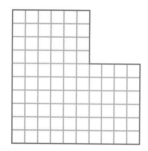

**3.** The size of the remaining paper represents the *difference* of the 10-by-10 square and the 4-by-4 square. Its area is $10^2 - 4^2$ square centimeters. How many square centimeters is this?

**4.** The odd-shaped figure you have left after cutting out the 4-by-4 square can be rearranged into a rectangle. You can do this by making a single cut in the paper. Try it. Sketch the resulting rectangle and label its length and width.

**5.** **Generalization** Repeat problems 2-4 for some other differences of squares. (For example, try cutting a 3-by-3 square out of a 7-by-7 square. Try several others.) Can the resulting shape always be rearranged into a rectangle, no matter what two numbers you use? Can you use fractions? What are the dimensions of the rectangle? If it can always be arranged into a rectangle, explain why. If not, explain when it is possible and when it is not possible. Give examples, using sketches.

### USING VARIABLES

Use the Lab Gear to do problems 6-9.

**6.** Trace the $x^2$-block on a piece of paper and cut out the square. Then trace a 1-by-1 square in the corner of the $x^2$-paper and cut it out. What difference is represented by the remaining paper?

**7.** Show how you can rearrange the remaining paper into a rectangle. Make a sketch showing the dimensions of the rectangle.

**8.** Repeat problems 6 and 7 for the following squares. You do not have to do the actual cutting unless you want to, but your sketches should be traced in the correct sizes.

   a. Cut a square having area 4 out of a square having area $x^2$.

   b. Cut a square having area $x^2$ out of a square having area $y^2$.

   c. Cut a square having area 9 out of a square having area $y^2$.

   d. Cut a square having area 25 out of a $y$-by-$y$ square.

**9.** Generalization Make a sketch showing what remains after a square having area $a^2$ has been cut out of a square having area $b^2$. Then show by sketching how this can be rearranged into a rectangle. What are the dimensions of this rectangle?

### FACTORING A DIFFERENCE OF SQUARES

When you cut a square out of a square, the area of the remaining paper is the *difference* of the two squares. When you rearrange this paper into a rectangle and write the area as *length · width,* you are writing this difference as a *product,* or factoring. Later in this course you will find this factoring technique helpful in solving equations.

**10.** Which of these is a difference of two squares?

   a. $4x^2 - 16y^2$

   b. $4x^2 + 16y^2$

   c. $(x - y)(x - y)$

   d. $(a - b)^2$

**11.** Write these differences as the product of two factors.

   a. $x^2 - 9$   b. $y^2 - 25$

   c. $25 - x^2$   d. $4x^2 - 16$

**12.** Factor.

   a. $9y^2 - 25$   b. $9 - 25x^2$

   c. $9y^2 - 25x^2$

**13.** Generalization In this lesson you found a technique for factoring a difference of two squares. However, in all the examples you have done, you have assumed that the first square was larger than the second. Does the pattern work if the first square is smaller than the second? That is, if $a$ is less than $b,$ is it still true that
$$a^2 - b^2 = (a - b)(a + b)?$$
Experiment, using some numbers, and explain your conclusions.

### REVIEW THE LAB GEAR MODEL

**14.** Use the corner piece to multiply $(y + 5)(y - 5)$. Remember to simplify.

**15.** Show $y^2 - 25$ with the Lab Gear. Show how you can add zero and rearrange the blocks so that the uncovered part forms a rectangle. What are the dimensions of the rectangle?

**16.** Explain how one can use the Lab Gear to factor

   a. $x^2 - 1$;   b. $y^2 - x^2$.

**17.** Summary Write a paragraph summarizing what you learned in this lesson about differences of squares. Use sketches and examples.

18. Arrange Lab Gear blocks to show a square having area $(x + 5)^2$.

    a. Using the blocks, remove a square having area $x^2$ out of the square having area $(x + 5)^2$, and rearrange the remaining blocks as a rectangle. Write its dimensions.

    b. Repeat part (a) and remove a square having area 25.

    c. What other squares can you remove from $(x + 5)^2$? Remove one, and rearrange the remaining blocks into a rectangle.

    d. Explain how parts (a), (b), and (c) are examples of the pattern you learned about earlier in this lesson.

19. Write each difference as a product of two factors.

    a. $(y + 4)^2 - y^2$
    b. $(y + 4)^2 - (y + 3)^2$
    c. $(y + 4)^2 - (y + 1)^2$

20. ◯ Factor. $(y + 2)^2 - (x + 5)^2$

---

**REVIEW** *SOLVING EQUATIONS*

Solve these equations using the cover-up method.

21. $\dfrac{5 - x}{7} = \dfrac{8}{14}$

22. $2 - \dfrac{x - 2}{3} = \dfrac{2}{3}$

23. $3 + \dfrac{2 + x}{5} = \dfrac{19}{5}$

24. $\dfrac{-7}{6} = \dfrac{x}{4}$

25. $6 - \dfrac{14}{x} = \dfrac{5}{2}$

26. $\dfrac{2 + x}{8} = \dfrac{5}{3}$

27. $\dfrac{1}{x} = 2$

28. $\dfrac{1 + x}{3} = \dfrac{2}{9}$

29. $\dfrac{4}{x} = 5$

30. $\dfrac{4}{x - 1} = 5$

31. $\dfrac{4}{3x - 1} = 5$

32. $\dfrac{4}{x + 4} = \dfrac{5}{6}$

# 7.A Cube Problems

## THE PAINTED CUBE

Lea made a cube by gluing together 27 Lab Gear 1-blocks.

1. Make a sketch of what this cube would look like. What are its dimensions?

Lea painted the cube red on all six sides. Later, Mary and Martin were annoyed when they discovered what Lea had done. They needed the 27 one-blocks to do a hard factoring problem. Besides, they didn't think she should have been gluing and painting Lab Gear blocks.

2. a. When Mary and Martin broke Lea's cube apart into the 27 original small cubes, how many of the 1-blocks did they find to be painted red on three sides?

   b. How many were painted red on only one side?

   c. How many were painted red on two sides?

   d. How many had no red paint on them?

3. Repeat problem 2 for a 4-by-4-by-4 cube.

4. **Report** Write a report about problems 2 and 3. It should include, but need not be limited to, the following:

   • Show how you solved problems 2 and 3. Include sketches.

   • Look for patterns in your answers. Use them to guess the answers for a cube of side 5 and a cube of side 6. How can you check whether or not you are right?

   • Make a generalization to an $n$-by-$n$-by-$n$ cube. Write expressions in terms of $n$ for the number of cubes with 0 sides painted, 1 side painted, 2 sides painted, and 3 sides painted. (Explain why the four expressions should add up to $n^3$, and check that they do.)

## CUBES IN CUBES

It is easy to see that there are 27 different 1-by-1-by-1 cubes in this 3-by-3-by-3 cube. It is harder to see how many different 2-by-2-by-2 cubes there are, because they overlap.

5. Figure out how many different 2-by-2-by-2 cubes there are in a 3-by-3-by-3 cube.

6. Think about a 4-by-4-by-4 cube. It contains how many

   a. 1-by-1-by-1 cubes?
   b. 2-by-2-by-2 cubes?
   c. 3-by-3-by-3 cubes?
   d. 4-by-4-by-4 cubes?
   e. cubes altogether?

7. Find how many cubes of each size there are in a 5-by-5-by-5 cube. Try to figure out a systematic way for counting the cubes.

8. **Report** Write a report about these cube problems. It should include, but not be limited to, the following:

   • Describe the strategy you used to answer problems 5, 6, and 7. Use sketches and explain your reasoning.

   • Make a generalization. In an $n$-by-$n$-by-$n$ cube, how many cubes of each size (1-by-1-by-1, 2-by-2-by-2, 3-by-3-by-3, and so on) would there be? Write expressions in terms of $n$.

   • Test your generalization by trying it for a 7-by-7-by-7 cube. How many smaller cubes of each size should there be, according to your generalization? If you add all these numbers, do you get the correct total of 784? Show your work.

# Remarkable Identities

**You will need:**

the Lab Gear

graph paper

graphing calculator (optional)

___REVIEW___ **MULTIPLYING PATTERNS**

**1.** Find these products.
   a. $(y - 3)(y + 3)$
   b. $(y + 5)(y - 5)$

**2.** ⚷ What is the pattern in problem 1?

**3.** Does the pattern still hold for $(2x - 1)(2x + 1)$? Explain.

**4.** Find these squares.
   a. $(y - 3)^2$     b. $(y - 5)^2$
   c. $(y + 3)^2$     d. $(y + 5)^2$

**5.** ⚷ What is the pattern in problem 4?

**6.** Does the pattern still hold for $(2x - 1)^2$ and $(2x + 1)^2$? Explain.

**THREE IDENTITIES**

**7.** True or False? The square of a sum is equal to the sum of the squares. Explain, using a sketch.

**8.** ⚷ Describe a shortcut for finding the square of a sum.

The expression $y^2 - x^2$ is the difference of squares. (Remember that shaded blocks are *upstairs.*)

The expression $(y - x)^2$ is the square of a difference.

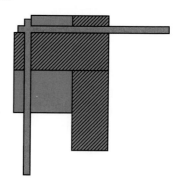

**9.** True or False? The square of a difference is equal to the difference of the squares. Explain.

**10.** ⚷ Describe a shortcut for finding the square of a difference.

**11.** Find the products.
   a. $(y + x)^2$
   b. $(y - x)^2$
   c. $(y - x)(y + x)$

As you know, identities are algebraic statements that are always true. The three that are shown in problem 11 are especially important and useful. You should memorize them. For example, using the second one,
$$(2x - 5)^2 = (2x)^2 - 2(2x)(5) + 5^2$$
$$= 4x^2 - 20x + 25.$$

**12.** Multiply by using one of the identities. You may check your answers with the Lab Gear or by setting up the multiplication as a table.
   a. $(3x - 2)^2$
   b. $(3x + 2)^2$
   c. $(3x - 2)(3x + 2)$

Even if you don't use the identities for multiplying, it is useful to memorize them in order to recognize them quickly when trying to factor a trinomial. Knowing them is also useful for understanding the solution of quadratic equations.

### A CASE OF MISTAKEN IDENTITY

Some of the most common mistakes of math students concern the identities you have learned about in this chapter. Even after having learned the identities, students often forget and write $(x + y)^2 = x^2 + y^2$ or $(x - y)^2 = x^2 - y^2$. This mistake causes math teachers to tear their hair in desperation.

13. **Report** Write an article or create a poster that you think would help other students avoid these mistakes. (Math teachers all over the world would greatly appreciate your help.) Include explanations, sketches, and examples. Make your article or poster appealing, eye-catching, or humorous so that other students will want to read it.

### FACTORING

14. Factor these trinomials.
   a. $9x^2 + 6x + 1$
   b. $x^2 - 6xy + 9y^2$
   c. $4x^2 + 4xy + y^2$
   d. $9x^2 - 25$
   e. $4x^2 - 4y^2$
   f. $a^2x^2 + 2acx + c^2$

15. Use the Lab Gear to make as many different rectangles as you can with $3x^2 + 12x + 12$. Write a product corresponding to each rectangle.

16. The figure below shows a box with a square base.
   a. Write an expression for the volume of the box in the form
      *Height · Area of Base.*
   b. Write an expression for the volume of the box in the form *Height · (Side)²*.

17. Each of these expressions gives the volume of a box that has a square base. For each one, write an expression of the form *Height · (Side)²*. You may want to use the Lab Gear.
   a. $3x^2 + 12x + 12$
   b. $8x^2 + 8x + 2$
   c. $3x^2 + 6xy + 3y^2$
   d. $2y^2 + 12y + 18$
   e. $xy^2 + 2xy + x$

18. Each of these polynomials gives the volume of a box that has a square base. For each one, write an expression of the form *Height · (Side)²*, without using the blocks. (Hint: The height of the blocks is the factor that is common to all three terms.)
   a. $27x^2 + 54x + 27$
   b. $60y^2 + 60y + 15$
   c. $50x^2 + 100xy + 50y^2$
   d. $16y^2 + 96y + 144$
   e. $6x^2y + 24xy + 24y$

### SQUARING TRINOMIALS

Do you think there is a pattern for the square of trinomials? Experiment with these problems.

**19.** $(x + y + 2)^2$

**20.** $(x + y - 5)^2$

**21.** Describe the pattern you discovered in problems 19 and 20.

**22.** What is $(a - b + c)^2$ equal to? Use the pattern you discovered, then check your answer by using the distributive law very carefully.

### CUBES OF SUMS

**23.** Find an identity for the cube of a sum. Lab Gear models using 3-D blocks may help. Explain why the cube of a sum is not the sum of the cubes.

### PUZZLE SUM OF SQUARES

**24.** ◯ $5x^2 + 20x + 25$

Think of the Lab Gear blocks representing this polynomial. The polynomial is not a perfect square, so you cannot rearrange it into a single square. However, it can be arranged into a *sum of squares*. Figure out how you would do it.

---

### REVIEW/PREVIEW  ALWAYS, SOMETIMES, OR NEVER TRUE?

**25.** On the same axes, graph $y = 12 - x$ and $y = 8 - x$.

**26.** Always, sometimes, or never true? (Explain your reasoning in each case.)
  a. $12 - x > 8 - x$
  b. $12 - x > 13$
  c. $8 - x > 12 - x$
  d. $4 > 8 - x$
  e. $-4 > 8 - x$

**27.** Always, sometimes, or never true? (If sometimes true, give the values of $x$ that make it true.)
  a. $x > 2x - 8$
  b. $2x - 5 > 2x - 8$
  c. $x < 2x - 5$

# How Many Solutions?

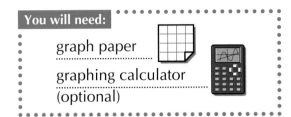

**You will need:**

graph paper

graphing calculator
(optional)

## LINEAR EQUATIONS

As you learned in Chapter 6, graphing is one way to find solutions to equations. For example, consider the equation $2x - 6 = -x$. This equation can be solved by graphing the lines $y = 2x - 6$ and $y = -x$ on the same axes.

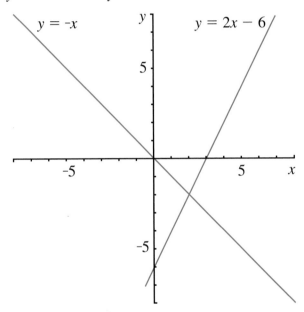

1.  a. From the graph above, estimate the point of intersection of the lines $y = 2x - 6$ and $y = -x$.

    b. Use algebra to solve the equation $2x - 6 = -x$.

2.  The linear equation $2x - 6 = 2x$ has *no solution*. Show that this is true by graphing the lines $y = 2x - 6$ and $y = 2x$. Explain how your graph shows that the equation has no solution.

3.  Tell how many solutions each equation has. Use graphs if necessary.
    a. $5x - 6 = 5x - 7$
    b. $5x - 6 = 0.5(10x - 12)$
    c. $5x - 6 = x$

4.  For all the equations in problem 3 that have one solution, find the solution.

5.  ⚷
    a. Write and solve a linear equation that has only one solution.
    b. Write a linear equation that has an infinite number of solutions.
    c. Write a linear equation that has no solution.

6.  ⚷ Is it possible for a linear equation to have two solutions? Three solutions? Explain your answers, using graphs if possible.

## QUADRATIC EQUATIONS

**Definition:** Second-degree equations are called *quadratic equations.*
**Example:** These are all quadratic equations.
$x^2 = 45$
$3x^2 - 15 = 6x + 2$
$6x^2 + 5x + 8 = 0$

You will learn several methods for solving quadratic equations. In this lesson, we will use graphing. Use a whole piece of graph paper for problems 7-11.

7.  Draw a pair of axes on a full page of graph paper. Show all four quadrants. Graph $y = x^2$ very carefully.

8.  On the same pair of axes, graph these lines and label them with their equations.
    a. $y = 6x - 12$
    b. $y = 6x - 9$
    c. $y = 6x - 5$

**9.** Label the point or points of intersection of each line with the graph of $y = x^2$.

One of the lines you drew touches the graph of $y = x^2$ at only one point.

┃ **Definition:** A line that touches a graph at only one point is *tangent* to the graph.

**10.** Which of the lines you drew is tangent to the graph of $y = x^2$ ?

**11.** Use the graphs to solve these equations.
   a. $x^2 = 6x - 12$
   b. $x^2 = 6x - 9$
   c. $x^2 = 6x - 5$

### HOW MANY INTERSECTIONS?

**12.** a. Draw a graph of $y = x^2$.
   b. On the same axes, draw a line that does not intersect $y = x^2$. Write the equation of the line.
   c. Repeat part (b) for another line that does not intersect $y = x^2$.

**13.** a. Draw a graph of $y = x^2$.
   b. On the same axes, draw a line that intersects $y = x^2$ at only one point. Write the equation of the line and label the point of intersection.
   c. Repeat part (b) for another line that intersects $y = x^2$ at only one point.

**14.** a. Draw a graph of $y = x^2$.
   b. On the same axes, draw a line that intersects $y = x^2$ at two points. Write the equation of the line and label the points of intersection.
   c. Repeat part (b) for another line that intersects $y = x^2$ at two points.

**15.** ⊷ Refer to your answers to problems 12-14. Use them to write and solve a quadratic equation that has
   a. one solution;
   b. two solutions;
   c. no solutions.

**16.** ◯ Use graphs to estimate the solutions to these equations.
   a. $x^2 = -6x - 11$
   b. $x^2 = -6x + 11$
   c. $-x^2 = 6x + 11$

**17.** ◯ Write the equation of a line that is tangent to $y = x^2$ at the point (-4, 16).

### WHICH GRAPH SHOULD YOU USE?

The solution of the equation $x^2 = 4$ can be found by graphing $y = x^2$ and $y = 4$ on the same pair of axes.

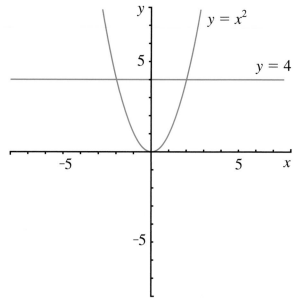

The equation $x^2 = 4$ can also be written as $x^2 - 4 = 0$. It can be solved by graphing $y = x^2 - 4$ and $y = 0$ on the same axes.

**18.** What is another name for the line $y = 0$?

As shown in the figure, the graphs intersect in two points. This means that the quadratic equation $x^2 = 4$ has two solutions.

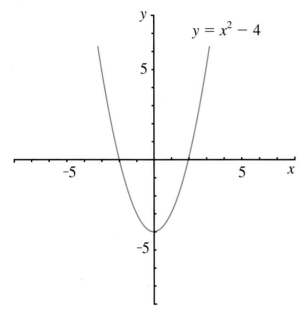

**19.** What are the two values of $x$ that satisfy the equation $x^2 = 4$? Where do they appear in each of the two graphs above?

**20.** Explain why all of these quadratic equations are equivalent.
$$x^2 = x + 6$$
$$x^2 - x = 6$$
$$x^2 - x - 6 = 0$$

**21.** Graph the parabola $y = x^2$ and the line $y = x + 6$ on the same pair of axes. Label the points of intersection.

**22.** Graph the parabola $y = x^2 - x$ and the line $y = 6$ on the same pair of axes. Label the points of intersection.

**23.** Graph the parabola $y = x^2 - x - 6$ and $y = 0$ on the same pair of axes. Label the points of intersection.

**24.** ⬥━ Compare your answers to problems 21-23.
a. What is the solution to the quadratic equation $x^2 - x - 6 = 0$?
b. Which of the three graphs do you think gave the easiest way to find the solution to this equation?

**25.** Find the solutions to these equations by graphing a parabola and a line on the same pair of axes. As you saw in problem 24, there may be more than one possible pair of graphs that can be used. You may use any pair that will work.
a. $x^2 = 3x + 4$
b. $x^2 - 5 = -4x$
c. $2x^2 = 18$

---

**DISCOVERY** **LAST DIGITS**

**26.** What is the last digit for each of these numbers: $0^{100}$, $1^{100}$, $2^{100}$, ..., $9^{100}$? Most of these numbers have too many digits for the last one to appear in your calculator, so you will have to figure out some other approach. (Hint: Try finding the last digits of smaller powers of these numbers.)

# LESSON 7.7 Equations With Squares

**You will need:**

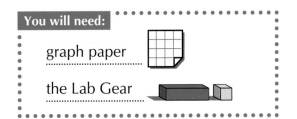

graph paper

the Lab Gear

This lesson is about solving equations. You will use two different methods to approach equations that involve the square of a binomial.

## GRAPHICAL SOLUTIONS

The graphs of $y = (x + 3)^2$ and $y = (x - 2)^2$ are shown below.

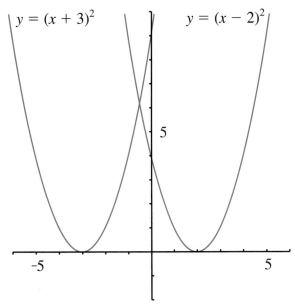

1. Explain why these two graphs never go below the *x*-axis. (Why is the value of *y* never negative?)

2. On a piece of graph paper, copy the two graphs. For more accuracy, calculate the coordinates of several points on each curve. Use the graphs to solve these equations.
   a. $(x + 3)^2 = 4$
   b. $(x - 2)^2 = 9$
   c. $(x - 2)^2 = 1$
   d. $(x + 3)^2 = -1$
   e. $(x - 2)^2 = 0$

3. Use your graphs to estimate the solutions to these equations.
   a. $(x + 3)^2 = 12$
   b. $(x - 2)^2 = 6$
   c. $(x - 2)^2 = -2$
   d. $(x + 3)^2 = 5$
   e. $(x + 3)^2 = (x - 2)^2$

4. ⚷
   a. Describe what you think the graphs of the functions $y = (x + 2)^2$ and $y = (x - 1)^2$ would look like. (Where would each one intersect the *x*-axis?)
   b. Check your guess by making tables of values and graphing the functions.

5. Use your graphs to find or estimate the solutions to these equations.
   a. $(x + 2)^2 = 9$
   b. $(x + 2)^2 = 2x + 3$
   c. $(x - 1)^2 = 5$
   d. $(x - 1)^2 = -x$

**EQUAL SQUARES**

The equation $x^2 = 25$ can be illustrated using the Lab Gear. Put out your blocks like this.

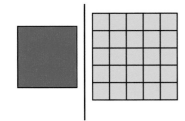

One way to get started with this equation is to remember that if the squares are equal, *their sides must be equal.* (This is true even though they don't look equal. Remember that $x$ can have any value.)

**6.** Solve the equation. If you found only one solution, think some more, because there are two.

**7.** Explain why there are two solutions.

**8.** Write the equation shown by this figure.

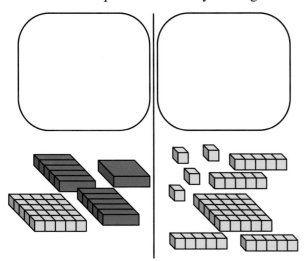

By rearranging the blocks, you can see that this is an *equal squares* problem, so it can be solved the same way. As you can see, $(x + 5)^2 = 7^2$. It follows that $x + 5 = 7$ or $x + 5 = -7$.

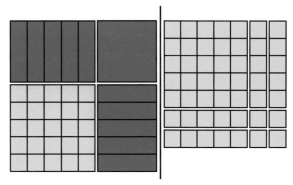

**9.** Solve the equation. There are two solutions. Check them both in the original equation.

Solve the equations 10-13 using the *equal squares* method. You do not have to use the actual blocks, but you can if you want to. Most equations, but not all, have two solutions.

**10.** $x^2 = 16$

**11.** $x^2 + 2x + 1 = 0$

**12.** $4x^2 = 36$

**13.** $4x^2 + 4x + 1 = 9$

Solve these equations without the blocks.

**14.** $4x^2 - 4x + 1 = -9$

**15.** $x^2 - 10x + 25 = 16$

**16.** $x^2 + 6x + 9 = 4x^2 - 4x + 1$

**17.** $-x^2 - 6x - 9 = -25$ (Hint: If quantities are equal, their opposites must be equal.)

**18.** ⟜ Explain why some problems had one, or no solution.

## 7.7

COMPARING METHODS

**19.** Summary

a. Compare the graphical method and the Lab Gear method for the solution of an equal-squares equation. Use examples that can be solved by both methods, and have 0, 1, and 2 solutions.

b. 💡 What is the meaning of the *x*-intercept in the graphical method? Where does that number appear in the Lab Gear method?

c. 💡 What is the meaning of the *x*- and *y*-coordinates of the intersections of the line and parabola in the graphical method? Where do these numbers appear in the Lab Gear method?

**20.** 💡 Create an equal-squares equation that has two solutions that are not whole numbers. Solve it.

---

**REVIEW** *FACTORING PRACTICE*

Factor these polynomials. One is difficult, one is impossible. The Lab Gear may help for some of the problems.

**21.** $xy + 6y + y^2$    **22.** $y^2 - 16$

**23.** $3x^2 + 13x - 10$  **24.** $4x^2 + 8x + 4$

**25.** $2x^2 + 2x + 1$    **26.** $y^2 - 5y + 6$

**27.** $y^2 - 4y + 4$     **28.** $x^2 + 8x + 12$

**REVIEW** *MULTIPLICATION PRACTICE*

You can multiply polynomials without the Lab Gear and without a table. Picture the table in your mind, and make sure you fill all its spaces. For example, to multiply

$$(2 - x)(7 - 3x + 5y)$$

you would need a 2-by-3 table. To fill the six cells of the table, you would multiply the 2 by 7, by -3*x*, and by 5*y*. Then you would multiply the -*x* by 7, by -3*x*, and by 5*y*. Finally, you

would combine like terms. While you think of the six cells of the table, what you actually write on paper looks like this.

$$(2 - x)(7 - 3x + 5y)$$
$$= 14 - 6x + 10y - 7x + 3x^2 - 5xy$$
$$= 14 - 13x + 10y + 3x^2 - 5xy$$

**29.** Look at the example above, and make sure you understand where each term came from.

Multiply these polynomials without using a table. Combine like terms.

**30.** a. $(2x - y)(y + 3x)$
 b. $(x - 5y)(3x + 2y)$
 c. $(ac - b)(2b + 2ac)$
 d. $(ab - c)(b - c^2)$

**31.** a. $(2x - y + 4)(5 - y)$
 b. $(2x^2 - y + 4)(5y - x^2)$
 c. $(2x - y^2 + 4)(5y - x^2)$
 d. $(a + b + c)(2a + 3b + 4c)$

# Power Play

## RAFFLE TICKETS

Erin is a senior at Alaberg High School and the director of the senior class play. To help pay for sets and costumes, she plans to raise money through a raffle. She is considering several plans for selling raffle tickets.

Erin's first idea was to have members of each class sell raffle tickets to the class below them. Erin would sell tickets to three 11th graders. Each of them would sell tickets to three 10th graders, who in turn would each sell tickets to three 9th graders, and so on. Erin started to draw a tree-diagram of her plan.

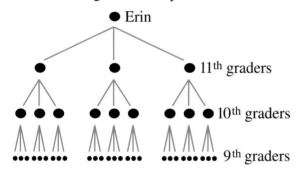

1. If Erin extended her plan all the way down to first grade, how many first graders would be buying tickets? Explain.

2. Make a table like the one following showing how many tickets would be bought by students in each grade. (The first entry in the table is based on the assumption that Erin bought one ticket for herself.) In the last column, express the number of tickets as a power of 3.

| Grade | Tickets (number) | Tickets (as a power of 3) |
|-------|------------------|---------------------------|
| 12th  | 1                |                           |
| 11th  | 3                | $3^1$                     |
| ...   |                  |                           |
| 1st   |                  |                           |

3. Give several reasons why Erin's plan is not practical.

## THE EXPONENT ZERO

The last column in your table above contained increasing powers of 3.

4. a. To follow the pattern, what should the exponent on the first power in the table be?

   b. Based on that pattern, what should $3^0$ be equal to?

5. a. Copy and complete this table.

| | |
|---|---|
| $5^5$ | 3125 |
| $5^4$ | |
| $5^3$ | |
| $5^2$ | |
| $5^1$ | |

   b. As you move down the columns, how can you get the next row from the previous one?

   c. Add another row to the bottom of the table. Explain how it fits the pattern.

**6.** Generalization You have found the values of $3^0$ and $5^0$. Using patterns in the same way, find the values of $2^0$ and $4^0$. What generalization can you make? ∎

**7.** Summary Many people think that a number raised to the zero power should be zero. Write a few sentences explaining why this is not true. ∎

## A BETTER PLAN

Erin needs a better scheme for selling raffle tickets. She decides to enlist the help of other seniors in the play. Each senior (including Erin) will buy a ticket for himself or herself, and sell a ticket to three juniors; each of the juniors will sell a ticket to three sophomores; and so on, down to the 8th grade.

Four more seniors help out:

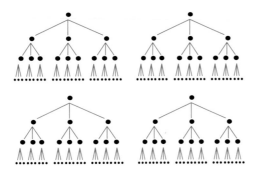

**8.** Assume Erin gets five seniors to help (including herself).

   a. How many 8th graders would buy tickets?

   b. How is this number related to the number of 8th graders who would buy tickets if Erin does not get any other seniors to help?

c. Express the answer to (a) as a number times a power of 3. Explain.

**9.** If Erin gets $K$ seniors to help (including herself), how many 8th graders would buy tickets? Express the answer in terms of $K$.

**10.** Assume five seniors are involved, including Erin. As before, each student at every step buys one ticket, but now each student sells two tickets instead of three.

   a. How many 8th graders would buy tickets?

   b. Express the answer to (a) as a number times a power. Should you use a power of 2, a power of 3, or a power of 5? Explain your answer.

**11.** ⟜ Assume $K$ seniors are involved and each student sells $M$ tickets.

   a. How many 8th graders would buy tickets? Express your answer in terms of $K$ and $M$.

   b. 💡 How many Nth graders would buy tickets? Express your answer in terms of $K$, $M$, and $N$.

**12.** Exploration Erin hopes to sell 1500 tickets altogether. Find several values for $K$ (the number of seniors) and $M$ (the number of tickets sold per person) that make it possible to sell at least 1500 tickets, without going below 7th grade. For each plan, indicate the number of students who would be involved at each grade level. Which of those plans do you think is the most realistic? ∎

REVIEW **WHICH IS GREATER?**

**13.** Which is greater?

  a. $5 \cdot 3^{35}$ or $3 \cdot 5^{35}$

  b. $5 \cdot 30^{35}$ or $30 \cdot 5^{35}$

  c. $5 \cdot 300^{35}$ or $300 \cdot 5^{35}$

**14.** Which is greater?

  a. $5^{35} \cdot 3^{35}$ or $15^{35}$

  b. $35^0$ or $0^{35}$

**15.** ⌐━ If $a$ and $b$ are each greater than 1, which is greater, $(ab)^{10}$ or $ab^{10}$? Explain.

REVIEW **A COMMUTATIVE LAW?**

Al announced, "I noticed that $4^2 = 2^4$ and $3^2 = 2^3$, so I generalized this using algebra to say $a^b = b^a$, always."

"That's a great discovery," said Beau. "This means that exponentiation is commutative!"

"Nice try, Al," said Cal. "It's true that $4^2$ and $2^4$ are both 16, but $3^2$ is 9 and $2^3$ is 8. They aren't equal."

Al was disappointed. "Round-off error," he muttered. "Close enough."

**16.** What did Beau mean when she said that exponentiation is commutative? Is she right or wrong? Explain, using examples to support your answer.

**17.** Is $4^2 = 2^4$ the only case where $a^b = b^a$? If it is, how can you be sure? If it isn't, how can you find others?

**18.** Exploration Which is greater, $a^b$ or $b^a$? Of course, the answer to this question depends on the values of $a$ and $b$. Experiment, and try to make some generalizations.

REVIEW/PREVIEW **CHUNKING**

**19.** Solve for $y$: $y^2 = 49$. (Remember there are two solutions.)

You can use the strategy of chunking to solve equations involving squares. For example, in problem 20, think of $(x + 3)$ as a chunk, and write two linear equations.

Solve.

**20.** $(x + 3)^2 = 49$

**21.** $(2p - 5)^2 = 49$

**22.** $(5 - 2p)^2 = 49$

**23.** $(6 + 2r)^2 = 49$

# 7.B Graphing Inequalities

## COMPOUND INEQUALITIES

**Definition:** An inequality that contains more than one inequality symbol is called a *compound inequality.*

**Example:** $3 < 2x < 8$ is read *2x is between 3 and 8.*

The figure shows the graphs of the line $y = 2x - 4$ and the horizontal lines $y = 2$ and $y = -2$.

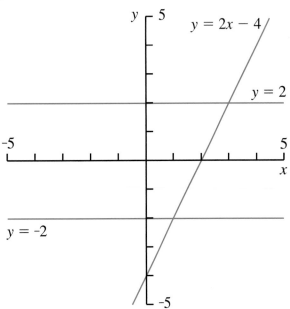

1. What are the coordinates of the points of intersection of $y = 2x - 4$ with each of the horizontal lines?

2. Look only at the part of the line $y = 2x - 4$ that is between the lines $y = 2$ and $y = -2$.
   a. Give the coordinates of some of the points on this part of the line.
   b. On this part of the line, how large can the $y$-coordinate get? How small?
   c. On this part of the line, how large can the $x$-coordinate get? How small?

We say that the *solution* of the compound inequality $-2 < 2x - 4 < 2$ is
$$1 < x < 3.$$
Notice that the solution is also a compound inequality, but it is simpler than the original one. It tells us what values of $x$ make the first inequality true.

3. Explain how the graph above can be used to show that the solution to the inequality is $1 < x < 3$.

4. a. Graph the horizontal lines $y = 3$, $y = 8$, and $y = 3x + 5$.
   b. Use your graph to find the solution of the compound inequality
$$3 < 3x + 5 < 8.$$

## QUADRATIC INEQUALITIES

Sometimes an inequality is not compound, but it has a compound solution. An example is the inequality $x^2 < 4$. The two graphs shown can be used to solve this inequality.

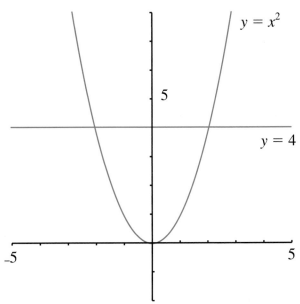

**5.** Look at the part of the graph of $y = x^2$ that is below the graph of $y = 4$.

 a. Give the coordinates of four points that lie on this part of the graph.

 b. On this part of the curve, how large can the $x$-coordinate get? How small?

 c. Write the solution to this inequality.

**6.** The same graph can also be used to solve the inequality $x^2 > 4$. In this case, the solution cannot be written as a compound inequality. Instead it is written in two parts,

$$x < -2 \text{ or } x > 2.$$

Explain why the solution has two parts.

**7.** On the same pair of axes, make an accurate graph of $y = x^2$, $y = 1$, and $y = 9$. Use your graphs to solve these inequalities.

 a. $x^2 < 9$    b. $x^2 > 9$

 c. $x^2 < 1$    d. $x^2 > 1$

 e. $1 < x^2 < 9$

**8.** Use the graph to estimate the solution to

$$x^2 > 5.$$

**9.** Solve these without a graph.

 a. $x^2 < 16$    b. $x^2 > 16$

 c. $x^2 > 0$    d. $x^2 < 0$

**10.** Report Write an illustrated report summarizing what you have learned in this assignment. Use examples, including at least one quadratic, and at least one compound, inequality.

# LESSON
## 7.9

# Powers and Large Numbers

Powers provide a shorthand for writing large numbers. Just as multiplication is repeated addition, raising to a power is repeated multiplication. For example,

$$12 \cdot 12 \cdot 12 \cdot 12 \cdot 12 \cdot 12,$$

which equals 2,985,984, can be written $12^6$. Not only is this shorter to write than either the repeated multiplication or the decimal number, it is shorter to key into a scientific calculator.

**Notation:** Calculators use $\boxed{\wedge}$, $\boxed{x^y}$, or $\boxed{y^x}$ for *exponentiation* (raising to a power). We will use $\boxed{\wedge}$ to refer to that key.

Calculators can calculate with exponents that are not positive whole numbers. For example, it is possible to get a value for a number like $3^{-2.4}$ using the key for powers on your calculator. (Try it.) In this lesson, you will consider only *positive whole numbers* for exponents. In later chapters, you will use other exponents.

### APPROXIMATING LARGE NUMBERS

1. **Exploration** Consider the number 123,456. Use your calculator to approximate the number as closely as you can with a power of 2, a power of 3, a power of 9, and a power of 10. How close can you get with each power? Repeat this experiment with four other numbers. (Use the same numbers as other students, so as to be able to compare your answers. Use only positive whole numbers having six or more digits.) Is it possible to get close to most large numbers by raising small numbers to a power?

For problems 2-4 find the powers of the following numbers (a-d), that are immediately below and above the given numbers.

a. 2          b. 3
c. 9          d. 10

**Example:** 691,737 (the population of Virginia, the most heavily populated state in 1790) is:
a. between $2^{19}$ and $2^{20}$
b. between $3^{12}$ and $3^{13}$
c. between $9^6$ and $9^7$
d. between $10^5$ and $10^6$

2. 3,929,214 (the population of the United States in 1790)

3. 48,881,221 (the number of people who voted for President Bush in 1988)

4. 178,098,000 (approximate number of Americans aged 18 or older in 1988)

### CLOSER APPROXIMATIONS

It is possible to combine powers with multiplication to get approximations that are closer than those you were able to get in the previous sections by using only powers. For example, the speed of light is approximately 186,282 miles per second. This number is more than $2^{17}$ and less than $2^{18}$, since

$$2^{17} = 131,072 \text{ and } 2^{18} = 262,144.$$

By multiplying 131,072 by a number less than 2, it is possible to get quite close to 186, 282.

$1.2 \cdot 131,072 = 157,286.4$ (too small)
$1.5 \cdot 131,072 = 196,608$ (too large)
$1.4 \cdot 131,072 = 183,500.8$ (too small, but pretty close)

5.  We showed that the speed of light can be roughly approximated by multiplying $2^{17}$ by 1.4. Find an even better approximation by changing the number by which you multiply, using more places after the decimal point.

You can approximate the speed of light in many different ways using powers of 2. For example:

$$93141 \cdot 2^1 = 186{,}282$$
$$46570 \cdot 2^2 = 186{,}280$$
$$23280 \cdot 2^3 = 186{,}240$$
$$45.5 \cdot 2^{12} = 186{,}368$$

We used $2^{17}$ in the example instead of some other power of 2 because it is the *largest* power of 2 that is less than 186,282. We approximated 186,282 by *multiplying that power of 2, by a number between 1 and 2.*

6.  Write an approximation to the speed of light using a power of 3 multiplied by a number between 1 and 3. (Hint: Begin by finding the largest power of 3 that is less than 186,282.)

7.  Write an approximation to the speed of light using a power of 9 multiplied by a number between 1 and 9.

8.  Write an approximation to the speed of light using a power of 10 multiplied by a number between 1 and 10.

9.  Combine a power and multiplication to get a close approximation to the length of the Earth's equator, which is 24,902 miles, to the nearest mile. You can use any base for the power, but multiply the power by a number between 1 and the base.

NAMES FOR LARGE NUMBERS

10. Write 100 and 1000 as powers of 10.

There are common names for some of the powers of ten. *Billion* in the U.S. means $10^9$, but in Britain it means $10^{12}$. The table gives the common names used in the U.S. for some powers of ten.

| Power | Name |
|---|---|
| $10^6$ | million |
| $10^9$ | billion |
| $10^{12}$ | trillion |
| $10^{15}$ | quadrillion |
| $10^{18}$ | quintillion |
| $10^{21}$ | sextillion |
| $10^{100}$ | googol |

11. ⌐— Someone might think a billion is two millions, and a trillion is three millions. In fact, a billion is how many millions? A trillion is how many millions? Explain.

SCIENTIFIC NOTATION

**Definition:** To write a number in *scientific notation* means to write it as a power of 10 multiplied by a number between 1 and 10. This is the most common way of writing large numbers in science and engineering.

12. ⌐— Explain why 10 is used for the base in scientific notation rather than some other number. Use examples.

## ▼ 7.9

**13.** Write in scientific notation.

   a. one million

   b. 67 million (the average distance from the sun to Venus in miles)

   c. 5.3 billion (an estimate of the world's population in 1990)

   d. twenty billion

   e. 3.1 trillion (the U.S. national debt in dollars as of June 1990)

   f. three hundred trillion

**14.** **Project** Find four large numbers that measure some real quantity. They should all be larger than 100,000,000. Encyclopedias, almanacs, and science books are good sources of such numbers.

   a. Tell what each number measures.

   b. Write the number in scientific notation.

---

### REVIEW   PRIME NUMBERS

There is only one polyomino rectangle of area 2, and only one of area 3. But there are two polyomino rectangles of area 4, corresponding to the products $2 \cdot 2 = 4$ and $1 \cdot 4 = 4$.

**15.** What is the smallest number that is the area of a polyomino rectangle in 3 different ways? Sketch the three rectangles and show the products.

**16.** Repeat the problem for 4 different ways.

**17.** Can you predict the smallest number that is the area of a polyomino rectangle in 5 different ways? Check your prediction.

> **Definition:** Numbers greater than 1 that can only make a rectangle with whole number dimensions in one way are called *prime numbers.*

**18.** Here is an ancient method, (invented by the Greek mathematician Eratosthenes,) of finding the prime numbers.

   a. On a list of numbers from 1 to 100, cross out the 1.

   Circle 2, cross out its multiples.

   Circle the first number that is not crossed out, cross out its multiples. Repeat, until all the numbers are either crossed out or circled.

   b. Explain how and why this method works to find the prime numbers.

**19.** A mathematician once suggested that *every even number greater than 2 may be the sum of two prime numbers.* No one knows why this should be true, but it has worked for every number that's ever been tried. Test this for yourself with at least ten even numbers. (This is known as *Goldbach's conjecture.* A conjecture is a guess that has not yet been proved true or false.)

# Using Scientific Notation

## WITH A CALCULATOR

Calculators can display numbers only up to a certain number of digits. For many calculators, ten digits is the limit.

**1.** What is the limit for your calculator?

**2.** What is the smallest power of 2 that forces your calculator into scientific notation?

On many calculators, the answer to problem 2 is $2^{34}$ which, according to the calculator, is equal to

$\boxed{1.717986918^{10}}$ or $\boxed{1.717986918\text{E}10}$ .

The expression on the left does *not* mean $1.717986918^{10}$, even though that's what it looks like. It is just calculator shorthand for $1.717986918 \cdot 10^{10}$. The actual value is 17179869184, which is too long to fit, so the calculator gives the approximate value of 17179869180, expressed in scientific notation. (For a number this large, this represents a very small error.)

**3.** Which power of 2 is displayed as $\boxed{2.814749767\text{E}14}$ ?

**4.** Find a power of 4 and a power of 8 that are also displayed as $\boxed{2.814749767\text{E}14}$ .

**5.** Find powers of 3, 9, 27, and 81 that are displayed in scientific notation, in the form ____ $\cdot 10^{17}$. If possible, find more than one solution for each number.

There are three ways to enter numbers in scientific notation into your calculator. For example, to enter $2 \cdot 10^3$, you can key in 2 $\boxed{*}$ 10 $\boxed{\wedge}$ 3, or 2 $\boxed{*}$ $\boxed{10^x}$ 3, or (depending on the calculator) 2 $\boxed{\text{EE}}$ 3, or 2 $\boxed{\text{EXP}}$ 3. We will refer to this last key as $\boxed{\text{EE}}$ .

**6.** Try all the methods listed that are available on your calculator. In each case, the calculator should respond with $\boxed{2000}$ after you press $\boxed{=}$ or $\boxed{\text{ENTER}}$.

**7.** ☞ Explain the purpose of the $\boxed{\wedge}$ and $\boxed{\text{EE}}$ keys. How are they different?

## HOW MUCH FARTHER, HOW MANY TIMES AS FAR?

The table shows the ten brightest objects in the sky, and their *average* distances from Earth, in miles. (The objects are listed in order of average brightness as seen from Earth.)

|          | Distance        |
|----------|-----------------|
| Sun      | $9.29(10^7)$    |
| Moon     | $2.39(10^5)$    |
| Venus    | $9.30(10^7)$    |
| Jupiter  | $4.84(10^8)$    |
| Sirius   | $5.11(10^{13})$ |
| Canopus  | $5.76(10^{14})$ |
| Arcturus | $2.12(10^{14})$ |
| Mars     | $1.42(10^8)$    |
| Vega     | $1.59(10^{14})$ |
| Saturn   | $8.88(10^8)$    |

**8.** If you were to divide the objects into two groups, based only on the value of the exponents of 10, what would be in each group? What is the actual significance of the two groups?

For each pair of objects given in problems 9-13, answer questions (a) and (b). If an answer is greater than 10,000, give it in scientific notation.

  a. The second object is *how many miles* farther from Earth than the first?
  b. The second object is *how many times* as far from Earth as the first?

**9.** The Moon, Venus

**10.** The Moon, Saturn

**11.** The Sun, Sirius

**12.** The Sun, Canopus

**13.** Sirius, Canopus

WITHOUT A CALCULATOR

**14.** Convert these numbers to ordinary decimal notation and add them without a calculator.

  a. $(4 \cdot 10^7) + (5 \cdot 10^6)$
  b. $(40 \cdot 10^6) + (5 \cdot 10^6)$

**15.** ⊶ Compare the two computations in problem 14. Which would have been easy to do without converting to ordinary decimal notation? Explain.

Without a calculator it is not easy to add and subtract in scientific notation. One way is to revert to ordinary decimal notation. Another is to write the two quantities with a common exponent for 10, as was done in problem 14b.

**16.** Add or subtract.

  a. $6.2 \cdot 10^3 + 5 \cdot 10^6$
  b. $6.2 \cdot 10^6 - 5 \cdot 10^3$
  c. $6.2 \cdot 10^5 + 5 \cdot 10^3$
  d. $6.2 \cdot 10^3 - 5 \cdot 10^6$

Without a calculator it can be tedious to multiply and divide large numbers. However, if the numbers are written in scientific notation it is easy to estimate the size of the answer.

For the following problems, 17-20:

  a. Convert the numbers to ordinary decimal notation.
  b. Multiply or divide.
  c. Write your answers in scientific notation.

**17.** $(3 \cdot 10^5) \cdot (6 \cdot 10^3)$

**18.** $(3 \cdot 10^3) \cdot (6 \cdot 10^5)$

**19.** $(6 \cdot 10^6) \div (3 \cdot 10^3)$

**20.** $(3 \cdot 10^6) \div (6 \cdot 10^3)$

---

**PREVIEW** *MULTIPLICATION AND EXPONENTS*

**21.** ◯
  a. In each of problems 17-20, look for a relationship between your answer and the original numbers. How could you have obtained your answer without converting from scientific notation?
  b. Explain a shortcut for multiplying and dividing numbers in scientific notation. Include an explanation of what happens to the exponent of 10.

**22.** ◯ Does the shortcut, described in problem 21b, work for multiplying $3(2^4)$ by $5(2^6)$? Explain, giving several examples of this type.

**REVIEW** *PERFECT SQUARE TRINOMIALS*

**23.** All of these are perfect square trinomials. Write each one as the square of a binomial.
  a. $c^2x^2 + 2bcxy + b^2y^2$
  b. $y^2 + 2xy + x^2$
  c. $y^2 + 2by + b^2$
  d. $0.25x^2 + 0.2x + 0.04$

# Using Large Numbers

## TRAVELING IN THE SOLAR SYSTEM

The table below gives the diameter and average distance from the Sun in kilometers (km) of each of the planets in the solar system. The Sun's diameter is also shown.

| | Diameter | Distance from Sun | Moons |
|---|---|---|---|
| Sun | $1.39(10^6)$ | | |
| Mercury | $4.88(10^3)$ | 57,700,000 | 0 |
| Venus | $1.21(10^4)$ | 108,150,000 | 0 |
| Earth | $1.23(10^4)$ | 150,000,000 | 1 |
| Mars | $6.79(10^3)$ | 227,700,000 | 2 |
| Jupiter | $1.43(10^5)$ | 778,300,000 | 17 |
| Saturn | $1.20(10^5)$ | 1,427,000,000 | 22 |
| Uranus | $5.18(10^4)$ | 2,870,000,000 | 15 |
| Neptune | $4.95(10^4)$ | 4,497,000,000 | 3 |
| Pluto | $6.00(10^3)$ | 5,900,000,000 | 1 |

1.  Convert the diameters to normal decimal notation.

2.  Convert the distances to scientific notation.

3.  Divide the planets into groups according to:
    a.  their diameters. How many groups are there? Explain.
    b.  their distance from the Sun. How many groups are there? Explain.
    c.  their number of moons. How many groups are there? Explain.

4.  Compare the groups you created in problem 3. Find a way to combine your decisions into an overall division of the planets into two or three groups, by *type of planet*. Name each group, and list its characteristics in terms of the data in the table.

5.  Light travels approximately 299,793 kilometers per second. Show your calculations, and give your answers in scientific notation. How far does light travel in
    a.  one minute?   b.  one hour?
    c.  one day?      d.  one year?

6.  Abe remembers learning in elementary school that it takes about eight minutes for light to travel from the Sun to the Earth. Figure out whether he remembers correctly. Show your calculations.

7.  Light from the Sun takes more than one day to reach which planets, if any?

8.  When Pluto is at its mean distance from the Sun, how long does it take light from the Sun to reach it?

9.  An *Astronomical Unit* is the distance from the Earth to the Sun. What is Pluto's distance from the Sun in Astronomical Units?

## SCALE MODELS

10. Make a scale drawing showing the distances of the planets from the Sun. Tell what your scale is, and explain why you chose it.

### Project

11. Decide what would be a good scale for a scale model of the solar system, so you could fit the model in your classroom. How large would each planet be? How far would each planet be from the Sun?

**12.** Decide what would be a good scale for a scale model of the solar system, so you could clearly see even the smallest planet. How far would each planet be from the Sun? How large would each planet be? What objects could you use to represent the planets?

**13.** Using a map of your town, figure out where you might place the planets and the Sun. Use the scale you calculated in problem 12.

**14.** The nearest star, Alpha Centauri, is 40 trillion kilometers away from the Sun. Where would it be in your model?

### DOWN TO EARTH

**15.** In 1986 people in the U.S. threw away about 64.7 million tons of paper and cardboard. Write this number in scientific notation.

The number 64.7 million is too large to mean anything to most people. The following problems illustrate some ways of bringing large numbers "down to earth."

For example, to understand how much paper and cardboard was thrown away in the U.S. in 1986, it helps to figure out how much was thrown away *per person.*

Since there are 2000 pounds in a ton, 64.7 million tons is

$(6.47 \cdot 10^7 \text{ tons}) \cdot (2 \cdot 10^3 \text{ lbs/ton})$
$= 12.94 \cdot 10^{10} \text{ lbs.}$

**16.** The U.S. population in 1986 was about 240 million people. Write this number in scientific notation. Then calculate how many pounds of paper and cardboard were thrown away *per person.*

**17.** The distance around the equator of the Earth is about 24,900 miles. Al bikes to and from school every day, about five miles each way. Biking back and forth to school, about how many school years would it take Al to cover the distance around the equator? (A school year has about 180 days.)

**18.** Biking back and forth to school, about how many school years would it take Al to cover
   a. the distance from the Earth to the moon?
   b. the distance from the Earth to the Sun?

**19.** The population of the U.S. was about 250 million in 1990. Approximately $5 \cdot 10^{11}$ cigarettes were smoked in the U.S.
   a. About how many cigarettes were smoked *per person?*
   b. About how many were smoked *per person, per day?*
   c. If 186 million U.S. residents did not smoke any cigarettes, how many cigarettes were smoked *per smoker, per day?*

# As the Crow Flies

**You will need:**

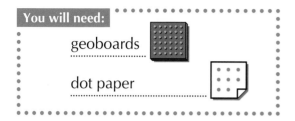

geoboards

dot paper

## SQUARE ROOTS

As you know, the square of a number is the area of a square that has that number for a side. For example, the square of 4 is 16, because a square having side 4 has area 16.

**1.** a. What is the area of a square having side 9?

b. What is the side of a square having area 9?

**2.** a. What is the area of a square having side 10?

b. What is the side of a square having area 10?

You can answer question 2b with the help of a calculator, by using trial and error. Or, you may answer it by using the $\boxed{\sqrt{\phantom{x}}}$ key.

**Definition:** The *square root* of a number is the side of a square that has that number for area.

For example, the square root of 4 is 2, because a square having area 4 has side 2.

**3.** a. What is the square of 11?

b. What is the square root of 11?

The square root of 11 is written $\sqrt{11}$. The number given by a calculator is an approximation of the exact value. Many calculators have an $\boxed{x^2}$ key.

**4.** ⚷ Use the $\boxed{x^2}$ key to calculate the square of 8.76. Write it down. Clear your calculator. Now use the $\boxed{\sqrt{\phantom{x}}}$ key to find the square root of the number. What answer did you get? Explain why this is so.

**5.** ⚷ Find a number for $\sqrt{5}$. Write it down. Now clear your calculator, enter the number, and use the $\boxed{x^2}$ key. What answer did you get? Compare your answer with other students' answers. Explain.

**6.** ⚷ Which number has more digits, $\sqrt{10.3041}$ or $\sqrt{2}$? Make a prediction and check it with your calculator. Explain your answer.

## DISTANCE ON THE GEOBOARD

To find the distance between two points on the geoboard, *as the crow flies,* you can use the following strategy.

- Make a square that has the two points as consecutive vertices.
- Find the area of the square.
- Find the side of the square.

In problems 7-9, express your answers two ways: as a square root, and as a decimal approximation (unless the answer is a whole number).

**Example:** Find the distance between (1, 0) and (0, 1).

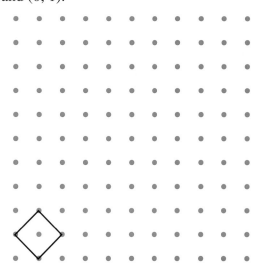

The area of the square is 2, so the distance between the two points is √2, or 1.41…

7. Find the distance between:
   a. (4, 3) and (6, 7);
   b. (4, 6) and (6, 4);
   c. (4, 5) and (4, 8).

8. Find the distance between the origin and (3, 1).

9. Find the distance between (5, 5) and (8, 9).

10. a. Find 12 geoboard pegs that are at a distance 5 from (5, 5). Connect them with a rubber band. Sketch the figure.
    b. Explain why someone might call that figure a *geoboard circle*.

11. How many geoboard pegs are there whose distance from (5, 5) is
    a. greater than 5?
    b. less than 5?

12. Choose a peg outside the *circle* and find its distance from (5, 5).

13. Find all the geoboard pegs whose distances from (4, 3) and (6, 7) are equal. Connect them with a rubber band. Sketch.

14. What are the distances between the pegs you found in problem 13 and (4, 3) or (6, 7)?

15. Generalization Describe a method for finding the distance between the origin and a point with coordinates $(x, y)$. Use a sketch and algebraic notation.

---

**DISCOVERY** *SUMS OF PERFECT SQUARES*

16. Any whole number can be written as a sum of perfect squares. Write each whole number from 1 to 25 as a sum of squares, using *as few squares as possible* for each one. (For example, $3^2 + 1^2$ is a better answer for 10 than $2^2 + 2^2 + 1^2 + 1^2$.)

17. 💡 You should have been able to write every number in problem 16 as a sum of *four or fewer* perfect squares. Do you think this would remain possible for large numbers? For very large numbers? Experiment with a few large numbers, such as 123, or 4321.

**DISCOVERY** *SUMS OF POWERS*

18. Write every whole number from 1 to 30 as a sum of powers of 2. Each power of 2 cannot be used more than once for each number. Do you think this could be done with very large numbers? Try it for 100.

19. Write every whole number from 1 to 30 as a sum of powers of 3 and their opposites. Each power can appear only once for each number. Do you think this could be done with very large numbers? Try it for 100.

Scientific notation will help you think about these two very large numbers.

one googol = 10,000,000,000,000,000,000,
000,000,000,000,000,000,000,000,000,000,
000,000,000,000,000,000,000,000,000,000,
000,000,000,000,000,000,000

1. How many zeroes does it take to write one googol? (Count them!)

one googolplex = 1 followed by one googol zeroes

2. Guess how large a sheet of paper one would need to write one googol zeroes.
   a. a sheet the size of a table?
   b. a sheet the size of a room?
   c. a sheet the size of a school?
   d. a sheet the size of a city?

3. Let's assume a zero takes up one square centimeter. How many zeroes could you fit on a piece of paper having area
   a. one square meter? (There are 100 centimeters in a meter. Use a sketch to figure out how many square centimeters in a square meter. Hint: There are more than 100 square centimeters in a square meter.)
   b. one square kilometer? (There are 1000 meters in a kilometer.)

   | **Notation:** cm$^2$ stands for square centimeter; km$^2$ for square kilometer.

4. a. The area of California is 4($10^5$) km$^2$. How many zeroes could fit on a sheet of paper this size?
   b. The area of the United States is nearly $10^7$ km$^2$. How many zeroes could fit on a sheet this size?

5. 30,000 sheets of thin paper make a pile one meter high. How many zeroes could be in such a pile, if each sheet is the size of the United States?

6. a. The moon is less than 4($10^5$) km away. How many zeroes, if our pile of paper extended that far?
   b. The sun is 1.5($10^8$) km away. How many zeroes, if our pile extended that far?
   c. The nearest star is 4($10^{13}$) km away. How many zeroes, if our pile extended that far?

7. What fraction of the total number of zeroes does our pile include?

8. Report  Write a report summarizing your answers to problems 3-6 above. Show your calculations and include any sketches that were useful in figuring out answers. Explain your reasoning. Then show how to figure out the correct answer to problem 2.

9. Project  Where in the universe would our pile of papers end if it did include one googol zeroes?

The word *googol* was created in 1938 by the eleven-year-old nephew of the American mathematician Edward Kasner. In one sense, a googolplex is the largest number that has a name. But in fact, even without creating any new names, you can name larger numbers. For example, the words *two googolplex* name a larger number.

10. What is the largest nameable number? Explain your reasoning.

# ◆ Essential Ideas

The window panes referred to below are those pictured in Lesson 2 of this chapter.

1. Sketch a window having length equal to twice its width that is made up of panes from the A.B. Glare Co. How many panes of each type (corner, edge, and inside) are there?

Use sketches or tables of values to help solve the following problem.

2. How many of each type of pane would you need for windows that are twice as long as they are wide? Your answer will depend on the width of the window. Let the width be $W$, and find expressions in terms of $W$ for:
   a. the length of the window;
   b. the number of inside panes;
   c. the number of edge panes;
   d. the number of corner panes.

3. Draw a pair of axes and label the $x$-axis *Width* and the $y$-axis *Number of Panes*. Then make a graph showing each of these as a function of $W$, the width of the window.
   a. the number of inside panes
   b. the number of edge panes
   c. the number of corner panes

4. As you increase the width of the window, which grows fastest, the number of inside panes, edge panes, or corner panes? Explain, referring to graphs or sketches.

5. The panes described in Lesson 2 cannot be used for windows of width 1.
   a. Explain why.
   b. Sketch the two types of panes that are needed in this case.
   c. Find the number of each type of pane for a window having width 1 and length $L$.

## MULTIPLY

6. Multiply these polynomials.
   a. $(3x - 5)(4x - 6)$
   b. $(5 - 3x)(6 - 4x)$
   c. $(3y + 3x - 1)(-2x + 2y)$
   d. $(x + y + z)(-x + y)$

7. Multiply and compare the results. What do you notice? Explain.
   a. $(ax - by)(ax - by)$
   b. $(by - ax)(by - ax)$
   c. $(ax - by)(by - ax)$

## REMARKABLE IDENTITIES

8. Find the missing terms.
   a. $(ax - \underline{\hspace{1cm}})^2 = \underline{\hspace{1cm}} - 2ax + 1$
   b. $b^2 - x^2 = (b - x)(\underline{\hspace{1cm}})$
   c. $y^2 - 10y + \underline{\hspace{1cm}} = (\underline{\hspace{1cm}})^2$
   d. $(ax + \underline{\hspace{1cm}})^2 = a^2x^2 + \underline{\hspace{1cm}} + b^2y^2$

## FACTOR

Factor. Look for a common factor and use an identity.

9.  a. $5x^2 + 20x + 20$
    b. $6y^2 + 12xy + 6x^2$
    c. $2x^2 + 60x + 450$

10. Find the middle term that will make each of these a perfect square trinomial. Then write it as the square of a binomial.
    a. $100a^2 + \underline{\hspace{1cm}} + 49b^2$
    b. $(1/9)x^2 + \underline{\hspace{1cm}} + (1/4)y^2$

11. Factor these polynomials.
    a. $4x^2 - 20x + 25$
    b. $4x^2 - 25$
    c. $25 - 4x^2$

12. 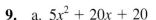 Factor these polynomials. (Hint: First look for common factors.)
    a. $5y^2 + 90xy + 45x^2$
    b. $48x - 27xy^2$
    c. $xy^2 - 6x^2y + 9x^3$

### SOLVING EQUATIONS WITH SQUARES

Solve for $x$. There may be no solution, one solution, or more than one solution.

13. $x^2 = 25$

14. $36x^2 = 49$

15. $x^2 - 6x + 9 = 0$

16. $x^2 - 6x + 9 = 1$

### GRAPHING INEQUALITIES

17. Use graphs to help you find the solution to each of these compound inequalities. In each case, you will need to graph two horizontal lines and one other line.
    a. $-3 < 4x - 3 < 5$
    b. $-3 < -4x + 3 < 5$
    c. $-5 < 4x - 3 < 3$
    d. $-5 < -4x + 3 < 3$

18. Use graphs and tables of values to solve these compound inequalities.
    a. $x - 2 < 3x - 4 < x + 5$
    b. $x - 2 < 3x - 4 < -x + 5$

### BILLIONS AND BILLIONS

The following was written on an ice cream package: $3 billion is 1% of the U.S. yearly defense budget. If you ate one ice cream cone per hour per day it would take you 342,466 years to consume 3 billion ice cream cones.

19. Check that the calculation is accurate.

20. Assuming that the information is accurate, what is the U.S. *hourly* defense budget?

### LIGHT-YEARS

21. A *light-year* is the distance light travels in one year. Figure out how far that is in kilometers, given that light travels approximately 299,793 kilometers per second. Use scientific notation.

### WHAT A BARGAIN

22. Say that a particularly expensive necklace costs one googol dollars.
    a. Fortunately, it's on sale at 99% off. How much does it cost now?
    b. What percent-off sale would be needed so that the necklace would cost ten billion dollars?

The spiral surface pattern of gastropod fossils

## *Coming in this chapter:*

**Exploration** A population is growing at a rate of about 2% per year. In how many years will the population double? Experiment with different starting values for the population. How does your answer depend on the starting value?

# GROWTH AND CHANGE

# Height and Weight

Dr. Terwit, a pediatrician, kept records of her son Joshua's height and weight from birth to age four years. We will use these numbers to learn about *rate of change*.

| Age | Height (cm) | Weight (kg) |
|---|---|---|
| birth | 51 | 3.4 |
| 3 mo | 60 | 5.7 |
| 6 mo | 66 | 7.6 |
| 9 mo | 71 | 9.1 |
| 12 mo | 75 | 10.1 |
| 15 mo | 79 | 10.8 |
| 18 mo | 82 | 11.4 |
| 2 yr | 88 | 12.6 |
| 2.5 yr | 92 | 13.6 |
| 3 yr | 96 | 14.6 |
| 4 yr | 103 | 16.5 |

### HEIGHT AS A FUNCTION OF AGE

1. Make a graph to represent height as a function of age. (Note that the ages given are not evenly spaced.)

2. What is the increase in height between:
   a. birth and three months?
   b. 15 months and 18 months?
   c. birth and one year?
   d. three years and four years?

3. Did Joshua's height grow faster or more slowly as he grew older? Explain your answer by referring to:
   a. the answers to problem 2;
   b. the shape of the graph.

4. If Joshua had grown the same number of centimeters every month, what would his average rate of growth be, in *centimeters per month*, between:
   a. birth and three months?
   b. 15 months and 18 months?
   c. birth and one year?
   d. three years and four years?

5. What was Joshua's *average rate of growth* in centimeters per month during his first four years? Compare this average with the averages you found in problem 4.

6. **Summary** Write a short paragraph summarizing the relationship between Joshua's age, his height, and the rate of his growth. In particular, explain the idea of average rate of growth and how it changed with his age.

**7.** **Project** Find out how many sizes there are for babies' and children's clothes in the age range studied here. Is what you find consistent with the information in the table?

### WEIGHT AS A FUNCTION OF AGE

This is a graph of weight as a function of age. The straight lines form four *steps* connecting some data points.

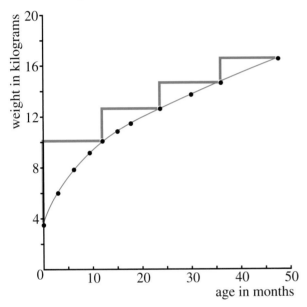

**8.** Use the data to answer these questions about the graph.
a. How high is each step? (Give your answer in kilograms.)
b. How wide is each step? (Give your answer in months.)
c. Explain the meaning of your answers to (a) and (b) in terms of the *yearly* change in Joshua's weight.

**9.** Find the average *monthly* weight gain between ages
a. two and two-and-a-half;
b. two-and-a-half and three;
c. two and three.

**10.** ⚷— Joshua's weight grew at a fairly constant monthly rate between ages one and four. Explain how this can be seen
a. on the graph;
b. numerically.

**11.** ⚷— However, his weight grew much more slowly between ages one and four than during his first year. Explain how this can be seen
a. on the graph;
b. numerically.

### WEIGHT AS A FUNCTION OF HEIGHT

This is a graph of weight as a function of height.

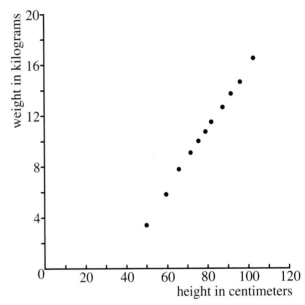

**12.** How much weight did Joshua gain for each centimeter he gained in height? Answer this question for the following periods:
a. birth and three months;
b. ages three and four;
c. on the average, over the four years.

**13.** Study the preceding graph and table and make calculations to find the time in Joshua's first four years when he gained
  a. the least weight per centimeter;
  b. the most weight per centimeter.

**14.** ☞ Compare the two graphs of weight (as a function of age and as a function of height). How are they alike? How are they different? Discuss the shape of the graphs, the units, and the rate of change.

Because the rate of change of weight as a function of height does not vary much, the data points fall close to a line. You could say that this data is nearly linear. In cases like this, it is a common statistical technique to approximate the data with a line. You will learn more about this in future lessons, but first you need to know more about lines and linear functions.

**15.** [Report] Write a report comparing the height and the rate of growth of boys and girls. Include a graph showing the heights of both boys and girls as a function of age, on the same axes. (Since the graphs are close to each other, you may want to distinguish them by using color.) Your report should include, but not be limited to, answers to these questions.
  - How many inches do boys and girls gain per year, on the average?
  - At what ages do they grow fastest?
  - How many inches do they gain per year during those growth spurts?

## BOYS AND GIRLS

The following table shows the average height in inches of boys and girls, ages 9 through 18.

|       | Height (in.) | |
|-------|--------------|-------|
| Age   | Girls        | Boys  |
| 9     | 52.3         | 53.3  |
| 10    | 54.6         | 55.2  |
| 11    | 57.0         | 56.8  |
| 12    | 59.8         | 58.9  |
| 13    | 61.8         | 61.0  |
| 14    | 62.8         | 64.0  |
| 15    | 63.4         | 66.1  |
| 16    | 63.9         | 67.8  |
| 17    | 64.0         | 68.4  |
| 18    | 64.0         | 68.7  |

# Focus on Function Diagrams

**REVIEW** *PARALLEL-LINE DIAGRAMS*

1.  a. Draw a function diagram such that its in-out lines are *parallel* and going uphill (from left to right).
    b. Find the function corresponding to the diagram, using an in-out table if you need it.

2.  Repeat problem 1 with parallel in-out lines going
    a. downhill;
    b. horizontally.

3.  🔑 For the functions you created in problems 1 and 2, when *x* increases by 1, by how much does *y* increase? Does it depend on the steepness of the lines?
    (To answer this, compare your functions with other students' functions.) Explain your answer.

Problems 4 through 9 refer to the function diagrams shown on the next page.

**THE FOCUS**

**Definition:** If an in-out line is horizontal, its input is called a *fixed point*.

For example, both *x* and *y* equal 12 in diagram (a), so 12 is a fixed point for that function.

4.  What are the fixed points for functions (b-p)?

**Definition:** In-out lines can be extended to the left or right. If all of them meet in a single point, that point is called the *focus*.

5.  **Exploration** Consider the function diagrams shown in figures (a-p). For each one, find the function. You may split the work with other students. Describe any patterns you notice. If you cannot find all the functions or patterns, you will get another chance at the end of the lesson. ∎

**MAGNIFICATION**

6.  Look at function diagram (h). By how much does *y* change when *x* increases by:
    a. 1?          b. 2?
    c. some amount *A*?

In function diagrams that have a focus, changes in *y* can be found by multiplying the changes in *x* by a certain number, called the *magnification*.

(change in *x*) · (magnification) = (change in *y*)

7.  a. What is the magnification for (h)?
    b. What other diagrams have the same magnification?

**Rule:** If *y* decreases when *x* increases, the magnification is negative.

8.  For which diagrams is the magnification equal to -3? (If *x* increases by 1, *y* *decreases* by 3.)

9.  Find the magnification for each function diagram. Note that the magnification can be positive or negative, a whole number or a fraction.

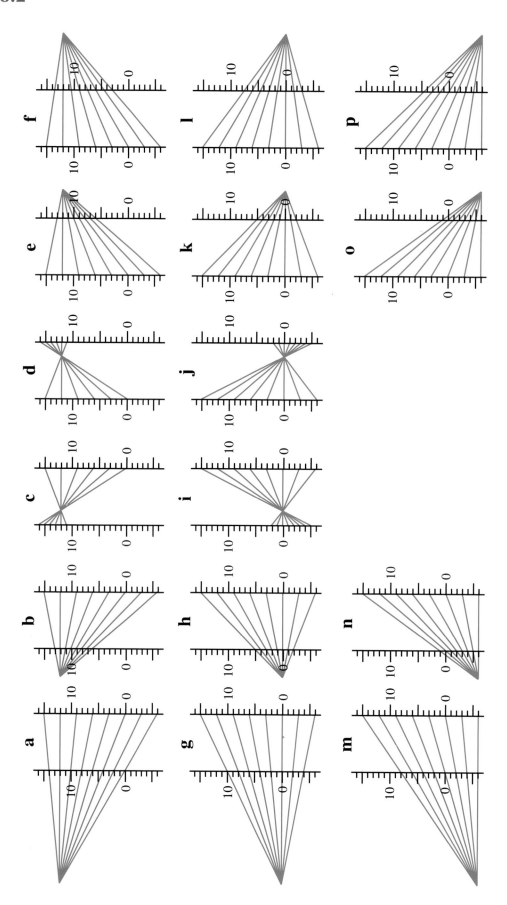

sixteen function diagrams

## THE *m* PARAMETER

You probably noticed that all the function diagrams represent functions of the form $y = mx + b$. It turns out that this is always true of function diagrams with a focus. As you may remember, the letters *m* and *b* in the equation are called *parameters*.

10. 🔑 Look at the equations you found in the Exploration, problem 5. What is the relationship between the magnification and the *m* parameter in those equations? Explain.

11. If you move the focus of a function diagram up, how does it affect the value of *m*? How about if you move it down?

12. Where would the focus be if *m* was
    a. a negative number?
    b. a number between 0 and 1?
    c. a number greater than 1?

13. What is a possible value of *m* if the focus is
    a. half-way between the *x*- and *y*-number lines?
    b. between the *x*- and *y*-number lines, but closer to *x*?
    c. between the *x*- and *y*-number lines, but closer to *y*?

14. What is a possible value of *m* if the focus is
    a. far to the left of the *x*-number line?
    b. close to the left of the *x*-number line?
    c. close to the right of the *y*-number line?
    d. far to the right of the *y*-number line?

15. 💡 In some parts of mathematics, parallel lines are said to meet at a point that is *at infinity*. In that sense, parallel-line diagrams could be said to have a focus at infinity. Is this consistent with your answer to problem 14? Explain.

## RATE OF CHANGE

Once again, look at the diagrams (a-p).

16. 🔑 On each diagram, *as x increases,* follow *y* with your finger. For what values of *m* does *y*
    a. go up?          b. go down?
    c. move fast?      d. move slowly?

The magnification is often called the *rate of change.*

17. What is the rate of change if *y* increases by 3 when *x* increases by:
    a. 1?          b. 6?          c. –10?

## THE *b* PARAMETER

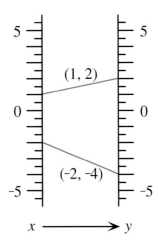

Two in-out lines are shown in the diagram. Each one is labeled with a number pair. The first number in the pair is the input, and the second number is the output.

> **Notation:** Any in-out line can be identified by a number pair. From now on, we will refer to lines on function diagrams this way. For example, the line connecting 0 on the *x*-number line to 0 on the *y*-number line will be called the (0, 0) line.

**18.** What can you say about the $b$ parameter if the focus is on the (0, 0) line?

**19.** Look at diagram (n). Its equation is $y = 3x + 12$.

   a. Name the in-out lines that are shown.

   b. Check that the pairs you listed actually satisfy the equation by substituting the input values for $x$.

   c. Among the pairs you checked was (0, 12). Explain why using 0 as input gave the $b$ parameter as output.

**20.** ⌐— In most of the diagrams (a-p), there is an in-out line of the form (0, ___). How is the number in the blank related to the $b$ parameter? Explain.

$y = mx + b$

**21.** If you did not find all the equations for the function diagrams (a-p), when working on problem 4, do it now. Hint: You may use what you learned about magnification and about the (0, ___) in-out line.

**22.** Summary  Write what you learned about function diagrams, the fixed point, the focus, magnification, and the parameters $m$ and $b$. Also mention parallel-line diagrams.

---

REVIEW  **BINOMIAL MULTIPLICATION**

Multiply and combine like terms.

**23.** $(3x + 1)(x - 2)$

**24.** $(2x - 3)(5 - x)$

**25.** $(5 + x)(3x - 3)$

**26.** $(2y - 2)(6 - y)$

**27.** $(3x - 1)(2 + x)$

**28.** $(3x + 1)(2 + x)$

**29.** $(6 + y)(2y + 4)$

**30.** $(y - 4)(2y + 2)$

**31.** $(y - 3)(y - 5)$

**32.** $(6 - x)(2x - 3)$

# 8.3 ▽ Slope

**You will need:**

geoboards

dot paper

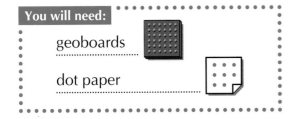

## GRADE AND SLOPE

Steep roads sometimes have a sign indicating how steep they are. For example, the sign may say **5% Grade**. This means that you gain 5 units of altitude (the *rise*) for every 100 units you move in the horizontal direction (the *run*).

1. On a 5% grade, how many units of altitude do you gain for every
   a. 200 units you move in the horizontal direction?
   b. 25 units you move in the horizontal direction?
   c. 1 unit you move in the horizontal direction?

5% grade (figure is not to scale)

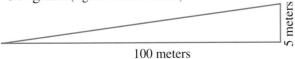

100 meters

5 meters

In math a 5% grade is called a *slope* of 0.05.

2. If the slope is 0.05, how many units do you move in the horizontal direction for every
   a. 30 units you gain in altitude?
   b. 0.05 units you gain in altitude?
   c. 0.5 units you gain in altitude?

3. The figure above is not to scale.
   a. What is the actual slope illustrated? (Use a ruler to measure the rise and the run.)
   b. Is it more or less steep than a 0.05 slope?

4. ⚷— A sign in the mountains says **6% Grade. Trucks Use Low Gear.** Explain what a 6% grade is. Use the words *slope, rise,* and *run* in your answer.

5. In a nonmountainous area, the steepest grade allowed on a freeway is 4%. With this grade, how many meters of altitude do you gain per
   a. kilometer traveled in the horizontal direction? ( A kilometer is 1000 meters.)
   b. meter traveled in the horizontal direction?

6. If you are climbing a mountain road with grade 5.5%, and you gain 1000 ft in altitude, how many miles have you traveled? (There are 5280 feet in a mile.)

> **Definition:** Slope is defined as the ratio of rise to run.   $\text{slope} = \dfrac{\text{rise}}{\text{run}}$

7. a. How many units of altitude do you gain for every 100 units traveled on a horizontal road?
   b. What is the grade of a horizontal road?
   c. What is the slope of a horizontal line?

A horizontal road has grade 0. This is because no matter how much you move in the horizontal direction, you do not gain any altitude. The rise is 0 for any run. For example, for a run of 1, the slope is 0/1 which equals 0.

## GEOBOARD SLOPE

The figure shows three geoboard right triangles. The side opposite the right angle in a right triangle is called the *hypotenuse.*

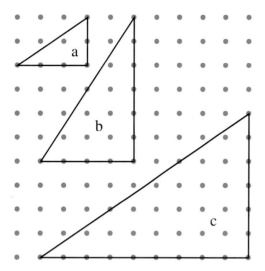

**8.** Find the slope of each hypotenuse in this figure.

**9.** How would you use the slope to find which hypotenuse is steeper? Which hypotenuses have the same steepness?

**10.** Two of the hypotenuses in the figure have the same slope. Explain why someone might make a mistake and believe all three have the same slope.

**Do not use horizontal or vertical lines in problems 11-16.** Start your lines at the origin.

**11. a.** What is the smallest slope you can find on a geoboard? Express it as a decimal.
  **b.** Sketch a right triangle, like the ones above, to illustrate it.

**12.** Repeat problem 11 for the greatest possible geoboard slope.

**13.** Find a line having slope 1, and sketch several right triangles for it.

**14.** Find every possible geoboard slope that is a whole number.

**15.** Find every possible geoboard slope that is greater than 1 and less than 2. Express your answers as decimals.

**16.** Find every possible geoboard slope that is greater than 0.5 and less than 1. Express your answers as decimals.

---
**SLOPES FROM COORDINATES**
---

You may make a right triangle on your geoboard to help you answer the following questions.

**17.** What is the slope of the line joining
  **a.** $(0, 0)$ and $(4, 5)$?
  **b.** $(1, 1)$ and $(5, 6)$?
  **c.** $(0, 1)$ and $(4, 5)$?
  **d.** $(1, 0)$ and $(5, 6)$?

**18.** What is the slope of the line joining
  **a.** $(0, 0)$ and $(8, 10)$?
  **b.** $(0, 2)$ and $(8, 10)$?
  **c.** $(2, 3)$ and $(3, 5)$?
  **d.** $(4, 6)$ and $(6, 10)$?

For problem 19, you cannot use the geoboard.

**19.** What is the slope of the line joining
  **a.** $(23, 34)$ and $(65, 54)$?
  **b.** $(1.2, 3.4)$ and $(5.6, 7.89)$?

**20.** Generalization Explain how to find the slope of the line joining $(a, b)$ and $(c, d)$.

---
**ROLLER COASTERS**
---

Abe and Bea disagree about which roller coaster is steeper, the Plunge of Peril or the Drop of Death.

"The Plunge of Peril," according to the ad for the Great American Super-Park, "drops you 111 feet in seconds, with a mere 20 feet of horizontal displacement."

Abe and Bea have a photograph of themselves standing in front of the Drop of Death. They measured the roller coaster on the photograph, and got a drop of 10.1 cm for a run of 1.8 cm.

**21.** Use what you know about slope to help them decide which roller coaster is steeper. Explain your method.

**22.** Project The Plunge of Peril and the Drop of Death were invented for this lesson. Find the slopes of some real roller coasters.

---

*DISCOVERY* **SLUMBER THEORY**

Number theory is the branch of mathematics that studies whole numbers and their properties. It has been the source of many challenging problems over the centuries. Slumber theory is a silly offshoot of number theory.

The key concept of slumber theory is that any whole number can be *sliced* into a sequence of whole numbers.

| **Example:** 365 can be sliced in four different ways:

3 | 6 | 5; 36 | 5; 3 | 65; or 365.

(Note that the slices are indicated by a vertical slash. Note also that in slumber theory, not slicing is considered a form of slicing.)

**23.** How many ways are there to slice a four-digit number?

A number is *slime* if it can be sliced into a sequence of primes.

| **Examples:** 5 is slime, since it is already prime. 2027 is slime (2 | 02 | 7) 4,155,243,311 is slime (41 | 5 | 5 | 2 | 43 | 3 | 11)

**24.** Which one of the following numbers is slime?
   a. 12          b. 345          c. 6789

**25.** 2 is the only even prime. Find the first three even slimes.

**26.** There are no prime squares. Find the first two slime squares.

**27.** There are no prime cubes. Find the first two slime cubes.

**28.** 2 and 3 are the only consecutive numbers that are both prime. Find the first three pairs of consecutive numbers that are both slime.

**29.** There is no triple of consecutive numbers that are all prime. Find the first two triples of consecutive numbers that are all slime.

**30.** Find the smallest number that is slime in more than one way. (In other words, it can be sliced into two different sequences of primes.)

**31.** Find the smallest number that is slime in more than two ways.

A number is a *super-slime* if you get a sequence of primes no matter how you slice it.

| **Example:** 53 is a super-slime since 53 and 5 | 3 are both sequences of primes.

**32.** ◯ Find all the super-slimes.

**You will need:**

graph paper

1. **Exploration** For problems (a-b), find the equations of lines that will create the given design.

a

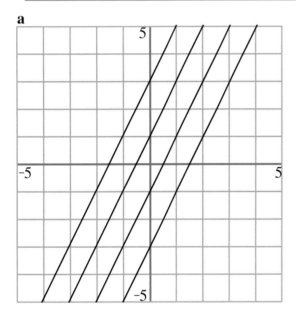

b

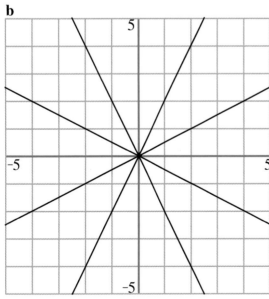

## THE SLOPE OF A LINE

**Definitions:** The *rate of change* of a function is defined as a ratio between the change in $y$ and the change in $x$.

$$\text{rate of change} = \frac{\text{change in } y}{\text{change in } x}$$

In the Cartesian plane, a change in $y$-coordinates is called a *rise*. A change in $x$-coordinates is called a *run*.

The *slope of a line* is the ratio obtained when you divide the rise by the run. If you move from left to right, the run is positive. From right to left, it is negative. If you move up, the rise is positive. Moving down, it is negative.

The figure shows right triangles for slopes 0.5, -0.5, 2, and -2.

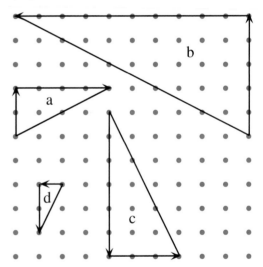

2. Match the slope to the triangle by finding the rise and the run as you move from one end of the hypotenuse to the other
   a. in the direction of the arrows;
   b. in the opposite direction.
   c. Do you get the same answers both ways?

3.  ⌐— What can you say about the slope of a line if, when you follow the line *from left to right,*
    a. it goes up?
    b. it goes down?
    c. it goes neither up nor down?

4.  Find two $(x, y)$ pairs that satisfy each equation. Use them to graph the line. Label the two points, and use them to find the slope.
    a. $y = 1.5x + 3$    b. $y = -1.5x + 3$
    c. $y = 2x + 3$    d. $y = -3x + 3$

5.  Think of the line with equation $y = 3x + 3$.
    a. Predict its slope.
    b. Check your prediction by graphing.
    c. For this function, when $x$ increases by 1, by what does $y$ increase?

6.  Repeat problem 5 for $y = -2x + 3$.

7.  ⌐— How is the coefficient of $x$ related to the slope?

### THE y-INTERCEPT OF A LINE

8.  For each of these equations, find the $y$-intercept.
    a. $y = 0.5x + 3$
    b. $y = 0.5x - 3$
    c. $y = 0.5x$
    d. $y = 0.5x + 1.5$

One way to find the $y$-intercept of a function is to graph it, and see where the graph meets the $y$-axis. Another way is to remember that *on the y-axis, the x-coordinate is 0.* In other words, all points on the $y$-axis are of the form $(0, \_\_\_)$. So to find the $y$-intercept of a function, it is enough to substitute 0 for $x$, and find the value of $y$.

For each of these linear functions, answer the following questions. Graph the functions if you need to check your answers.
    a. When $x = 0$, what is $y$?
    b. When $x$ increases by 1, by how much does $y$ increase? (If $y$ decreases, think of it as a negative increase.)
    c. What are the slope and $y$-intercept?

9.  $y = x + 2$    10. $y = -4 - 3x$

11. $y = -x$    12. $y = 9$

13. $y = \frac{6x - 7}{8}$    14. $y = -2(x - 3)$

### SLOPE AND y-INTERCEPT

**Definition:** $y = mx + b$ is called the *slope-intercept form* for the equation of a line.

For each equation below, tell whether it is in slope-intercept form.
    a. If it is, name $m$ and $b$.
    b. If not, put it in slope-intercept form, then name $m$ and $b$.

15. $y = 5x - 6$    16. $y = -4(x - 7)$

17. $y = \frac{5x - 6}{3}$    18. $y = \frac{x - 7}{-4}$

19. $y = 3(5x - 6)$    20. $y = -4x - 7$

21. $y + 4 = x$    22. $y + x = 4$

23. Without graphing each pair of lines, tell whether or not their graphs would intersect. Explain.
    a. $y = 2x + 8$    $y = 2x + 10$
    b. $y = -2x + 8$    $y = 2x + 10$
    c. $y = -2$    $y = 10$
    d. $y = x/4$    $y = 0.25x + 10$
    e. $y = 2(5x - 3)$    $y = 10x$

**24.** For (a-c), give the equation of a line that satisfies the following conditions.

a. It passes through the point (0, -2), and goes uphill from left to right.

b. It passes through the origin and (4, -6).

c. It does not contain any point in the third quadrant, and has slope -1.5.

Compare your answers with your classmates' answers.

**25.** Write three equations of the form $y = mx + b$. For each one, tell how much $x$ changes when $y$ changes by:

a. 1;          b. 5;          c. $K$.

**26.** ◑━ Did your answers to problem 25 depend on the parameter $m$, the parameter $b$, or both?

**27.** ◑━ What can you say about the signs of the slope and $y$-intercept of a line that does not contain any points in:

a. the first quadrant?

b. the second quadrant?

c. the third quadrant?

d. the fourth quadrant?

**28.** Report Explain how to use the slope-intercept form to predict the slope and $y$-intercept of a line. Make sure you give examples as you answer the following questions.

• What is the value of $y$ when $x = 0$?

• When $x$ increases by 1, by how much does $y$ increase?

• How about when $x$ increases by $d$?

• If two lines are parallel, what do their equations have in common?

• If two lines meet on the $y$-axis, what do their equations have in common?

• How is the slope-intercept form useful for graphing lines quickly?

---

**PREVIEW** *WHAT'S THE FUNCTION?*

**29.** Think of the line that has slope -2 and passes through (1, 4).

a. By graphing, find any other point on the line.

b. Look at the graph to find the $y$-intercept.

c. What is the equation of the line?

**30.** Graph the line $y = 2x - 5$. Then graph each line, (a-c), and find its slope, $y$-intercept, and equation.

a. any line parallel to $y = 2x - 5$

b. the line parallel to it that passes through the origin

c. the line parallel to it that passes through the point (1, 4)

# 8.A Slope-Intercept Form

### HORIZONTAL AND VERTICAL LINES

1. **REVIEW** What is the equation of:
   a. a horizontal line through (2, 3)?
   b. a vertical line through (2, 3)?
   c. the *x*-axis?
   d. the *y*-axis?

2. What is the slope of a horizontal line?

To find the slope of a vertical line, notice that the run is 0 for any rise. For example, for a run of 1, the slope should be 1/0, which is not defined. For this reason, vertical lines do not have a slope.

3. a. Explain why vertical lines do not have a *y*-intercept.
   b. Explain why the equations of vertical lines cannot be written in slope-intercept form.
   c. How does one write the equation of a vertical line?

### FINDING m AND b

4. What are the equations of these lines, (a-d)?

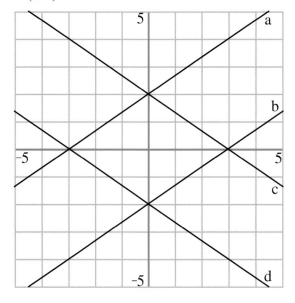

5. a. What are the equations of the two lines in the graph below?
   b. What can you say about the equations of lines that pass through the origin and each of the regions A-H? (Your answers should be in the form: For lines in regions A and E, *b* = ___ and *m* is between ___ and ___.)

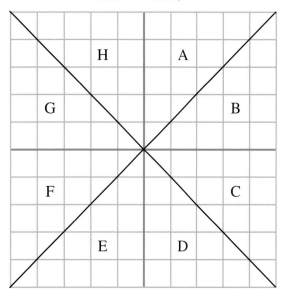

6. What can you say about *m* if the graph is a very steep line, nearly vertical?

7. This table lists three points that all lie on one line. Find *m* and *b* without graphing.

| x | y |
|---|---|
| -3 | 7 |
| 0 | 6 |
| 3 | 5 |

**8.** a. One of these tables lists three points which do not all lie on the same line. Which table is it? Explain how you can tell without graphing, by thinking about slope.

  b. Find $m$ and $b$ for the other two tables.

| x | y |
|---|---|
| -1 | -7 |
| 1 | 1 |
| 3 | 9 |

| x | y |
|---|---|
| -1 | 2 |
| 1 | 4 |
| 3 | 5 |

| x | y |
|---|---|
| -1 | 8 |
| 1 | 0 |
| 3 | -8 |

**9.** For equations (a-e), find $m$ and $b$ without graphing. (You may use graphing to check your answers.)

  a. $y = -2$
  b. $y = 9x$
  c. $y = 2 - 3x$
  d. $y = 4(5x - 6)$
  e. $y = \dfrac{7x + 8}{9}$

**10.** **Report** Summarize what you know about slope-intercept form for linear functions. Illustrate your report with graphs and function diagrams. Use the words: equation, fixed point, focus, function, grade, graph, horizontal, linear, magnification, negative, parallel, parameters, positive, rate of change, ratio, slope, table, vertical, y-intercept.

# LESSON 8.5 Ideal Population Growth

## MATHEMATICAL MODELS

Exponents are useful for making mathematical descriptions of many kinds of growth, including population growth and spread of infectious disease. A mathematical description, or *mathematical model,* usually involves simplifying the real-world situation. Even though some of the idealized situations you study in this course may seem unrealistic, they will help you learn techniques that can be applied to more complicated real-world data.

Bacterial growth is one such situation. In research laboratories, bacteria used for biological studies are grown under controlled conditions. Although no real populations would grow as predictably as the ones described in this chapter, bacterial populations over short periods of time do approximate this kind of growth.

## A DOUBLING POPULATION

1. A colony of bacteria is being grown in a laboratory. It contains a single bacterium at 12:00 noon (*time 0*), and the population is doubling every hour. How long do you think it would take for the population to exceed 1 million? 2 million? Write down your *guesses* and compare them with other students' guesses.

2. Make a table of values showing how the population in problem 1 changes as a function of time. Find the population one hour from now, two hours from now, etc. Extend your table until you can answer the questions asked in problem 1. How close were your guesses?

3. Add a third column to your table, writing the population each time as a power of 2.

4. What would the population be after $x$ hours? (Write this as a power of 2.)

## HOW MUCH MORE THAN? HOW MANY TIMES AS MUCH?

To determine the rate at which the population is increasing, we compare the populations at different times.

5. Compare the population after 8 hours with the population after 5 hours.
   a. *How much more* is the population after 8 hours? (Compare by subtracting.)
   b. *How many times* as much is it? (Compare by dividing.)
   c. Which of your answers in (a) and (b) can be written as a power of 2? What power of 2 is it?

6. Repeat problem 5, comparing the population after 7 hours with the population after 3 hours.

7. ⚷ One of the questions, *How much more than?* or, *How many times as much?* can be answered easily with the help of powers of 2. Which question? Explain.

8. Make the comparisons below, answering the question: How many times as much? Write your answers as powers of 2.
   a. Compare the population after 12 hours with the population after 10 hours.
   b. Compare the population after 9 hours with the population after 4 hours.
   c. Compare the population after 4 hours with the population after 12 hours.

9. Compare each pair of numbers. The larger number is how many times as much as the smaller number? Write your answer as a power. In (d), assume $x$ is positive.
   a. $2^6$ and $2^9$    b. $2^9$ and $2^{14}$
   c. $2^{14}$ and $2^6$    d. $2^x$ and $2^{x+3}$

### A TRIPLING POPULATION

A colony of bacteria being grown in a laboratory contains a single bacterium at 12:00 noon (time 0). This population is *tripling* every hour.

**10.** Make the comparisons below, answering the question: How many times as much? Write your answers as powers of 3. (Hint: It may help to start by making a table showing how the population changes as a function of time.)

a. Compare the population after 12 hours with the population after 10 hours.

b. Compare the population after 9 hours with the population after 4 hours.

c. Compare the population after 4 hours with the population after 12 hours.

**11.** Compare each pair of numbers. How many times as much as the smaller number is the larger? Write your answer as a power. In (d), assume $x$ is positive.

a. $3^6$ and $3^9$  b. $3^9$ and $3^{14}$
c. $3^{14}$ and $3^6$  d. $3^x$ and $3^{x+5}$

**12.** By what number would you have to multiply the first power to get the second power? Write your answer as a power.

a. $3^5 \cdot \underline{\quad} = 3^{15}$  b. $3^8 \cdot \underline{\quad} = 3^{15}$
c. $3^{11} \cdot \underline{\quad} = 3^{15}$  d. $3^0 \cdot \underline{\quad} = 3^{15}$

### MULTIPLYING AND DIVIDING POWERS

In a power, the exponent tells how many times the base has been used as a factor. For example, $4^2$ means $4 \cdot 4$, and $4^3$ means $4 \cdot 4 \cdot 4$, therefore:
$$4^2 \cdot 4^3 = (4 \cdot 4) \cdot (4 \cdot 4 \cdot 4) = 4^5.$$
Use this idea to multiply powers.

**13.** Write the product as a power of 3.

a. $3^7 \cdot 3^3 =$  b. $3^5 \cdot 3^5 =$
c. $3^8 \cdot 3^2 =$  d. $3^8 \cdot 3^0 =$

**14.** Write the product as a power of 5.

a. $5^4 \cdot 5^3 =$  b. $5^4 \cdot 5^6 =$
c. $5^4 \cdot 5^9 =$  d. $5^0 \cdot 5^0 =$

When you divide, the quotient tells you how many times as much the numerator is than the denominator. For example, $4^5/4^2$ means *what times $4^2$ equals $4^5$?* Since $4^2 \cdot 4^3 = 4^5$, you have $4^5/4^2 = 4^3$. Use this idea to divide powers.

**15.** Write the quotient as a power of 2.

a. $\dfrac{2^{11}}{2^6}$  b. $\dfrac{2^6}{2^3}$

c. $\dfrac{2^{11}}{2^3}$  d. $\dfrac{2^{11}}{2^0}$

**16.** Write the quotient as a power of 3.

a. $\dfrac{3^7}{3^5}$  b. $\dfrac{3^6}{3^4}$

c. $\dfrac{3^{x+2}}{3^x}$  d. $\dfrac{3^{11}}{3^0}$

**17.** Use what you have learned in this lesson to find $x$.

a. $5^x \cdot 5^3 = 5^9$
b. $2^3 \cdot x^4 = 2^7$
c. $\dfrac{8^{66}}{8^x} = 8^{54}$
d. 💡 $\dfrac{10^{x+3}}{10^4} = 10^{a+1}$

**18.** Summary

a. Describe the patterns you found in multiplying and dividing powers.

b. Give examples to show how patterns can make it easier to multiply and divide powers.

c. In each multiplication and division problem, 15-17, *the bases of the powers are the same*. Does the pattern you described in (a) work if the bases are not the same? Explain, using examples.

**19.** Generalization Use the patterns you found in this lesson to rewrite each expression as a single power.

a. $5^x \cdot 5^y$  b. $a^x \cdot a^y$

c. $\dfrac{3^y}{3^x}$  d. $\dfrac{6^{x+5}}{6^x}$

e. $6^x \cdot 6^x$  f. $6^0 \cdot 6^x$

# LESSON 8.6

# Comparing Populations

## EXPONENTIAL GROWTH

Three populations of bacteria are being grown in a laboratory. At time 0: Population A had 10 bacteria; Population B had 100 bacteria; and Population C had 300 bacteria. All three double every hour.

1. Complete the table below to show how the three populations increase as a function of time for the first six hours of growth after time 0.

### Population

| Time | A | B | C |
|------|------|------|------|
| 0 | 10 | 100 | 300 |
| 1 |  |  |  |

The populations are doubling, which means they are being repeatedly multiplied by 2. Powers of 2 provide a good shorthand for writing the populations.

2. Make another table of the populations of A, B, and C for the first six hours of growth after time 0. This time, use multiplication and a power of 2 to write each population. (Example: For A, the population after four hours is $10 \cdot 2^4$.)

3. Write the expressions for the populations of A, B, and C after:
   a. $x$ hours;
   b. $x + 3$ hours.

**Definitions:** This kind of growth is called *exponential growth.* Exponential growth involves *repeated multiplication* by a number. To describe exponential growth, we specify the *starting population* and the *rate of growth.*

For example, if the starting population is 4 and the population triples every hour, this table shows how the population changes as a function of time.

| Time | Population | Exponential Expression |
|------|------------|------------------------|
| 0 | 4 | $4 \cdot 3^0$ |
| 1 | $4 \cdot 3 = 12$ | $4 \cdot 3^1$ |
| 2 | $4 \cdot 3 \cdot 3 = 36$ | $4 \cdot 3^2$ |
| 3 | $4 \cdot 3 \cdot 3 \cdot 3 = 108$ | $4 \cdot 3^3$ |
| $x$ | $4 \cdot 3 \cdot ... = ?$ | $4 \cdot 3^x$ |

### Generalizations

4. Write an expression for the population after six hours of growth
   a. if the starting population is 100 and the population is tripling every hour;
   b. if the starting population is 100 and the population is being multiplied by $r$ every hour;
   c. if the starting population is $p$ and the population is being multiplied by $r$ every hour.

**5.** 🗝 Write an expression for the population after $x$ hours of growth for each situation in problem 4.

**6.** The population of B after five hours is $100 \cdot 2^5$.

    **a.** Find the population of B at 8 hours, 11 hours, and 14 hours. By how much is the population being multiplied over each three-hour period?

    **b.** Compare the population of B after $x$ hours with its population after $x + 3$ hours by simplifying this ratio.

$$\frac{10 \cdot 2^{x+3}}{10 \cdot 2^x}$$

**7.** The population of A at six hours is $10 \cdot 2^6$.

    **a.** Compare the population of A after $x$ hours with its population after $x + 5$ hours by simplifying this ratio.

$$\frac{10 \cdot 2^{x+5}}{10 \cdot 2^x}$$

    **b.** Check your answer to part (a) by comparing the population of A at 6 hours, 11 hours, and 16 hours.

**8.** Simplify these ratios.

    **a.** $\dfrac{400 \cdot 2^7}{400 \cdot 2^3}$     **b.** $\dfrac{100 \cdot 2^{15}}{100 \cdot 2^8}$

**9.** Simplify these ratios. It may help to substitute values for $x$ and look for a pattern.

    **a.** $\dfrac{400 \cdot 2^{x+7}}{400 \cdot 2^x}$     **b.** $\dfrac{100 \cdot 2^{3x}}{100 \cdot 2^x}$

**10.** Solve for $x$. $\dfrac{35 \cdot 2^{x+6}}{35 \cdot 2^x} = 2^x$

**11.** **a.** Use the tables you made in problems 1 and 2 to compare the size of A with the size of B at several times. In each case, B is how many times as large? Does this ratio increase, decrease, or remain the same as time goes on?

    **b.** Repeat part (a), comparing C with B.

**12.** Simplify these ratios.

    **a.** $\dfrac{400 \cdot 2^x}{200 \cdot 2^x}$     **b.** $\dfrac{10^0 \cdot 2^{x+4}}{500 \cdot 2^{x+4}}$

**13.** Solve for $x$. $\dfrac{300 \cdot 2^a}{x \cdot 2^a} = 30$

**14.** Compare these populations using ratios.

    **a.** B at 10 hours and A at 3 hours

    **b.** C at 3 hours and A at 6 hours

    **c.** A at 12 hours and B at 7 hours

    **d.** 💡 C at 1/2 hour and A at 1 hour

**15.** Compare these populations using ratios.

    **a.** B at $x$ hours and A at $x + 2$ hours

    **b.** C at $h$ hours and A at $2h$ hours

    **c.** A at $h$ hours and B at $h - 5$ hours

**16.** Simplify these ratios.

    **a.** $\dfrac{400 \cdot 2^{x+4}}{25 \cdot 2^x}$     **b.** $\dfrac{10 \cdot 2^{4x}}{150 \cdot 2^x}$

**17.** Solve for $x$.

    **a.** $\dfrac{30 \cdot 2^{a+4}}{x \cdot 2^a} = 60$

    **b.** $\dfrac{300 \cdot 2^{a+3}}{x \cdot 2^a} = 24$

## POPULATION PROJECTIONS

In 1975 the population of the world was about 4.01 billion and was growing at a rate of about 2% per year. People used these facts to project what the population would be in the future.

**18.** Copy and complete the table, giving projections of the world's population from 1976 to 1980, assuming that the growth rate remained at 2% per year.

| Year | Calculation | Projection (billions) |
|------|-------------|------------------------|
| 1976 | $4.01 + (0.02)4.01$ | 4.09 |

**19.** Find the ratio of the projected population from year to year. Does the ratio increase, decrease, or stay the same?

**20.** There is a number that can be used to multiply one year's projection to calculate the next. What is that number?

**21.** Use repeated multiplication to project the world's population in 1990 from the 1975 number, assuming the same growth rate.

**22.** Compare your answer to problem 21 with the actual estimate of the population made in 1990, which was about 5.33 billion.

   a. Did your projection over-estimate or under-estimate the 1990 population?

   b. Was the population growth rate between 1975 and 1990 more or less than 2%? Explain.

**23.** At a growth rate of 2% a year, how long does it take for the world's population to double?

### REVIEW  FACTORING COMPLETELY

**Example:** $16 - 4x^2$ is a difference of two squares, so it can be factored:

$$(4 - 2x)(4 + 2x).$$

However, each of the binomials can be factored further, like this:

$$2(2 - x) \cdot 2(2 + x) = 4(2 - x)(2 + x)$$

Here is another way to factor the same expression:

$$4(4 - x^2) = 4(2 - x)(2 + x).$$

The final expression is the same one we got using the first method. It cannot be factored any further, so we say we have *factored completely*.

Factor each expression completely.

**24.** $3t^2 - 27s^2$

**25.** $5x^2 - 180$

**26.** $x^3y - xy^3$

# Percent Increase

**You will need:**

graph paper

## AN ALGEBRA TUTOR'S SALARY

Bea did so well in algebra that she got a job as an algebra tutor. Her starting salary, as she had no experience, was $10 per week.

1. As Bea got more experience, her salary increased. She got a raise of $1 per week. Copy and complete the table for the first ten weeks that Bea worked.

| Weeks | Salary | Amount increase | Percent increase |
|-------|--------|-----------------|------------------|
| 0 | $10 | | |
| 1 | $11 | $1 | 10 |
| 2 | $12 | $1 | 9 |
| 3 | $13 | $1 | 8.33 |

2. a. Explain how to calculate the number in the last column.
   b. Explain why the number in the last column decreases each week.

3. Compare Bea's original salary with her salary for the tenth week.
   a. What was the total amount of increase in her salary?
   b. What percent of her original salary is this total increase? (This is the total *percent increase*.)
   c. What percent of her original salary is her salary in the tenth week? (Your answer should be a number greater than 100. Why?)

Abe also got a job as an algebra tutor. He heard that Bea was getting a weekly raise of $1. Since $1 is 10% of $10, Abe asked for a weekly raise of 10%. The first week Bea and Abe both got the same raise.

4. Copy and complete the table for the first ten weeks that Abe worked.

| Weeks | Salary | Amount increase | Percent increase |
|-------|--------|-----------------|------------------|
| 0 | $10 | | |
| 1 | $11 | $1 | 10 |
| 2 | $12.10 | $1.10 | 10 |
| 3 | $13.31 | $1.21 | 10 |

5. a. Explain how to calculate the numbers in the third column of the table above.
   b. Explain why the numbers in the third column increase each week.

6. Repeat problem 3 for Abe's salary.

7. On the same pair of axes, make graphs of Abe's and Bea's weekly salaries as a function of weeks of experience.

8. ⚷
   a. Each week's salary for Bea can be obtained from the previous week's salary by *adding* a number. Find this number and use it to write an equation that gives Bea's salary ($S$) as a function of weeks of experience ($W$).
   b. Each week's salary for Abe can be obtained from the previous week's salary by *multiplying* by a number. Find this number, experimenting with your calculator if necessary, and use it to write an equation that gives Abe's salary as a function of weeks of experience.

**9.**

   a. Write each equation you wrote on the graphs it belongs to.

   b. Compare the graphs. Which is straight? Which is curved?

   c. Which function describes linear growth? Which describes exponential growth?

**10.** Repeat the analysis you did for Abe's and Bea's salaries if Bea's raise were $2 and Abe's raise were 20%.

### EQUATIONS WITH PERCENTS

A state has 5% sales tax. If you paid $12.60 for something, including tax, what was the price without tax? If the price without tax is $x$, and the increase due to tax is 0.05 of $x$, then

$$x + 0.05x = \$12.60.$$

**11.** ◆━ Remember that $x$ can be written $1x$.

   a. Combine like terms on the left side of the equation. (Or factor out the $x$.)

   b. Then solve for $x$.

**12.** Solve for $x$.

   a. $1.2x = 240$

   b. $x + 0.4x = 18.2$

   c. $x + 0.06x = 23.85$

   d. $1.7x = 78.2$

**13.** Solve for $x$.

   a. $(1.10)(1.10)x = 67.76$

   b. $(1.10)(1.10)(1.10)x = 13.31$

The Skolar family eat out once a month. Usually they take turns figuring out the tip, also called the *gratuity*.

**14.** At one restaurant, they ordered food totaling $35.95 and received a bill for the total amount they owed. The total was $43.86, and the bill said "tax and gratuity included." Sue wrote this equation.

$$35.95 + p(35.95) = 43.86$$

   a. Explain the equation. What does $p$ represent?

   b. Solve for $p$. Is your answer reasonable? Discuss.

**15.** Another night the Skolar family had $23.00 to buy dinner. Assuming they'd need 25% of the cost of the dinner to cover the tax and tip, Michael wrote this equation.

$$d + 0.25d = 23.00$$

   a. Explain the equation. What does $d$ represent?

   b. Solve for $d$.

**16.** Now assume the Skolars had $23.00 for their meal and needed only 20% of the cost of the dinner to cover the tax and tip. How much can their actual food order be? Write and solve the equation.

### EQUATIONS AND THE PRICE OF WIDGETS

**17.** A certain retail store sells widgets at the wholesale price, plus a 35% markup. If the wholesale price is $W$, what is the retail price of the widget? Express your answer as a function of $W$ in two ways: as an addition and as a multiplication.

**18.** The wholesale cost of widgets went up by 8.5%. If the old wholesale price was $W$, express as a function of $W$,

   a. the new wholesale price;

   b. the new retail price;

   c. the retail price including a 5% sales tax.

**19.** ◯ After the price increase in the wholesale cost a certain customer purchased a widget at the retail store for $15.71, including tax.

   a. What was the wholesale price on that widget?

   b. How much would the customer have saved by buying a widget before the wholesale price increase?

---

**REVIEW** *SOLVING EQUATIONS*

**20.** Solve for $x$.

   a. $\dfrac{3^x}{3^2} = 3^5$

   b. $\dfrac{10^{2x-5}}{10^2} = 10^5$

   c. $\dfrac{p^{x-3}}{p^2} = p^6$

**REVIEW** *EQUATIONS AND INEQUALITIES*

Use the techniques you have learned to solve these equations and inequalities. You can use trial and error, the cover-up method, tables, graphs, or the Lab Gear. Show your work.

**21.** $5y > 2y + 57$

**22.** $3s + 7 = 4 + 3s$

**23.** $3(m + 4) + 3(m - 4) = 54$

**24.** $7 + y = 7y$

**25.** $\dfrac{10x + 4}{6} + 7 = -4$

**26.** $\dfrac{4x}{5} = 2 - x$

**27.** $\dfrac{3}{3x} = \dfrac{7}{4x - 2}$

**28.** $(2p + 3)^2 = (4p - 2)(p - 8)$

**29.** $(2p - 1)(3p + 2) = (6p - 1)(p + 1)$

**30.** $\dfrac{x}{x + 1} = 2$

**31.** ◯ $\dfrac{5}{x} + \dfrac{x}{5} = 2$

# Percent Decrease

## A CASHIER'S QUANDARY

Sherman's Department Store ran the following ad in the newspaper.

---

### 3-HOUR EARLY-BIRD SPECIAL!

★ ★ ★ ★ ★

This week, all merchandise has been discounted 30% for our year-end clearance sale.

For three hours only, from 9AM to 12 noon on Saturday, get amazing additional savings! We will take an *additional* 20% off the sale price at the cash register.

---

G.D. and Cal were working during the three-hour sale. At the end of the sale, they compared receipts and discovered that they had sold some of the same items, but they had charged customers different prices for them. They made the following table.

| Original price | Cal charged | G.D. charged |
|---|---|---|
| $139.99 | $78.39 | $70.00 |
| $49.95 | $27.97 | $24.98 |
| $18.89 | $10.57 | $9.44 |
| $5.29 | $2.96 | $2.65 |
| $179.00 | $100.24 | $89.50 |

1. **Exploration** How was Cal calculating the sale price? How was G.D. calculating the sale price? Explain, showing sample calculations. Who do you think was right, and why? ▪

## LATE PAPER POLICIES

Mr. Peters, an algebra teacher, has a *10% off* late paper policy. This means that for each day that a paper is late, the student receives 90% of the credit that he or she would have received the day before. For example, if you turned in a perfect paper (assume a score out of 100) one day late, you would receive $(0.90)(100) = 90$ as your score. If you turned the paper in two days late, you would receive $(0.90)(90) = 81$ as your score.

2. Copy and extend Mr. Peters's table to show the score you would receive on a perfect paper that is up to ten days late.

### Mr. Peters's Late Policy

| Days late | Score |
|---|---|
| 0 | 100 |
| 1 | 90 |
| 2 | 81 |

3. a. Explain how you figured out the scores in the table. Show some sample calculations.
   b. After how many days would your score for a late paper drop below 50?
   c. Would your score ever reach 0? Explain.

Mr. Riley, another algebra teacher, has a *10 points off* policy. This means that you lose ten points for each day that your paper is late.

**4.** Copy and extend Mr. Riley's table to show the score you would receive on a perfect paper that is up to ten days late.

### Mr. Riley's Late Policy

| Days late | Score |
|:---:|:---:|
| 0 | 100 |
| 1 | 90 |
| 2 | 80 |

**5.** a  After how many days would your score for a late paper drop below 50?

   b. Would your score ever reach 0? Explain.

**6.** Graph the data in the two tables showing how the score decreases as a function of the number of days late. Use the same axes for both graphs so that you can compare them.

**7.** ◉━ Write an equation that gives your score (*S*) on a perfect paper as a function of the number of days late (*D*)

   a. in Mr. Peters's class;

   b. in Mr. Riley's class.

**8.** ◉━

   a. One of the equations you wrote in problem 7 should have an exponent. (If it doesn't, check your work.) Which equation has an exponent, the *percent off* policy, or the *points off* policy?

   b. Write each equation you wrote in problem 7 on the corresponding graph. Does the equation containing an exponent correspond to the straight graph or to the curved graph?

**9.** Compare Mr. Riley's policy with Mr. Peters's policy. Which one do you prefer, and why? Give reasons why some students might prefer one policy and some students another.

### DISCOUNTER INTRODUCES REDUCTIONS!

A store offers a 5% discount to students. If something costs $15.00 after the discount is taken, how much does it cost without the discount? You can use percent decrease and algebra to solve this problem. If the price before the discount is $x$, and the decrease due to the discount is $0.05x$, then

$$x - 0.05x = \$15.00.$$

**10.** ◉━ Remember that $x$ can be written $1x$.

   a. Combine like terms on the left side of the equation. (Or factor the $x$.)

   b. Then solve for $x$.

**11.** Solve for $x$.

   a. $0.2x = 240$

   b. $x - 0.8x = 18.2$

   c. $x - 0.06x = 23.50$

   d. $x - 0.75x = 22.5$

**12.** Solve for $x$.

   a. $(0.75)(0.75)x = 11.25$

   b. $(0.65)^3 x = 4.12$

Look back at the ad for Sherman's Store.

**13. a.** If the clearance sale price is $13.50, what was the original price, before the 30% discount?

   **b.** If the original price was $20.95, what is the 30% discount price?

**14.** Report Let $x$ be the original price of an item. Write two algebraic expressions for the early-bird price, one that will give the amount Cal would charge, and one for the amount G.D. would charge. Explain how you figured out these two expressions. Show that they work, by substituting the prices from the table into the expression.

---

**REVIEW** *RATE OF CHANGE*

**15.** Find a function $y = mx + b$ for which

   **a.** $y$ increases when $x$ increases;

   **b.** $y$ increases when $x$ decreases;

   **c.** $y$ never increases.

**16.** Find a function $y = mx + b$, with $m$ positive, for which $y$ changes

   **a.** faster than $x$;

   **b.** more slowly than $x$;

   **c.** at the same rate as $x$.

**17.** $\bigcirc$ $y = x^7$ and $y = 2^x$ are having a race. When $x = 1$, $x^7 = 1$ and $2^x = 2$, so $y = 2^x$ is ahead. When $x = 3$, $x^7 = 2187$ and $2^x = 8$, so $y = x^7$ is ahead. As $x$ gets larger and larger, who will win the race? Use your calculators and make a table to find out.

# 8.B Simple and Compound Interest

Money in a savings account usually earns either *simple* or *compound* interest. For example, suppose you invest $100 and earn 5% interest per year. If you earn *simple* interest, you will earn $5 for every year that the money is invested, since 5 is 5% of 100. If you earn *compound* interest, you will earn $5 for the first year the money is invested. In the next year, if you keep the entire $105 in the bank, you will earn 5% interest on $105. In other words, compound interest pays you interest on the interest as well as on the original investment.

The table shows what would happen to your investment in both cases for the first few years.

### Total account balance, with:

| Year | Simple interest | Compound interest |
|------|-----------------|-------------------|
| 0 | 100 | 100 |
| 1 | 105 | 105 |
| 2 | 110 | 110.25 |
| 3 | 115 | 115.76 |

1.  a.  With simple interest, your account balance for each year can be obtained by *adding* a certain amount to the amount from the previous year. Find this amount.

    b.  With compound interest, your account balance for each year can be obtained by *multiplying* by a certain amount each year. Find this amount.

2.  Write two equations (one for simple interest and one for compound interest) giving the account balance as the function of the year for:

    a.  5% interest on the amount $100;

    b.  12% interest on the amount $100;

    c.  12% interest on the amount $500.

3.  **Report** Write a report comparing simple and compound interest. Your report should include, but not be limited to, the following:
    - Equations for simple and compound interest that give the account balance as a function of time invested. Show how to change the equations if you change the amount of money invested or the interest rate. Explain how you figured out the equations.
    - A comparison of how the amount in the account grows in each case. Which grows linearly and which grows exponentially? Explain how you know.
    - An analysis of an example: Choose an amount to invest and an interest rate, and make a table or graph comparing the amount you would have in the account with simple and with compound interest. Assume you leave the money and the interest in the account for 25 years. Use a graph to illustrate.

4.  Find a formula for the difference in the account balance after $n$ years for two accounts that start with an original investment of $s$ dollars at $p$ percent interest, if one account earns simple interest and the other earns compound interest.

5.  Say you have some money invested at 7% compound interest. How many *months* does it take for your investment to double? (Find a formula, then use decimal exponents on your calculator to find out what fraction of a year past a whole number of years it will take.)

*Chapter 8 Growth and Change*

# Equal Powers

**In this lesson, use only whole number exponents.**

1. **Exploration** The number 64 can be written as a power in at least three different ways, as $2^6$, $8^2$, or $4^3$.

   a. Find some numbers that can be written as powers in two different ways.

   b. Find another number that can be written as a power in three different ways.

### POWERS OF 3 AND 9

2. Using your calculator if necessary, try to find a power of 3 that is equal to each power of 9 below. If any are impossible, say so. Fill in the exponent.

   a. $9^2 = 81 = 3^?$

   b. $9^5 = 59049 = 3^?$

   c. $9^{10} = 3^?$

   d. $9^0 = 3^?$

3. Using your calculator if necessary, try to find a power of 9 that is equal to each power of 3 below. If any are impossible, say so. Fill in the exponent.

   a. $3^8 = 6561 = 9^?$

   b. $3^5 = 243 = 9^?$

   c. $3^{14} = 9^?$

   d. $3^0 = 9^?$

4. ⌗

   a. Can every power of 9 be written as a power of 3? If so, explain why. If not, show some that can and some that can't, and explain the difference.

   b. Can every power of 3 be written as a power of 9? If so, explain why. If not, show some that can and some that can't, and explain the difference.

### POWERS OF 2, 4, 6, AND 8

5. Find two powers of 2 (other than 64) that can be written as powers of 8.

6. If the same number is written as both a power of 2 and a power of 8, how do the exponents compare? Explain and give examples.

7. Find at least three powers of 2 that can be written as powers of 4. Compare the exponents and describe what you notice.

8. Find at least two powers of 2 that can be written as powers of 16. Compare the exponents and describe what you notice.

9. ⌗

   a. Which powers of 2 can be written as powers of 8? Explain, giving examples.

   b. Which powers of 8 can be written as powers of 2? Explain, giving examples.

   c. Find the smallest number (besides 1) that can be written as a power of 2, a power of 4, and a power of 8. Write it in all three ways. How do you know that it is the smallest?

10. ⌗ Can you find a number that can be written as a power of 2, a power of 4, and a power of 6? If so, find it. If not, explain why it is impossible.

### WRITING POWERS USING DIFFERENT BASES

11. Write each number as a power using a smaller base.

   a. $8^2$        b. $27^3$        c. $25^3$

   d. $16^4$       e. $49^2$        f. $2^0$

**12.** Write each number as a power using a larger base.

a. $3^2$      b. $9^4$      c. $4^8$

d. $5^8$      e. $6^6$      f. $95^0$

**13.** If possible, write each number as a power using a different base. (Do not use the exponent 1.) If it is not possible, explain why not.

a. $3^4$           b. $3^3$

c. $4^5$           d. $3^5$

**14.** Repeat problem 13 for these numbers.

a. $5^4$           b. $5^3$

c. $25^2$         d. $26^4$

**15.** | Summary | If you exclude the exponent 1, when it is possible to write a number in two or more ways as a power? Does it depend on the base, the exponent, or both? Explain. (Give examples of some equivalent powers and of numbers that can be written as powers in only one way.)

**16.** | Generalization | Fill in the exponents.

a. $9^x = 3^?$      b. $4^x = 2^?$

c. $8^x = 2^?$      d. $16^x =$

e. $25^x =$

### A POWER OF A POWER

Since $9 = 3^2$, the power $9^3$ can be written as $(3^2)^3$. The expression $(3^2)^3$ is a *power of a power* of 3.

**17.** a. Write $25^3$ as a power of a power of 5.

b. Write $8^5$ as a power of a power of 2.

c. Write $9^4$ as a power of a power of 3.

There is often a simpler way to write a power of a power. For example:

$$(3^5)^2 = (3^5)(3^5)$$
$$= (3 \cdot 3 \cdot 3 \cdot 3 \cdot 3)(3 \cdot 3 \cdot 3 \cdot 3 \cdot 3)$$
$$= 3^{10}$$

**18.** a. Show how $(2^5)^3$ can be written with one exponent as a power of 2.

b. Write $(3^4)^2$ as a power of 3.

**19.** ⚷ Is $(4^5)^3$ equal to $4^8$, to $4^{15}$, or to neither? Explain.

### Generalizations

**20.** Fill in the exponents.

a. $(x^2)^3 = x^?$      b. $y^4 = (y^2)^?$

c. $y^{10} = (y^5)^?$      d. $y^6 = (y^3)^?$

e. $(x^4)^3 = x^?$

**21.** Fill in the exponents.

a. $(y^2)^x = y^?$      b. $(y^3)^x = y^?$

c. $(x^4)^y = x^?$      d. $y^{ax} = (y^x)^?$

The generalization you made in problem 21 is one of the *laws of exponents*. It is sometimes called the *power of a power law:*

$$(x^a)^b = x^{ab}, \text{ as long as } x \text{ is not } 0.$$

**22.** ⚷ Explain how the ideas you discussed in problem 15 are related to the power of a power law.

# Working With Monomials

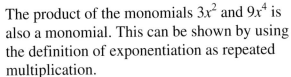

The product of the monomials $3x^2$ and $9x^4$ is also a monomial. This can be shown by using the definition of exponentiation as repeated multiplication.

$$3x^2 = 3 \cdot x \cdot x \text{ and } 9x^4 = 9 \cdot x \cdot x \cdot x \cdot x$$
so
$$3x^2 \cdot 9x^4 = 3 \cdot x \cdot x \cdot 9 \cdot x \cdot x \cdot x \cdot x = 27x^6$$

1. Find another pair of monomials whose product is $27x^6$.

2. **Exploration** If possible, find at least two answers to each of these problems. Write $27x^6$ as:
   a. the product of three monomials
   b. the sum of three monomials
   c. a monomial raised to a power
   d. the quotient of two monomials
   e. the difference of two monomials

## PRODUCT OF POWERS

The monomial $48x^9$ can be written as a product in many different ways. For example, $16x^6 \cdot 3x^3$ and $12x^5 \cdot 4x^3 \cdot x$ are both equal to $48x^9$.

3. Write $48x^9$ in three more ways as a product of two or more monomials.

4. Write $35x^4$ as a product in which one of the factors is
   a. a third-degree monomial;
   b. a monomial with a coefficient of 7;
   c. $5x^0$;
   d. $35x^3$.

5. Write $7.2 \cdot 10^8$ in three ways as the product of two numbers in scientific notation.

6. Write $x^5$ in three ways as a product of two or more monomials.

7. **Generalization** Study your answers to problem 6. Then fill in the exponent.
$$x^a \cdot x^b = x^?$$
Explain.

8. If possible, write each expression more simply. If it is not possible, explain why not.
   a. $3x^5 \cdot 6x^4$     b. $x^5 \cdot y^7$
   c. $y^7 \cdot y^3$       d. $4a^4 \cdot 9a^3$

The generalization you made is one of the laws of exponents. It is sometimes called the *product of powers* law. It says that
$$x^a \cdot x^b = x^{a+b}, \text{ as long as } x \text{ is not } 0.$$
However, notice that it works only when the bases are the same.

## POWER OF A PRODUCT

The expression $x^4 \cdot y^4 \cdot z^4$ is the product of three powers. Since the bases are not the same, we cannot use the product of powers law. However, notice that since the exponents are the same, it is possible to write a product of powers as a single power
$$x^4 y^4 z^4 = x \cdot x \cdot x \cdot x \cdot y \cdot y \cdot y \cdot y \cdot z \cdot z \cdot z \cdot z$$
$$= xyz \cdot xyz \cdot xyz \cdot xyz$$
$$= (xyz)^4$$

9. Write $16a^2b^2$ as the square of a monomial. (Hint: First rewrite 16 as a power.)

10. Write $p^3q^3$ as the cube of a monomial.

11. If possible, write each expression as a single power. If it is not possible, explain why not.
    a. $32n^5m^5$       b. $x^2y^3$
    c. $(2n)^7 \cdot (3m)^7$   d. $(ab)^4 \cdot (bc)^4$

The generalization you used above is another of the laws of exponents. It is sometimes called the *power of a product* law. It says that
$$x^a y^a = (xy)^a,$$ as long as x and y are not 0.
However, notice that it works only when the exponents are the same.

**12.** Write without parentheses.
  a. $(6y)^2$     b. $(3xy)^4$
  c. $(5xyz)^3$   d. $(2x)^3$
  e. $(2xy)^3$    f. $(2xyz)^3$

**13.** Write $64x^3 y^6 z^9$ as the cube of a monomial.

### POWER OF A RATIO

**14.** Write 49/25 as the square of a ratio.

Study this example.
$$\left(\frac{x}{y}\right)^3 = \frac{x}{y} \cdot \frac{x}{y} \cdot \frac{x}{y} = \frac{x \cdot x \cdot x}{y \cdot y \cdot y} = \frac{x^3}{y^3}$$
This law of exponents is called the *power of a ratio* law. It says that
$$\frac{x^a}{y^a} = \left(\frac{x}{y}\right)^a,$$ as long as x and y are not 0.

However, notice that it works only when the exponents are the same.

**15.** Write as a power of a ratio.
  a. $8x^3/y^6$     b. $16x^4/x^{10}$

**16.** Write as a ratio of monomials.
  a. $(5x/7z)^9$     b. $(2xy/yz)^2$

### RATIOS OF MONOMIALS

Consider the ratio $6x^5/4x^7$. By multiplying numerator and denominator by x, you can get the equivalent ratio $6x^6/4x^7$. Or you can get an equivalent ratio in lowest terms by noticing that
$$\frac{6x^5}{4x^7} = \frac{3}{2x^2} \cdot \frac{2x^5}{2x^5} = \frac{3}{2x^2}.$$

**17.** Explain the example above.

**18.** Write in lowest terms.
  a. $8x^8/6x^9$     b. $7x^7/5x^4$

In some cases, a ratio can be simplified to a monomial. For example,
$$\frac{150x^6}{50x^4} = 3x^2.$$

**19.** a. Explain this example.
  b. Write $3x^2$ as a ratio of monomials in three other ways.

**20.** Write $12y^3$ as a quotient of two monomials in which
  a. one is a fourth-degree monomial;
  b. one has a coefficient of 5;
  c. one is a monomial of degree 0.

**21.** Write $1.2 \cdot 10^4$ in three ways as the quotient of two numbers in scientific notation.

**22.** a. Write $x^5$ as a ratio in three ways.
  b. Find three ratios equivalent to $1/x^5$.

**23.** Generalization Study your answers to problem 22. Compare the situations in (a) and (b). Explain how to simplify a ratio whose numerator and denominator are powers of x.

**24.** Fill in the exponent, assuming $p > q$.
$$\frac{x^p}{x^q} = x^?$$

**25.** Write these ratios in lowest terms.
  a. $3x^5/6x^4$     b. $x^5/y^7$
  c. $y^3/y^7$       d. $45a^4/9a^3$

**26.** 💡 Write as a power of 6. $\dfrac{6^{x-5}}{6^{5-x}}$

### SOLVING EQUATIONS

Solve for x.

**27.** a. $\dfrac{5^{2x}}{5^x} = 5^7$     b. $\dfrac{(7^2)^x}{7^4} = 7^6$

**28.** a. $\dfrac{(3 \cdot 5)^3}{108 \cdot 5^x} = \dfrac{1}{20}$     b. $\dfrac{3^3 \cdot 4^7}{3 \cdot 4^x} = \left(\dfrac{3}{4}\right)^2$

**29.** 💡
  a. $\dfrac{3 \cdot 4^{6p}}{9 \cdot 4^x} = \dfrac{1}{3 \cdot 4^{4p}}$     b. $\dfrac{15h^x}{12h^a} = \dfrac{5}{4h^6}$

# Negative Bases, Negative Exponents

In previous lessons, we have considered only whole number exponents. Does a negative exponent have any meaning? To answer this, consider these patterns.

| | |
|---|---|
| $3^4 = 81$ | $(1/3)^4 = 1/81$ |
| $3^3 = 27$ | $(1/3)^3 = 1/27$ |
| $3^2 = 9$ | $(1/3)^2 = 1/9$ |
| $3^1 = 3$ | $(1/3)^1 = 1/3$ |
| $3^0 = 1$ | $(1/3)^0 = 1$ |
| $3^{-1} = ?$ | $(1/3)^{-1} = ?$ |

**1.** a. Look at the powers of 3. How is each number related to the number above it? Following this pattern, what should the value of $3^{-1}$ be?

b. Now look for a pattern in the powers of 1/3. As the exponent increases, does the value of the power increase or decrease? Following this pattern, what should the value of $(1/3)^{-1}$ be?

c. Compare the values of $3^{-1}$, $3^1$, $(1/3)^1$ and $(1/3)^{-1}$. How are they related?

d. Use the pattern you found to extend the table down to $3^{-4}$ and $(1/3)^{-4}$.

Another way to figure out the meaning of negative exponents is to use the product of powers law. For example, to figure out the meaning of $3^{-1}$, note that:

$$3^{-1} \cdot 3^2 = 3^1$$
$$3^{-1} \cdot 9 = 3$$

But the only number that can be multiplied by 9 to get 3 is 1/3, so $3^{-1}$ must equal 1/3.

**2.** Find the value of $3^{-1}$ by applying the product of powers law to $3^1 \cdot 3^{-1}$.

**3.** Use the same logic to find the value of:
a. $3^{-2}$;      b. $3^{-x}$.

**4.** Are the answers you found in problem 3 consistent with the pattern you found in problem 1? Explain.

**5.** Summary People who have not studied algebra (and, unfortunately, many who have) think that $5^{-2}$ equals a negative number, such as −25.

a. Write a convincing argument using the product of powers law to explain why this is not true.

b. Show how to find the value of $5^{-2}$ using a pattern like the one in problem 1.

**6.** a. Show that $5x^2$ and $5x^{-2}$ are not reciprocals, by showing that their product is not 1.

b. Find the reciprocal of $5x^2$.

A bacterial culture doubles every hour. At this moment it weighs 10 grams.

**7.** What did it weigh
a. 1 hour ago?
b. 2 hours ago?
c. $x$ hours ago?

**8.** ⚷
a. Explain why the weight of the bacteria culture $x$ hours from now is given by
$$W = 10 \cdot 2^x.$$

b. Explain the meaning of substituting a negative value for $x$.

9. Show your calculations, using the equation in problem 8, to find out:
   a. how much it will weigh in three hours;
   b. how much it weighed three hours ago.

In 1975 the world population was about 4.01 billion and growing at the rate of 2% per year.

10. ⌿— If it continued to grow at that rate, write a formula for the world population after $x$ years.

If it had been growing at the same rate before 1975, we could estimate the population in previous years by using negative values of $x$ in the formula.

11. Use your calculator to find the value of $(1.02)^4$ and its reciprocal, $(1.02)^{-4}$.

12. Show your calculations using the equation in problem 10 to estimate the population in:
   a. 1971;          b. 1979.

13. Assume the world population had been growing at this rate since 1925.
   a. Estimate the world population in 1925.
   b. Compare this number with the actual world population in 1925, which was about 2 billion. Was the population growth rate between 1925 and 1975 more or less than 2%? Explain.

### RATIO OF POWERS

Negative exponents often arise when simplifying ratios of monomials.

This law of exponents is sometimes called the *ratio of powers* law:

$$\frac{x^a}{x^b} = x^{a-b} \text{ , as long as } x \text{ is not } 0.$$

However, notice that it works only when the bases are the same.

**Examples:**

$$\frac{x^6}{x^7} = x^{6-7} = x^{-1} \text{ or } \frac{1}{x^1}$$

$$\frac{x^{3a}}{x^{5a}} = x^{3a-5a} = x^{-2a} \text{ or } \frac{1}{x^{2a}}$$

14. Simplify.
   a. $4x^6/5x^7$          b. $2x^8y^3/2xy$
   c. $y^3/y^7$            d. $45a/9a^5$

15. Simplify these ratios.
   a. $\dfrac{400a^5}{25a^2}$          b. $\dfrac{400x^3}{200x^8}$
   c. $\dfrac{3m^6}{9m^3}$            d. $\dfrac{9R^a}{3R^a}$

16. ◯
   a. Write as a power of 4, $4^{3+x}/4^{3-x}$.
   b. Write as a power of 7, $7^{5x-5}/7^{5x-6}$.

17. Solve for $x$.
   a. $\dfrac{7^4}{7^{x+2}} = 7^3$
   b. $\dfrac{3 \cdot 5^{x+2}}{12 \cdot 5^2} = \dfrac{1}{20}$

18. Divide without using your calculator. Then, if your answer is not already in scientific notation, convert it to scientific notation.
   a. $\dfrac{4.2 \cdot 10^5}{3.0 \cdot 10^2}$          b. $\dfrac{3.0 \cdot 10^4}{1.5 \cdot 10^6}$
   c. $\dfrac{1.5 \cdot 10^3}{3.0 \cdot 10^6}$          d. $\dfrac{9 \cdot 10^a}{3 \cdot 10^b}$

### OPPOSITES

The expression $(-5)^3$ has a negative base. This expression means *raise -5 to the third power.* The expression $-5^3$ has a positive base. This expression means *raise 5 to the third power and take the opposite of the result.*

**19.** 🔑 Which of these expressions represent negative numbers? Show the calculations or explain the reasoning leading to your conclusions.

$-5^3$   $(-5)^3$   $-5^2$   $(-7)^{15}$   $(-7)^{14}$

$-5^{-3}$   $(-5)^{-3}$   $-5^{-2}$   $(-7)^{-15}$   $(-7)^{-14}$

**20.** 🔑
   a. Is $(-5)^n$ always, sometimes, or never the opposite of $5^n$? Explain, using examples.
   b. Is $-5^n$ always, sometimes, or never the opposite of $5^n$? Explain, using examples.

**EARLY PAPERS**

Ms. Kem has a policy that penalizes students for turning in papers late. Her students are trying to convince her to give them extra points for turning in their papers early. Some students propose a policy based on adding points. Others propose one based on increasing by a percentage.

**21.** If you were her student, what kind of early paper policy would you propose?

**22.** Using your policy, what would your score be, if your paper were $x$ days early?

## REVIEW WHICH IS GREATER?

Or are they equal?

**23.** a. $x - 0.30x$    b. $0.70x$

**24.** a. $(0.70)(0.70)x$    b. $x - 0.50x$

**25.** a. $(0.90)(0.90)(0.90)x$
   b. $x - 0.10x - 0.10x - 0.10x$

## REVIEW EQUATION SOLVING

Solve for $x$.

**26.** a. $(0.85)(0.85)(0.85)(0.85)x = 18.79$
   b. $x - 0.2x = 160$
   c. $0.80x = 500$

**27.** $\dfrac{50b^3}{xb} = 2b^2$

**28.** $\dfrac{20a^{m+1}}{10a^m} = 2a^x$

## REVIEW WHAT'S THE FUNCTION?

**29.** Find the slope of the line that goes through each pair of points. Then find the equation for the line. (Hint: A sketch may help.)
   a. $(0, 1)$ and $(2, 3)$
   b. $(0, 4)$ and $(0.5, -6)$
   c. $(0, 7)$ and $(-0.8, 0.9)$

**30.** In problem 29
   a. how did you find the $y$-intercept?
   b. how did you find the slope?

**31.** 💡 Find the equation for the line
   a. having slope 0.9, passing through $(2, -1)$;
   b. having slope 3.4, passing through $(6.7, 9)$;
   c. passing through $(8, 2)$ and $(1.3, -5.4)$.

# Small and Large Numbers

1. Using a power of ten, write the reciprocal of each number.
   a. $10^2$          b. $10^4$          c. 0.001

## SMALL NUMBERS IN SCIENTIFIC NOTATION

Any decimal number can be written in many ways as a product of a decimal number and a power of 10. For example, 43,000 can be written:

$$0.43 \cdot 10^5$$
$$4.3 \cdot 10^4$$
$$43 \cdot 10^3$$
$$430 \cdot 10^2$$
$$4300 \cdot 10^1$$

2. Write 43,000 as a product of a decimal number and
   a. $10^0$;          b. $10^{-1}$;          c. $10^{-2}$.

3. a. Write 0.065 in three ways as a product of a decimal number and a power of 10. At least one way should use a negative exponent.
   b. Write 0.065 in scientific notation. (Remember that scientific notation requires multiplying a number greater than or equal to 1 and less than 10 by a power of 10.)

4. Which of these numbers would require a negative exponent when written in scientific notation? Explain why.
   0.0123     0.123     12.3     1230

5. ⚷ How can you tell by looking at a decimal number whether or not it will require a negative exponent when it is written in scientific notation?

## RECIPROCALS

Al and Abe, having nothing else to do, were arguing about reciprocals. Abe said, "If $10^{-4}$ is the reciprocal of $10^4$, then $2.5 \cdot 10^{-4}$ is the reciprocal of $2.5 \cdot 10^4$." Al said, "I can prove that you're wrong by finding their product."

6. If $2.5 \cdot 10^{-4}$ is the reciprocal of $2.5 \cdot 10^4$, what should their product be?

7. ⚷ Settle the argument between Al and Abe. If Abe has not found the correct reciprocal of $2.5 \cdot 10^4$, find it for him. Explain.

8. Find an approximation for the reciprocal of $4.6 \cdot 10^{-6}$. Give your answer in scientific notation.

## UNITS AND RECIPROCALS

9. Dick walks at the rate of about five miles in one hour. What fraction of an hour does it take him to walk one mile?

10. Stanley can run about ten miles in one hour. What fraction of an hour does it take him to run one mile?

11. A snail travels at the rate of 0.005 miles per hour. How many hours does it take the snail to slither one mile?

Notice that your answers to problems 9-11 are the reciprocals of the rates given. This is not a coincidence. In each case, the rate is given in *miles/hour* and you are asked to find *hours/mile*. Since the units are reciprocals, the rates will also be reciprocals.

12. Sound travels through air at the rate of $1.088 \cdot 10^3$ feet per second at sea level. How long does it take sound to travel one foot?

13. Sound travels much faster through granite than through air. Its speed is about $1.2906 \cdot 10^4$ feet per second. How long does it take sound to travel one foot through granite?

## UNITS IN THE METRIC SYSTEM

The metric system of measurement is based on powers of ten. Prefixes indicating powers of ten are used for all measurements within the metric system. Conversion between units is easy, since it involves multiplying by powers of ten.

**Example:** The prefix *kilo* means to multiply the basic unit of measure by $10^3$, or 1000. A kilogram is 1000 grams, a kilometer is 1000 meters, and so on. This table lists some of these prefixes.

| To Multiply by | Prefix |
|:---:|:---:|
| $10^{12}$ | tera- |
| $10^9$ | giga- |
| $10^6$ | mega- |
| $10^3$ | kilo- |
| $10^2$ | hecto- |
| $10^1$ | deka- |
| $10^0$ | — |
| $10^{-1}$ | deci- |
| $10^{-2}$ | centi- |
| $10^{-3}$ | milli- |
| $10^{-6}$ | micro- |
| $10^{-9}$ | nano |
| $10^{-12}$ | pico- |

14. Express the size of each object in terms of a more appropriate unit of measurement.
    a. A redwood tree is 80,023 millimeters high.
    b. A protozoan is 0.0000002 kilometers in diameter.
    c. A football player weighs 95,130 grams.

15. At the San Andreas fault in Northern California, the ground is moving about $5 \cdot 10^{-5}$ kilometers per year. How long will it take to move one kilometer?

16. ◯ If hair grows at the rate of about $10^{-8}$ miles per hour, how long would it take your hair to reach ankle length? (Why is this problem harder than the previous ones?)

# 8.C Applying the Laws of Exponents

Tina overslept and had to skip breakfast, so she didn't do very well on her math test. Besides, she had forgotten to study the laws of exponents. In fact, she missed *all* the problems.

---

Test        Name: *Tina A.*

### Exponents

Instructions: Simplify. Your answer should have only one exponent. Not all are possible.

a. $2^4 \cdot 3^4 = 5^4$

b. $3^{15} + 6^{15} = 9^{15}$

c. $3x^2 \cdot 2x^3 = 5x^5$

d. $\dfrac{x^7}{y^3} = \left(\dfrac{x}{y}\right)^4$

e. $10x^5 \cdot 8x^9 = 80x^{45}$

f. $(2x)^7 = 2x^7$

g. $12x^3 \cdot 4y^7 = 48(xy)^{10}$

h. $\left(\dfrac{3^7}{3^5}\right)^3 = 1^6$

i. $(3x^2)^3 = 3x^5$

j. $x^3 + x^2 = x^5$

---

1. Summarize the five laws of exponents given in Lessons 9, 10, and 11.

2. Correct Tina's test. For each problem, write the correct answer. If one or more of the laws of exponents was used, tell which law (or laws) was used. If the expression cannot be simplified, say so.

3. Take Tina's make-up test for her. Be careful! (Remember, make-up tests are always harder.)

---

Make-up Test        Name: *Tina A.*

### Laws of Exponents

Instructions: Show all work leading to your answer.

a. Write without parentheses: $(4x^2y^3z)^3$

Perform each operation, and *if possible* write the result as a power of 5.

b. $5^{11} - 5^9$

c. $5^{x+3}/5^x$

d. $5^5 \cdot \underline{\quad} = 5^{15}$

e. $5^7 + 5^3$

If possible, write as a power of 12.

f. $3 \cdot 4^3$

g. $(3 \cdot 4)^5$

h. $2 \cdot 6^8$

i. $2^8 \cdot 6^8$

j. $2^8 \cdot 6^5$

Which expression is not equal to the other two?

k. $3^{100}$     $6^{75}$     $9^{50}$

l. $(y^2)^4$     $(y^4)^2$     $y^4y^2$

m. $a^7$     $a^3 + a^4$     $a^3 \cdot a^4$

Write the opposite of the reciprocal of $(1/2)^5$

n. using a negative exponent;

o. using a positive exponent.

---

# ◆ Essential Ideas

The table shows the estimated population of North America from 1650 to 1950.

| Year | Population (thousands) |
|------|------------------------|
| 1650 | 5000 |
| 1750 | 5000 |
| 1850 | 39,000 |
| 1900 | 106,000 |
| 1950 | 219,000 |

**1.** What is the population increase in each 100-year period?

**2.** Graph the data.
   a. What is the meaning of slope for this data?
   b. Is the slope constant or does it increase or decrease? Explain.

**3.** Estimate the population of North America in the year
   a. 1800;        b. 2000.
   Explain how you arrive at your estimates.

SAME DIAGRAM, DIFFERENT SCALE

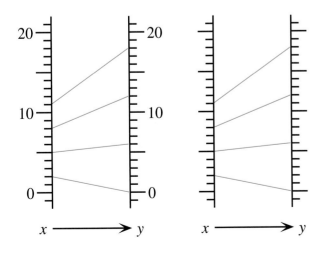

**4.** Make an in-out table for the function diagram on the left. What is the function illustrated?

**5.** The function diagram on the right is the same, except that the number lines are not labeled. Copy the diagram, and put labels on it, using the same scale on both the *x*- and *y*-number lines. Make an in-out table, and find the function .

**6.** Repeat problem 5 two times. For each diagram, make an in-out table and find the function.

**7.** Summary
   a. For the functions you found in problems 4-6, when *x* increases by 1, what does *y* increase by? Does it depend on the scale you used?
   b. Compare the functions you found in problems 4-6. How are they the same? How are they different? Explain.

SLOPE AND INTERCEPT

The following questions are about the graph of $y = mx + b$.

**8.** Describe the line if $b = 0$ and
   a. $m > 1$          b. $0 < m < 1$
   c. $m = 0$          d. $-1 < m < 0$
   e. $m < -1$

**9.** In which quadrants does the line lie if
   a. $b > 0, m > 0$?   b. $b < 0, m > 0$?
   c. $b > 0, m < 0$?   d. $b < 0, m < 0$?

**10.** How would lines be the same or different if
   a. they have the same value for *b* and different values for *m*?
   b. they have the same value for *m* and different values for *b*?

### LINEAR AND EXPONENTIAL GROWTH

**11.** Two populations are growing exponentially. At time 0, both have populations of 100. If one is growing twice as fast as the other, how do their populations compare after:

a. 2 hours?    b. 3 hours?

c. $x$ hours?

**12.** `Report` A recent college graduate was offered a job with a salary of $20,000 per year and a guarantee of a 5% raise every year. She was about to accept the job when she received another offer for an identical job with a salary of $22,000 per year and a guarantee of a $1200 raise each year. Explain how you would help her decide which job to accept.

### LAWS OF EXPONENTS

**13.** If possible, write as a power of 4.

a. $2 \cdot 2^6$      b. $(2 \cdot 2)^6$

c. $2 \cdot 2^5$      d. $2^7 \cdot 2^5$

e. $2^5 \cdot 2^5$

**14.** If possible, write as a power of 6.

a. $2 \cdot 3^5$      b. $(2 \cdot 3)^5$

c. $36^7$      d. $36^0$

**15.** If possible, write as a power of 3.

a. $9 \cdot 3^5 \cdot 3^2 \cdot 3^0$

b. $9 \cdot 3^5 \cdot 3^2 \cdot 2^0$

c. $9 \cdot 3^5 \cdot 2^2 \cdot 2^0$

d. $81 \cdot (3^5)^4 \cdot 6^0$

**16.** If possible, write as a single monomial.

a. $8a^{12} - 2(3a^3)^4$

b. $\left(\dfrac{6t^3}{4}\right)^2 - t^5$

**17.** Find values of $a$, $b$, and $c$ so that

a. $(a \cdot b)^c > a \cdot b^c$;

b. $(a \cdot b)^c = a \cdot b^c$;

c. $(a \cdot b)^c < a \cdot b^c$.

**18.** Find the number or expression that makes each equation true. Write your answer as a power.

a. $(3x)^4 = \underline{\quad} \cdot x^4$

b. $(5t)^3 = \underline{\quad} \cdot t^3$

c. $(12xy)^3 = \underline{\quad} \cdot (3xy)^3$

**19.** Simplify each ratio.

a. $(2x^5)/x^5$      b. $(2x)^5/x^5$

c. Explain why your answers to (a) and (b) are different.

**20.** Find the number that makes each equation true. Write your answer as a power.

a. $100 \cdot (2R)^5 = \underline{\quad} \cdot 100 \cdot R^5$

b. $20 \cdot (2x)^7 = \underline{\quad} \cdot 20 \cdot x^7$

c. $(2xyz)^{10} = \underline{\quad} \cdot (xyz)^{10}$

**21.** Find the number that makes each equation true. Write your answer as a power.

a. $100 \cdot (3R)^5 = \underline{\quad} \cdot 100 \cdot R^5$

b. $20 \cdot (3x)^7 = \underline{\quad} \cdot 20 \cdot x^7$

c. $(3xyz)^{10} = \underline{\quad} \cdot (xyz)^{10}$

**22.** ⚲ Find the reciprocal. Check by showing that the product is 1.

a. $14x^3y^3$      b. $-3a^5$

c. $\dfrac{1}{3b^2}$

Because of variables in the exponents, these problems are more challenging.

**23.** Simplify.

a. $\dfrac{9 \cdot 10^{a+5}}{3 \cdot 10^a}$      b. $\dfrac{3 \cdot 10^{b+2}}{9 \cdot 10^b}$

c. $\dfrac{9 \cdot R^{a+5}}{3 \cdot R^a}$      d. $\dfrac{12 \cdot y^{b+2}}{10 \cdot y^b}$

**24.** Write as a power of 5.

a. $\dfrac{5^{2x-2}}{5^{x-5}}$      b. $\dfrac{5^{x-5}}{5^{2x-2}}$

**25.** Write as a power of 4. $\left(\dfrac{4^{3+x}}{4^{3-x}}\right)^3$

## VERY SMALL NUMBERS

A proton weighs $1.674 \cdot 10^{-24}$ grams, an electron weighs $9.110 \cdot 10^{-28}$ grams, and Ann weighs 48 kilograms.

**26.** Which is heavier, a proton or an electron? How many times as heavy?

**27.** Ann weighs the same as how many
   a. electrons?
   b. protons?

**28.** The mean distance between the Earth and the sun is $1.50 \cdot 10^{11}$ meters. This length is called one *astronomical unit* (AU) and is a convenient unit for measuring distances in the solar system. The distance $10^{-10}$ meters is called one *angstrom* (after the Swedish physicist Anders Angstrom). It is a convenient unit for measuring atoms. How many angstroms are in one AU?

The scroll-like spirals in the capital of a Greek column

## Coming in this chapter:

**Exploration** There are four geoboard segments that start at the origin and have length 5. Find their endpoints. Use this to help you solve the following problem: If you know that two sides of a geoboard triangle are of length 5, what are the possible lengths for the third side?

# MEASUREMENT AND SQUARE ROOTS

## LESSON 9.1

# Distance

**You will need:**

graph paper

### TAXICAB DISTANCE

1. Assume you can travel only horizontally and vertically on the Cartesian plane, never letting your $x$- or $y$-coordinates decrease.
   a. Find at least three ways to get from the origin to (3, 4).
   b. Does the travel distance depend on the path you found in part (a) or is it the same for all of them? Explain.

**Definition:** The *taxicab distance* between two points in the Cartesian plane is the length of the *shortest path* between them that consists of *only* horizontal and vertical segments. Taxicab distance gets its name because it models distance in a city with a network of perpendicular streets.

**Example:** The taxicab distance from (10, 8) to (5, 4) is 9.

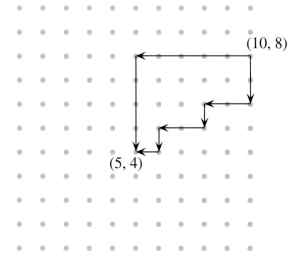

2. What is the taxicab distance between:
   a. (1, 2) and (6, 7)?
   b. (1, 2) and (1, 7)?
   c. (1, 7) and (6, 2)?
   d. (−1, −7) and (6, −2)?
   e. (1.2, 3.4) and (5.67, 8.9)?

3. a. Find all the points that are at taxicab distance 5 from (5, 5). Sketch them.
   b. Describe the shape you found in part (a). Some math teachers call this shape a *taxicab circle*. Explain why.
   c. What else might this shape be called?

4. Describe the set of points whose taxicab distance from (5, 5) is
   a. greater than 5;
   b. less than 5.

### TAXICAB vs. EUCLIDEAN DISTANCE

Euclidean distance (named after the ancient Greek mathematician Euclid) is the straight-line distance ("as the crow flies") we studied in a previous lesson.

5. A crow and a taxicab go from the origin to (5, 5). How far does each have to travel?

6. ⚷ Give examples, if possible, and explain.
   a. When are Euclidean and taxicab distances between two points equal?
   b. When is Euclidean distance greater than taxicab distance?
   c. When is taxicab distance greater?

7. ⚷ *A straight line is the shortest path between two points.* Explain how this statement is relevant to problem 6.

*Chapter 9 Measurement and Square Roots*

**8.** Sketch all the points that are at the same taxicab distance from both (4, 3) and (6, 7).

**9.** Sketch all the points that are at the same Euclidean distance from both (4, 3) and (6, 7).

**10.** ◯ Find all points $P$ such that:
- the taxicab distance from $P$ to (4, 3) is greater than the taxicab distance from $P$ to (6, 7), **but**
- the Euclidean distance from $P$ to (6, 7) is greater than the Euclidean distance from $P$ to (4, 3).

Explain, using sketches and calculations.

### ABSOLUTE VALUE

**11.** Find the Euclidean distance between:
a. (1, 2) and (6, 2);
b. (6, 2) and (1, 2);
c. (6.7, 3.45) and (8.9, 3.45).

**12.** ⌘— Explain in words how to find the distance between $(x_1, y)$ and $(x_2, y)$ if:
a. $x_1 > x_2$;  b. $x_1 < x_2$.

If the $y$-coordinates of two points are the same, the distance between the two can be found by subtracting the $x$-coordinates. If the result of the subtraction is negative, use its opposite, since distance is always positive. This is called the *absolute value* of the difference.

**13.** Find the absolute value of the difference between:
a. 2 and 5;  b. 3 and -9;
c. -2 and -5;  d. -3 and 9.

**14.** ⌘— Explain how you find the distance between two points whose $x$-coordinates are the same. Give an example.

**Definition:** The *absolute value* of a number $x$ is the distance from $x$ to 0 on the number line.

**Example:** The absolute value of 3 is 3. The absolute value of -3 is also 3.

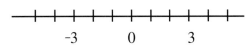

-3    0    3

**15.** Find the absolute value of:
a. 12;  b. -1/4.

**Notation:** The absolute value of a number $z$ is written $|z|$. For example:
$$|2| = 2 \qquad |-2| = 2$$

The absolute value of a difference can be written using the same symbol. For example, the absolute value of the difference between $a$ and $b$ is written $|a - b|$.

**16.** Find the absolute value of:
a. $3 - -5$;  b. $-5 - 3$.

**17.** ⌘— What is the distance between $x$ and 3 on the number line?
a. Explain in words how to find it.
b. Write a formula, using absolute value notation.

**18.** Using absolute value notation, the distance between $(x_1, y)$ and $(x_2, y)$ can be written $|x_1 - x_2|$ or $|x_2 - x_1|$. Explain.

**19.** Use absolute value notation to write the distance between $(x, y_1)$ and $(x, y_2)$.

**20.** Use absolute value notation to write the taxicab distance between $(x_1, y_1)$ and $(x_2, y_2)$.

Find the volume and surface area of each of these buildings (including the underside).

**21.**

**22.**

**23.**

**24.**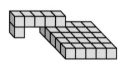

**25.**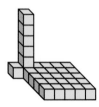

**26.**

Tina was thirsty, so Tina and Lana decided to make lemonade. They planned to make a lot, so they could sell some of it at a roadside stand.

Tina started making lemonade using the "taste" method. She added 21 cups of water to 16 cups of lemonade concentrate, but it tasted too lemony. Then she noticed directions on the lemonade package:

> Add water to taste. Most people like a mixture that is 1/5 to 1/4 concentrate.

**27.** How much water should she add to get a mixture that is 1/5 concentrate?

**28.** Lana tasted the lemonade after Tina had added water to get a mixture that was 1/5 concentrate. It didn't taste lemony enough. How much lemonade concentrate should they add now to get a mixture that is 1/4 concentrate?

# The Pythagorean Theorem

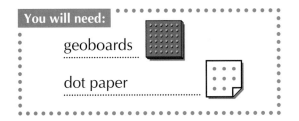
## RIGHT TRIANGLES

The corner of a piece of paper can be used to measure a *right angle*.

1. The figure shows three triangles, having a total of nine angles. To do the following problems, you may copy the figure onto your geoboard.

    a. Give the coordinates of the vertex of the right angle.

    b. Give the coordinates of the vertex of the angle that is greater than a right angle.

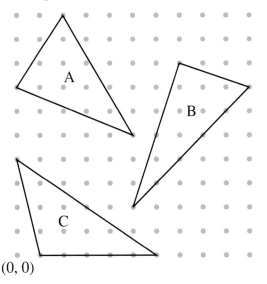

(0, 0)

**Definitions:** An angle that is greater than a right angle is called *obtuse*. An angle that is less than a right angle is called *acute*. A triangle that contains an obtuse angle is called an *obtuse triangle*. A triangle that contains three acute angles is called an *acute triangle*. A triangle that contains a right angle is called a *right triangle*.

2. Which triangle in the preceding figure is acute? Right? Obtuse?

**Definition:** The two sides forming the right angle in a right triangle are called the *legs*.

The figure shows a right triangle. Three squares have been drawn, one on each of the sides of the triangle.

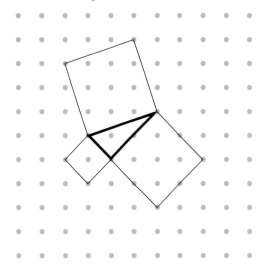

3. What is the area of each of the three squares?

4. **Exploration** Working with other students, make eight figures like the one above (on geoboards or dot paper). Each figure must be based on a different right triangle. For each one, find the areas of the three squares. Fill out a table like the one below. Study the table for any pattern.

**Areas of:**

| Square on short leg | Square on long leg | Square on hypotenuse |
|---|---|---|
| ... | ... | ... |

The pattern you probably discovered is called the Pythagorean theorem, after the ancient Greek mathematician Pythagoras. The pattern is about the relationship of the squares on the legs to the square on the hypotenuse for a right triangle.

5. Make an acute triangle on a geoboard or dot paper. Draw a square on each of its sides. Is the sum of the areas of the two smaller squares equal to, greater than, or less than the area of the large square?

6. Repeat problem 5 with an obtuse triangle.

7. **Summary** Explain the following equation.
$$\text{leg}^2 + \text{leg}^2 = \text{hyp}^2$$
(Is it true of any triangle? For those triangles for which it is true, what does it mean?)

---

**FINDING DISTANCES FROM COORDINATES**

The Pythagorean theorem provides us with a way to find distances in the Cartesian plane. (*Distance* usually refers to Euclidean distance.)

**Example:** What is the distance between (3, 8) and (7, 2)? First sketch the points.

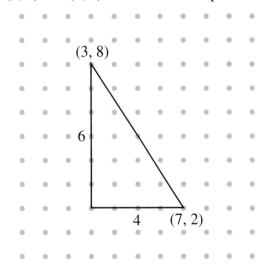

You can see on the sketch that the length of the legs is 4 for the horizontal leg, and 6 for the vertical leg. Since the triangle shown is a right triangle, we can use the Pythagorean theorem, ($\text{hyp}^2 = \text{leg}^2 + \text{leg}^2$). In this case,
$$\text{distance}^2 = 4^2 + 6^2 = 16 + 36 = 52$$
so, distance $= \sqrt{52} = 7.21\ldots$

8. For the example, if you did not sketch the figure, how could you find the lengths of the legs directly from the coordinates?

Note that the lengths of the legs have been called the *rise* and the *run* when discussing slope. However keep in mind that rise, run, and slope can be positive, negative, or zero, while distances cannot be negative.

9. Consider the two points (3, -4) and (4, -9). Use a sketch if you need to.
   a. Find the rise between them.
   b. Find the run between them.
   c. Find the slope of the line that joins them.
   d. Find the taxicab distance between them.
   e. Find the Euclidean distance between them.

10. Use any method to find the (Euclidean) distance between:
    a. (-1, 2) and (-1, -7);
    b. (-1, 2) and (5, 2);
    c. (-1, 2) and (5, -7);
    d. (-1, 2) and (-1, 2).

11. ☞ For which part of problem 10 is the Pythagorean theorem helpful? Explain.

12. Find the distances between:
    a. (8, 0) and (0, -8);
    b. (-8, 0) and (3, -8);
    c. (1.2, 3.4) and (-5.6, 7.89).

The mathematician Leonardo of Pisa, also known as Fibonacci, posed this problem in 1202.

**13.** 💡 Two towers of height 30 paces and 40 paces are 50 paces apart. Between them, at ground level, is a fountain towards which two birds fly from the tops of the towers. They fly at the same rate, and they leave and arrive at the same time. What are the horizontal distances from the fountain to each tower?

---

### REVIEW  *MORE SURFACE AREA*

Imagine these buildings are made by gluing Lab Gear blocks together. The surface area is the total area of all the exposed faces, even the bottom of the building. Find the surface areas.

**14.**

**15.**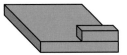

**16.**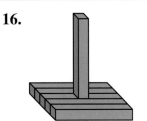

**17.**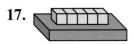

**18.**

# Radicals

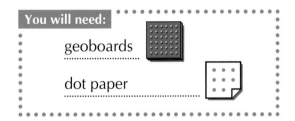
## SQUARES AND ROOTS

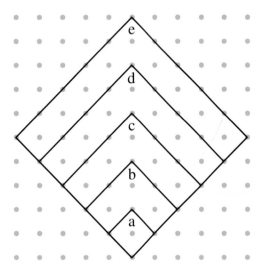

The figure shows five squares. For each one, find

1. its area;

2. its side, written twice: as the square root of the area, and as a decimal number.

The sides of the larger squares are multiples of the side of the smallest square. For example, square (b) has a side that is equal to two times the side of square (a). You can write,
$$\sqrt{8} = \sqrt{2} + \sqrt{2} = 2\sqrt{2}.$$
Note that $2\sqrt{2}$ means 2 times $\sqrt{2}$, just as $2x$ means 2 times $x$. You can check the equation with a calculator.
$$\sqrt{8} = 2.828427125\ldots$$
$$2\sqrt{2} = 2.828427125\ldots$$

3. Write equations about the sides of squares (c), (d), and (e). Check their correctness with a calculator.

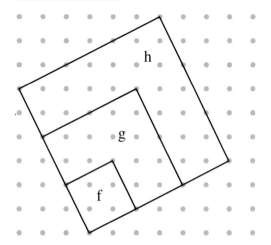

The figure shows three squares. For each one, find

4. its area;

5. its side, written twice: as the square root of the area, and as a decimal number.

6. Write equations involving square roots based on the figure. Check your equations on a calculator.

7. 🔑 True or False? Use a sketch on dot paper to explain your answers.
   a. $\sqrt{2} + \sqrt{2} = \sqrt{4}$
   b. $4\sqrt{2} = \sqrt{8}$

8. 🔑 Is $\sqrt{2 + 2} = \sqrt{4}$ ? Explain.

## RECTANGLES AND ROOTS

**In this section do not use decimal approximations.**

9. The figure shows three rectangles. For each one, write *length · width = area*.

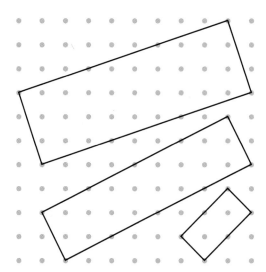

**10.** For each rectangle above:

   a. What is the side of a square having the same area?

   b. Sketch this square on dot paper.

Some multiplications involving square roots can be modeled by geoboard rectangles. For example, $2\sqrt{5} \cdot 3\sqrt{5}$ is shown in this figure.

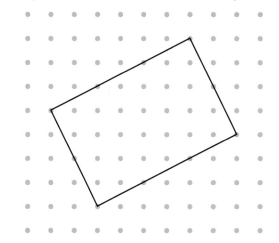

**11.** Find the product of $2\sqrt{5} \cdot 3\sqrt{5}$ by finding the area of the rectangle.

**12.** Multiply.

   a. $2\sqrt{2} \cdot 3\sqrt{2}$     b. $3\sqrt{2} \cdot 4\sqrt{2}$

   c. $4\sqrt{2} \cdot 5\sqrt{2}$     d. $\sqrt{2} \cdot 2\sqrt{2}$

**13.** Multiply.

   a. $\sqrt{2} \cdot \sqrt{18}$     b. $\sqrt{18} \cdot \sqrt{50}$

   c. $\sqrt{50} \cdot \sqrt{8}$     d. $\sqrt{8} \cdot \sqrt{32}$

---

Using the fact that $\sqrt{a} \cdot \sqrt{a} = a$ makes it easy to multiply some quantities involving radicals. For example:

$$6\sqrt{5} \cdot 2\sqrt{5} = 6 \cdot 2 \cdot \sqrt{5} \cdot \sqrt{5} = 12 \cdot 5 = 60$$

**14.** Multiply.

   a. $5\sqrt{2} \cdot \sqrt{2}$     b. $5\sqrt{2} \cdot 4\sqrt{2}$

   c. $3\sqrt{5} \cdot \sqrt{5}$

**15.** 🔑 Explain your answers by using a sketch of a geoboard rectangle.

   a. Is $\sqrt{4} \cdot \sqrt{2} = \sqrt{8}$?

   b. Is $\sqrt{5} \cdot \sqrt{20} = \sqrt{100}$?

> ### MULTIPLYING SQUARE ROOTS

Is it always true that $\sqrt{a} \cdot \sqrt{b} = \sqrt{ab}$? We cannot answer this question in general by making geoboard rectangles. A multiplication like $\sqrt{2} \cdot \sqrt{5}$ cannot be shown that way because it is not possible to find those lengths on the geoboard at a right angle to each other.

**16.** Guess how to write $\sqrt{2} \cdot \sqrt{5}$ as a square root. Check your guess with a calculator.

**17.** **Generalization** If $a$ and $b$ are positive,

   a. give a rule for multiplying $\sqrt{a} \cdot \sqrt{b}$;

   b. explain how to multiply $c\sqrt{a} \cdot d\sqrt{b}$.

**18.** Multiply.

   a. $3\sqrt{5} \cdot 2\sqrt{6}$

   b. $(2\sqrt{11})(-11\sqrt{2})$

> ### SIMPLE RADICAL FORM

**Definitions:** The square root symbol ($\sqrt{\phantom{x}}$) is called a *radical sign,* or simply *radical.* A *radical expression* is an expression that includes a radical.

Examples:

$$\sqrt{3}, \; 4\sqrt{7}, \; 1 + \sqrt{6}, \text{ or } \frac{\sqrt{2}}{x}$$

**19.** Write each of these in at least two ways as the product of two radical expressions.

   a. $\sqrt{70}$     b. $\sqrt{63}$

   c. $6\sqrt{80}$     d. $24\sqrt{105}$

**20.** Write each of these as the product of two radicals, one of which is the square root of a perfect square.
   a. $\sqrt{75}$
   b. $\sqrt{45}$
   c. $\sqrt{98}$
   d. $\sqrt{28}$

> **Definition:** Writing the square root of a whole number as a product of a whole number and the square root of a smallest possible whole number is called putting it in *simple radical form*.

For example, in simple radical form,
   $\sqrt{50}$ is $5\sqrt{2}$      $\sqrt{20}$ is $2\sqrt{5}$.

(Note that when using a calculator to find an approximate value, simple radical form is not simpler!)

**21.** Write in simple radical form.
   a. $\sqrt{75}$
   b. $\sqrt{45}$
   c. $\sqrt{98}$
   d. $\sqrt{28}$

---

**GEOBOARD LENGTHS**

Since 50 is a little more than 49, $\sqrt{50}$ is a little more than 7. A calculator confirms this: $\sqrt{50} = 7.07\ldots$

**22.** Estimate the following numbers, and check your answer on a calculator.
   a. $\sqrt{65}$
   b. $\sqrt{85}$

These numbers may help you with the next problem.

---

**23.** Exploration  There are 19 geoboard line segments that start at the origin and have length 5, 10, $\sqrt{50}$, $\sqrt{65}$, or $\sqrt{85}$. Find them, and mark their endpoints on dot paper. ∎

---

**24.** If you know two sides of a geoboard triangle are of length 5, what are the possibilities for length for the third side?

**25.** Repeat problem 24 for the following side lengths.
   a. 10
   b. $\sqrt{50}$
   c. $\sqrt{65}$
   d. $\sqrt{85}$

# LESSON 9.4

# Radical Operations

**You will need:**

geoboards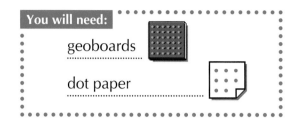

dot paper

---

### MULTIPLICATION

1. **Exploration** Using only multiplication, write at least three radical expressions that equal each of the following.
   a. $2\sqrt{3}$         b. 6

Even though you are often asked to simplify expressions, it is sometimes just as important to know how to "complicate" them. For example, $3\sqrt{7}$ is equivalent to all these radical expressions.

$$\sqrt{9}\sqrt{7} \qquad \sqrt{9 \cdot 7} \qquad \sqrt{63}$$
$$\sqrt{3}\sqrt{3}\sqrt{7} \qquad \sqrt{3}\sqrt{21}$$

2. Write at least two other radical expressions equivalent to:
   a. $5\sqrt{2}$;         b. $2\sqrt{5}$;
   c. $6\sqrt{10}$;        d. $10\sqrt{6}$.

3. Write each as the square root of a number. (For example, $3\sqrt{7} = \sqrt{63}$.)
   a. $2\sqrt{2}$         b. $2\sqrt{7}$
   c. $5\sqrt{6}$         d. $4\sqrt{3}$

4. Write each as the product of as many square roots as possible. (For example, $3\sqrt{6} = \sqrt{3} \cdot \sqrt{3} \cdot \sqrt{2} \cdot \sqrt{3}$.)
   a. $5\sqrt{10}$         b. $7\sqrt{5}$
   c. $\sqrt{30}$          d. $10\sqrt{22}$

5. What number times $\sqrt{6}$ equals $3\sqrt{10}$?

To answer problem 5, Tina wrote:

$$\underline{\qquad} \cdot \sqrt{6} = 3\sqrt{10}$$
$$\underline{\qquad} \cdot \sqrt{3}\sqrt{2} = \sqrt{3}\sqrt{3}\sqrt{2}\sqrt{5}$$

"First I wrote everything as a product of square roots," she explained. "Then it was easy to see that the missing factors were $\sqrt{5}$ and $\sqrt{3}$, so the answer must be $\sqrt{15}$."

Erin politely told Tina that her method seemed unnecessarily complicated. Erin wrote:

$$\underline{\qquad} \cdot \sqrt{6} = 3\sqrt{10}$$
$$\underline{\qquad} \cdot \sqrt{6} = \sqrt{9}\sqrt{10}$$
$$\underline{\qquad} \cdot \sqrt{6} = \sqrt{90}$$

"My goal was to write $3\sqrt{10}$ as the square root of something. Once I found that $3\sqrt{10} = \sqrt{90}$, it was easy from there. I could use the rule that $\sqrt{a} \cdot \sqrt{b} = \sqrt{ab}$ to see that the answer was $\sqrt{15}$," she explained.

6. What number times $2\sqrt{10}$ equals $10\sqrt{2}$? Find the answer by using
   a. Tina's method;
   b. Erin's method.

7. What number times $\sqrt{8}$ equals 4?

8. What number times $2\sqrt{2}$ equals $4\sqrt{3}$?

---

### DIVISION

9. Divide 5 by $2\sqrt{5}$.

"That's not fair," said Tina. "Ms. Kem never taught us to divide with radicals." "That's true," said Erin, "but we know that multiplication and division are inverse operations." She wrote:

$$\underline{\qquad} \cdot 2\sqrt{5} = 5$$
$$\underline{\qquad} \cdot \sqrt{4}\sqrt{5} = \sqrt{25}$$

10. Finish solving the problem using Erin's method.

Another way to solve this problem is to use the following trick: *Write an equivalent fraction without a square root in the denominator.* In this case, we multiply both the numerator and denominator by $\sqrt{5}$.

---

$$\frac{5}{2\sqrt{5}} \cdot \frac{\sqrt{5}}{\sqrt{5}} = \frac{5 \cdot \sqrt{5}}{2 \cdot 5} = \frac{\sqrt{5}}{2}$$

**11.** Explain why $\sqrt{5}$ was chosen as the number by which to multiply.

**12.** Divide.

a. $\dfrac{3}{2\sqrt{6}}$    b. $\dfrac{24}{\sqrt{6}}$    c. $\dfrac{3\sqrt{10}}{5\sqrt{3}}$    d. $\dfrac{5\sqrt{3}}{3\sqrt{10}}$

### MORE ON SIMPLE RADICAL FORM

Using the fact that $\sqrt{a} \cdot \sqrt{b} = \sqrt{ab}$, we can write $\sqrt{63}$ as $\sqrt{21} \cdot \sqrt{3}$. We can also write it as $\sqrt{9} \cdot \sqrt{7}$, which is especially convenient because 9 is a perfect square. Therefore:
$$\sqrt{63} = \sqrt{9} \cdot \sqrt{7} = 3\sqrt{7}.$$
This last expression is in simplest radical form.

**13.** Write in simple radical form.

a. $\sqrt{200}$    b. $\sqrt{147}$
c. $\sqrt{700}$    d. $\sqrt{275}$

### ADDITION AND SUBTRACTION

**14.** Use dot paper to illustrate the addition $\sqrt{5} + 2\sqrt{5}$.

**15.** Using the figure you made in problem 14, explain how to decide which of the two equations $\sqrt{5} + \sqrt{20} = \sqrt{25}$ and $\sqrt{5} + \sqrt{20} = \sqrt{45}$ is correct.

**16.** Check your answer to problem 15 with a calculator.

**17.** ⚷ True or False? Explain.

a. $16 + 9 = 25$
b. $\sqrt{16 + 9} = \sqrt{25}$
c. $\sqrt{16} + \sqrt{9} = \sqrt{25}$
d. $\sqrt{16} + \sqrt{9} = \sqrt{16 + 9}$

**18.** ⚷ If $a$ and $b$ are positive numbers, is it always, sometimes, or never true that $\sqrt{a} + \sqrt{b} = \sqrt{a + b}$? Explain, with examples.

The figure shows a right triangle, a square having area $a$, a square having area $b$, and a third square.

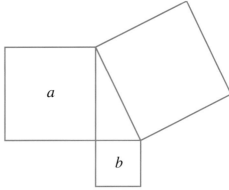

**19.** In terms of $a$ and $b$,

a. what is the area of the third square? Explain.

b. What are the sides of the triangle?

**20.** ⚷ If $a$ and $b$ are positive numbers, is it always, sometimes, or never true that $\sqrt{a} + \sqrt{b} > \sqrt{a + b}$? Explain, using the figure.

As you see, sums of radical expressions cannot usually be simplified. However, in some cases, simple radical form can help.

**21.** Simplify, then add or subtract.

a. $\sqrt{18} + \sqrt{32}$
b. $\sqrt{18} - 4\sqrt{20}$
c. $\sqrt{60} - \sqrt{135}$
d. $\sqrt{45} + \sqrt{125}$

You can add or subtract square roots only if they are the roots of the same number. This is similar to combining like terms when adding polynomials.

**22.** Simplify, then add or subtract, if possible.

a. $5 + 5\sqrt{68} + \sqrt{17}$
b. $6 - 6\sqrt{15} + \sqrt{90}$
c. $\sqrt{8} + \sqrt{16} + \sqrt{32} - \sqrt{64}$
d. $\sqrt{10} + \sqrt{20} - \sqrt{30} + \sqrt{40} - \sqrt{50}$

# 9.A Geoboard Distances

 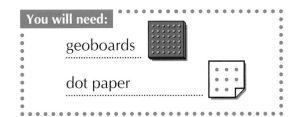
**1.** Find the distance between the origin and each geoboard peg. Use radical expressions for your answers, not decimal approximations. Arrange your results in a table like the one below, with the peg coordinates along the sides. In each space write the peg's distance from the origin. Some examples have been entered to get you started. To speed this up, work with a partner and look for patterns.

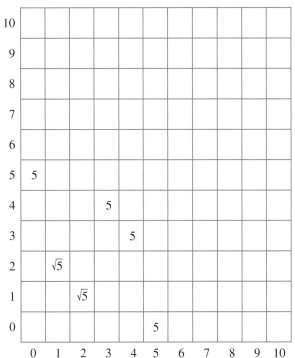

**2.** Describe the patterns you see in the table.

**3.** Find the numbers in the table that are not in simple radical form. Put them in that form and describe the patterns you notice.

**4.** What is the distance from the origin to the furthest peg on a geoboard having dimensions

    a. 20 by 20?      b. $n$ by $n$?

    c. 20 by 30?      d. $m$ by $n$?

**5.** On a 20-by-20 geoboard, what would be the largest multiple of:

    a. $\sqrt{2}$?          b. $\sqrt{5}$?

    c. $\sqrt{10}$?

**6.** Notice that all the multiples of $\sqrt{2}$ lie on a line. What is the slope of this line?

**7.** a. Why are there two lines containing multiples of $\sqrt{5}$?

    b. What are the slopes of these lines?

**8.** Repeat problem 7(b) for multiples of:

    a. $\sqrt{10}$;      b. $\sqrt{17}$.

**9.** List the geoboard distances that are on the line through the origin having slope

    a. 5;          b. 3/4.

**10.** Report Summarize your results from this lesson. Describe and explain the patterns you noticed and the generalizations you made.

# The Square Root Function

**You will need:**

graph paper

graphing calculator
(optional)

## ROOTS OF NUMBERS < 1

The large square in the figure has dimensions
1-by-1 unit. It is divided into 11 smaller
squares. For the square on the top left, you
could write the following equations, relating
the length of its side to its area.

　a.　$1/4 = (1/2)^2$　　b.　$1/2 = \sqrt{1/4}$
　c.　$0.25 = 0.5^2$　　d.　$0.5^2 = \sqrt{0.25}$

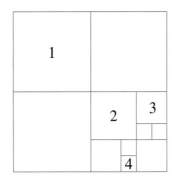

**1.** Explain the above equations.

**2-4.** For each numbered smaller square, write
equations of the form:
　a.　area $=$ side$^2$, using fractions
　b.　side $= \sqrt{\text{area}}$, using fractions
　c.　area $=$ side$^2$, using decimals
　d.　side $= \sqrt{\text{area}}$, using decimals

## DIAGRAMS FOR SQUARES AND ROOTS

The function diagrams for the same function
could look quite different with different scales.

**a.**

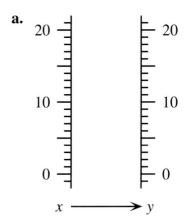

**b.**

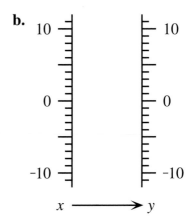

**c.**

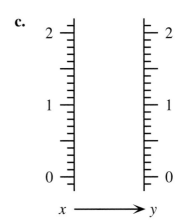

**5.** Make three function diagrams for the
function $y = x^2$, using the scales given in
the figure. Use nine in-out pairs for each.

Problems 6 and 7 are about $y = x^2$.

*Chapter 9 Measurement and Square Roots*

**6.** In the function diagrams below, how far would you have to extend the *y*-number line in the positive direction so that every value you can see on the *x*-number line has a corresponding *y*-value on the diagram? How about in the negative direction?

**7.** In the function diagrams below, how far would you have to extend the *x*-number line, if at all, so that every value you can see on the *y*-number line has a corresponding *x*-value on the diagram?

**a.**

**a.**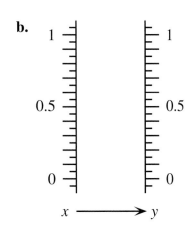

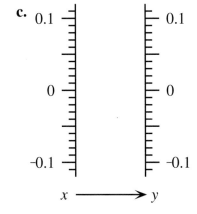

**b.**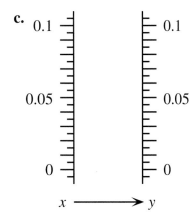

**c.**

**Definitions:** The *domain* of a function is the set of the values that the input can take. The *range* of a function is the set of the values the output can take.

**Example:** The domain of $y = x^2$ is *all numbers*, since any number can be squared.

**8.** 🔑 Explain why the range of the function $y = x^2$ is all nonnegative numbers.

**Notation:** $\sqrt{x}$ represents the nonnegative number whose square is $x$.

**Example:** $\sqrt{4}$ represents only 2, even though $(-2)^2$ also equals 4. However we can write
$$-2 = -\sqrt{4}.$$

**9.** Using the same scales as in problem 5, make three function diagrams for the function $y = \sqrt{x}$.

**10.** 🔑 For which scale is the function diagram not a mirror image of the corresponding one for $y = x^2$? Explain.

**11.** 🔑 What are the domain and the range of the square root function? Explain.

**12.** 🔑 To *be* or to *have*, that is the question.
  a. Which numbers have a square root?
  b. Which numbers have a square?
  c. Which numbers can be a square?
  d. Which numbers can be a square root?

GRAPHS FOR SQUARES AND ROOTS

**13.** Make tables of at least eight $(x, y)$ pairs each for these two functions and graph them on the same axes. Use three values of $x$ between 0 and 1, as well as negative values and whole numbers.
  a. $y = x^2$     b. $y = \sqrt{x}$

**14.** On the same axes, graph the line $y = x$.

**15.** The curve representing $y = x^2$ is called a *parabola*. What would you call the curve representing $y = \sqrt{x}$?

**16.** Which of your three graphs grows
  a. faster and faster?
  b. more and more slowly?
  c. always at the same rate?

**17.** If extended to the right, how high would the curve representing $y = \sqrt{x}$ go? (Can you find an $x$ such that $\sqrt{x}$ is larger than 100? Than 1000?) Explain.

**18.** 🔑
  a. What numbers are greater than their squares?
  b. What numbers are less than their square roots?
  c. What numbers are equal to their square roots?
  d. What numbers are equal to their squares?

**19.** Solve the equations.
  a. $x^2 = 5$          b. $x^2 = -5$
  c. $\sqrt{x} = 5$      d. $\sqrt{x} = -5$
  e. $-\sqrt{x} = -5$

**20.** Solve the inequalities. (Be careful! Some have compound solutions.)
  a. $x^2 < 4$          b. $\sqrt{x} < 2$
  c. $x^2 < \sqrt{x}$    d. $x^2 > 6$

**21.** Solve the equations and inequalities.
  a. $P^2 = 456$        b. $P^2 < 456$
  c. $\sqrt{K} = 789$   d. $\sqrt{K} < 789$

**22.** Report Summarize what you know about the functions $y = x$, $y = x^2$, and $y = \sqrt{x}$. Use graphs, diagrams, and examples. Include answers to these questions.
  • Which is greatest and which is least among $x$, $x^2$, or $\sqrt{x}$? Explain how the answer depends on the value of $x$.
  • What are the domains and ranges of these three functions?

**23.** 💡 Sketch the graphs of $y = \sqrt{x}$ and $y = \sqrt{-x}$. Think about domain and range!

### MORE SQUARE ROOT GRAPHS

Use a graphing calculator if you have one.

**24.** Graph these equations on the same pair of axes.

a. $y = 4\sqrt{x}$　　b. $y = \sqrt{4x}$

c. $y = \sqrt{4}\sqrt{x}$

**25.** In problem 24, which graphs are the same? Explain.

**26.** Graph these equations on the same pair of axes.

a. $y = \sqrt{x + 9}$　　b. $y = \sqrt{x} + 3$

c. $y = \sqrt{x} + \sqrt{9}$

**27.** In problem 26, which graphs are the same? Explain.

### PUZZLES  *PACKING SQUARES*

**28.** A 10-by-10 square can be divided into 11 smaller ones, with no overlaps and no space left over (as in the figure at the very beginning of the lesson). Divide each of the following squares into 11 smaller squares. (The side lengths of the smaller squares must be integers.)

a. 11-by-11　　b. 12-by-12

c. 13-by-13

### DISCOVERY  *WALKING DISTANCE*

Use graph paper as the map of a city. The horizontal and vertical lines represent streets.

**29.** In your group, agree on the location of various buildings, such as a supermarket, a hospital, a school, a fast food outlet, a bank, etc. Mark them on dot paper. Make a list of their coordinates.

Make up a problem about finding a good place for a couple to live in your city. Assume that they do not want to drive, and that they work in different places. Each student should choose a different job for each member of the couple.

a. Where should they live if they want to minimize the total amount of distance walked to work?

b. Where should they live if, in addition, they want to walk equal amounts?

# Midpoints

## MEETING HALFWAY

1. Linda works at the corner of Galbrae Avenue and 15th Street. Micaelia works at the corner of Galbrae Avenue and 38th Street. The streets between 15th and 38th are all consecutively numbered streets. Linda and Micaelia agree to meet after work. If they both want to walk the same distance, where should they meet?

2. Change Micaelia's workplace in problem 1. Make her meeting place with Linda at a street corner, not the middle of a block.

3. For what values of $n$ is the halfway point between 15th Street and $n$th Street in the middle of the block, and for what values is it at a street corner?

4. Find the point on the number line halfway between:

   a. 1.5 and 6.8;    b. 1/3 and 1/2.

5. 🔑 Describe how to find the point on the number line halfway between $a$ and $b$. Use a sketch and explain.

6. 💡 Explain how to find the point on the number line
   a. 1/3 of the way from 4 to 6;
   b. 1/4 of the way from 4 to 7.

## FINDING A FORMULA

Sue and Ruth were trying to find the number halfway between 5 and 11.4. Ruth used this method: First she found the distance between 11.4 and 5, which is 6.4.  Next she took half of that, which is 3.2. Last she added 3.2 to 5.

7. Use a sketch of the number line to explain Ruth's method.

8. If $B > A$, what is the distance between $A$ and $B$ on the number line? What is half that distance?

9. The formula for Ruth's method is
$$\text{midpoint} = \frac{B - A}{2} + A.$$
   Explain.

10. Ruth's formula can be rewritten as two fractions with a common denominator.
$$\text{midpoint} = \frac{B - A}{2} + \frac{2A}{2}$$
   Write it as one fraction in lowest terms.

11. Explain the formula you found in problem 10 in words.

12. Sue's method for finding the midpoint between two points on the number line is to take the average of the two points. Does that method work? Test it on some examples, and explain what you find out.

13. **Summary** Compare Ruth's method with Sue's method. Use examples, sketches, and algebra. Does either method work all the time? Which one do you prefer? Do they work when $A$ and/or $B$ are negative?

## THE MIDPOINT OF LINEAR GROWTH

Between ages 10 and 12, Sue's growth in height was approximately linear as a function of age. This means that the rate of change of height per year was approximately constant.

### Sue's Growth (Height)

| Age (years) | Height (cm) |
| --- | --- |
| 10 | 146 |
| 11 | — |
| 12 | 161 |

**14.** Estimate Sue's height at age 11.

**15.** Based on the data, do you think her weight increased linearly as a function of age? If so, estimate her weight at ages 10½ and 11½.

### Sue's Growth (Weight)

| Age (years) | Weight (lbs) |
| --- | --- |
| 10 | 90 |
| 11 | 101 |
| 12 | 112 |

**16.** Joel kept a record of his height and weight. When he was 5'5" tall, he weighed 130 pounds. When he was 5'7" tall, he weighed 142 pounds. If his weight increased as a linear function of his height, how much did he weigh when he was 5'6" tall?

## MIDPOINT OF A LINE SEGMENT

**17.** On a graph, plot and label the midpoint of the segment joining each pair of points.
a. (5, 3) and (8, 7)
b. (-5, -3) and (8, -7)
c. (-5.5, 3.5) and (8, 7)
d. (1/4, 3) and (3/4, -7)

**18.** ⌘ Using a sketch, explain how to find the coordinates of the midpoint of the segment joining the points (*a*, *b*) and (*c*, *d*). Check your method for positive and negative numbers. Try to write a formula.

## PREVIEW SURFACE AREA SEQUENCES

For each sequence of buildings, find the volume and surface area of the first four buildings. Then, describe and sketch the fifth building, and find its volume and surface area.

**19.** a.  b.  c.  d.

**20.**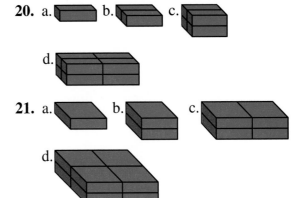

**21.**

# Halfway Measures

1. **Exploration** Janet and Marne had savings accounts. Marne was earning simple interest, and Janet was earning compound interest. Surprisingly, both accounts grew from $650.00 to $805.24 in four years. What was the annual interest rate for each account?

2. How much money was in each account after two years?

3. One account increased by the same *amount* every two years. What was the amount?

4. The other account increased by the same *percent* every two years. What was the percent?

5. **Summary** One account was an example of linear growth, the other was an example of exponential growth. In equal time intervals, one account showed constant differences, while the other showed constant ratios. Explain.

Dick and Stan had data about the population of their school. There were 325 students in 1980 and 742 students in 1988. They wanted to estimate the population in 1984.

Dick assumed that the population had grown linearly. This means that for equal time intervals the difference in population would be the same. Algebraically,

$$P_{1984} - P_{1980} = P_{1988} - P_{1984}.$$

6. Use algebra to find $P_{1984}$.

7. If Dick's assumption was correct, what was the population in 1986?

Stan assumed that the population had grown exponentially. This means that for equal time intervals, the population ratios would be the same. Algebraically,

$$\frac{P_{1984}}{P_{1980}} = \frac{P_{1988}}{P_{1984}}$$

$$\frac{P_{1984}}{325} = \frac{742}{P_{1984}}$$

8. Solve for $P_{1984}$. (Hint: Multiply both sides by 325 and then by $P_{1984}$.)

9. If Stan's assumption was correct, what was the population in 1986? Explain your reasoning and show your calculations.

10. Assume Stan's assumption was correct and also that the population grew at the same rate from 1980 to 1992. Make a table showing an estimate of the population at two-year intervals during this time period.

Solve these problems in two ways, assuming
  a. that the growth is linear;
  b. that the growth is exponential.
  c. Discuss which assumption is more reasonable, or whether neither one is credible.

11. A tree was 6 feet high in 1930 and 21 feet high in 1980. How high was it in 1955?

12. A tumor was estimated to weigh about 4 grams in January and 7 grams six months later. If it continued to grow in the same way, how much would it weigh after three more months?

**13.** Generalization A growing population is $P_1$ at a certain time and $P_2$ at a later time. Use algebra to find its size halfway between these two times, assuming

   a. linear growth;

   b. exponential growth.

### USING AN EQUATION

A population grew from 1000 to 2197 in three years.

**14.** Assume linear growth.

   a. How much did the population grow each year?

   b. Make a table showing the population at the end of one, two, three, and four years.

   c. Write an equation expressing the population as a function of the number of years.

   d. Use the equation to find out the population after 27 months. (Hint: First figure out how many years that is.)

**15.** Assume exponential growth.

   a. By how much was the population multiplied each year?

   b. Make a table showing the population at the end of one, two, three, and four years.

   c. Write an equation relating the population to the number of years.

Your equation should be in the form $P = 1000b^x$, with $x$ indicating the number of years.

**16.** Use the equation and your calculator to find the population after:

   a. 27 months;   b. 2.5 years;

   c. 1 month.

---

### REVIEW/PREVIEW

#### CALCULATOR PREDICTIONS

**17.** a. Predict how your calculator will respond if you try to use it to compute $\sqrt{-9}$.

   b. Explain your prediction.

   c. Check whether you were right.

For each problem, 18-24, two expressions are given.

   a. Predict which is greater or whether they are equal.

   b. Explain your prediction.

   c. Use your calculator to check whether you were right.

**18.** $\sqrt{2} + \sqrt{8}$ or $\sqrt{18}$

**19.** $\sqrt{27}$ or $3\sqrt{3}$

**20.** $2\sqrt{3}$ or $\sqrt{2\cdot3}$

**21.** $\sqrt{3} + \sqrt{3}$ or $\sqrt{6}$

**22.** $\sqrt{2}/\sqrt{3}$ or $\sqrt{2/3}$

**23.** $\sqrt{2}\sqrt{3}$ or $\sqrt{2\cdot3}$

**24.** $\sqrt{3} + \sqrt{3} + \sqrt{3}$ or $3\sqrt{3}$

**25.** 

   a. Predict how your calculator will respond if you try to use it to compute $49^{.5}$ (49 to the power one-half).

   b. Explain your prediction.

   c. Use your calculator to check whether you were right.

# The Exponent 1/2

## THE HALFWAY GROWTH FACTOR

1. A bacterial population is growing exponentially. It is multiplied by nine every day.
   a. Copy and complete the table of the population at half-day intervals.

   | Time | Population |
   |------|-----------|
   | 0    | 100       |
   | 0.5  | —         |
   | 1    | 900       |
   | 1.5  | —         |
   | 2    | —         |

   b. Write an equation giving the population as a function of time (measured in days).

2. Repeat problem 1 for a population that is multiplied by 25 every day.

3. For problems 1 and 2:
   a. By how much was the population multiplied in half a day?
   b. How are these numbers related to the equation?

4. A tumor that is growing exponentially triples in ten years. By how much is it multiplied in five years?

5. **Generalization** An exponentially growing tumor is multiplied in size by $B$ every ten years and by $H$ every five years. How are $B$ and $H$ related? Explain.

## A FRACTIONAL EXPONENT

6. Find $x$.
   a. $2^5 \cdot 2^5 = 2^x$
   b. $2^3 \cdot 2^3 = x^6$
   c. $(2^4)^2 = 2^x$

7. Find $x$.
   a. $9^x \cdot 9^3 = 9^6$
   b. $9^x \cdot 9^x = 9^2$
   c. $9^x \cdot 9^x = 9^1$
   d. $B^x \cdot B^x = B^1$

8. Find $x$.
   a. $(9^x)^2 = 9^6$    b. $(9^x)^2 = 9^1$
   c. $(B^x)^2 = B^6$    d. $(B^x)^2 = B^1$

9. ☞ Problems 6-8 suggest a meaning for the exponent 1/2. Explain it.

10. Using this meaning of the exponent 1/2, find the following. (Avoid using a calculator if you can.)
    a. $16^{\frac{1}{2}}$          b. $400^{\frac{1}{2}}$

    c. $25^{-\frac{1}{2}}$          d. $2^{\frac{1}{2}}$

11. ☞ Does it make sense to use the exponent 1/2 in the equations you found in problems 1 and 2? Explain your answer.

12. A colony of bacteria was growing exponentially. It weighed 6 grams at noon and 15 grams at 8 P.M. How much did it weigh at 4 P.M.? Explain.

Rules for operations with radicals can be derived from laws of exponents using the fact that

$$x^{\frac{1}{2}} = \sqrt{x}.$$

The following rules assume $a$ and $b$ are nonnegative.

| **Exponent Rule** | **Radical Rule** |
|---|---|
| $a^{\frac{1}{2}} \cdot a^{\frac{1}{2}} = a^1$ | $\sqrt{a}\,\sqrt{a} = a$ |
| $a^{\frac{1}{2}} \cdot b^{\frac{1}{2}} = (ab)^{\frac{1}{2}}$ | $\sqrt{a}\,\sqrt{b} = \sqrt{ab}$ |
| $\dfrac{a^1}{a^{\frac{1}{2}}} = a^{\frac{1}{2}}$ | $\dfrac{a}{\sqrt{a}} = \sqrt{a}$ |
| $\dfrac{a^{\frac{1}{2}}}{b^{\frac{1}{2}}} = \left(\dfrac{a}{b}\right)^{\frac{1}{2}}$ | $\dfrac{\sqrt{a}}{\sqrt{b}} = \sqrt{\dfrac{a}{b}}$ |

13. Check all the radical rules by using $a = 16$ and $b = 9$.

The last rule is especially useful for simplifying rational expressions involving radicals. To be in simple radical form, an expression cannot have any radicals in the denominator or fractions under the radical sign.

**Examples:**

$$\frac{\sqrt{16}}{\sqrt{8}} = \sqrt{\frac{16}{8}} = \sqrt{2}$$

$$\sqrt{\frac{144}{169}} = \frac{\sqrt{144}}{\sqrt{169}} = \frac{12}{13}$$

$$\frac{\sqrt{48}}{\sqrt{32}} = \frac{\sqrt{3}}{\sqrt{2}} = \frac{\sqrt{3}}{\sqrt{2}} \cdot \frac{\sqrt{2}}{\sqrt{2}} = \frac{\sqrt{6}}{2}$$

14. Write problems 14-15 in simple radical form. You can check the answers on your calculator.

a. $\dfrac{\sqrt{60}}{\sqrt{30}}$  b. $\dfrac{\sqrt{450}}{\sqrt{18}}$

c. $\dfrac{\sqrt{18}}{\sqrt{2}}$  d. $\dfrac{\sqrt{20}}{\sqrt{5}}$

15. a. $\sqrt{\dfrac{25}{125}}$  b. $\sqrt{\dfrac{32}{48}}$

c. $\sqrt{\dfrac{3}{75}}$  d. $\sqrt{\dfrac{1}{12}}$

16. **Exploration** Use your calculator to make a list of the square roots of the powers of ten, from $\sqrt{10^1}$ to $\sqrt{10^{10}}$. Explain any pattern you discover.

17. 🔑 Explain the pattern you found in problem 16 by using a law of exponents and the exponent 1/2. (Hint: It is not one of the laws listed before problem 13.)

18. Write in simple radical form.

a. $\sqrt{9(10^8)}$  b. $\sqrt{4(10^7)}$

c. $\sqrt{3(10^6)}$  d. $\sqrt{2(10^5)}$

*CHALLENGE* **ESTIMATING POPULATION**

19. The population of California was 3,426,861 in 1920 and 15,717,204 in 1960. Assume it grew exponentially and estimate the population in:

a. 1940;  b. 💡 1949.

# 9.B Skidding Distance

Police use a formula to estimate the speed a car was traveling before an accident by measuring its skid marks. This is the formula.

$$S = \sqrt{30df}$$

*S* is the speed the car was traveling (in mph).

*d* is the distance the car skidded (in feet).

*f* is a special number (called the *coefficient of friction*) that depends on the road surface and road conditions.

The number *f* is determined by the police when they investigate an accident. For a dry tar road, *f* is usually about 1.0, so the formula is

$$S = \sqrt{30d(1.0)} \quad \text{(dry tar road)}.$$

For a wet tar road, f is about 0.5, so the formula is

$$S = \sqrt{30d(0.5)} \quad \text{(wet tar road)}.$$

1.  Make tables of values and a graph to show speed as a function of the length of the skid marks. Put both curves on the same axes and use a range for *d* that will give you values of *S* up to 125 mph.

2.  Why is the coefficient of friction less for a wet road than for a dry road? How does that affect the graph?

**Police Report**

| Weather | Skid marks (ft) |
|---------|-----------------|
| wet     | 112             |
| dry     | 321             |
| wet     | 459             |
| wet     | 173             |
| dry     | 100             |
| dry     | 132             |

3.  This table shows a summary of accidents from a police report. All the accidents took place on tar roads. Use formulas or graphs to estimate how fast the cars were going. Explain how you made your estimates.

4.  A police report stated that a car had left 150-foot skid marks on a tar road, but the report did not state the weather. Estimate how fast the car was probably traveling if the road had been wet. Then estimate the speed if the road had been dry.

5.  There are two sets of skid marks on the same road. The second set is twice as long as the first. Do you think the second car was going twice as fast as the first? If not, was it going less than twice as fast or more than twice as fast? Explain.

6.  The coefficient of friction for a dry concrete road is about 0.8 and for a wet concrete road about 0.4. If a car had been traveling at 50 mph before it skidded, estimate the lengths of skid marks it would have left on each type of road (tar or concrete) and in each type of weather (wet or dry). Compare your answers and comment on the differences you find.

7.  Report Imagine that you are responsible for giving a lecture on skidding distance to a class of police cadets who are being prepared to join the highway patrol. You are asked to provide an illustrated two-to-three-page report summarizing the information that you think is important for them to know. Use examples. You may also make a poster to help make your talk more interesting and understandable.

# Radical Expressions

## MAKING RADICAL GEAR

This figure shows how to make *radical gear* from dot paper, to help model multiplications like

$$2\sqrt{5} \cdot (\sqrt{5} + 2).$$

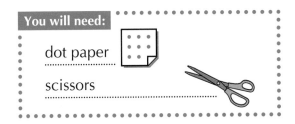

Draw some radical gear on dot paper. Cut it out, then use it in the corner piece to do these multiplications.

1. Multiply.
   a. $2\sqrt{5} \cdot (\sqrt{5} + 2)$
   b. $\sqrt{5} \cdot (2\sqrt{5} + 2)$
   c. $4\sqrt{5} \cdot (\sqrt{5} - 1)$
   d. $3\sqrt{5} \cdot (2\sqrt{5} - 1)$

2. Multiply.
   a. $(2\sqrt{5} + 1) \cdot (\sqrt{5} + 2)$
   b. $(2 + \sqrt{5}) \cdot (\sqrt{5} + 2)$
   c. $(2\sqrt{5}) \cdot (2\sqrt{5})$
   d. $(2\sqrt{5})(2 + \sqrt{5})$

3. Multiply.
   a. $(2\sqrt{5} + 1) \cdot (2\sqrt{5} - 1)$
   b. $(\sqrt{5} + 1) \cdot (\sqrt{5} - 1)$
   c. $(3\sqrt{5} - 1) \cdot (\sqrt{5} + 1)$
   d. $3 + \sqrt{5}(2\sqrt{5} - 1)$

## APPLYING THE DISTRIBUTIVE LAW

**Rule:** As you probably noticed, when multiplying radical expressions, *the radicals are handled as if they were variables* .

**Example:** You can set up a table to multiply $(\sqrt{3} - 2)(\sqrt{2} - \sqrt{3})$.

|            | $\sqrt{3}$   | $-2$          |
|------------|--------------|---------------|
| $\sqrt{2}$ | $\sqrt{6}$   | $-2\sqrt{2}$  |
| $-\sqrt{3}$| $-3$         | $2\sqrt{3}$   |

So the product is $\sqrt{6} - 2\sqrt{2} + 2\sqrt{3} - 3$.

4. Multiply.
   a. $7\sqrt{3} \cdot (\sqrt{6} - \sqrt{3})$
   b. $(7 + \sqrt{3}) \cdot (\sqrt{6} - \sqrt{3})$
   c. $7 + \sqrt{3} \cdot (\sqrt{6} - \sqrt{3})$
   d. $(8 - 2\sqrt{3}) \cdot (\sqrt{3} + 4)$

5. Find the missing terms.
   a. $(1 + \sqrt{3})\underline{\quad} = 3 + \sqrt{3}$
   b. $\sqrt{5} \cdot \underline{\quad} = 10 + 4\sqrt{5}$
   c. $(6 + \sqrt{7})(\underline{\quad} + \sqrt{7}) = 55 + 14\sqrt{7}$
   d. $(\sqrt{6} + \sqrt{2}) \cdot \underline{\quad} = 2\sqrt{3} + 2$
   e. $(\sqrt{15} - \sqrt{2}) \cdot \underline{\quad} = 5\sqrt{3} - \sqrt{10}$

## DISAPPEARING RADICALS

6. Find the product. Simplify your answer.
   a. $(x - y)(x + y)$
   b. $(x - \sqrt{5})(x + \sqrt{5})$
   c. $(\sqrt{3} - x)(\sqrt{3} + x)$
   d. $(\sqrt{3} - \sqrt{5})(\sqrt{3} + \sqrt{5})$

7. 🔑 Explain why there are no radicals in the simplified form of any of the answers to problem 6.

8. For each binomial, find a binomial to multiply it by so that the result has no radicals.
   a. $(\sqrt{7} - \sqrt{8})$    b. $(\sqrt{x} + \sqrt{y})$
   c. $(2 - \sqrt{y})$

### FRACTIONS AND RADICALS

**Definition:** To *rationalize* the denominator (or numerator) of a fraction is to write an equivalent fraction with *no radicals* in the denominator (or numerator).

9. Rationalize the denominator. $\dfrac{1}{2 + \sqrt{3}}$

10. 🔑 In problem 9, Gerald tried to multiply the numerator and denominator by $(2 + \sqrt{3})$. Explain why this did not work.

11. 🔑 Daniel used the idea in the section **Disappearing Radicals** to rationalize the denominator. Explain what he did, and why it did work.

12. Rationalize the denominator.
   a. $\dfrac{1}{\sqrt{2} + 3}$
   b. $\dfrac{1}{3 - \sqrt{3}}$
   c. $\dfrac{4}{\sqrt{5} - \sqrt{6}}$
   d. $\dfrac{5}{\sqrt{5}}$

13. Rationalize the numerator.
   a. $\dfrac{7 - \sqrt{5}}{4}$    b. $\dfrac{\sqrt{7} - \sqrt{5}}{4}$

### REVIEW CALCULATOR EXPERIMENTS

14. Use your calculator to compute
   $$(\sqrt{9876} - \sqrt{9866})(\sqrt{9876} + \sqrt{9866}).$$
   Comment on the answer.

15. 🔑 Bernard believes that the square root of the square of a number is the number itself.
   a. Is he right or wrong? Explain.
   b. What's the square root of the square of -543? Make a prediction, then use your calculator to check.

16. Choose any number. Find its square root on your calculator. Then find the square root of the result. Continue this until you notice something happening. What is happening? Can you explain it? What starting numbers does it work for?

17. 🔑 Always, sometimes, or never? Explain, using examples.
   a. $x^2 > x$        b. $1/x^2 > 1/x$
   c. $\sqrt{x} < x$        d. $1/\sqrt{x} > 1/x$
   e. $\sqrt{x} < x^2$        f. $1/\sqrt{x} > 1/\sqrt{x^2}$

### REVIEW GEOBOARD PUZZLES

18. If two sides of geoboard triangle are $\sqrt{2}$ and $\sqrt{5}$, what are the possibilities for:
   a. the third side?
   b. the area?

19. Find the geoboard figure having the least area, if its perimeter is
   a. 20;        b. $4\sqrt{65}$;
   c. $10 + 2\sqrt{65}$;    d. $10\sqrt{2} + 2\sqrt{85}$.

**You will need:**

graph paper

### BIGGER BOXES

The Real Bag Company makes cardboard boxes. One of the boxes is called the Banker's Box. It has the dimensions: length, 16 in.; width, 12 in.; height, 10 in. Another box, the Square Pak box, has the dimensions: length, 12 in.; width, 12 in.; height, 10 in. Sid, a Real Bag Box Division Manager, decides that new boxes need to be manufactured, the Caterer's Crate and the Great Pak.

**1. Exploration**

   a. The Caterer's Crate will have two dimensions the same as the Banker's Box, and the third dimension multiplied by two. Sid asks his colleague Li Ann whether the volume of the box would be increased the most by multiplying the length, the width, or the height by two. What should she answer? Explain.

   b. The Great Pak will have a square base and a volume that is double that of the volume of the Square Pak. Sid asks his colleague Annette (who owns a calculator) to find three choices for the dimensions of the new box. What should she answer? Explain.

### STRETCHING POLYOMINOES

Sid, Annette, and Li Ann like to spend their lunch breaks working geometric puzzles. (They should have become math teachers.) Here is a puzzle they have been working on, using the tetrominoes.

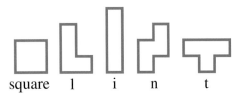

square   l   i   n   t

For each of the tetrominoes, they created three new polyominoes. The first one by doubling all horizontal dimensions, the second one by doubling all vertical dimensions, and the third one by doubling both horizontal and vertical dimensions. For example, the t tetromino led to the creation of three new polyominoes.

   a. original

   b. doubled horizontally

   c. doubled vertically

   d. doubled both ways

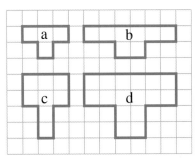

**2. Exploration** Draw all 15 *stretched* tetrominoes. For each one, find its area and perimeter. Keep your work clearly organized, so you can find a pattern to the areas and perimeters. (The area pattern is the easier of the two.) You will need to refer to this data to do the problems in the next two sections.

## PERIMETER

Call the perimeter of a tetromino $p$. It is made up of some horizontal segments and some vertical segments.

Let $h$ = total length of the horizontal segments.
Let $v$ = total length of the vertical segments.

**3.** Express $p$ in terms of $h$ and $v$.

**4.** a. Find $h$ and $v$ for the t tetromino.
   b. Show that the perimeter of the vertically stretched t tetromino is $h + 2v$.
   c. What is the perimeter of the horizontally stretched t tetromino in terms of $h$ and $v$?
   d. What is the perimeter of the horizontally and vertically stretched t tetromino in terms of $h$ and $v$?

**5.** 🗝 In problem 4 you found formulas that related the perimeters of the three stretched t tetrominoes to the perimeter of the original t tetromino. Explain why these formulas work for all the tetrominoes.

**6.** 🗝 What is the sum of the perimeters of the two polyominoes that were stretched in only one dimension? Use factoring to see how this sum is related to the original perimeter.

**7.** `Generalization`
   a. Repeat the perimeter investigation, but stretch the tetrominoes by tripling dimensions. You do not need to draw the tripled tetrominoes, just use algebra. Find a formula relating the perimeters of the tripled tetrominoes to $h$, $v$, and $p$ for the original tetromino.
   b. Repeat this investigation, but this time stretch by a factor of $n$.

## AREA

**8.** 🗝 Refer to your data on the area of the 15 stretched (doubled) tetrominoes, and experiment with other polyominoes. If the original area of a polyomino is $A$, what is the area of the polyomino stretched by doubling
   a. horizontally?
   b. vertically?
   c. both horizontally and vertically ?

**9.** a. Draw the l and t tetrominoes, with both their horizontal and vertical dimensions doubled.
   b. Repeat part (a), tripling the dimensions instead of doubling.

**10.** `PUZZLE` Tile the blown-up tetrominoes you drew with copies of the original l and/or t tetrominoes. Example:

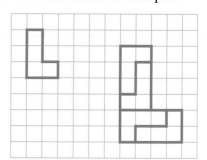

**11.** How many tetromino tiles did you need to cover the blown-up tetrominoes? How is this related to the area of the blown-up tetrominoes?

**12.** a. Draw a pentomino.
   b. Draw a copy of it, with horizontal and vertical dimensions multiplied by two.
   c. Repeat with the original dimensions multiplied by three.
   d. Repeat with the original dimensions multiplied by four.

**13.** Predict the area of each figure you drew in problem 12. Check your predictions.

**14.** Generalization When both horizontal and vertical dimensions are multiplied by *k*, by what is the area multiplied? Explain.

---

> **BACK TO WORK**

After their lunch break, Sid, Li Ann, and Annette had to attend to more box problems.

**15.** They created a new box by multiplying all the dimensions of the Banker's Box by two. Make a sketch of the original box and the new box. What would the volume of the new box be? How many times greater is this than the volume of the Banker's Box?

**16.** If they created a new box by multiplying all the dimensions of the Square Pak by three, what would its volume be? How many times greater is this than the volume of the Square Pak?

**17.** Generalization When all the dimensions are multiplied by *k*, by what is the volume multiplied?

**18.** What are the dimensions of a box that is a perfect cube and has the same volume as the Square Pak? Explain.

**19.** What are the dimensions of a box that is a perfect cube and has double the volume of the Square Pak? Explain.

---

> **REVIEW** *SCIENTIFIC NOTATION*

**20.** In June of 1990 the national debt of the United States was $3.1 trillion. The population of the U.S. at the same time was about 250 million. Therefore, the debt per person was

$$\frac{3.1 \text{ trillion}}{250 \text{ million}}.$$

  a. Express both of these numbers in scientific notation.

  b. What was the debt per person? Express your answer in ordinary decimal notation and in scientific notation.

> **REVIEW** *WHAT'S YOUR SIGN?*

Do not use a calculator for these problems.

**21.** Is *x* positive or negative, or is it impossible to know? Explain.
  a. $(-2)^x = -524,288$
  b. $2^x = 1/131,072$
  c. $(-2)^x = 262,144$
  d. $x^{11} = -177,147$
  e. $x^{12} = 531,441$
  f. $x^{13} = 1/1,594,323$

REVIEW  THE CHESSBOARD

According to an old legend, a King decided to reward the inventor of the game of chess. "I am immensely rich. Whatever you ask for will be yours." The inventor replied, "All I ask is for one cent on the first square of the chessboard; two cents on the next square; four cents on the next square; and so on, doubling the amount each time, until the last square on the chessboard." (The legend actually specifies grains of rice, not cents.)

**22.** Find out how many cents the King owed the inventor. Express the final answer two ways: in terms of a power of two, in cents; and as a number of dollars, in scientific notation.

**23.** Project  Is the money paid the inventor as much as the budget of:
   a. a toy store?
   b. a multi-national corporation?
   c. the State of New York?
   d. the United States?

DISCOVERY  DECIMAL EXPONENTS

**24.** Use decimal exponents (to the nearest hundredth) to approximate 100 as a power of:
   a. 2          b. 3          c. 4
   d. 8          e. 9          f. 10

REVIEW  EQUAL RATIOS

Solve for $N$.

**25.** $\dfrac{3N - 2}{5} = \dfrac{N + 2}{2}$

**26.** $\dfrac{3N - 2}{15} = \dfrac{N + 2}{6}$

Solve for $x$. If you cannot find an exact value, approximate to nearest thousandth.

**27.** $\dfrac{x}{8} = \dfrac{3}{4}$

**28.** $\dfrac{4}{10} = \dfrac{400}{x}$

**29.** $\dfrac{1}{x} = \dfrac{x}{2}$

REVIEW  DISTRIBUTIVE LAW PRACTICE

Find these products.

**30.** $2y(2x - y + 6)$

**31.** $3x(2x - 3)$

**32.** $(y - 4)(y + 3)$

## PIZZA PRICES

Lana and Tina were studying for their semester exam one Sunday afternoon. They needed more energy and decided to order a pizza. They called Pinky's and Primo's to compare prices.

### Pinky's Prices

| Size | Diameter | Price |
|------|----------|-------|
| small | 8 in. | $4.25 |
| medium | 12 in. | $8.50 |
| large | 14 in. | $10.20 |

### Primo's Prices

| Size | Diameter | Price |
|------|----------|-------|
| small | 10 in. | $6.44 |
| medium | 12 in. | $8.84 |
| large | 14 in. | $9.91 |

1. **Exploration** Assuming the pizzas are of the same thickness and similar quality, which is the better buy for the large pizza? The medium pizza? The small pizza? Explain, showing your calculations.

The area of a circle is given by the formula $\pi r^2$, where $r$ is the radius, and $\pi$ is approximately equal to the number 3.1415926536.

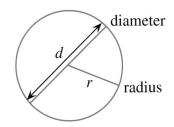

**Example:** A circle having diameter 14 in. has a radius of 7 in. Its area is $\pi(7)^2$, or $49\pi$ square inches.

2. Use your calculator to find the area of a circle having diameter 14 in., to the nearest tenth of a square inch. (Scientific calculators have a $\pi$ key.)

Tina thought Pinky's medium pizza looked expensive. "It's twice as expensive as an 8-inch pizza," she said. "For twice as much, I ought to be able to get a 16-inch pizza."

3. a. Find the area of a 16-inch pizza. Compare it with the area of an 8-inch pizza. How many times as large is it?

   b. How many times as large is a 12-inch pizza as an 8-inch pizza? Show your calculations.

   c. Comment on Tina's remark.

4. a. Copy and complete the tables below, giving an approximation for the area of each pizza and the price per square inch.

   b. Which pizza is the best buy, based on price per square inch?

### Pinky's

| Diameter (in.) | Area (sq in.) | Price | Price per sq in. |
|----------------|---------------|-------|------------------|
| 8 | $16\pi$ | $4.25 | — |
| 12 | — | $8.50 | — |
| 14 | — | $10.20 | — |

**Primo's**

| Diameter (in.) | Area (sq in.) | Price | Price per sq in. |
|---|---|---|---|
| 10 | — | — | — |
| 12 | — | — | — |
| 14 | — | — | — |

**5.** Compare the areas of these pizzas. How many times as big is the larger than the smaller?

a. a 12-inch pizza and a 6-inch pizza

b. a 14-inch pizza and a 12-inch pizza

**6.** 🔑 To compare a pizza having radius $r$ with a pizza having radius $2r$, you can use the ratios of the areas. Simplify this ratio.

$$\frac{\pi(2r)^2}{\pi(r)^2}$$

**7.** `Generalization` Write and simplify the ratios to compare the area of:

a. a pizza having radius $r$ with a pizza having three times this radius;

b. a pizza having radius $r$ with a pizza having radius $kr$.

**8.** 🔑 If you double the diameter of a pizza, why does the price more than double?

**9.** 🔑 For a party Tina was going to buy ten 8-inch pizzas from Pinky's, but she got mixed up and bought eight 10-inch pizzas from Primo's instead. Did she have the right amount of pizza, too much, or too little? Explain, showing your calculations.

**BAKING BROWNIES**

An hour after they had polished off their pizza, Lana and Tina were having trouble concentrating on studying exponents. "Maybe we're just hungry," said Lana. "I'm feeling a little faint," Tina agreed. "We should probably bake some brownies."

The recipe said to use an 8-inch-square pan.

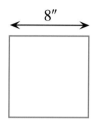

Lana wanted to double the recipe. "OK," said Tina, "but we'll need a 16-inch-square pan."

**10.** a. Using the same scale, make a sketch of an 8-by-8-inch pan and a 16-by-16-inch pan.

b. How many 8-by-8 pans would fit inside a 16-by-16 pan?

c. Comment on Tina's remark.

**11.** 🔑 How many times as big is the larger than the smaller square? (The measurement refers to the side length.)

a. a 12-inch square and a 6-inch square

b. a 14-inch square and a 12-inch square

**12.** `Generalization` What is the ratio of the areas of two squares, if the ratio of the sides is

a. 5?          b. $k$?

**13.** 💡

a. Write the ratio of the area of a circle having diameter $s$ to that of a square having side $s$.

b. Simplify the ratio. Which is larger, the circle or the square? How many times as large is it?

**PUZZLES** *MORE POLYOMINO TILINGS*

**14.** Draw all the tetrominoes with their dimensions doubled. Tile the blowups with the l and/or t tetrominoes.

**15.** Repeat with the tripled tetrominoes.

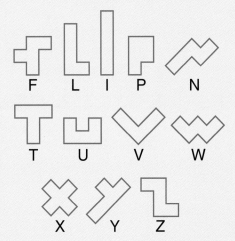

F  L  I  P  N

T  U  V  W

X  Y  Z

**16.** Draw all the pentominoes with their dimensions doubled. Tile the blowups with the P and/or N pentominoes.

**17.** Repeat with the tripled pentominoes.

**Projects**

**18.** Can you use the same tiles to cover bigger and bigger blown-up tetrominoes and pentominoes? Experiment and report on your discoveries.

**19.** What is the smallest rectangle you can tile with a given pentomino? Experiment and report on your discoveries.

**REVIEW** *A SQUARE NUMBER OF SQUARES*

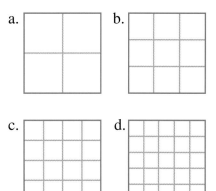

a.  b.

c.  d.

Each of the four large squares has area 75. Each has been divided into a square number of smaller squares.

**20.** Find the area of each small square.

**21.** Express the side of each small square as a square root.

**22.** Explain why $\sqrt{75} = 5\sqrt{3}$, using
   a. the figure;
   b. radical rules;
   c. decimal approximations.

**23.** Divide a square having area 72 into a square number of smaller squares, in such a way that you can use the figure to help write $\sqrt{72}$ in simple radical form.

**LESSON**
**9.12**

# Similar Figures

**You will need:**

the Lab Gear

## RATIO OF SIMILARITY

The polycubes in this figure were obtained by doubling the dimensions of the original tetracube in succession: first the height, then the length, and finally the width.

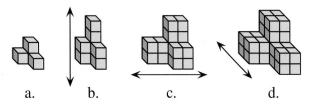

a.   b.   c.   d.

**1.** Find the volume and surface area of each of these polycubes.

> **Definitions:** Two figures are *similar* if *all* the dimensions of one can be obtained by multiplying the dimensions of the other by the same number, called the *ratio of similarity.*

(In Chapter 3, similar figures were defined as being enlarged or shrunk *without distortion*. That definition is equivalent to this one.)

**2.** 🔑 Which two of the four polycubes are similar to each other? Explain.

**3.** Sketch buildings similar to this tetracube, but larger, with ratio of similarity

    a. 2              b. 3

The two buildings you sketched in problem 3 are similar to each other.

**4.** You could get the dimensions of the larger building by multiplying the dimensions of the smaller one by what number?

**5.** You could get the dimensions of the smaller building by multiplying the dimensions of the larger one by what number?

**6.** 🔑 Either of the numbers you found in problems 4 and 5 could be considered the ratio of similarity. How are the two numbers related? Explain this.

## AREA, PERIMETER

**7.** Make a list of pairs of similar polyominoes in this figure. (Hint: There are six pairs.)

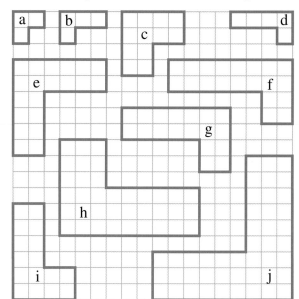

For each pair of similar polyominoes you found, find

**8.** the ratio of similarity;

**9.** the ratio of the areas.

**10.** 💡 Give the dimensions of a rectangle similar to the domino shown above, but larger, such that the ratio of areas is

    a. 25;        b. 9;

    c. 2;        d. 5.

### 11. Generalization

a. If the ratio of similarity of two figures is $R_S$, what is the ratio of areas? Explain.

b. If the ratio of areas is $R_A$, what is the ratio of similarity? Explain.

12. ✏— Using the data from problems 7-8, find the relationship between the ratio of similarity and the ratio of perimeters.

13. Make a figure using three 2-D Lab Gear blocks (including some blue blocks).

a. Sketch the figure.

b. Find its perimeter and area.

c. Use blocks to make a figure similar to the original figure.

d. Predict its perimeter and area.

e. Check your prediction.

### VOLUME, SURFACE AREA

14. ✏— True or False? Explain each one.

a. Any two rectangles are similar.

b. Any two squares are similar.

c. Any two cubes are similar.

15. Build the following cubes using the Lab Gear: $1^3$, $5^3$, $(x + 1)^3$, and $y^3$. Find the volume and surface area of each cube.

16. There are six pairs of similar buildings among the four cubes you built. For each pair, find

a. the ratio of similarity;

b. the ratio of surface areas;

c. the ratio of volumes.

### 17. Generalization

If you know the ratio of similarity between two figures, $R_S$, explain how you can find

a. the ratio of surface areas, $R_A$;

b. the ratio of volumes, $R_V$.

18. What should be the dimensions of a cubical box that would hold 27 times as much as a box having dimensions 2 in.-by-2 in.-by-2 in.?

19. 💡 Repeat problem 18 for a cubical box that would hold 10 times as much as a box having dimensions 2 in.-by-2 in.-by-2 in.

### TRAIN SETS

Model train sets come in different scales. The scale is the ratio of similarity between the model and the actual train that is being modeled. This table shows some of the available scales.

| Name | Scale |
|------|-------|
| Z | 1/220 |
| N | 1/160 |
| O | a quarter inch to one foot |
| HO | an eighth of an inch to one foot |
| LGB | half an inch to one foot |

20. Order the scales from smallest to largest.

21. The LGB scale is also known as 1/25. Comment on this.

George wanted to buy an HO set that would cover an area of 15 square feet.

22. How much area would be covered by the actual train being modeled by this set?

23. How much area would be covered by a similar set in each of the other scales?

24. How many times heavier or lighter do you estimate a similar set would be in each of the other scales? (Assume that you can estimate the ratio of weights by using the ratio of volumes.)

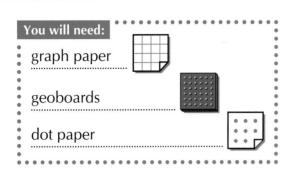

**You will need:**

graph paper

geoboards

dot paper

In the world of geometric puzzles, half a unit square (cut along the diagonal), is called a *tan*.

Figures created by combining tans are called *polytans*. Here are the ditans.

The tans must be combined side-to-side. The following arrangements are not acceptable.

1. Find all four tritans.

2. 💡 Find all fourteen tetratans.

3. Tetratans are usually called *SuperTangrams*. Find the perimeter and area of each SuperTangram, using radical expressions when appropriate. Rank the perimeters from shortest to longest.

This figure shows one of the SuperTangrams and four blown-up versions of it.

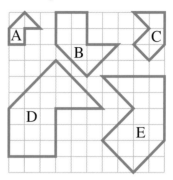

4. Find the perimeter and the area for the SuperTangram and each blowup.

5. Compare shape A with shape C.
   a. What is the ratio of similarity?
   b. Verify your answer to part (a) by showing that multiplying the perimeter of A by the ratio of similarity yields the perimeter of C.

6. Repeat problem 5 for each other pair of shapes in the figure. (You should find nine more ratios of similarity.)

7. **Report** Write a report summarizing your work in problems 3-6. Include a discussion of:
   • using the Pythagorean theorem;
   • perimeter and area of similar figures;
   • operations with radical expressions.

## MIDPOINTS

**8.** Draw five geoboard segments whose midpoints are on a peg.

**9.** Make a triangle such that all of its sides have their midpoints on a peg. Connect the midpoints, making a smaller triangle. Study the figure, looking for parallel lines, equal segments, and similar figures.

**10.** Find the slopes of lines you believe are parallel. Find the lengths of the segments you believe are equal. Find the ratio of similarity for figures you believe are similar.

**11.** Make a quadrilateral such that all of its sides have their midpoints on a peg. Make the quadrilateral as irregular as you can, avoiding equal or parallel sides. Connect the midpoints, making a smaller quadrilateral. Study the figure, looking for parallel sides and equal segments.

**12.** Find the slopes of lines you believe are parallel. Find the lengths of the segments you believe are equal.

**13.** Report Write a report on midpoints of triangles and quadrilaterals. Do you think what you found in the case you investigated will always be true? Explain.

**14.** ♀ Try to make a triangle such that exactly two of its sides have their midpoints on pegs. If you find such a triangle, draw it on dot paper. If you believe such a triangle does not exist, explain why.

# ◆ Essential Ideas

**1.** On the number line, what is the distance between:
   a. 12 and −34?   b. 12 and 34?
   c. 12 and $x$?

**2.** On the number line, what points are at distance 7.5 from 6.89?

**3.** On the number line, what point is halfway between:
   a. 12 and −34?   b. 12 and 34?
   c. 12 and $x$?

**4.** (5, 6) is the midpoint of a segment from what point to:
   a. (7, −8)?   b. (−9.1, 2.34)?

**5.** What is the biggest possible difference between taxicab and Euclidean distance between two geoboard pegs on a 10-by-10 geoboard? (Give a decimal approximation.)

**6.** On graph paper, show as many points as possible that are at distance 10 from the origin, using
   a. taxicab distance;
   b. Euclidean distance.

**7.** What is the distance from (5, 6) to:
   a. (7, −8)?   b. (−9.1, 2.34)?

## THE PYTHAGOREAN THEOREM

**8.** How long is the diagonal of a square if the side of the square is
   a. 10?   b. $x$?

**9.** How long is the side of a square if the diagonal is
   a. 10?   b. $x$?

**10.** How long is the other leg of a right triangle, if the first leg is half the hypotenuse, and the hypotenuse is
   a. 10?   b. $x$?

## FROM ONE POINT TO ANOTHER

**11.** Given the two points (1, 2.3) and (−4.5, 6), find
   a. the taxicab distance between them;
   b. the slope of the line that joins them;
   c. the Euclidean distance between them.

## SQUARE ROOTS

**12.** ⚷ Explain why $\sqrt{-4}$ is not a real number.

**13.** ⚷ Is $\sqrt{-x}$ a real number? Explain.

**14.** a. Give three values of $x$ for which $-x$ represents a positive number.
   b. Make a table of values and graph $y = \sqrt{-x}$.
   c. What is the domain of $y = \sqrt{-x}$?

**15.** Hal noticed something interesting. He saw that if he squared a number and took its square root, he would get back the same number. Jacob said he could find many numbers for which that wouldn't work. Can you? List some.

**16.** Ruth thought you could write:
$$-\sqrt{25} = \sqrt{-25} \text{ and } -\sqrt{-25} = \sqrt{25}.$$
Explain why she is wrong.

**17.** Which is greater? Explain.
   a. $\sqrt{80}$ or $8\sqrt{10}$
   b. $\sqrt{40} + \sqrt{40}$ or $\sqrt{80}$
   c. $\sqrt{63} - \sqrt{28}$ or $\sqrt{63 - 28}$
   d. $\dfrac{\sqrt{4}}{\sqrt{9}}$ or $\sqrt{\dfrac{4}{9}}$

## MULTIPLYING AND DIVIDING

**18.** What is the area of a rectangle having sides
   a. 3 and $\sqrt{6}$?
   b. $\sqrt{3}$ and $\sqrt{6}$?
   c. $4\sqrt{3}$ and $5\sqrt{6}$?
   d. $(4 + \sqrt{3})$ and $5\sqrt{6}$?

**19.** A rectangle has area $8\sqrt{7}$. Give three possibilities for the sides.

**20.** 💡 A rectangle has area $15 + 6\sqrt{7}$. Give three possibilities for the sides.

**21.** Write without radicals in the denominator.
   a. $\dfrac{2}{\sqrt{3}}$
   b. 💡 $\dfrac{4}{\sqrt{5} + 6}$

## ADDING AND SUBTRACTING

**22.** True or False? Explain.
   a. $36 + 64 = 100$
   b. $\sqrt{36 + 64} = \sqrt{100}$
   c. $\sqrt{36} + \sqrt{64} = \sqrt{100}$
   d. $\sqrt{36 + 64} = \sqrt{36} + \sqrt{64}$

**23.** Simplify, then add or subtract.
   a. $\sqrt{8} + \sqrt{72}$
   b. $\sqrt{20} - \sqrt{5}$
   c. $\sqrt{30} - \sqrt{36} + \sqrt{120} + \sqrt{121}$
   d. $15 - \sqrt{15} + 60 - \sqrt{60}$

## THE MIDPOINT OF GROWTH

**24.** Joel invested $200 in 1970 and forgot about it. In the year 2010 he discovered that he had $5227 in the account. How much did he have in the account in 1990 if he was getting
   a. simple interest?
   b. compound interest?

## RADICAL RULES

**25.** If $a$ and $b$ are nonnegative, write an expression equivalent to each of the following. Explain each rule with an example.

   a. $\sqrt{a}\,\sqrt{a}$
   b. $\sqrt{a}\sqrt{b}$
   c. $a/\sqrt{a}$
   d. $\sqrt{a}/\sqrt{b}$

**26.** Simplify.
   a. $\sqrt{2^9}$
   b. $\sqrt{2^{10}}$

**27.** 💡 Simplify $\sqrt{2^n}$ assuming $n$ is
   a. even;
   b. odd.

## SIMILAR FIGURES

**28.** Assume you want to use a copy machine to blow up a picture from a 3-inch-by-5-inch index card to 4-inch-by-6-inch card.
   a. What percent setting should you use so that you get as large an image as possible, but one which does not extend beyond the edge?
   b. How much is the area increased at that setting?

**29.** Answer the questions in problem 28 about blowing up a picture from a 3-inch-by-5-inch size to an 8.5-inch-by-11-inch size.

**30.** Assume you want to use a copy machine to reduce an image so its area gets divided by two. What percent setting should you use?

Assume that the amount of material needed to make clothes is proportional to the surface area, while the amount of food needed is proportional to the volume.

**31.** How many times as much material would be needed to dress a five-foot Alice as a ten-inch Alice?

**32.** How many times as much food would be needed to feed a five-foot Alice as a ten-inch Alice?

# CHAPTER 10

The spiral groove of a record, from the outer rim to the inner

## Coming in this chapter:

Exploration I have pennies, dimes, and quarters, and two bags to put them in. I put all the coins of one kind into one bag, and coins of the other two kinds into the other. There is the same number of coins in each bag, and the total value of each bag's contents is the same. How much money might I have?

# SATISFYING CONSTRAINTS

# The Van Pool

**You will need:**

graph paper

In the town of Braun a group of people decided to organize a van pool to get to and from work and school. They estimated mileage costs to be about $11 per day, so the total cost including the bridge toll would be $12 per day round trip. Then they had to discuss how to share costs. They agreed that children and adults might have different fares.

1. **Exploration** Say there are three children and four adults in the van pool. Find several possible fares you could charge children and adults.

## SHARING COSTS

In the following problems, let $x$ stand for a child's daily fare, and let $y$ stand for an adult's daily fare.

2. If only one adult and one child joined the van pool, there is more than one possible pair of values for $x$ and $y$.
   a. List three possible $(x, y)$ pairs.
   b. Plot these $(x, y)$ pairs on coordinate axes.
   c. Make a graph showing all possible $(x, y)$ pairs. Label the $x$-intercept and the $y$-intercept.

3. Repeat problem 2, assuming that one child and two adults join the van pool. Use the same axes for your graph.

4. Repeat problem 2, assuming that two adults and three children join the van pool. Use the same axes for your graph.

5. a. Write equations for the graphs you drew in problems 2-4.
   b. For each equation, interpret the coefficients of $x$ and $y$ and the constant term in terms of the situation.
   c. Find the $x$-intercept and the $y$-intercept on each of your graphs. Interpret them in terms of the situation.

## NEGOTIATIONS

In this section, assume that the van pool has four children and three adults.

6. a. Make a table showing several possible $(x, y)$ pairs representing the daily fare for children and adults. Draw a graph that shows all possible $(x, y)$ pairs.
   b. Label and interpret the $x$-intercept and the $y$-intercept on your graph.
   c. Write an equation for the graph.

The members of the van pool discussed how to divide the cost among themselves. Some thought the adults' and children's fares should be different, and others thought they should be the same. They discussed several possible plans.

In each case described in problems 7-12:

    a. Figure out what the daily fare for adults and for children would be. Show your work.

    b. Plot a point on the graph from problem 6 to represent your solution.

**7.** Frances suggested that adults pay twice as much as children because they have more money.

**8.** John thought that adults should pay $1 more than children.

**9.** Kathleen said that adults should pay $2 more than children.

**10.** Joanna argued that there was no reason to have different fares, since an adult and a child each occupy one seat.

**11.** Allan thought it was unfair to have adults pay more than children, since adults take turns driving the van. He argued that children should pay twice as much as adults.

**12.** Louise remembered that van pools are exempt from the bridge toll, so she subtracted $1 from the total cost. She agreed with Allan that children should pay twice as much as adults.

### INFLATION

The cost of commuting kept increasing. Since the van could legally carry nine people, including the driver, the members decided to let two more children join the pool. They had six children and three adults. Over the years, the cost went up, first to $14, then to $15, and finally to $18 per day.

**13.** On the same pair of axes, draw three graphs, one for each of the three values for the total cost.

**14.** Label each graph with its equation.

**15.** Assume that the adults' fare is twice the children's fare. Mark the points on your graph representing those fares for adults and children, if the total cost is the following amounts:

    a. $14        b. $15        c. $18

**16.** ⚷ Look at the three points you marked in problem 15. You should be able to connect all of them with a straight line.

    a. Find an equation that fits your line.

    b. Interpret your equation. (What do the coefficients mean in terms of the problem?)

**17.** Repeat problems 15-16, assuming that the children's fare is twice the adults' fare.

**RECIPES**

These are the instructions on a can of orange juice concentrate.

> Mix one part juice concentrate
> with three parts water.

**18.** How much concentrate should you use to make
 a. 6 cups of orange juice?
 b. 10 cups of orange juice?

**19.** Using this recipe, how much of each ingredient would you need to make 160 cups of punch for the 80 people who are expected at the piano recital?

> ❀ **Piano Recital Punch** ❀
> • • • • • • • • • • • • • • • • • • • • • • • • • • • • •
>
> *Mix:*
> 4 parts iced tea, sweetened
> 4 parts apple juice
> 4 parts cranberry juice
> 2 parts orange juice
> 1 part lemon juice
>
> *Garnish with lemon and orange slices.*

**20.** How much Piano Recital Punch could you make if you had an unlimited amount of the other ingredients but only
 a. 3/4 cup of lemon juice?
 b. 3 cups of orange juice?

**EXPONENTS**

**21.** Write without parentheses.
 a. $(4x^2)^3$  b. $(4x^2y)^3$

**22.** Simplify each ratio.
 a. $\dfrac{80 \cdot 2^{x+2}}{4 \cdot 2^x}$

 b. $\dfrac{4 \cdot 2^{x+2}}{80 \cdot 2^{x+1}}$

 c. $\dfrac{4 \cdot 2^{x+1}}{80 \cdot 2^{x+2}}$

**23.** Use your calculator to compare $3 \cdot 2^x$ and $2 \cdot 3^x$. Which is greater for different values of $x$? For what value of $x$ are they equal?

# How Much of Each Kind?

### AT THE LAUNDROMAT®

1. **Exploration** Some dimes and quarters have a total value of $3.95. How many of each coin might there be? (Find all the possibilities.) What is the fewest coins there could possibly be? The most? Explain, showing your method of thinking about this problem and commenting on any patterns you notice.

Dan needs nickels and quarters to do his laundry at Science and Math Quick Wash. He has a five-dollar bill. The table shows one possible combination of coins he might get if he asks for change in nickels and quarters only. (The value is given in cents.)

| Nickels | | Quarters | | Total Coins | |
|---|---|---|---|---|---|
| no. | value | no. | value | no. | value |
| 45 | 225 | 11 | 275 | 56 | 500 |

2. Add at least six more possibilities to the table and comment on any patterns you notice. (If you don't see any patterns, add more possibilities until you do.)

3. What is the fewest coins Dan might get? The most?

4. Would it be possible for Dan to have an even number of coins? An odd number? Explain.

5. Would it be possible for Dan to have the same number of quarters as nickels? If so, how many of each would he have?

If Dan gets $x$ nickels and $y$ quarters, the entry in the table would look like this.

| Nickels | | Quarters | | Total Coins | |
|---|---|---|---|---|---|
| no. | value | no. | value | no. | value |
| $x$ | $5x$ | $y$ | $25y$ | — | — |

6. a. Explain the meaning of the expressions $5x$ and $25y$ in the table.

   b. Complete the entry, giving the total number of coins and their value *in terms of x and y*.

Any possible whole number pair of values $(x, y)$ giving a possibility for the number of nickels and quarters that Dan might get in change will satisfy this *equation*,

$$5x + 25y = 500.$$

For example, it is easy to show by substitution that the pair (45, 11) satisfies this equation: $5(45) + 25(11) = 500$. This pair also satisfies this condition, or *constraint:*

   The total number of coins is 56.

7. Is there another $(x, y)$ pair that satisfies the same equation and the same constraint? If so, what is it?

8. Find $(x, y)$ pairs that satisfy both the equation $5x + 25y = 500$ and the constraints given. (You may want to extend the table you made. You can save work by looking for patterns in your table.) Some may not be possible.

   Constraints:

   a. The total number of coins is 80.

   b. There are 20 times as many nickels as quarters.

   c. There are 12 more nickels than quarters.

   d. There are 8 more quarters than nickels.

9. Each of the constraints in problem 8 can be expressed as an equation in $x$ and $y$. Write each equation.

10. At Science and Math Quick Wash, the machines take three quarters and one nickel to wash and one quarter to dry. If Dan wants to do as many loads as possible,
    a. how many loads of wash will he be able to do?
    b. what change should he request for his five-dollar bill? (Find all possible answers.)

**CRANBERRY-APPLE JUICE**

Nelson works for the G. Ale Bar Company, a chain of soda fountains. He is trying to create a special recipe to make a best-selling juice. For a taste test, he wants to prepare several 20-cup batches of different mixtures of pure apple juice with a cranberry-apple juice that is 50% apple and 50% cranberry.

| Apple juice | | Cranberry-apple | | Mixture | |
|---|---|---|---|---|---|
| apple | cran | apple | cran | apple | cran |
| 15 | 0 | 2.5 | 2.5 | 17.5 | 2.5 |
| 8 | 0 | 6 | 6 | 14 | 6 |
| 6 | 0 | — | — | — | — |
| — | — | 8 | — | — | — |
| — | — | — | 9.5 | — | — |
| $x$ | — | $0.50y$ | — | $x+0.50y$ | — |

11. Copy and complete the table. Add several more numerical possibilities. (The last row is based on $x$ cups of apple juice and $y$ cups of cranberry-apple.)

12. 🔑 What are the largest and smallest amounts of cranberry juice possible in one of Nelson's mixtures? What about apple juice? Explain.

13. For the mixture in the first row, what percent *of the total* is cranberry? (Be careful! You can't get the answer by dividing 2.5 by 17.5)

14. Add a **% cran** column to your table, and repeat problem 13 for all the rows.

15. What are the largest and smallest *percentages* of cranberry juice possible in one of Nelson's mixtures? What about apple juice? Explain.

16. Explain why the expression $x + 0.50y$ represents the total amount of apple juice in the mixture.

17. What is the expression for the total amount of cranberry juice in the mixture? Explain.

18. Explain why $x + y$ equals 20 for every possibility listed in the table.

19. What does the $x + 0.50y = 10$ mean in this situation? Is there an $(x, y)$ pair that satisfies this equation? Explain.

For each equation, 20-25:
  a. Interpret the equation in terms of this situation.
  b. If possible, find a value of $x$ and of $y$ that satisfies the equation, given the constraint that $x$ and $y$ add up to 20.

20. $0.50y = 4$

21. $x + 0.50y = 15$

22. $x + 0.50y = 4$

23. $x + 0.5y = 11.5$

24. 💡 $x + 0.50y = 0.75(x + y)$

25. 💡 $x + 0.50y = 0.25(x + y)$

26. 🔧 Which of the equations 20-25 were impossible to solve? Would they have been possible if the total amount had been 30 cups? Explain.

# Two Variables, Two Equations

the Lab Gear

## MYSTERY CONTAINERS

The Lab Gear may help you solve this problem.

1. A crate contains two small containers and three large containers. The total weight of the crate is 16 pounds.

   a. What are some possible weights of the small and the large containers? How many possible weights are there?

   b. Find the weight of four small containers and six large containers.

   c. Two containers are removed from the crate, and it is weighed again. Now it weighs ten pounds. Using this additional information, find possible weights for the small container and the large container. Comment on your answers.

## ONE EQUATION, ONE CONSTRAINT

The workmat shows the equation

$$y + 4x = 12.$$

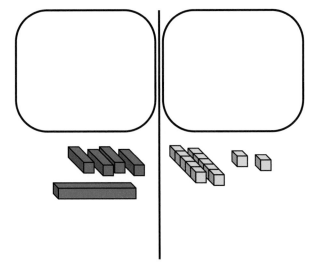

2. Using trial and error, find some values of $x$ and $y$ that make the equation true. (How many possible values are there?)

One of the $(x, y)$ pairs satisfying this equation also satisfies the constraint, or condition, that $y$ is twice $x$. If $y$ is twice $x$, then each $y$-block can be replaced with two $x$-blocks.

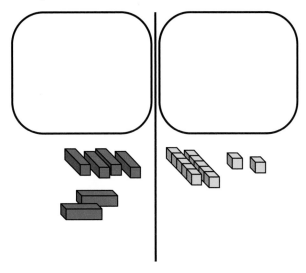

The resulting equation is $6x = 12$.

3. Solve for $x$ in the equation above. Then find the $(x, y)$ pair that satisfies both the equation $y + 4x = 12$ and the constraint that $y = 2x$.

For each problem, 4-7, model the equation on the workmat with the blocks. Then use the blocks to find an $(x, y)$ pair that satisfies both the equation and the constraint. Check your final answers in the original equations.

4. $4x - 7 = y + 3$
   Constraint: $y$ is two more than $x$.

5. $2y + x = 5$
   Constraint: $x$ is six less than $y$.

6. $2x + y = 9$
   Constraint: $x$ is three more than $y$.

**7.** $2y + x = 4$

Constraint: $x$ and $y$ add up to six.

For each problem you just solved, the constraint could have been written as an equation. For example, the constraint that the sum of $x$ and $y$ is six can be written $x + y = 6$. This means that in each of problems 4-7, you found an $(x, y)$ pair that *satisfied both of two given equations*. We say that you *solved* a system of simultaneous equations.

### SIMULTANEOUS EQUATIONS

Solve each system of simultaneous equations. If you want to use the Lab Gear, begin by modeling the first equation with the blocks. Then use the second equation to substitute blocks for the $y$-blocks or for the $x$-blocks. Check your answers.

**8.** $\begin{cases} 2x - y = 2 \\ y = 3x \end{cases}$  **9.** $\begin{cases} 4x + y = 10 \\ y = 6x - 20 \end{cases}$

**10.** $\begin{cases} x - 4y = 23 \\ x = -5y - 4 \end{cases}$  **11.** $\begin{cases} 3y + 2x = 7 \\ 3y = 4x - 5 \end{cases}$

### MIND READING

What numbers am I thinking of?

**12.** Their sum is 7. Their difference is 3.

**13.** Their sum is 18. The second is twice as large as the first.

**14.** The first minus the second is 3. Twice the first, minus twice the second is 6.

**15.** ☛ One of problems 12-14 has more than one answer. How many answers does it have? Why?

◆◆◆◆◆◆◆◆◆◆◆◆◆◆◆◆◆◆◆◆◆◆◆◆◆◆◆◆◆◆◆

### REVIEW/PREVIEW  *EVALUATING*

**16.** Two $(x, y)$ pairs that satisfy the equation $2x + 3y = 16$ are given in the table below. Copy and complete the table.

| $x$ | $y$ | $2x + 3y$ | $x + y$ | $x - y$ | $4x + 6y$ | $x + 1.5y$ |
|-----|-----|-----------|---------|---------|-----------|------------|
| -1  | 6   | 16        | 5       | —       | —         | 8          |
| 2   | 4   | 16        | —       | -2      | 32        | —          |
| –   | 5   | 16        | —       | —       | —         | —          |
| –   | -6  | 16        | —       | —       | —         | —          |
| –   | –   | 16        | —       | —       | —         | —          |
| -4  | –   | 16        | —       | —       | —         | —          |

**17.** ☛ Study the table you made. In which columns are all the values the same? Why?

### REVIEW/PREVIEW  *SOLVING FOR y*

Set up these problems with the Lab Gear, and rearrange the blocks so that $y$ is by itself on one side of the equation. Write equations to show your steps. In some cases, you will need to finish the problem without the blocks.

**18.** $-4x + y = 6$  **19.** $4x + 2y = 10$

**20.** $-6x + y = 4$  **21.** $-6x + 3y = 9$

**22.** $6x - 3y = 12$  **23.** $x + 2y = 8$

**24.** $x - y = 1$  **25.** $6x - 5y = 0$

**26.** ☛ Explain how to solve for $y$ (without the Lab Gear), with the help of an example.

**27.** **Generalization** Solve for $y$.
$$Ax + By = C$$

**CONSECUTIVE NUMBERS**

**28.** Compute, and look for a pattern.

    a. $1 \cdot 2 \cdot 3 + 2$

    b. $2 \cdot 3 \cdot 4 + 3$

    c. $4 \cdot 5 \cdot 6 + 5$

    d. $(5 - 1) \cdot 5 \cdot (5 + 1) + 5$

    e. $9 \cdot 10 \cdot 11 + 10$

    f. $(10 - 1) \cdot 10 \cdot (10 + 1) + 10$

**29.** 💡 Use algebra to explain the pattern.

**30.** The product of three consecutive numbers divided by their sum is 1. What are the numbers?

**31.** Repeat problem 30, if the product divided by the sum is the following:

    a. 5                 b. 16

**32.** 💡 What can you say about the middle number if the product of three consecutive numbers divided by their sum is a whole number?

**NINE FACTORS**

**33.** **Project** The number 1 has one whole number factor, itself; 2 has two factors, 1 and 2; 3 has two factors; and 4 has three factors. (What are they?) Find some numbers having *nine factors*. Explain.

# LESSON 10.4 Solving Systems

**You will need:**

the Lab Gear

**Definitions:** In real-world applications we often need to find a solution that satisfies two or more equations simultaneously. We call the group of equations a *system of simultaneous equations*. To *solve a system* means to find the $(x, y)$ pairs that satisfy every equation in the group.

In this course, you will learn techniques for solving systems of two equations. In later courses you will learn how to solve systems of more than two equations.

In an earlier chapter, you studied equivalent equations. *Equivalent equations have all the same solutions.*

1. Find some $(x, y)$ solutions to these equations.
   a. $y = 2x + 6$
   b. $3y = 6x + 18$

2. Use algebra to show that the two equations in problem 1 are equivalent.

### SOLVING TECHNIQUES: SUBSTITUTION

**Example:** Solve the system.
$$\begin{cases} 5x + 3y = -15 \ (A) \\ y = 2x + 6 \quad (B) \end{cases}$$

The figure shows how to model the system on two workmats.

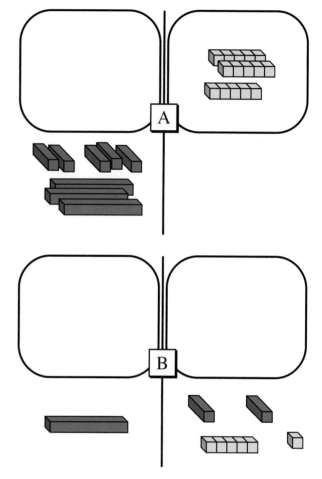

By multiplying both sides of Equation (B) by 3, you get Equation (C), which is equivalent to Equation B.

$$3y = 6x + 18 \quad (C)$$

The figure shows how to model Equation (C) on the second workmat.

▲ **376**

*Chapter 10 Satisfying Constraints*

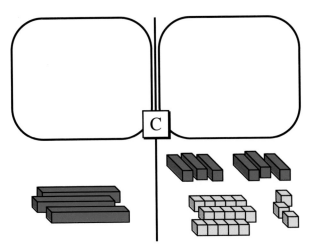

Since $3y = 6x + 18$, we can replace the $3y$ in the first equation with $6x + 18$ to get a new equation that has only $x$-blocks and yellow blocks.

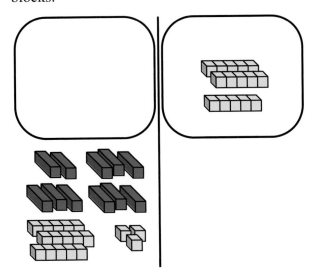

**3.** Write the new equation. Then solve for $x$.

**4.** a. Substitute the value of $x$ into Equation (B) and solve for $y$.

b. Substitute this $(x, y)$ pair into Equation (A). If it doesn't satisfy the equation, check your work to find your mistake.

c. Write the $(x, y)$ pair that is the solution to the system.

Solve each system, 5-10. If you use the Lab Gear, you may set up the first equation with the blocks. Then use the second equation to eliminate the $x$- or $y$-blocks by substitution. In some cases, you may first need to write an equation equivalent to the second equation.

**5.** $\begin{cases} 5y - 4x = -9 \\ 5y = 3x - 7 \end{cases}$  **6.** $\begin{cases} 5x + 3y = -15 \\ y = 2x + 6 \end{cases}$

**7.** $\begin{cases} 5x - 3y = -29 \\ x = 2 - 2y \end{cases}$  **8.** $\begin{cases} 2x + 3y = 9 \\ 4x = 6 - 2y \end{cases}$

**9.** $\begin{cases} 4x - y = 5 \\ 3y = 6x + 3 \end{cases}$  **10.** $\begin{cases} 6x - 2y = -16 \\ 4x + y = 1 \end{cases}$

**SOLVING TECHNIQUES:**
**LINEAR COMBINATIONS**

Here is another technique for solving systems.

**Example:** Solve the system.

$$\begin{cases} x + 2y = 11 & \text{(A)} \\ x - 2y = 3 & \text{(B)} \end{cases}$$

The figure shows two workmats, with one equation modeled on each.

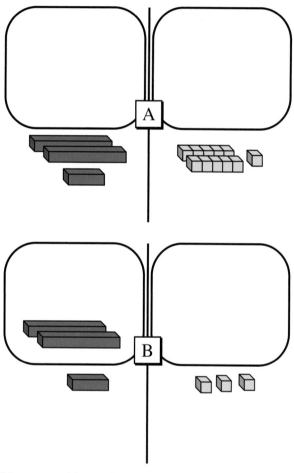

You can add equal quantities to both sides of Equation (A) to get an equivalent equation. For example, you could add 3 to both sides, or even $x - 2y$ to both sides. Also, since Equation (B) says that $x - 2y = 3$, you could add 3 to one side and $x - 2y$ to the other side, as shown on the figure.

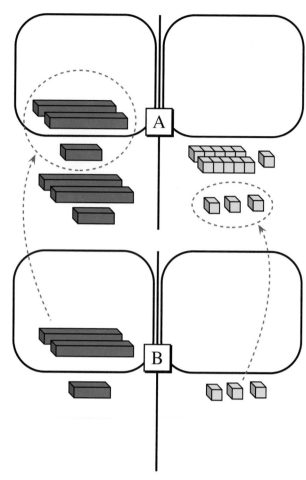

**11.** Write the equation shown in equation (A) in the figure. Simplify and solve for $x$. (What happened to $y$?)

**12.** Find the $(x, y)$ pair that is the solution to the system. Check by substituting into both of the original equations.

Solving the system in the example was easier than solving most systems, since when you added one equation to the other there were no $y$'s left. The next example is more difficult.

**Example:** Solve the system.

$$\begin{cases} 2y - 6x = 16 & \text{(A)} \\ 4x + y = 1 & \text{(B)} \end{cases}$$

By multiplying both sides of Equation (B) by -2, you get Equation (C), which is equivalent to Equation (B). Here is the new system, which is equivalent to the original.

$$\begin{cases} 2y - 6x = 16 & \text{(A)} \\ -8x - 2y = -2 & \text{(C)} \end{cases}$$

**13.** 🔑 Why was Equation (B) multiplied by -2?

**14.** Solve the system. Show your work. Check your answers by substituting into both equations of the original system.

Mr. Richards gave the class this hard system to solve.

$$\begin{cases} 3x + 5y = 17 & \text{(A)} \\ 2x + 3y = 11 & \text{(B)} \end{cases}$$

Charlotte suggested multiplying the first equation by 3 and the second equation by -5 to get a new system.

**15.** Use Charlotte's method to write a new system. Solve the system and check your answer.

**Definition:** The equation you get by adding multiples of the two equations together is called a *linear combination* of the two equations.

Leroy thought it would be easier if they got a linear combination by multiplying by smaller numbers. He suggested multiplying the first equation by -2 and the second equation by 3.

**16.** Use Leroy's method to write a new system. Solve the system.

**17.** 🔑 Compare the two ways you solved this problem. Which do you prefer? Can you think of a third way? Explain.

**SYSTEMATIC PRACTICE**

Solve these systems. Some have one $(x, y)$ solution. Others have an infinite number of solutions, or no solution.

**18.** $\begin{cases} 5x + 7y = 1 \\ x + 7 = 1 \end{cases}$  **19.** $\begin{cases} 3 - x = 4y \\ x = -2y - 9 \end{cases}$

**20.** $\begin{cases} 8x - 4y = 0 \\ 2x = y \end{cases}$  **21.** $\begin{cases} y = 4 + x \\ y = 7x + 10 \end{cases}$

**22.** $\begin{cases} 4x - y = 2 \\ y = 4x + 1 \end{cases}$  **23.** $\begin{cases} 6x - 2y = -16 \\ 4x + y = 1 \end{cases}$

# 10.A Juice Experiments

Nelson is continuing his quest for the perfect juice. You have been hired as a consultant to the G. Ale Bar Company to assist him. He ran out of apple juice and is making the 20-cup batches for the taste test using two kinds of juice.

**Fruity Flavor:** 50% cranberry and 50% apple

**Berry Blend:** 20% cranberry and 80% apple

| Fruity Flavor | | Berry Blend | | Mixture | |
|---|---|---|---|---|---|
| apple | cran | apple | cran | apple | cran |
| 5 | 5 | 8 | 2 | 13 | 7 |
| 7.5 | 7.5 | 4 | 1 | 11.5 | 8.5 |
| $0.50x$ | — | $0.80y$ | — | — | — |

1. Make a table like the one above. List at least six possible mixtures. Add two columns to the table, showing the percents of cranberry and apple in the mixture.

2. Find the minimum and the maximum amount of cranberry juice possible in one of Nelson's mixtures. Then find the minimum and the maximum *percent*.

3. Repeat problem 2 for apple juice.

How many cups of Fruity Flavor and Berry Blend would you need to use to make 20 cups each of the cranberry-apple mixtures in 4-7? (Some are impossible.)

4. 30% cranberry, 70% apple

5. 25% cranberry, 75% apple

6. 10% cranberry, 90% apple

7. Choose your own percentages.

8. In the last line of the table, what is the meaning of $x$ and $y$?

9. For Nelson's mixtures, what is the sum of $x$ and $y$?

For each equation, 10-15:
   a. Write, in words, an interpretation of it in terms of the situation.
   b. If possible, find a value of $x$ and of $y$ that satisfies the equation, keeping in mind the answer to problem 9.

10. $0.50x + 0.20y = 7$

11. $0.50x + 0.80y = 8$

12. $0.50x + 0.80y = 0.25(x + y)$

13. $0.50x + 0.20y = 0.25(x + y)$

14. $x + y = 25$

15. $x - y = 10$

16. Report Write an illustrated report summarizing the results of this investigation. Your report should include, but not be limited to, answers to the following questions:
   • What determines the maximum and the minimum amount of each kind of juice possible in the mixture?
   • What determines the maximum and the minimum percent of each kind of juice in the mixture?
   • How could you use systems of equations to solve problems like 4 through 6? Give examples.

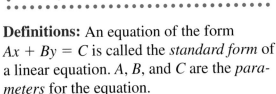

# Standard Form

**You will need:**

graph paper

graphing calculator
(optional)

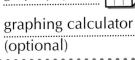

**Definitions:** An equation of the form $Ax + By = C$ is called the *standard form* of a linear equation. $A$, $B$, and $C$ are the *parameters* for the equation.

In this lesson you will investigate how the values of the parameters affect the graphs of linear equations in standard form.

### INTERCEPTS

Do not use graphing calculators for this section. These equations of lines are in standard form. For each equation:

  a. Find the parameters $A$, $B$, and $C$.

  b. Find the *x*-intercept and the *y*-intercept.

  c. Graph the line by plotting the intercepts.

**1.** $3x + 2y = 12$     **2.** $3x - 2y = 18$

**3.** $x + y = 6$         **4.** $x - y = 6$

**5.** $-3x + 4y = 10$

**6.** **Generalization**

  a. Explain how to find the *x*-intercept and the *y*-intercept of the line whose equation is $Ax + By = C$.

  b. A fast way to graph a line is by finding and plotting the intercepts. Show how to use this technique to graph a line of the form $Ax + By = C$. (Choose specific values for $A$, $B$, and $C$.)

**7.**  a. Write the equation of a line that has *x*-intercept $(6, 0)$. Graph it and find its *y*-intercept.

  b. Write the equation of a line that has *y*-intercept $(0, -4)$. Graph it and find its *x*-intercept.

  c. Write the equation of a line that has *y*-intercept $(0, 4)$ *and* *x*-intercept $(-6, 0)$.

**8.** **Generalization** Show how to find the equation of a line having intercepts $(p, 0)$ and $(0, q)$.

### THE CASE WHEN $A = B$

**9.**  a. Graph $x + y = 10$.

  b. On the same axes, graph $2x + 2y = 10$.

  c. In the equations you graphed in parts (a) and (b), what are $A$, $B$, and $C$?

  d. When you doubled $A$ and $B$ in the equation but left $C$ the same, how did the graph change?

**10.** Draw the graphs of at least two other equations of the form $Ax + By = C$ for which $A$ is equal to $B$ and $C = 10$. Label the graphs with their equations.

**11.**  Compare all the graphs you drew in problems 9-10. (What stayed the same, and what changed? How do the graphs compare in steepness?)

**12.**  a. Graph $x + y = 4$.

  b. On the same axes, graph $2x + 2y = 8$.

  c. In the equations you graphed in parts (a) and (b), what are $A$, $B$, and $C$?

**13.**  

  a. When you doubled $A$, $B$, and $C$, how did the graph change?

  b. If you triple $A$, $B$, and $C$, what will the equation be? How do you think the graph will change? Explain.

### VARYING A

**14.** a. Graph $x + 2y = 5$.

    b. Graph $2x + 2y = 5$ on the same axes.

    c. Draw several more graphs, changing the value of $A$, leaving $B$ equal to 2, and $C$ equal to 5. Use both positive and negative values for $A$.

**15.** ⚷— Compare all the graphs you drew in problem 14.

    a. When you changed the value of $A$ in the equation, what features of the graph changed and what stayed the same? Did the steepness change? Did the intercepts change?

    b. How are the graphs having a positive value of $A$ different from the graphs having a negative value of $A$?

    c. Is it possible to pick a value of $A$ so that the graph will be a horizontal line? A vertical line? Explain.

**16.** Show what you think the following graphs would look like. You don't have to graph them accurately, but you should make a rough sketch and explain your work.

    a. $500x + 2y = 5$

    b. $-500x + 2y = 5$

    c. $0.01x + 2y = 5$

    d. $-0.01x + 2y = 5$

### VARYING B

**17.** a. Graph $2x + y = 8$.

    b. Graph $2x + 2y = 8$ on the same axes.

    c. Draw several more graphs, changing the value of $B$, leaving $A$ equal to 2, and $C$ equal to 8. Use both positive and negative values for $B$.

**18.** ⚷— Compare all the graphs you drew in problem 17.

    a. When you changed the value of $B$ in the equation, what features of the graph changed and what stayed the same? Did the steepness change? Did the intercepts change?

    b. How are the graphs having a positive value of $B$ different from the graphs having a negative value of $B$?

    c. Is it possible to pick a value of $B$ so that the graph will be a horizontal line? A vertical line? Explain.

**19.** Show what you think the following graphs would look like. You don't have to graph them accurately, but you should make a rough sketch and explain your work.

    a. $2x + 100y = 8$

    b. $2x - 100y = 8$

    c. $2x + 0.02y = 8$

    d. $2x - 0.02y = 8$

### VARYING C

**20.** Where do you think the graph of $3x + 2y = 5$ will intersect the graph of $3x + 2y = 6$? You may want to check your prediction by graphing.

**21.** ⚷— Describe what will happen to the graph of $3x + 2y = 6$ when you change the value of $C$ but keep $A$ and $B$ constant. What will change and what will stay the same? Make several graphs to convince yourself that your answers are correct.

**22.** Report Write a report summarizing what you learned in this lesson. Explain how the values of the parameters $A$, $B$, and $C$ affect the graph of $Ax + By = C$, specifically its slope and intercept. Use examples.

**DIFFERENCES OF PERFECT SQUARES**

**23.** `Project` The number 17 can be written as the difference of the squares of whole numbers, $9^2 - 8^2$. Which other whole numbers can be written as the difference of two squares of whole numbers? Which cannot? Look for patterns, and try to explain what you discover.

**SIDES OF SQUARES**

**24.** The length of a side of a square is given. Find the area of the square.

a. $\sqrt{2}$      b. $2 + \sqrt{2}$

c. $2 - \sqrt{2}$      d. $2\sqrt{2}$

e. $\sqrt{2}/2$      f. $2/\sqrt{2}$

**25.** The side lengths of two squares are given. Which of the two squares has the larger area? Explain how you know.

a. $\sqrt{10} - \sqrt{5}$ and $\sqrt{5}$

b. $2\sqrt{8}$ and $\sqrt{16}$

**26.** Which has the larger area, or are they the same?

a. a rectangle with sides $\sqrt{2}$ and $\sqrt{5}$ or a square with side $\sqrt{10}$

b. a rectangle with sides $\sqrt{4}$ and $\sqrt{8}$ or a square with side $2\sqrt{2}$

**27.** Which has the larger perimeter, or are they the same?

a. a rectangle with sides $\sqrt{10}$ and $\sqrt{5}$ or a square with side $2\sqrt{5}$

b. a rectangle with sides $2 + 2\sqrt{2}$ and $\sqrt{2}$ or a square with sides $2 + \sqrt{2}$

# Line Intersections

## POINTS ON LINES

1. On the same pair of axes, make accurate graphs of these three equations.
   a. $3x + 5y = 9$     b. $6x + y = 18$
   c. $4x + 2y = 30$

2. There is a point on each of the lines in problem 1 where the $y$-value is three times the $x$-value.
   a. Find these points. Show your work.
   b. The three points you found in part (a) should all lie on one straight line. What is the equation of this line?

3. Graph the line $4x + 2y = 6$. Then mark and label a point on the line for which
   a. the $y$-coordinate is four times the $x$-coordinate;
   b. $y$ is twice $x$;
   c. $x$ is three less than $y$;
   d. $y$ is three less than $x$.

4. Add the graphs of the following lines to the axes you used in problem 3. Notice where each one intersects the line $4x + 2y = 6$.
   a. $y = 4x$          b. $y = 2x$
   c. $x = y - 3$       d. $y = x - 3$

5. Find the point on the line $2x - y = 6$ for which
   a. the $y$-coordinate is one more than the $x$-coordinate;
   b. the $x$-coordinate is 2/3 of the $y$-coordinate.

6. ☞ Explain the method you used to solve problem 5.

## HOW MANY INTERSECTIONS?

7. Graph these three lines on the same pair of axes. Describe what you observe.
   a. $x + 3y = 9$
   b. $2x + 6y = 18$
   c. $x + 3y = 10$

8. Graph the line $2x - 3y = 4$. Then write an equation that has
   a. the same graph;
   b. a parallel graph.

For each pair of equations 9-12 tell whether the two graphs will be
   a. the same graph;
   b. parallel graphs;
   c. intersecting graphs.

9. $2x + 9 = y$          10. $x - y = 7$
   $-4x - 18 = -2y$          $x + y = 7$

11. $x + 6 = y$          12. $x + y = 9$
    $x + y = 6$              $x + y = 7$

13. **Summary** Explain how to tell without graphing whether the equations of two lines have the same graph, parallel graphs, or intersecting graphs. Give examples.

## HOW MANY SOLUTIONS?

Some pairs of equations 14-19 represent parallel lines. Some represent intersecting lines. Others represent the same line. *Without graphing*, find the point of intersection of each pair of lines, if it exists.

14. $2x - 3y = 7$          15. $x = 6 + 3y$
    $3x - 4y = 15$             $3y = 3 + x$

*Chapter 10 Satisfying Constraints*

**16.** $y - 12 = 4x$
  $2y - 8x = 24$

**17.** $y = 42 - 4x$
  $6x = 50 + 5y$

**18.** $y - 12 = 4x$
  $2y = 8x + 24$

**19.** $2y - 2x = 7$
  $y - x = 3.5$

**20.** **Summary** Explain, giving examples, and compare what happens when you try to solve the system if
   a. the lines are parallel;
   b. the equations represent the same line;
   c. the lines meet in one point.

### ADDING LINES

**21.** a. Graph the two lines on the same pair of axes.
$$3x + y = 7$$
$$-2x + y = -8$$
   b. Label the point of intersection.
   c. Add these two equations to get a third equation. Graph it on the same pair of axes. What do you notice?

**22.** a. Graph these two lines on the same pair of axes.
   (A)   $5x - 2y = 3$
   (B)   $2x + y = 3$
   b. Label the point of intersection.
   c. Get a third equation by adding.
   (A) + (B) + (B)

Graph this equation on the same pair of axes. What do you notice?

**23.** Solve the system. $\begin{cases} 5x - 2y = 3 \\ 2x + y = 3 \end{cases}$

**24.** ◯ Here are two equations of lines.
$$2x + 3y = 5$$
$$x + 2y = 4$$

Use addition of these equations to get the equation of a *horizontal* line that passes through their intersection.

**25.** Solve the system. $\begin{cases} 2x + 3y = 5 \\ x + 2y = 4 \end{cases}$

**26.** **Summary** Explain how "adding lines" to get horizontal and vertical lines is related to solving systems of equations.

### MORE MIND READING

**27.** ⚷ Which of these problems has one solution? Which has an infinite number of solutions? Which has no solution? Explain.
   a. I'm thinking of two numbers. Their sum is 10. Twice the first plus twice the second is 20.
   b. I'm thinking of two numbers. Their sum is 6. Their difference is 10.
   c. I'm thinking of two numbers. The second is 5 more than the first. The second minus the first is 6.

REVIEW  SLOPE-INTERCEPT FORM

**28.** ⊶ The following questions are about the graph of  $y = \frac{2}{3}x - 1$ .

 a.  Where does it meet the $y$-axis?

 b.  If you move 2 units up and 3 units to the right from the $y$-intercept, where are you? Is that point on the graph? Explain.

 c.  If you move 2 units up and 3 units to the right from the point you found in part (b), where are you? Is that point on the graph? Explain.

 d.  Start anywhere on the line. Move 6 units up and $m$ units to the right, to end up on the graph. What is $m$? Explain.

**29.** ⊶ Describe a fast way to graph a line whose equation is given in slope-intercept form. Use an example.

**30.** Write these equations in slope-intercept form.

 a.  $3y = 4(2 - x)$

 b.  $4 - 3x = y - 2$

 c.  $y - 4 = 3(x - 2)$

 d.  $\dfrac{y}{2} = \dfrac{2 - 4x}{6}$

# Using Simultaneous Equations

## WRITING EQUATIONS

Some problems can be solved by solving systems of equations.

**Example:** The members of the advanced music class of Alaberg High School gave a spring concert. Afterwards they wanted to know how many adults had attended the concert. They knew they had sold 351 tickets, and receipts totaled $1078.50. If adult tickets were $4.00 and student tickets were $2.50, how many of each kind had they sold?

*Identify the variables:*

   Let $x$ = the number of adult tickets.
   Let $y$ = the number of student tickets.

*Write the equations:*

   $x + y = 351$
   $4.00x + 2.50y = 1078.50$

1. Interpret the two equations in terms of this problem.

2. Solve the system. Interpret your answer.

3. The following year 536 tickets were sold, with total receipts of $1656.50. If the ticket prices were the same, how many of each type were sold? Write and solve a system of equations.

4. 🗝 Compare the system you wrote in problem 3 with the one in the example. What is the same, and what is different? Explain.

Writing and solving a system of equations is an efficient way to solve the problems in this lesson. However, there are other ways to solve them, such as using tables, graphs, or by trial and error. Regardless of what method you use, show your work clearly and express your solutions in terms of the original problem.

## GADGETS AND WIDGETS

5. Ken walked into Kate's Store. "How much for five of those gidgets and eight of those gadgets?" he asked. "That would be $11.27 without tax," Kate replied. "Oops," said Ken. "I really need eight of the gidgets and five of the gadgets." The total was $11.87 before tax. What was the cost of a gidget? What was the cost of a gadget?

6. It takes 2.5 kg of copper and 4 kg of nickel to manufacture a widget. A smidget requires 7 kg of copper and 3 kg of nickel. How many widgets and how many smidgets could you manufacture if you had
   a. 74 kg of copper and 61 kg of nickel?
   b. 80 kg of copper and 43 kg of nickel?

## MOZART

7. Liza planned to tape a 12-hour Mozart Marathon. She wanted to use a combination of 90-minute and 60-minute tapes and to fill each one completely.
   a. What possible combinations of tapes could she use?
   b. If she used a total of ten tapes, and filled all of them completely, how many of each did she use?

8. Shelly earned some money assisting with preparations for Mozart's 200th birthday party. She made $6 per hour for addressing invitations and $8 per hour for helping to set up the stage and auditorium for the concert. She received a total of $352. How many hours did she work at each job?

## COLLEGE APPLICATIONS

9. Garabel College newspaper reported that 1089 students had applied to the college in the two-year period 1992-1994. There were 20% more applicants in the 93-94 school year than in the 92-93 school year. How many students applied to Garabel in each of the two years?

10. The number of students applying to Garabel in 92-93 was a 12% increase over the number in 91-92. How many students applied in 91-92?

11. Ms. Pavlov, the Director of Admissions, congratulated the admissions staff. "We had 32% more applicants in 93-94 than in 91-92." What is wrong with her statement?

12. 💡 The admissions department is expanding. Their budget has been increased by $1800 per week to hire new staff. They will hire some part-time student interviewers and tour guides at $5.25 per hour and student secretaries at $6.50 per hour. Interviewers and tour guides work approximately 10 hours per week, and secretaries work 15 hours per week. If they need one secretary for every five interviewers and tour guides, how many of each should they hire?

## MEXICAN FOOD

At La Brea's Mexican Restaurant, you can buy a Family Feast of eight enchiladas and twelve tamales for $19.60. The Couple's Combo has four tamales and four enchiladas, and sells for $8.00.

13. Based on these prices, what price would you recommend for the Single's Special, which has two tamales and one enchilada?

14. Mr. G. La Brea wants to add a new item to the restaurant's menu. How should he price the Double Dozen, which has a dozen enchiladas and a dozen tamales?

## CHEMISTRY

15. One solution is 80% acid. Another is 20% acid. Rosemary wants 500 liters of a solution that is 70% acid. How much of each solution should she use?

## GEOMETRY

16. 💡 A 30-cm string loop goes around two thumbtacks that are ten cm apart. A third thumbtack is added, so that the loop makes a right triangle. How far is the new tack from the old ones?

17. 💡 A rectangle has perimeter 30. If you add 3 to the width, and subtract 4 from the length, the area does not change. What are the length and width of the original rectangle?

## PROBLEMATIC PROBLEMS

Systems of simultaneous linear equations are an important and widely-used application of mathematics. Usually they involve many variables and are solved with the help of more advanced math, plus computers or programmable calculators. The lessons in this chapter were intended to give you an introduction to this sort of mathematics. However, some of the problems in this lesson are not very realistic.

18. **Report** Discuss:
- How could some of the problems be solved (or avoided) without using algebra?
- Which problems are backwards? (You are given information that could have been figured out only by someone who already knew the answer to the problem.)
- Which problems seem to start from unrealistic numbers?
- Which problems could arise in the real world?
- Which problems are really puzzles created to help you learn algebra?

# LESSON
## 10.8

# Lines Through Points

**You will need:**

graph paper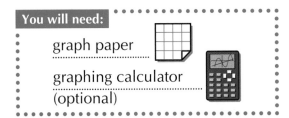

graphing calculator (optional)

1. **Exploration** The linear equation $y = x - 1$ has (2, 1) as a solution. Make up several more linear equations in $x$ and $y$ that have (2, 1) as a solution. Compare your solutions with those of other students. How many different linear equations have this solution?

## FINDING COORDINATES

Hint: The problems in this section and the following one can be solved by graphing carefully.

2. A line having slope ‑2 passes through the point (‑4, 3). Give the coordinates of three more points on the line.

3. A line having slope ‑3 passes through the point (5, 12). The points $(a, 5)$ and $(0, b)$ are on the same line. Find $a$ and $b$.

4. A line passes through (2, 1) and (‑2, ‑1). Give the coordinates of three more points on the line.

5. The points (7, ‑2) and (6, 2) are on a line. The points $(a, 5)$ and $(0, b)$ are on the same line. Find $a$ and $b$.

## LINES THROUGH A POINT

6. Which of the following lines pass through the point (1, ‑1)?
   a. $5x - 5y = 10$     b. $5x + 5y = 10$
   c. $2x - 3y = 6$     d. $-3x + 2y = 6$

7. The line $y = mx - 1$ passes through the point (3, 2). What is $m$?

8. The line $y = (-1/3)x + b$ passes through the point (3, 2). What is $b$?

## FINDING THE EQUATION OF A LINE

9. Graph the line that passes through the points (1, 3) and (3, 8). Find its equation.

Ellen and Sandor wanted to find the equation of a line passing through (4, 5) and (8, ‑3) *without using graphing*.

10. Ellen could tell by imagining the graph that the slope of the line must be negative and the $y$-intercept must be greater than 5. Explain.

Ellen knew that the equation could be written in slope-intercept form as $y = mx + b$. "All I have to do is find $m$ and $b$," she thought. Using the point (4, 5), she substituted values for $x$ and $y$ and wrote this equation in $m$ and $b$,

$$5 = m(4) + b$$

which she rewrote as $5 = 4m + b$.

11. What equation in $m$ and $b$ did she write, using the point (8, ‑3)?

**12.** a. Find the values of $m$ and $b$ that satisfy both of Ellen's equations.

b. Write the slope-intercept equation of the line passing through the points.

Sandor knew that the equation could be written in standard form as $Ax + By = C$. He substituted values for $x$ and $y$ and wrote two equations. One was $A(4) + B(5) = C$, which he rewrote as $4A + 5B = C$.

**13.** a. What was the other equation?

b. Find some values of $A$, $B$, and $C$ that satisfy both equations. (Many solutions are possible.)

c. Write in standard form an equation of the line passing through the points.

d. Compare your answer to (c) with other students' answers.

**14.** Show that Ellen and Sandor got equivalent answers, one in slope-intercept form and the other in standard form.

**15.** Find the equation of a line having slope 1.5 that passes through the point $(0.5, 4)$.

**16.** Find the equation of the line through the points $(2.3, 4.5)$ and $(-6, -7)$. (You may round off the parameters.)

**17.** Summary Explain, with examples, your strategies for finding the equation of a line,

a. when you know its slope and the coordinates of a point on it;

b. when you know the coordinates of two points on it.

### CELSIUS-FAHRENHEIT CONVERSION

Water freezes at 0° Celsius, which is 32° Fahrenheit. Water boils at 100° Celsius, which is 212° Fahrenheit.

**18.** A temperature reading can be converted from Fahrenheit to Celsius by using the formula $C = mF + b$. Find $m$ and $b$ by using the fact that $C = 0$ when $F = 32$, and $C = 100$ when $F = 212$.

**19.** Find a formula for converting Celsius to Fahrenheit.

**20.** What is the relationship between the formulas that you found in problems 18-19?

**21.** When the temperature increases by $n$ degrees on the Celsius scale, by how much does it increase on the Fahrenheit scale? Explain.

## ADDING POINTS

A line passes through the points (2, 4) and (6, 8). If you add the *x*-coordinates and the *y*-coordinates of these points you get the point (8, 12). Call this point the *sum* of the points.

**22.** What point is the *difference* of the points?

**23.** a. Find the equation of the line through (2, 4) and (6, 8).

b. Does this line also pass through the sum and the difference of (2, 4) and (6, 8)?

**24.** Write the equation of any line and find the coordinates of two points on the line. Find their sum and difference. Does the line pass through the sum and difference points?

**25.** Find the equation of a line such that the sum and the difference of any two points on the line is also on the line. To find this line, it may help to experiment with graphs. Compare your answers to problems 23-24 with other students' answers.

**26.** Summary What kinds of lines contain the sum and the difference of any two points on the line? Explain, giving examples and counter-examples.

**27.** What's wrong with this reasoning? (Hint: Think about problems 18-26.)

$$0°C = 32°F$$
$$100°C = 212°F$$
Adding equals to equals:
$$100°C = 244°F$$

DISCOVERY REAL WORD PROBLEM

**28.** Rearrange the letters in the sentence

> I'm a pencil dot.

to create an appropriate mathematical two-word phrase. (Hint: The second word has five letters.)

# 10.B Fitting a Line

**You will need:**

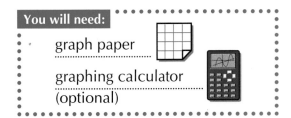

graph paper
...................................................
graphing calculator
...................................................
(optional)

These data are about *average* 45-year-olds.

| Height | Weight (lbs) | |
| --- | --- | --- |
| | **Men** | **Women** |
| 4'10" | | 118 |
| 5' | | 123 |
| 5'2" | 140 | 129 |
| 5'4" | 149 | 136 |
| 5'6" | 158 | 143 |
| 5'8" | 167 | 150 |
| 5'10" | 176 | 158 |
| 6' | 186 | 168 |
| 6'2" | 197 | |
| 6'4" | 208 | |

**1.** On the same axes, graph weight as a function of height for men and women.

The points appear to lie on two straight lines. However by looking at the differences between consecutive entries, you can see that for women, a two-inch difference in height means five more pounds between 4'10" and 5', while it means six more pounds between 5' and 5'2". This shows that the slope changes, and therefore the points are not lined up exactly.

**2.** Between what heights is the relationship between height and weight linear? In other words, between what heights do the points lie exactly on a line?

  a. Answer this for men and for women.

  b. Find the slope of those lines.

  c. Find the equations of the lines, in the form $W = mH + b$. (Express heights in inches.)

The equations you found can be used to predict the average weight for 45-year-old men and women *in that range.*

**3.** Use the equation you found to calculate the weights of a man and a woman who are each 5'5" tall. Check that your answers are consistent with the data in the table.

**4.** The unit of height is the inch, the unit of weight is the pound. What is the unit and meaning of the slope in these graphs?

**5.** In what ranges is the slope less? Greater? Explain why, in terms of the real-world meaning of the data.

It is more difficult to find a linear function relating weight to height if you try to do it over the whole range. Finding such a function is called *fitting a line to the data.* The equation of such a line is useful as an approximate formula.

**6.** **Exploration** Draw a line that is close to all the data points for the men. Find its equation. (Start out by finding two points on the line you drew and use their coordinates. They do not need to be points from the table.) Do this again for the women. Compare your answers with those of other students.

**7.** Report Explain how you found a linear equation for these data. Your report should answer the following questions, but not be limited to them.

- In a paragraph, summarize the information contained in the table.
- Why is it impossible to find an exact formula relating weight and height?

- What is the meaning of slope in this context?
- What does your formula predict for the weight of a 5′ man? Of a 6′2″ woman? Are those predictions probably too high or too low?

*DISCOVERY* **BEYOND SQUARE ROOTS**

**8.** With which of the following numbers of blocks could you build a single cube with no blocks left over? If you could build a cube, give its dimensions. (You may want to use the Lab Gear or make a sketch.)

a. 8      b. 81
c. 216      d. 729

Say that we have:
$$64^x \cdot 64^x \cdot 64^x = 64.$$

Using the product of powers law of exponents it is easy to see what $x$ must be:
$$64^{1/3} \cdot 64^{1/3} \cdot 64^{1/3} = 64^1.$$

**9.** a. What must be the value of $64^{1/3}$? (Hint: What number could you substitute for it in this equation?)
b. Use the same reasoning to find the value of $27^{1/3}$.

The 1/3 power of a number is called the cube root of a number. Explain why.

**10.** Use a law of exponents to simplify.
a. $64^{2/3}$
b. $8^{4/3}$
c. $64^{1/4}$

Kathryn counted 41 wheels in the preschool yard. All of them were on bikes and trikes. (She did not count training wheels.)

1.  Make a table showing some possible numbers of bikes and trikes.

2.  Jana counted a total of 16 bikes and trikes in the same yard. How many of each kind were there?

Bill is on vacation and wants to write to his friends. He is going to write letters and post-cards, and wants to spend no more than $4.75 on postage. Postcard stamps are 19 cents, and letter stamps are 29 cents.

3.  a.  If Bill writes only cards, how many can he write?

    b.  If he writes only letters, how many can he write?

    c.  If he has 20 friends and wants to write as many letters and as few postcards as possible, how many of each kind should he send?

4.  Which of these equations have the same set of $(x, y)$ solutions as each other? Make two groups. Show your work.
    a.  $2x + 3y = 0.4$    b.  $10x = 2 - 15y$
    c.  $15x + 10y = 5$    d.  $x + 1.5y = 0.2$
    e.  $y = -1.5x + 0.5$  f.  $3x + 2y = 1$

5.  Write in standard form, $y = 6x + 7$.

6.  What is the equation of a line having slope 8 that passes through $(9, 11)$?

Solve each system. Check first to see if you can tell that the system has no solution or an infinite number of solutions.

7.  $\begin{cases} 6m - 4b = 0 \\ 5m + 8b = 0 \end{cases}$    8.  $\begin{cases} 4m - 3b = 2 \\ 3m + 4b = 5 \end{cases}$

9.  $\begin{cases} 3a + 8b = 20 \\ 3a + b = 13 \end{cases}$    10.  $\begin{cases} 6m - 2n = 12 \\ n = 3m - 4 \end{cases}$

11.  Jeanne saw some cows and chickens. She had nothing to do, so she counted their legs and heads, over and over. Here are her results.

     The first time: 93 legs, 31 heads

     The second time: 66 legs, 16 heads

     The third time: 82 legs, 29 heads

     She counted accurately only one time. Which time was it? How many cows and how many chickens were there? Comment.

12.  Jonathan saw some three-legged stools and four-legged chairs. He was bored, so he counted their legs. There were 59 legs. Then he put six pennies on each stool, and eight nickels on each chair. (He thought it would make a good math problem.)

     a.  He used 118 coins. Can you tell how many chairs and stools there were? Explain.

     b.  The total value of the coins was $3.74. Can you tell how many chairs and stools there were? Explain.

     c.  How many of each kind of coin did he use?

## GOING NUTS

The G. Ale Bar Company also sells nuts. Cashews are $4.95 a pound, and peanuts are $1.95 a pound.

**13.** Ginger was asked to create a mix of cashews and peanuts that would cost $2.95 a pound. What percent of the mix should be peanuts and what percent should be cashews?

## CREATING SYSTEMS OF EQUATIONS

**14.** Create a system of equations that has the solution $x = 2$, $y = 7$. Compare your answer with other students' answers.

**15.** Create two different systems of equations that have the solution $x = 4$, $y = -1$. Compare answers.

**16.** Explain your strategy for making up a system of equations having a given $(x, y)$ solution.

**17.** Make up a word problem having two variables. The problem should have a unique solution. You might use one of the following themes: different-sized bottles or cans, alien creatures having different numbers of eyes or arms. Or choose anything else you want. Be creative, but make sure the math works out.

## EQUATIONS AND GRAPHS

**18.** The graphs of $y = 2x + 3$ and $y = -4x - 5$ meet at a point having $x$-coordinate -4/3. Solve the system.
$$\begin{cases} y = 2x + 3 \\ y = -4x - 5 \end{cases}$$

**19.** One of (2.5, 0.5) and (0.5, 2.5) is the solution to the system $\begin{cases} 6x + 2y = 8 \\ 9x - y = 2 \end{cases}$

Where do the graphs of $6x + 2y = 8$ and $9x - y = 2$ intersect?

## POINTS ON A LINE

Susan connected (6, 0) to (2, 10) with a rubber band on her geoboard. (5, 3) and (4, 5) appeared to be on the line she formed. She wondered whether they really were.

**20.** Find the equation of the line through (6, 0) and (2, 10). Use algebra to check whether (5, 3) and (4, 5) are on it.

**21.** Mark thought the question could be answered without finding the equation of a line, by using the slope of the line connecting one point to another. Use his method and explain it.

## A HEIGHT-WEIGHT FORMULA?

Many people do not like to reveal their weight, but most people don't mind telling their height. Lewis thought it would be useful to have a formula giving weight as a function of height. Lewis is 5 feet 6 inches tall and weighs 141 pounds. He made up a formula that relates his weight (in pounds) to his height (in inches).
$$W = 2(H) + 9$$

**22.** Verify that this formula works for Lewis's height and weight.

**23.** Lewis's friend Doug weighs 162 pounds and is 6 feet 1 inch tall. Does Lewis's formula work for Doug? Explain.

**24.** Find a formula that works for both Lewis and Doug.

**25.** Find two people who will tell you their height and weight. Find a formula that relates their weights to their heights.

**26.** Check whether the formula you found in problem 25 works to predict your weight from your height. Comment.

A spiral staircase

## *Coming in this chapter:*

**Exploration** On graph paper, you want to go from (0, 0) to (*p*, *q*), where *p* and *q* are positive whole numbers. If you travel only up and to the right, following graph paper lines, how many ways are there to do it? If you travel in a straight line, how many graph paper squares do you cross?

# INTERPRETING RATIOS

# Sums of Geometric Sequences

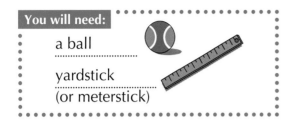

a ball
.............................
yardstick
.............................
(or meterstick)

## THE BOUNCING BALL

When you drop a ball, it bounces back, but not quite to the height from which you dropped it.

1.  Do an experiment in which you drop a ball from various heights and see to what height it bounces back. Use a yardstick or meterstick to make your measurements. Make a table like this.

| Dropped from | Bounced to | Ratio | Difference |
|---|---|---|---|
| —— | —— | —— | —— |

2.  As you vary the height, what remains closer to constant, the ratio or the difference?

For a certain "ideal" ball, the bounce-height to drop-height ratio (or *bounce ratio*) is consistently 0.8. The ball is dropped from a height of two meters.

3.  a.  How high does it bounce on the first, second, and third bounces?
    b.  How many bounces until it bounces to fewer than 80 centimeters?
    c.  How many bounces until it bounces to fewer than 10 cm?

4.  What is the total distance traveled by the ball (both down and up) if someone catches it at the top of its bounce after:
    a.  2 bounces?  b.  20 bounces?

5.  Make a guess about the total distance traveled by the ball after 200 bounces. Justify your guess.

Say the bounce ratio is $r$. Then we have:

$$\frac{bounce\ height}{drop\ height} = r$$

Or: *bounce height* $= r \cdot$ *drop height*

Assume that the initial drop height is $H$.

6.  How high does the ball bounce on the first, second, third, and fourth bounces? Express your answers in terms of $H$ and $r$.

To analyze the problem of the total distance traveled, it is easier to separate the upwards and downwards motions. First find the downwards distance traveled in the first four bounces.

$$D_4 = H + Hr + Hr^2 + Hr^3$$

As you see, the terms of the sum form a *geometric sequence* having first term $H$ and *common ratio* $r$.

7.  Write an expression for $D_6$ the downwards distance traveled in the first six bounces.

8.  🔑 What is the last exponent in the expression for the downwards distance traveled in the first $n$ bounces? Explain why the exponent is not the same as the number of bounces.

9.  Write an expression for the upwards distance traveled in:
    a.  the first four bounces, $U_4$;
    b.  the first six bounces, $U_6$.

10. 🔑 What is the last exponent in the expression for the upwards distance traveled in the first $n$ bounces? Why does this differ from the expression for the downwards distance?

## FINDING THE SUM

Here is a shortcut for calculating the sum of a geometric sequence. We will use the example of the ideal ball having bounce ratio 0.8, dropped from a height of two meters, and caught at the top of its fourth bounce. First write the downwards motion.

Eq. 1: $D_4 = 2 + 2(0.8) + 2(0.8)^2 + 2(0.8)^3$

Do not calculate the sum! You will soon see why.

*Multiplying* both sides by 0.8, we get:

Eq. 2: $D_4(0.8) = 2(0.8) + 2(0.8)^2 + 2(0.8)^3 + 2(0.8)^4$

*Subtracting* one equation from the other:

Eq. 1-Eq. 2: $D_4 - D_4 \cdot (0.8) = 2 - 2(0.8)^4$

**11.** ● Explain why there are so few terms after subtracting.

**12.** *Solve* for $D_4$. (Hint: Factor, then divide.)

**13.** Use this *multiply-subtract-solve* technique to find $U_4$. You found an expression for $U_4$ in problem 9.

**14.** What is the total distance traveled by the ball in four bounces?

When adding only four terms, the multiply-subtract-solve technique is not much of a shortcut. However, when adding large numbers of terms, it is extremely convenient. For example, for 20 bounces, you would start by writing:

$D_{20} = 2 + 2(0.8) + ... + 2(0.8)^{18} + 2(0.8)^{19}$

**15.** ● Explain why in this case the last terms do not contribute very much to the sum.

**16.** Use the multiply-subtract-solve technique to check the correctness of your answers for problems 4b and 5.

## OTHER BOUNCE RATIOS

**17.** What is the total distance traveled in 200 bounces by a ball having the following bounce ratios, after being dropped from a height of two meters?
   a. a super-ball, having bounce ratio 0.9
   b. a flat basketball, having bounce ratio 0.3

**18.** Repeat problems 3-5 for a real ball. (First, you must find the bounce ratio, perhaps by averaging the ratios you found in problem 1.) Verify your predictions for problem 3 with experiments.

An absent-minded professor invents a hyper-ball having a bounce ratio of 1.1.

**19.** Repeat problems 3-5 for the hyper-ball.

**20.** Repeat problems 3-5 for a defective hyper-ball having a bounce ratio of only 1.

**21.** Summary  Summarize what you learned about the sum of geometric sequences.
   a. Explain the multiply-subtract-solve method. (What does one multiply by? What does one subtract? What does one solve for, and how?)
   b. What is the effect of the common ratio on the sum? (What if $r$ is less than 1? What if it is equal to 1? What if it is greater than 1?)

**22.** Generalization  Use the multiply-subtract-solve technique for each sum $S$.
   a. $S = a + ar + ar^2 + ... + ar^{n-1}$
   b. $S = a + ar + ar^2 + ... + ar^n$

**23.** a. Replace each box with one of the numbers: 1, 2, 3, 4. (Use each number exactly once.)

$$\frac{\square}{\square} + \frac{\square}{\square}$$

How many possible arrangements are there?

   b. Which arrangement gives the smallest sum? What is the smallest sum?

   c. Which arrangement gives the largest sum? What is the largest sum?

   d. Are the arrangements that give the smallest and the largest answer *unique*? That is, is there only one arrangement that gives the same sum?

**24.** Repeat problem 23 for $\frac{\square}{\square} - \frac{\square}{\square}$, this time finding the arrangements that give the smallest and the largest difference. How are the smallest and the largest difference related? Explain.

**25.** Repeat problem 23 for $\frac{\square}{\square} \cdot \frac{\square}{\square}$, this time finding the arrangements that give the smallest and the largest product. How are the smallest and the largest product related? Explain.

**26.** Repeat problem 23 for $\frac{\square}{\square} \div \frac{\square}{\square}$, this time finding the arrangements that give the smallest and the largest quotient. How are the smallest and the largest quotient related? Explain.

**27.** Choose four numbers $a$, $b$, $c$, $d$ such that $a < b < c < d$. Repeat problems 23-26 for these numbers. Compare your answers with other students' answers. Were you able to use the answers from problems 23-26 to help you?

**28.** Report Write a report summarizing your findings in problems 23 through 27. Describe the strategies you used for finding the smallest and the largest values. Explain why you were sure that they were the smallest and the largest.

# LESSON 11.2

# Decimals and Fractions

**1.** How do you convert a fraction to a decimal number? Give examples.

When converting fractions to decimals, sometimes you get a *terminating* decimal like 3.4125, and sometimes you get a *repeating* decimal, like 7.8191919.... This last number is often written $7.8\overline{19}$.

Problems 2 and 3 are easier if you work with lowest-term fractions.

**2.** **Exploration** For what fractions do you get a repeating decimal? Does it depend on the numerator or the denominator? (Hint: Pay attention to the prime factorization of the numerator and the denominator.)

**3.** **Exploration** For repeating decimals, is there a pattern to the number of digits in the repeating part? What is the longest possible repeating string for a given denominator? (Hint: Use long division rather than a calculator to explore this.)

**4.** 💡 Explain why the decimals obtained as a result of a division *must* repeat or terminate.

**5.** 🔑 Explain why some calculators give a decimal that does not seem to repeat for 2/3: 0.6666666667.

**Example:** 3.4125 can be converted to a fraction by multiplying it by $10^4$, which gets rid of the decimal, and then dividing by $10^4$, which gets us back to the original number.

$$\frac{34{,}125}{10{,}000}$$

**6.** Convert these decimals to fractions.
   a. 6.0           b. 3.2
   c. 0.015        d. 3.41

The case of repeating decimals is more difficult. Take $7.8\overline{19}$. Clearly, it is greater than 7.81 and less than 7.82. So it is between 781/100 and 782/100.

To find a single fraction it is equal to, we can rewrite it as:

$$7.80\overline{19}$$
$$= 7.8 + 0.0\overline{19}$$
$$= 7.8 + 0.019 + 0.00019 + 0.0000019 + ...$$

Observe that:

$$0.00019 = 0.019(0.01)$$
$$0.0000019 = 0.019(0.01)^2$$

**7.** Write the next term in the sum as a decimal, and as a product of 0.019 and a power of 0.01.

As you see, $7.8\overline{19}$ is the sum of 7.8 and a geometric sequence with first term 0.019 and common ratio 0.01. The sum of the first three terms of the geometric sequence can be written:

$$S = 0.019 + 0.019(0.01) + 0.019(0.01)^2$$

Multiply both sides by 0.01:

$$S(0.01) = 0.019(0.01) + 0.019(0.01)^2 + 0.019(0.01)^3$$

Subtract:

$$S(1 - 0.01) = 0.019 - 0.019(0.01)^3$$

Solve:

$$S = \frac{0.019 - 0.019(0.01)^3}{0.99}$$

Multiplying numerator and denominator by 1000:

$$S = \frac{19 - 19(0.01)^3}{990}$$

$$7.8\overline{19} = 7.8 + S$$

$$= 7.8 + \frac{19 - 19(0.01)^3}{990}$$

$$= \frac{7.8(990) + 19 - 19(0.01)^3}{990}$$

So

$$= \frac{7741 - 19(0.01)^3}{990}$$

$$= \frac{7741 - 0.000019}{990}$$

The sum is very close to 7741/990.

**8.** Use the multiply-subtract-solve technique to add:

a. the first 4 terms;

b. the first 5 terms.

**9.** ⚷— The numerator differs from 7741 by $19(0.01)^n$ if we add up the first $n$ terms. Explain.

If we use large values for $n$, we find that the sum can get as close to 7741/990 as we want. (Even with fairly small values of $n$, the sum of the first $n$ terms differs from 7741/990 by a *very* small number.) Mathematicians say that the whole infinite sum *converges* to 7741/990, and they agree that we can write an equality:

$$7.8\overline{19} = 7741/990.$$

**10.** Check that this equality is correct, by converting the fraction back to a decimal.

A quick way to find the fraction is to use the multiply-subtract-solve technique on the decimal itself:

$$R = 7.8191919...$$

$$0.01\,R = 0.0781919...$$

Subtract:

$$R - 0.01R = 7.8191919... - 0.0781919...$$

$$(1 - 0.01)R = 7.819 - 0.078$$

(Notice that the infinite sequence of 19s disappeared.)

$$0.99R = 7.741$$

$$R = \frac{7.741}{0.99} = \frac{7741}{990}$$

**11.** Convert to a fraction.

a. $0.\overline{65}$        b. $4.\overline{321}$

---

**RATIONAL NUMBERS**

**Definition:** A *rational number* is a number that can be written as a fraction having an integer numerator and denominator.

**Examples:** 7, 0.5, and –0.66666... are rational numbers, because they can be written as 7/1, 1/2, and –2/3.

Show that the following numbers are rational.

**12.** a. 0.3

b. 0.3333...

**13.** a. 0.142857

b. $0.\overline{142857}$

**14.** a. 0.0909090...

b. 0.9090909...

**15.** a. 0.1111111...

b. 0.2222222...

**16.** ⚷— Mathematicians believe that 0.99999... = 1. Explain why.

# LESSON
## 11.3

# Stairs and Squares

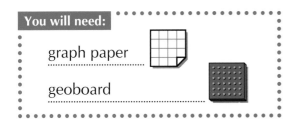

graph paper

geoboard

### STAIR SAFETY

In most houses, stairs have a riser (or rise) of eight inches and a tread (or run) of nine inches. However, safety experts claim that such stairs are the cause of many accidents. They recommend what they call 7/11 stairs: a riser of seven inches, and a tread of eleven inches.

1. What are the slopes of the stairs described in the previous paragraph? (Express the answer as a decimal.)

2. If a staircase makes a vertical rise of about nine feet from one floor to the next, how much horizontal distance does it take
   a. for 8/9 stairs?
   b. for 7/11 stairs?

3. Why do you think 8/9 stairs are more common?

4. **Exploration** Donna wants to build a staircase that is less steep than an 8/9 staircase would be, but that does not take up as much horizontal space as a 7/11 staircase would. What are the possibilities for the riser and tread of Donna's stairs? Make the following assumptions:
   • The riser and tread must each be a whole number of inches.
   • The riser should be between six and nine inches, inclusive.
   • The tread should be between eight and twelve inches, inclusive.
   Express your answer numerically and graphically.

### STAIRS ON LINES

To build a staircase on the graph of a line:
   a. Sketch the graph.
   b. Find the coordinates of a point on the graph. Call this point the starting point.
   c. Find two numbers (the rise and the run) such that if you draw a step having those dimensions, you end up on the line.

The figure shows a staircase for the line $y = -x + 2$.

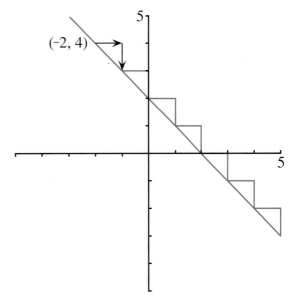

The starting point is $(-2, 4)$, the rise is $-1$, and the run is $1$.

5. Create a staircase for the same line, using a different starting point and a different rise and run.

6. Create *two* staircases for each line. They must have a different starting point and a different rise and run.
   a. $y = -4 + 3x$
   b. $y = -0.5x$
   c. $y = 9$

## 11.3

d. $y = \dfrac{6x - 7}{8}$

e. $y = -2(x - 3)$

7.  Find a rise and a run for a staircase connecting the following pairs of points:
    
    a.  (3, -5) and (2, 2.5)
    
    b.  (-3, 5) and (2, 2.5)

8.  A staircase having the given rise and run starts at the given point. What is the equation of the corresponding line?
    
    a.  rise = 4, run = 6, point = (-3, 6)
    
    b.  rise = -2, run = -3, point = (0, 8)

### LATTICE POINTS AND FRACTIONS

**Definition:** A *lattice point* is a point on the Cartesian plane having integer coordinates.

**Examples:** (2, 3) is a lattice point, but (4.5, 6) is not.

9.  The graph of each of the following equations is a line through the origin. Find two other lattice points on each line.
    
    a.  $y = 7x$   b.  $y = \frac{2}{3}x$
    
    c.  $y = 4.5x$   d.  $y = 6.78x$

If a line passes through the origin and the lattice point (9, 8), it will also pass through the lattice points (9n, 8n) for all integer values of n.

10. If a line passes through the origin and the point (2.4, 3.6),
    
    a.  what are the lattice points on the line that are closest to the origin?
    
    b.  what is a general description of all the lattice points on the line?
    
    c.  what is the equation of the line?

11. Do all lines through the origin pass through another lattice point sooner or later? Discuss.

| Generalizations |

12. What is the slope of a line that passes through the origin and a lattice point (p, q), where $p \neq 0$?

13. Describe the lattice points on the line $y = (p/q)x$, where $p \neq 0$.

### GEOBOARD DIAGONALS

If you connect (0, 0) to (5, 3) with a straight line, you go through seven unit squares.

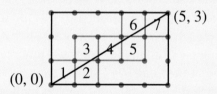

14. | Exploration | If you connect (0, 0) to (p, q) with a straight line, how many unit squares do you go through? Experiment and look for patterns. (Assume p and q are positive whole numbers.) Keep a record of your work.

**Definition:** A *lattice line* is a line having equation $x = b$ or $y = b$, where b is an integer.

The following problems are about the diagonal connecting (0, 0) to (p, q). Give answers in terms of p and q.

15. a.  How many horizontal lattice lines does it cross? (Look at some specific cases and make a generalization. Do not guess.)
    
    b.  How many vertical lattice lines does it cross?

**16.** How many lattice points does it cross,

    a. if the greatest common factor of $p$ and $q$ is 1?

    b. if the greatest common factor of $p$ and $q$ is $n$, where $n > 1$? (Experiment and reason. Do not guess.)

**17.** The diagonal starts in the first unit square, then every time it crosses a lattice line it enters a new square.

    a. If it crosses no lattice points, how many squares does it go through altogether?

    b. If it crosses $n$ lattice points, how many squares does it cross?

**18.** Report How many squares do the diagonals of geoboard rectangles go through? Write an illustrated report, including examples.

---

### DISCOVERY  SLOPE RELATIONSHIPS

| Lines | Slopes |
|---|---|
| parallel | opposite |
| perpendicular | opposite of reciprocal |
| symmetric across horizontal line | reciprocal |
| symmetric across the line $y = x$ | reciprocal of opposite |
| symmetric across vertical line | same |

The first column shows possible relationships between two lines. The second column shows possible relationships between the slopes of two lines.

**19.** Project Experiment to find out if it is possible to match relationships in the first column with relationships in the second column. (For example, parallel lines have the same slope.) Support your answers with examples, sketches, and explanations.

# Irrational Numbers

In Lesson 2 you learned how to show that any terminating or repeating decimal can be converted to a fraction. In other words, you know how to show that terminating or repeating decimals are rational numbers.

If a decimal is neither repeating nor terminating, it represents an *irrational number* (one that is not rational).

For example, the number

       0.010110111011110111110...,

created by inserting one, two, three, ... 1's between the 0's, never ends or repeats. Therefore it cannot be written as a fraction, because if it were, it would have to terminate or repeat.

1.  Create an irrational number that is
    a. greater than 1 and less than 1.1;
    b. greater than 1.11 and less than 1.12.

While most numbers we deal with every day are rational, and even though there is an infinite number of rational numbers, mathematicians have proved that most real numbers are irrational.

$\sqrt{2}$ and $\sqrt{3}$ are familiar examples of irrational numbers. They cannot be written as a fraction having whole number numerators and denominators. In order to prove this, we will need to review prime factorization.

## PRIME FACTORIZATION

Every whole number can be written as a product of prime factors.

**Example:** $990 = 99 \cdot 10$
$$= 9 \cdot 11 \cdot 2 \cdot 5$$
$$= 2 \cdot 3 \cdot 3 \cdot 5 \cdot 11$$

Note that 990 has a total of five prime factors. (Three is counted twice since it appears twice.)

2.  Start the factorization of 990 by writing $990 = 3 \cdot 330$. Do you get the same prime factors?

3.  Start the factorization of 990 a third way. Do you get the same prime factors?

Each whole number greater than 1 has *only one* prime factorization. Find it for the following numbers:

4.  12

5.  345

6.  💡 6789

7.  Find the prime factorization of several perfect squares. Try to find one having an odd number of prime factors.

Take the numbers 6 and 8. We have
$$6 = 2 \cdot 3 \text{ and } 8 = 2^3.$$

Six has two prime factors, an even number. Eight has three prime factors, an odd number. When we square them, we get:
$$6^2 = (2 \cdot 3)^2 = 2^2 \cdot 3^2$$
$$8^2 = (2^3)^2 = 2^6$$

8.  🔑 Explain why any perfect square *must* have an even number of prime factors.

9.  🔑 Explain why any number that is equal to twice a perfect square *must* have an odd number of prime factors.

## THE SQUARE ROOT OF TWO

This section explains why $\sqrt{2}$ is not a rational number. The way we are going to do this is to show that if it were, it would lead to an impossible situation. This is called proof by contradiction.

If $p$ and $q$ were nonzero whole numbers and we had

$$\frac{p}{q} = \sqrt{2}$$

It would follow that $\left(\frac{p}{q}\right)^2 = \left(\sqrt{2}\right)^2$

$$\frac{p^2}{q^2} = 2$$

$$p^2 = 2q^2$$

**10.** Explain each step in the previous calculations.

**11.** Explain why $p^2$ must have an even number of prime factors.

**12.** Explain why $2q^2$ must have an odd number of prime factors.

**13.** Explain why $p^2$ cannot equal $2q^2$.

We conclude that there can be no whole numbers $p$ and $q$ such that $\sqrt{2} = p/q$, and therefore $\sqrt{2}$ is irrational.

**14.** ☞ Use the same method to show that $\sqrt{3}$ is irrational.

**15.** ☞ Show why the method does not work to prove that $\sqrt{4}$ is irrational.

**16.** Does the decimal expansion of $\sqrt{2}$ terminate or repeat?

**17.** Does the line $y = \sqrt{2}x$ pass through any lattice points?

**18.** ☞ Do all lines through the origin eventually pass through a lattice point? Discuss.

**19.** Research $\pi$ is probably the world's most famous irrational number. Find out about its history.

**DISCOVERY** *SUM FRACTIONS*

**20.** Find two lowest-term fractions having different denominators whose sum is 8/9.

**DISCOVERY** *COMPARING COUPONS*

**21.** Which is a better deal, 15% off the purchase price, or $1 off every $5 spent? Make a graph that shows how much you save with each discount, for various purchases from $1 to $20. Write about your conclusions.

**You will need:**

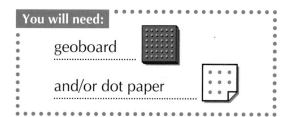

geoboard
...........................

and/or dot paper
...........................

1. Using your geoboard or dot paper, make an 8-by-8 square. Calculate its area and perimeter.

2. Now make a square that is nested in the original square, like in the diagram. Its vertices should be the midpoints of the sides of the original square. Find its area and perimeter.

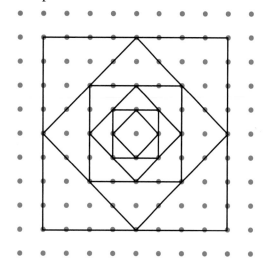

3. Continue the process, making smaller and smaller nested squares. As you work, extend and complete a table like the following one up to Square #5. When the numbers involve square roots, write them in simple radical form.

| Square # | Area | Side | Perimeter |
|----------|------|------|-----------|
| 1 | 64 | 8 | 32 |

4. Look for a pattern in each of the columns. Describe the patterns for the
   a. areas;
   b. sides;
   c. perimeters.

5. Use the pattern you found in problem 4. For the 10th nested square, find
   a. the area;
   b. the side;
   c. the perimeter.

6. ⚪ Repeat problem 5 for the $n$th nested square.

7. For the first ten squares, what is the sum of:
   a. the areas;
   b. the sides;
   c. the perimeters.

8. ⚪ Repeat problem 7 for the first $n$ squares.

9. ⚪ With larger and larger values of $n$, the sums get closer and closer to a certain number. What is that number for:
   a. the areas?
   b. the sides?
   c. the perimeters?

10. **Report** Write a report on nested squares.

# Dice Games

## TWO GAMES

1. **Exploration** Play these two games with another person. To play a game, roll a pair of dice 20 times. After each roll, add the numbers on the uppermost faces. Keep track of how many rolls each player wins. (See below.) Whoever wins the most rolls, wins that game.

Game One: If the sum is 3, 5, 7, 9, or 11, Player A wins. If the sum is 2, 4, 6, 8, 10, or 12, Player B wins.

Game Two: If the sum is 5, 6, 7, 8, or 9, Player A wins. If the sum is 2, 3, 4, 10, 11, or 12, Player B wins.

For each game, who wins more often? Why?

## TWO-DICE SUMS

If you roll a red die and a blue die, there are many possible outcomes. We will use (4, 3) to refer to the outcome in which 4 dots appear uppermost on the red die and 3 dots appear uppermost on the blue die. Likewise (3, 4) refers to 3 on the red die and 4 on the blue die.

(4, 3)

(3, 4)

Both of the outcomes in the figure show a sum of seven.

2. Copy and extend this table to show all possible two-dice sums. For each sum, list all the possible ways it can be obtained, and give the total number of ways. The sums of 2 and 7 have been done to get you started.

| Sum | 2 | ... | 7 | ... | 12 |
|---|---|---|---|---|---|
| Possible ways | | | (1, 6) | | |
| | | | (2, 5) | | |
| | | | (3, 4) | | |
| | | | (4, 3) | | |
| | | | (5, 2) | | |
| | (1, 1) | ... | (6, 1) | ... | ... |
| # of ways | 1 | ... | 6 | ... | ... |

3. Which sums have the most ways of occurring? Which sums have the fewest ways of occurring?

4. **Summary** Analyze the games in problem 1 using the table you made. Explain why some sums are more likely to occur than others and how this determines who wins more often.

**Definition:** A game is *fair* if each of the players is equally likely to win.

5. ☞ Is Game One fair? How about Game Two? Explain.

## OUTCOMES AND EVENTS

**Definition:** We call one roll of the dice an *experiment.* Each of the different possibilities you listed in the table is called an *outcome* of the experiment.

6. When you roll a red die and a blue die, how many outcomes are possible?

7. If you flip a penny and a nickel, how many outcomes (heads and tails) are possible? Make a list.

8. 💡 If you roll a red, a blue, and a yellow die, how many outcomes are possible?

When an experiment is performed, we are usually interested in whether or not a particular *event* has occurred. An event consists of one or more outcomes.

In the two-dice experiment, an example of an event could be: *The sum of the dots is even.* This event was important in Game One of problem 1. In that game, 36 outcomes were possible. However, we were not interested in the individual outcomes, but only in which of the two events had occurred: an even sum or an odd sum.

9. In what events were we interested in Game Two of problem 1?

10. The outcome of a two-dice experiment is (3, 2). Which of the following events occurred?
    a. The difference is even.
    b. The product is even.
    c. One die shows a multiple of the other.
    d. The sum is a prime number.

The table you made in problem 2 was organized to show these *events*: the sum of the dots is 2, the sum of the dots is 3, etc. In that table, each column corresponds to one event. A table like the following one is another way to represent the two-dice experiment. It is organized around the *outcomes*. Each cell corresponds to one outcome.

Blue Die

|  | 1 | 2 | 3 | 4 | 5 | 6 |
|---|---|---|---|---|---|---|
| 1 | (1, 1) | (1, 2) | (1, 3) | (1, 4) | (1, 5) | (1, 6) |
| 2 | (2, 1) | (2, 2) | (2, 3) | (2, 4) | (2, 5) | (2, 6) |
| ... | ... | ... | ... | ... | ... | ... |

Red Die

In the two-dice experiment, figure out how many outcomes make up each event in problems 11-14.

You can make the same kind of table to help answer problems 11-14. For example, to think about problem 11a, you would write the products in the cells.

Blue Die

|  | 1 | 2 | 3 | 4 | 5 | 6 |
|---|---|---|---|---|---|---|
| 1 | 1 | 2 | 3 | 4 | 5 | 6 |
| 2 | 2 | 4 | ... | ... | ... | ... |

Red Die

11. a. The product is even.
    b. The difference is even.
    c. One die shows a multiple of the other.

12. a. The sum is 2, 3, or 4.
    b. The sum is 9, 10, or 12.

13. a. a double
    b. not a double

14. a. The sum is prime.
    b. The product is prime.
    c. The difference is prime.

## CREATE DICE GAMES

**15.** Name two events in the two-dice experiment that each consist of nine outcomes.

**16.** Name an event in the two-dice experiment that consists of:
a. 17 outcomes;
b. 19 outcomes.

**17.** ◆── Create a dice game that is fair. Write the rules. Then write an explanation of why the game is fair.

**18.** ◆── Create a dice game that appears to favor one player, but that actually favors the other. Or, make up a dice game that appears to be fair, but that actually favors one player. Write the rules and an explanation of the game.

**DISCOVERY** *THREE QUANTITIES, THREE CONSTRAINTS*

These problems were invented by algebra students. You may want to use colored slips of paper to solve them. In each one, there are three unknown quantities and three constraints. Try to find the three unknown quantities.

**19.** The red and yellow marbles add up to 5.
Blue and red add up to 7.
There are 8 yellows and blues altogether.

**20.** The blue and red add up to 9.
There are two times as many yellows as blues.
There are 15 marbles altogether.

**21.** Blue + 9 = Black
Blue times 3 = Red
Black + 1 = Red

**22.** $A + B = 11$
$A + C = 7$
$B + C = 6$
How many of each?

# What is Probability?

**You will need:**

two coins

This lesson will introduce you to three interpretations of probability.

## RELATIVE FREQUENCY

While waiting for his food at the Slow Food Café, Zoltan asked himself, "What is the probability of getting at least one head when tossing two coins?" He thought it might be 1/2, since there was an equal chance of getting heads or tails, or 1/3, since there were three possibilities (two heads, one head, no heads). He decided to find out by doing an experiment. Here are his notes on the first eight tosses (or *trials*).

HH, HT, TT, HT, HH, TT, TH, TT...

He made a table of the results. A *success* is a toss where one or two heads appeared.

**Definition:** The *relative frequency* of the successes is the ratio of successes to trials.

| Trials so far | Successes so far | Relative frequency |
|:---:|:---:|:---:|
| 1 | 1 | 1/1 = 1.00 |
| 2 | 2 | 2/2 = 1.00 |
| 3 | 2 | 2/3 = 0.67 |
| 4 | 3 | 3/4 = 0.75 |
| 5 | 4 | 4/5 = 0.80 |
| 6 | 4 | 4/6 = 0.67 |
| 7 | 5 | 5/7 = 0.72 |
| 8 | 5 | 5/8 = 0.63 |

He graphed the results, with relative frequency on the *y*-axis, and trials on the *x*-axis.

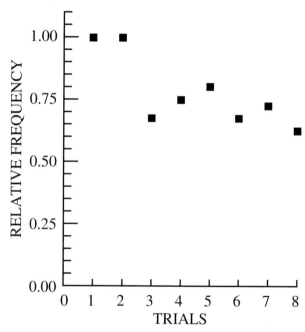

*Chapter 11 Interpreting Ratios*

1. Toss a pair of coins 30 times. Make a table like Zoltan's.

2. Make a graph like Zoltan's for the data in your table.

3. ☞ If you tossed the coins 100 times, what do you think your graph would look like? What if you tossed them 500 times? Explain.

> **First Definition:** The *probability* of an event is often interpreted to mean the relative frequency with which that event occurs if the experiment is repeated many, many times.

> **Example:** If you roll a die many times, you expect the relative frequency of threes to be approximately 1/6.

4. ☞ Explain why the relative frequency of an event is a number from 0 to 1.

### EQUALLY LIKELY OUTCOMES

This definition is the most common interpretation of probability.

> **Second Definition:** The *probability* of an event $A$ is
> $$P(A) = \frac{e}{t}$$
> where:
> $e$ = the number of equally likely outcomes in the event.
> $t$ = the total number of equally likely outcomes possible.

> **Example:** In the two-dice experiment, say that event $D$ is the event that the sum is 8. Then
> $$D = \{(2, 6), (3, 5), (4, 4), (5, 3), (6, 2)\}$$

> Since $D$ consists of five equally likely outcomes, and the total number of equally likely outcomes is 36,
> $$P(D) = \frac{5}{36}.$$

5. For the two-dice experiment, find an event having the following probabilities:
   a. $\frac{2}{36}$
   b. $\frac{1}{12}$

6. For the two-dice experiment, find the probability of these events.
   a. The product is more than 25.
   b. The product is less than 50.
   c. The sum is 7 or 11.

7. ☞ Explain why any probability $p$ will always satisfy the inequality $0 \le p \le 1$.

8. For the two-dice experiment, find an event having the following probabilities:
   a. 0
   b. 1

9. List all the equally likely outcomes in Zoltan's two-coin experiment. (Hint: Think of the coins as a penny and a nickel. Make a table.)

10. ☞ What is the probability that there will be at least one head when tossing two coins? Explain.

### THEORETICAL vs. OBSERVED PROBABILITY

Zoltan graphed his results another way. This time he put the number of successes on the y-axis and the number of trials on the x-axis.

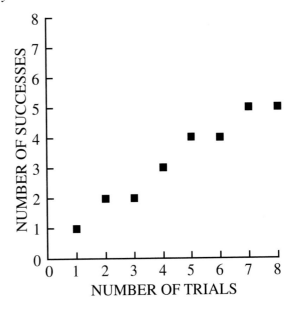

**11.** Make a graph like Zoltan's for the data in the table you made in problem 1.

**12.** On your graph, draw lines having equations:

*successes = trials*
*successes = 0.75 · trials*
*successes = 0.67 · trials*
*successes = 0.50 · trials*

**13.** ⚷ What do rise and run each measure on this graph? What does slope represent?

On a graph like this, the *theoretical probability*, as predicted by the analysis of equally likely outcomes, can be represented as a line through the origin, having slope equal to the probability. The *observed probability* as seen in the experiment is represented by the slope of the line through the origin and the corresponding data point. Note that data points rarely land exactly on the theoretical line.

**14.** Which line that you drew in problem 12 represents the theoretical probability? Explain.

**15.** ⚷ Add a line representing the theoretical probability to the graph you made in problem 2. Explain.

A third interpretation of probability is *subjective probability*. This is the probability that a person assigns to an event based on his or her own knowledge, beliefs, or information about the event. Different people may assign different probabilities to the same events.

**Example:** Before Mark took his driving test, Karen said, "I think you've got about a 60% chance of passing."

What subjective probability would you assign for each of the following events? Explain your reasons.

**16.** It will be cloudy on a night with a full moon this month.

**17.** You will be assigned no math homework this Friday.

**18.** School will be cancelled next week due to bad weather.

**19.** Exactly half of the students in your math class next year will be boys.

# 11.7 Random Walks

**You will need:**

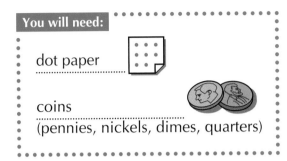

dot paper

coins
(pennies, nickels, dimes, quarters)

The Mad Probabilist takes a random walk on dot paper. Starting at the origin, he goes from lattice point to lattice point, flipping a coin each time to determine where to go next.

- *Heads* means to move east, increasing just the *x*-coordinate by 1.
- *Tails* means to move north, increasing just the *y*-coordinate by 1.

The map shows the path H, H, T, T, H, T, H, H.

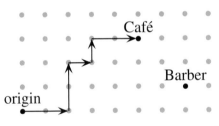

1. **Exploration** Find another sequence of heads and tails that would get the Mad Probabilist from the origin to (5, 3), where the Slow Food Café is located. Compare your sequence with that of a classmate. How many ways are there to reach (5, 3)?

### A FOUR-COIN EXPERIMENT

2. If you toss a penny, a nickel, a dime, and a quarter, which do you think is most likely to occur: 0 heads, 1 head, 2 heads, 3 heads, 4 heads? Or are they all equally likely? Explain your reasoning.

3. Use a penny, a nickel, a dime, and a quarter. Toss them and record the number of heads. Repeat this experiment 20 times.

If you toss a penny, a nickel, a dime, and a quarter, the event *three heads* consists of the following equally likely outcomes: HHHT, HHTH, HTHH, and THHH, depending on which coin comes up tails.

4. Find all possible equally likely outcomes when tossing four coins.

5. Count the outcomes for each of these events: 0 heads, 1 head, 2 heads, etc.

6. 🔑 Are the results of your experiment in problem 3 consistent with your analysis in problems 4 and 5? Comment.

If you toss one coin, there are two equally likely possible outcomes, H and T. In Lesson 6 you studied the tossing of two coins, (HH, HT, TH, TT), and in problems 5-6 the tossing of four coins.

7. Figure out how many equally likely outcomes are possible if you toss
   a. three coins;    b. five coins.

8. **Generalization** How many equally likely outcomes are possible if you toss *n* coins? Explain.

Tossing the same coin repeatedly works in a similar way. For example, one possible string of eight tosses is: TTHTHTTH, just as one possible outcome of tossing eight coins is TTHTHTTH.

9. If you toss one coin eight times, how many possible outcomes are there? How about *n* times?

### THE MAD PROBABILIST

**10.** How many moves does it take the Mad Probabilist to get to (5, 3)?

**11.** Generalization How many moves does it take him to get to ($p$, $q$)? Explain.

**12.** a. Where might he be after six moves?

b. Make a list of the points he could get to in seven moves.

**13.** ⬤━ How would you describe the set of points you listed in problem 12b? (How many points does it consist of? What equation relates their coordinates?) Explain.

**14.** Generalization Describe the set of points he could reach in $n$ moves. Explain.

**15.** ⬤━ Which is greater, the number of possible points he could end up on after eight tosses of a coin, or the number of possible strings of eight tosses? Explain.

### MAKING A MAP

The Mad Probabilist wants to calculate the *probability* of getting to a lattice point like (5, 3). He decides to make a map on a piece of dot paper. He draws diagonal lines to separate the points he may reach in one, two, three, etc., moves.

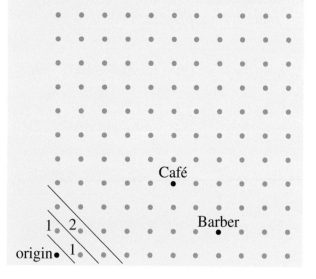

Then he writes how many ways there are to reach each point on the map. For example, there is only one way to get to (1, 0): a toss of H. There is only one way to get to (0, 1): T. There is only one way to get to (2, 0): HH. There are two ways to get to (1, 1): HT or TH.

As he makes his map, he finds it helpful to ask himself for each point, "Where could I have come from to get here?"

**16.** Continue the Mad Probabilist's map, until you get to (5, 3).

The Mad Probabilist reasons, "At the end of eight moves, I will be at one of these points, one of which is the Slow Food Café." He marks the points on his map. "The outcomes are eight-move paths; the event is those paths that end up at (5, 3). To find out the probability of this event, I need a numerator and a denominator." He writes:

$$P(5, 3) = \frac{\text{\# of paths that get to (5, 3)}}{\text{\# of 8-move paths}}$$

**17.** What is $P(5, 3)$? In other words, what is the probability the Mad Probabilist's random walk will end up at the Slow Food Café?

**18.** What is the probability it will end up at (7, 1), where the barbershop is? Explain.

**19.** Summary Explain how you can find the probability of getting to any lattice point in the first quadrant.

*Chapter 11  Interpreting Ratios*

This is one of the most important arrays of numbers in mathematics. It is called Pascal's triangle.

```
1
1   1
1   2   1
1   3   3   1
1   4   6   4   1
1   5   10  10  5   1
1   6   15  20  15  6   1
1   7   21  35  35  21  7   1
1   8   28  56  70  56  28  8   1
```

**20.** Exploration Study this triangle, looking for patterns. Explain any patterns that you find.

**21.** Find a pattern that will enable you to write the next row in the triangle.

**22.** Find the pattern in the third column.

**23.** Find the pattern in the sums of the rows.

**24.** 💡 Find the pattern in the sums of the upward diagonals.

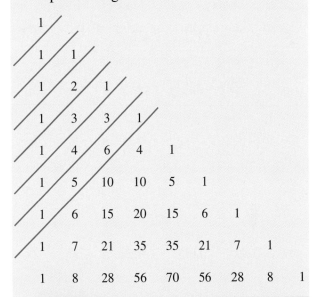

**25.** Report Write an illustrated report about the patterns you found in Pascal's triangle. Include a section on the relationship between Pascal's triangle and coin-tossing experiments.

# Unit Conversion

**You will need:**

graph paper

1. Find the missing numerator and denominator in each equation. (You should be able to solve most of these without multiplying or dividing.) Compare your answers with other students' answers.

   a. $\frac{2}{3} \cdot \frac{5}{7} \cdot \frac{\triangle}{\square} = \frac{2}{3}$

   b. $\frac{2}{3} \cdot \frac{\triangle}{7} \cdot \frac{5}{\square} = \frac{2}{3}$

   c. $\frac{7}{12} \cdot \frac{14}{11} \cdot \frac{12}{5} \cdot \frac{\triangle}{\square} = \frac{7}{11}$

   d. $\frac{1}{3} \cdot \frac{5}{x} \cdot \frac{2}{5} \cdot \frac{x}{2} \cdot \frac{\triangle}{\square} = \frac{8}{3}$

   e. $\frac{8}{7} \cdot \frac{3}{x} \cdot \frac{7}{6} \cdot \frac{y}{\square} \cdot = \frac{y}{x}$

   f. $\frac{a}{b} \cdot \frac{\triangle}{a} \cdot \frac{b}{\square} = \frac{x}{y}$

---

### TWO RULERS

Alice had a new ruler. Oliver suggested she measure it with another ruler, as in this figure.

Alice's ruler

| 0 | 1 | 2 | 3 | 4 | 5 | 6 |
|---|---|---|---|---|---|---|
| 0 | 2 | 4 | 6 | 8 | 10 | 12 | 14 |

Oliver's ruler

Oliver and Alice had to write about functions for algebra. They decided to use the rulers as a way to get tables of *x*- and *y*-values. Here are the tables they got from the ruler setup.

| Alice | | Oliver | |
|---|---|---|---|
| *x* | *y* | *x* | *y* |
| 1 | 2.5 | 1 | 0.4 |
| 2 | 5.1 | 2 | 0.8 |
| 3 | 7.6 | 3 | 1.2 |

2. Describe the pattern for the numbers in each table.

3. What do you think the units of each ruler are?

4. Write a function of the type *y* = *an expression in terms of x* for each table. (Because of measurement error, this may have to be an approximation.)

5. 🔑 If you were to graph these functions, explain why the graph would
   a. be a line;
   b. pass through the origin.

6. According to an almanac, 1 inch = 2.54 centimeters, exactly. Using that information, what is the exact length of a centimeter, in inches?

When converting inches to centimeters, we multiply by 2.54. When converting centimeters to inches, we multiply by 1/2.54. As you can see from the equations, this conversion of units involves direct variation.

**Definition:** In the case of unit conversion, the proportionality constant (the number you multiply by) is called the *conversion factor*.

Conversion factors have units. For example, the conversion factor from inches to centimeters is 2.54 *cm/in*.

7. ⚷— What is the conversion factor from centimeters to inches? (Include its unit.) Explain.

### MULTIPLYING BY ONE

When converting a quantity from one unit to another, the way the quantity is measured is changed, not the amount of it. We can think of the conversion factor as having the value 1.

**Example:** Two miles are how many feet?

$$2 \text{ miles} \cdot \frac{5280 \text{ feet}}{1 \text{ mile}} = 10{,}560 \text{ feet}$$

The conversion factor is 5280/1 and its units are feet/mile. Since 5280 feet = 1 mile, the numerator equals the denominator in the fraction, so we can think of this conversion as multiplying by a form of 1. To make the units work out, we multiplied by feet and divided by miles.

In problems 8-10, when writing a conversion factor, include its unit.

8. a. What is the conversion factor used to convert feet to miles?

   b. Mount Everest, the world's tallest peak, is 29,028 feet high. How many miles is that?

9. ⚷—
   a. What is the conversion factor used to convert seconds to minutes?

   b. What is the conversion factor used to convert minutes to seconds?

   c. How are the answers to (a) and (b) related? Explain.

10. Convert 1000 inches to:
    a. feet;        b. miles;
    c. meters;      d. kilometers.

### TWO-STEP CONVERSIONS

In science, speeds are sometimes given in feet per second. To convert feet per second to miles per hour, there are two steps:
- Convert feet to miles.
- Convert seconds to hours.

The steps can be combined:

$$\frac{\text{feet}}{\text{second}} \cdot \frac{1 \text{ mile}}{5280 \text{ feet}} \cdot \frac{3600 \text{ seconds}}{1 \text{ hour}} = \frac{\text{miles}}{\text{hour}}$$

We chose the conversion factors in order to divide by feet and multiply by seconds so that those units did not appear in the final answer.

11. Convert the speed of sound in cold water (4938 feet per second) to miles per hour. Show your calculations.

12. ⚷— To convert feet per second to miles per hour, what single number could you multiply by? Explain how you obtained this conversion factor.

13. Find the conversion factor between each of these common measures of speed. Show all your work. Summarize your results in a table like this one. Give approximations to the nearest thousandth. (Note: m/sec means meters per second.)

|        |        | To:   |       |        |        |
|--------|--------|-------|-------|--------|--------|
|        |        | mi/hr | km/hr | m/sec  | ft/sec |
| From:  | mi/hr  | —     | —     | —      | —      |
|        | km/hr  | —     | —     | —      | —      |
|        | m/sec  | —     | —     | —      | —      |
|        | ft/sec | —     | —     | —      | —      |

14. ⚷— In your table, find pairs of numbers that are reciprocals of each other. Explain why they should be reciprocals.

15. Use your table to convert
    a. the speed of light (299,792,500 m/sec) into miles per hour;
    b. the speed of sound in cold air (1,088 ft/sec) into miles per hour.

16. A fast runner can run a mile in four minutes. How fast is that in miles per hour?

17. **Project** Find out how fast students in your class walk, skip, run, move backwards, etc., by timing how long it takes them to cover a measured distance. Convert the speeds to miles per hour.

18. **Project** Find out how fast cars drive on a nearby street or road, by timing how long it takes them to cover a measured distance. Convert the speeds to miles per hour.

**REVIEW** *SOLVING SYSTEMS*

Solve each system. Check first to see if you can tell that the system has no solution or an infinite number of solutions.

19. $\begin{cases} 2x + 6 = 3y \\ 4y = 12 - 3x \end{cases}$

20. $\begin{cases} -m - b = 25 \\ -m + b = 13 \end{cases}$

21. $\begin{cases} 2r + 2s = 60 \\ r - 2s = 5 \end{cases}$

22. $\begin{cases} 2m + n = -1 \\ m + 3n = -18 \end{cases}$

23. $\begin{cases} r - s = 1 \\ r + 3s = -11 \end{cases}$

24. $\begin{cases} \frac{2}{3}x + \frac{2}{5}y = 4 \\ x - 2y = 5 \end{cases}$

25. $\begin{cases} y = \frac{3}{7}(x - 8) \\ y - 4 = \frac{3}{7}(x + 6) \end{cases}$

# 11.B Calibrating a Speedometer

You can check the accuracy of a car's speedometer by using a stopwatch and the mile markers on a highway. The driver should maintain a steady speed while a passenger uses a stopwatch to time the travel time between mile markers. This travel time tells you the number of seconds it takes you to go one mile, which you can convert to miles per hour.

1. Convert 0.123 hours to minutes and seconds.

2. Convert 4.567 hours to hours, minutes, and seconds.

3. A car is traveling at 55 miles per hour.
   a. What fraction of an hour does it take to go one mile?
   b. How many minutes and seconds does it take to go one mile?
   c. How many seconds does it take to go one mile?

4. How would you convert
   a. miles per hour to miles per second?
   b. miles per second to miles per hour?
   c. miles per second to seconds to go one mile?
   d. seconds to go one mile to miles per second?

5. If it takes you 65 seconds to go one mile, how many miles per hour are you going? Explain how you figured this out, showing calculations.

6. Describe a general strategy for converting seconds per mile to miles per hour.

7. Make a table like this one to help people check their speedometers.

| Seconds between mile markers | Speed in mi/hr |
|---|---|
| ... | ... |

8. a. Graph the ordered pairs in the table you made.
   b. Let $y$ stand for the speed in mi/hr, and $x$ stand for the number of seconds between markers. Write an equation relating $x$ and $y$.

Say that the person in charge of timing can be off by one second in starting the stopwatch, and one second in stopping it.

9. What is the maximum error in using the table, resulting from the inaccuracy in timing?

10. If, instead of measuring the time to go one mile, you measure the time to go four miles and use the average one-mile time, what is the maximum error?

11. Report Write an explanation for the general public of how to check the accuracy of a speedometer. Include your table, some illustrations, and an explanation of what to do to get an exact answer between values given in the table.

## SUMS

1. Find each sum.

   a. $\frac{1}{2} + \left(\frac{1}{2}\right)^2 + \left(\frac{1}{2}\right)^3$

   b. $\frac{1}{2} + \left(\frac{1}{2}\right)^2 + \left(\frac{1}{2}\right)^3 + \left(\frac{1}{2}\right)^4$

   c. $\frac{1}{2} + \left(\frac{1}{2}\right)^2 + \left(\frac{1}{2}\right)^3 + \left(\frac{1}{2}\right)^4 + \left(\frac{1}{2}\right)^5$

   d. $\frac{1}{2} + \left(\frac{1}{2}\right)^2 + \left(\frac{1}{2}\right)^3 + ... + \left(\frac{1}{2}\right)^n$

2. This sum goes on for ever. (We call it an *infinite series*.) Use the pattern you found in problem 1 to estimate the sum of this infinite series.

$$\frac{1}{2} + \left(\frac{1}{2}\right)^2 + \left(\frac{1}{2}\right)^3 + ...$$

3. Estimate the sums of these infinite series.

   a. $\frac{1}{3} + \left(\frac{1}{3}\right)^2 + \left(\frac{1}{3}\right)^3 + ...$

   b. $\frac{1}{4} + \left(\frac{1}{4}\right)^2 + \left(\frac{1}{4}\right)^3 + ...$

   c. $\frac{1}{k} + \left(\frac{1}{k}\right)^2 + \left(\frac{1}{k}\right)^3 + ...$

   (Assume that $k$ is a positive integer.)

## GEOMETRIC SEQUENCES

4. Some of the following sequences are geometric; find their common ratio. Some are arithmetic; find their common difference.

   a. 2/3, (2/3)², (2/3)³, (2/3)⁴, ...
   b. 1/3, 4/3, 7/3, 10/3, ...
   c. 10, 10/8, 10/64, 10/512, ...
   d. 10, 80, 640, 5120, ...
   e. 1/3, 8/3, 64/3, 512/3, ...

5. Find the sum of the first 50 terms for the sequences in problems 4a and e.

6. Two of the sequences in problem 4 are such that if you add the entire infinite sequence, the sum converges to a finite number.

   a. Explain how you can tell which sequences they are.

   b. Find the sum they each converge to.

## INHERITANCE

The brothers Able and Earl inherited from their father an acre of land, which they divided equally. Each brother willed his land to his family. Able's family was large, and Earl's was small. Able's family needed more land, so they bought 40% of the land belonging to Earl's family. In the next generation, Able's family again bought 40% of Earl's family land. This continued for several generations.

7. Copy and and extend this table to show the amount of land owned by each family up to the eighth generation.

| Generation | Able's land | Earl's land |
|:---:|:---:|:---:|
| 1 | 0.5 | 0.5 |
| 2 | 0.7 | 0.3 |

8. Study the data. At this rate, will Able's family ever own the whole acre? Explain.

## DECIMALS AND FRACTIONS

9. Write as a fraction.

   a. $0.\overline{21}$
   b. $0.3\overline{21}$
   c. $0.\overline{321}$

**10.** Find whole numbers $p$ and $q$ such that:
 a. $0.45 < p/q < 0.46$
 b. $0.\overline{4} < p/q < 0.45$

PRIME FACTORIZATION

**11.** Explain why the square of an even number must be a multiple of four.

**12.** Explain why the square of an odd number must be odd.

**13.** Explain why the double of an odd number is an even number, but not a multiple of four.

LATTICE POINTS

Imagine that you are standing at the origin, and that you cannot see lattice points that are hidden behind other lattice points. For example, you cannot see $(2, 2)$ because $(1, 1)$ is in the way. Let us call $(1, 1)$ *visible* and $(2, 2)$ *hidden*.

**14.** List three visible lattice points and three hidden ones. Explain.

**15.** By looking at its coordinates, how can you tell whether a lattice point is visible?

**16.** Give the equation of a line that includes no lattice points except the origin.

**17.** Give the equation of a line that includes no lattice points at all.

**18.** Which line on an 11-by-11 geoboard contains the greatest number of visible lattice points?

GAMES AND PROBABILITY

**19.** If you choose a letter at random from the alphabet, what's the probability that it's a vowel?

**20.** If you choose a month at random, what's the probability that its name
 a. begins with J?
 b. contains an R?

**21.** Assume that you draw one card from an ordinary deck of 52 playing cards. What's the probability that you draw
 a. a 7?
 b. a heart?
 c. a 7 or a heart?
 d. a 7 of hearts?

**22.** Which game, if either, is fair? Explain.
 a. Roll a pair of dice and multiply the numbers on the uppermost faces. If the product is 18 or greater, Player A wins. If the product is less than 18, Player B wins.
 b. Toss three coins. If the number of heads is even, Player A wins. If it is odd, Player B wins.
 c. Repeat part (b) for six coins.

UNIT CONVERSION

**23.** Given that 1 pound is approximately 454 grams, 1 kilogram is approximately how many pounds?

**24.** Find conversion factors for converting the following measurements. (Note: Even though these problems look different, you can use the technique you learned in Lesson 8. Remember that in.$^2$ means in. $\cdot$ in.)
 a. in.$^2$ to ft$^2$      b. ft$^2$ to in.$^2$
 c. in.$^3$ to cm$^3$      d. cm$^3$ to in.$^3$

**25.** The density of water is approximately 1 gram/cm$^3$. What is it in pounds/ft$^3$?

# CHAPTER 12

The spiral coils of car springs

## Coming in this chapter:

**Exploration**  By measuring people's feet and asking for their shoe size, find a formula relating foot length, in inches, to shoe size,

　　　a.  for men;
　　　b.  for women.

# MATHEMATICAL MODELING

# The U.S. Population, 1890–1990

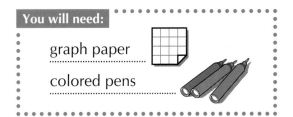

You will need:

graph paper

colored pens

The Bureau of the Census conducts a census every ten years, as required by the U.S. Constitution. Census results are now used for many purposes, but their original purpose was primarily to determine how many seats each state would be allocated in the House of Representatives. As population patterns change, these seats are divided up differently among the states. Here are some census results from 1890 through 1990.

### Census Table

| Year | Population | # increase | % increase |
|------|-----------|-----------|-----------|
| 1890 | 62,979,766 | 12,790,557 | 25.5 |
| 1900 | 76,212,168 | 13,232,402 | 21.0 |
| 1910 | 92,228,496 | 16,016,328 | 21.0 |
| 1920 | 106,021,537 | 13,793,041 | 15.0 |
| 1930 | 123,202,624 | 17,181,087 | 16.2 |
| 1940 | 132,164,569 | 8,961,945 | 7.3 |
| 1950 | 151,325,798 | 19,161,229 | 14.5 |
| 1960 | 179,323,175 | 27,997,377 | 18.5 |
| 1970 | 203,302,031 | 23,978,856 | 13.4 |
| 1980 | 226,545,805 | 23,243,774 | 11.4 |
| 1990 | 248,709,873 | 22,164,068 | 9.8 |

### EXAMINING DATA

1. Use the information given to estimate the 1880 population.

2. Write a paragraph describing anything interesting you see in the data. What factors affect population growth? Can you think of historical events that might be associated with periods of low or high growth rates?

3. Over what ten-year period was
   a. the number increase the smallest? The largest?
   b. the percent increase the smallest? The largest?

4. From 1890 to 1990, what was the overall
   a. number increase?
   b. percent increase?

5. Using a large piece of graph paper, make a graph of the population as a function of time. You will add to this graph when you do other problems in this lesson. Choose the scale carefully.

6. Approximately when did the population reach its halfway point between 1890 and 1990? Explain how you calculated this, and show the point on your graph. Is the halfway point in population before or after the halfway point in years?

### MAKING PREDICTIONS

If you had lived in 1890 and wanted to predict the population of the United States in 1900 and 1990, you might have assumed that the increase for every future ten-year period would be the same as it had been in the ten-year period from 1880 to 1890. (We will call 1880-1890 the *base period*.)

*Chapter 12 Mathematical Modeling*

**7.** For each assumption below, make a table showing what the population would have been in each decade.

   a. The number increase in each decade was the same as in the base period.

   b. The percent increase in each decade was the same as in the base period.

**8.** In this problem, add to the graph you made in problem 5. Use a different color for each set of data.

   a. Graph the data in your table from problem 7a. Write a description on your graph telling what assumption was used to obtain the numbers.

   b. Repeat part (a) for the data in your table in problem 7b.

**9.** 🗝 Compare the three graphs.

   a. Which of the two assumptions in problem 7 gave a closer prediction of the population in 1900? How close was each estimate?

   b. Which predicted the population in 1990 more accurately? How close was each estimate?

Say you were living in 1940, had access to the data for the period 1890-1940, and wanted to predict the population for 1950 and 1990.

**10.** a. Why might you *not* want to use the growth from 1930 to 1940 to help you make the predictions?

   b. What numbers might you choose instead to model a constant number increase? What about a constant percent increase?

**11.** Repeat problem 7, starting with the 1940 population and using the numbers you chose in problem 10. Do you get better predictions?

**12.** 🗝 Predict the population of the U.S. in the years 2000 and 2040. Explain how you arrive at your numbers.

### ESTIMATING MISSING DATA

It is very expensive to conduct a census of the entire population, and it cannot be done every year. However, census data can be used to estimate the population in other years.

**13.** Use the 1940 and 1950 data to estimate the population in 1945 assuming

   a. linear growth;

   b. exponential growth.

**14.** Use the 1930 and 1950 data to estimate the population in 1940 assuming

   a. linear growth;

   b. exponential growth.

**15.** Use the 1890 and 1990 data to estimate the population in 1940 assuming

   a. linear growth;

   b. exponential growth.

**16.** 🗝 Compare your answers to problems 14 and 15. Did you get closer to the actual 1940 population using

   a. the 1930 and 1950 data or the 1890 and 1990 data?

   b. the linear model or the exponential model?

### EXAMINING ASSUMPTIONS

**Definitions:** When we know data points and use them to determine data values between those points, the process is called *interpolation*. When we know data points and try to use them to predict data values at a later or earlier time, the process is called *extrapolation*.

**17.** Which of the problems in this lesson involved extrapolation? Which ones involved interpolation?

It is important to examine assumptions when analyzing from data. People who analyze data often make incorrect projections and draw wrong conclusions because of making inappropriate assumptions.

**18.** Report Write a report summarizing what you learned in this lesson. Your report should include but not be limited to comments on:

- the suitability of the linear and exponential models as applied to the growth of the U.S. population during this century;
- the validity of results from extrapolating and interpolating using these models;
- a comparison of the accuracy of short-term and long-term predictions;
- how ideas outside of mathematics can help improve the quality of a mathematical model.

**REVIEW** *LINE THROUGH TWO POINTS*

**19.** Find the equation of the line through:
    a.  (0, 0) and (12, 34);
    b.  (5, 6) and (7, 11);
    c.  (8.9, –10) and (12.3, –4.3).

# The Median-Median Line

**You will need:**

graph paper

## FITTING A LINE

The table shows fuel efficiency data for 28 automobiles equipped with manual transmission.

**Highway vs. City Mileage**

| EPA Fuel Efficiency Data for 28 Cars with Manual Transmission | | |
|---|---|---|
| Car | miles per gallon | |
| | City | Highway |
| Corvette | 16 | 25 |
| Firebird | 17 | 26 |
| Thunderbird | 17 | 24 |
| Nissan 300ZX | 18 | 24 |
| Subaru XT | 18 | 25 |
| Stealth | 19 | 24 |
| Saab 9000 | 19 | 25 |
| Sunbird | 19 | 28 |
| Volvo 740 | 20 | 26 |
| Shadow | 20 | 28 |
| Probe | 21 | 27 |
| Sonata | 21 | 28 |
| Nissan NX | 22 | 28 |
| Colt Vista | 22 | 29 |
| Celica | 22 | 30 |
| Eclipse | 23 | 32 |
| Accord | 24 | 29 |
| Acclaim | 24 | 34 |
| Capri | 25 | 31 |
| Cabriolet | 25 | 32 |

| Car | miles per gallon | |
|---|---|---|
| | City | Highway |
| Impulse | 26 | 33 |
| Geo Prizm | 28 | 34 |
| Colt 5-speed | 29 | 35 |
| Escort | 29 | 36 |
| Sentra | 29 | 37 |
| Colt 4-speed | 31 | 36 |
| Civic CRX | 32 | 36 |
| Tercel | 33 | 37 |

**1.** Explain the meaning of the words *city mileage* and *highway mileage*.

Can average highway mileage be predicted from average city mileage? A graph of highway mileage versus city mileage shows that the data points lie approximately in a straight line. In this lesson you will learn a formal method for fitting a line to data. You can then use this line to make predictions for other cars.

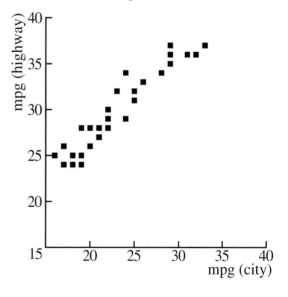

**2.** On your own graph paper, make a full-page graph of the data. Your graph should have both scales starting at (0, 0). Use vertical lines to divide the data points into three approximately equal sets of points, as shown in the following graph. There are ten points in the first set, eight in the middle set, and ten in the third set.

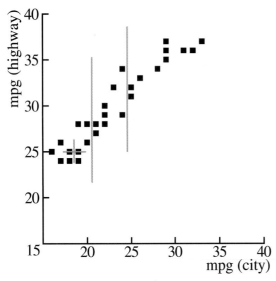

Look at the first set of data points. In your table, this is (16, 25) through (20, 28). It is easy to see on the graph that the median of the *x*-values in this first set of points is 18.5, and the median of the *y*-values is 25. The median point is marked with a +. Five points are to the left of it and five to the right. Five points are below it, (or even with it), and five are above, (or even with it).

**3.** Plot the point (18.5, 25) on your graph to show the medians of the *x*-values and *y*-values. Mark it with a +.

**4.** Find the median of the *x*-values and the median of the *y*-values for the second set of points. Mark it with a +.

**5.** Repeat for the third set of points.

The three +'s do not all lie exactly on the same line, but we can find a line that is close to all of them.

**6.** Place your ruler next to the first + and the third +, as if you were going to connect them with a line, but do not draw a line. Instead, move your ruler slightly toward the second +, about one-third of the way. Then draw the line.

**7.** Using two points on the line, find its equation. (Use points on the line, not actual data points — unless they happen to lie on the line.)

The line for which you found the equation is called the *median-median* line. Its equation provides an approximate relationship between city and highway mileage for a given car.

EXAMINING THE MODEL

**Summary**

**8.** What is the slope of the fitted line? What is its meaning in terms of this application?

**9.** What is the *y*-intercept of your line? What is its meaning in terms of this application?

**10.** Find two data points that are at least two units above the fitted line. What cars do they represent? What does it mean for points to be above the fitted line?

**11.** Find two data points that are at least two units below the fitted line. What cars do they represent? What does it mean for points to be below the fitted line?

**12.** Find two data points that are exactly on the line, or very near it. What cars do they represent? What does it mean for points to be on or near the fitted line?

## USING THE MODEL

**13.** Using your model (the equation of your fitted line), predict the highway mileage for a car that got city mileage of:

a. 30 miles per gallon;

b. 27 miles per gallon.

**14.** For a city mileage of 26, what is the

a. actual highway mileage based on the data?

b. predicted highway mileage based on the fitted line?

**15.** For a highway mileage of 28,

a. what range of city mileages might you expect, based on the data?

b. what city mileage would you expect, based on the fitted line?

## EXTENDING THE MODEL

**16.** Use the equation of the fitted line to predict highway mileage, if the city mileage is the following:

a. 53  b. 11

**17.** Based on your model, what city mileage would you expect for highway mileage of:

a. 58?  b. 15?

| Car | miles per gallon | |
|---|---|---|
| | City | Highway |
| Lamborghini | 9 | 14 |
| Ferrari | 10 | 15 |
| BMW M5 | 11 | 20 |
| Suzuki Swift | 45 | 50 |
| Civic HF | 49 | 52 |
| Geo Metro | 53 | 58 |

This table shows data for cars with very high and very low mileage.

**18.** ⚷

a. Does your model seem to work for very high and very low values?

b. For what range of values does your model work well? Explain.

## YOUR OWN DATA

**19.** **Project** Collect your own data (at least twenty *pairs* of numbers), either from an almanac, newspaper, or magazine, or by surveying people you know. Graph the data. *If the points seem to fall more or less in a line*, find the median-median line and find an equation for it. In any case, write a paragraph about what you find out. The following are possible topics, but you may choose any two variables which are related.

a. arm span vs. height

b. weight vs. height

c. height vs. shoe size

d. points scored vs. time on the court

e. hits vs. times at bat

**You will need:**

graph paper

There is no safe way to drive after drinking. Alcohol reaches a person's brain very soon after it has been absorbed into the bloodstream, and it impairs vision, hearing, muscular coordination, judgment, and self-control.

A person can begin to show mild effects from drinking alcohol when the blood alcohol concentration (BAC) is as low as 0.02%. Most people do not experience impairment until the BAC is about 0.05%, but each situation is different. A person who is tired or sick, or has taken drugs or medicines, may experience impairment with a lower BAC. In any case, a BAC of 0.10% is very unsafe for driving.

### A FORMULA

Blood alcohol concentration depends on many factors, but it can be estimated by using a person's weight and the amount of alcohol consumed, using this formula.

$$B = \frac{7.6 \cdot A}{W}$$

**B** = blood alcohol level, or BAC (in %).
**A** = alcohol consumed (in ounces).
**W** = body weight (in pounds).

The number 7.6 in the formula was derived by taking into account physiological factors (such as the percentage of alcohol that will be absorbed into the blood) and conversion of units.

**Definition:** We say that $y$ is *inversely proportional* to $x$ if the product of $x$ and $y$ is constant. Expressed algebraically
$xy = k$ or $y = k/x$ for some constant $k$.

1. In the formula is $B$
   a. directly or inversely proportional to $W$?
   b. directly or inversely proportional to $A$?

2. Use the formula to estimate the blood alcohol concentration of:
   a. a 152-pound person who consumed one ounce of alcohol;
   b. a 190-pound person who consumed two ounces of alcohol.

3. a. Solve the formula for $W$ in terms of the other two variables.
   b. Use your equation to estimate the weight a person would have to be in order to have a blood alcohol concentration of 0.05 after drinking three ounces of alcohol.

4. a. Solve the formula for $A$ in terms of the other two variables.
   b. Estimate the amount of alcohol a person probably consumed if he or she weighed 170 lbs. and had a BAC of 0.10.

### GRAPHING BAC vs. ALCOHOL

The formula has three variables, so we cannot graph it on a two-dimensional Cartesian coordinate system. However, we can use two-dimensional graphs to study this problem by fixing the value of one variable and graphing the resulting function.

5.  a. Substitute 152 for $W$ in the formula to find the function that expresses how BAC depends on the amount of alcohol consumed for a 152-pound person.

    b. Make a graph of the function you wrote in part (a). Label the $y$-axis *BAC (%)* and the $x$-axis *Alcohol (oz)*.

    c. Label your graph so people can see what it refers to.

6.  Repeat problem 5 for three other reasonable weights. Use the same axes for all four graphs.

7.  🔑 Describe the four graphs you drew. For a given body weight, is BAC directly proportional or inversely proportional to the amount of alcohol consumed? Explain.

### GRAPHING BAC vs. WEIGHT

8.  a. Substitute 1 for $A$ in the formula to find the function that expresses how BAC depends on weight for people who have consumed one ounce of alcohol.

    b. Make and label the graph of the function you wrote in part (a).

9.  Repeat problem 8 for three other amounts of alcohol (between two ounces and eight ounces). Use the same axes for all four graphs.

10. 🔑 Describe the four graphs you drew. For a given amount of alcohol, does the BAC vary directly or inversely as the weight of the person? Explain.

### THE EFFECT OF TIME

Alcohol does not stay in a person's blood forever. The amount remaining as time passes depends on many factors. A rule of thumb is that 40 minutes after drinking, blood alcohol starts to decrease at the rate of 0.01% per 40 minutes. In using this rule, you must remember to account for the first 40 minutes.

**Example:** Using the formula, a woman's blood alcohol level was estimated to be about 0.06%. Eighty minutes later she might expect it to be about 0.05%.

11. A man's blood alcohol concentration was estimated to be about 0.09%. How long would he have to wait for his BAC to drop below 0.02%?

12. A woman's blood alcohol concentration was estimated to be about 0.12%. How long until her BAC was below 0.04%?

### SAFE DRIVING GUIDELINES

13. A 115-pound woman had two ounces of alcohol to drink. Her 240-pound companion drank three ounces. Two hours later, do you think either person could drive safely? If so, which one? Explain your answer.

14. People know how much they have had to drink, but they do not know how much alcohol they have consumed. Calculate the amount of alcohol in each of these drinks.

    a. 12 ounces of beer that is 4% alcohol

    b. 4 ounces of wine that is 12% alcohol

    c. 6 ounces of wine that is 12% alcohol

    d. 4 ounces of a drink that is 20% alcohol

15. 🔑 A woman drank two 12-ounce beers. She weighs about 120 pounds. How long should she wait before driving? Explain.

16. Report Write a report that will give information to people to help them use good judgment in driving if they have been drinking. Include the following components in your report:

    • Summarize what you learned about blood alcohol concentration in your investigation. You may wish to include graphs or tables.

- Make a chart or diagram that you think will help give people information about blood alcohol concentration. They should be able to look up their weight and the amount they have had to drink in your table and estimate their BAC. Include information on the amount of alcohol in some typical drinks.

17. Research Find out about the DUI (driving under the influence of alcohol or drugs) laws in your state. In some states the laws are different for people under age 18 or 21. You may want to find statistics about the relationship between BAC and the chance of being involved in an accident.

- Summarize what you find out about DUI laws.
- Give your own opinion about the DUI laws in your state.

REVIEW COMPARING FRACTIONS

Explorations

18. Find several values of $x$ for which:

    a. $\dfrac{x}{40} > \dfrac{40}{x}$      b. $\dfrac{x}{40} < \dfrac{40}{x}$

19. Which is greater?

    a. $\dfrac{x}{40}$ or $\dfrac{x}{45}$      b. $\dfrac{40}{x}$ or $\dfrac{45}{x}$

20. Which is greater?

    a. $\dfrac{d}{40} - \dfrac{d}{45}$ or $\dfrac{d}{40} - \dfrac{d}{50}$

    b. $\dfrac{d}{40} - \dfrac{d}{45}$ or $\dfrac{d}{45} - \dfrac{d}{50}$

# 12.4

# Mathematical Models in Science

## HEATING AND COOLING GASES

Doing science often means finding mathematical models that fit experimental data. In 1787 the French scientist Jacques Charles discovered that when a gas is kept at constant pressure, it expands when heated and contracts when cooled. For gases under constant pressure, *volume is a linear function of temperature*.

At a certain pressure a gas has a volume of 500 cubic centimeters at 27°C. Kept at the same pressure, it expands to 605cc at 90°C.

1.  Find an equation that gives the volume ($V$) of this gas as a linear function of the temperature ($T$).

2.  Find the volume of the gas at 0°C.

3.  When kept at this pressure, how much does this gas expand for every 1°C increase in temperature?

When they get cold enough, gases condense (turn into liquids). If they did not, the temperature for which the volume would be 0 is called *absolute zero*, the lowest possible temperature.

4.  Use the equation you wrote in problem 1 to figure out what temperature absolute zero must be.

This graph shows how the volume of a certain gas varies with temperature, when kept at constant pressure. Each line represents a different pressure. The point where the red line ends and the blue line starts is the condensation point. Only the red lines represent actual data.

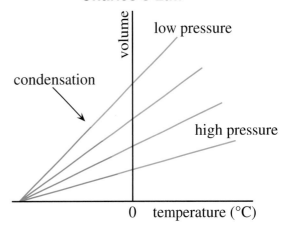

**Charles's Law**

## Summary

5.  As the pressure increases, what happens to the slopes of the lines? What does this mean in terms of the application?

6.  What is the meaning of the $y$-intercept of the lines? As the pressure increases, how does it change?

7.  How does the condensation point vary with pressure?

8.  Why do all the blue lines intersect at one point? What is the point's significance?

STRETCHING IT

The length of a spring is related to the weight that hangs from it. The following figure shows a graph from an experiment with a certain spring.

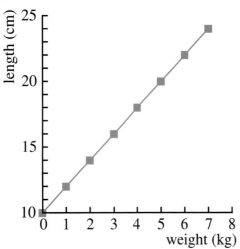

9.  a. What was the length of the spring before any weight was added?

    b. How many centimeters did the spring stretch for each kilogram of weight?

    c. What is the equation that relates length to weight?

10. ⚷ Can the graph be indefinitely extended to the right? Explain.

11. ⚷ This graph shows data for two other springs. Which spring is stiffer? Which one is longer? Explain.

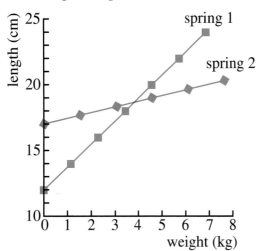

DEPENDENCE AND INDEPENDENCE

Paul, a forest lover, knew how to estimate the temperature from listening to cricket chirps. His grandmother had taught him to count the number of chirps per minute, divide by 4, and add 40 to get the temperature in Fahrenheit.

12. Write an equation for the temperature ($T$) as a function of the number of chirps ($C$).

13. What would Paul estimate the temperature to be if he counted 180 chirps per minute?

14. According to the model, at what temperature would the crickets cease to chirp?

Since the number of chirps depends on the temperature, and not vice-versa, we call number of chirps the *dependent* variable and temperature the *independent* variable.

In algebra we usually call the independent variable $x$ and use the horizontal axis for it. We call the dependent variable $y$ and use the vertical axis for it. Likewise, we often express the relationship between the two variables by writing the dependent variable as a function of the independent variable.

15. Write an equation for the dependent variable (number of chirps) as a function of the independent variable (temperature). Hint: Use your equation from problem 12 and solve for $C$ in terms of $T$.

In an experiment the independent variable is the variable we change or manipulate. Then we observe and record the effect on the dependent variable.

16. ⚷ Which variable is dependent and which is independent in problem 9? Explain.

For each experiment, problems 17-20, do the following:

   a. Discuss the relationship you expect between the two variables.

   b. Identify the dependent and independent variables.

   c. Carry out the experiment and collect the data in a table.

   d. Make a graph.

   e. Interpret the graph.

   f. If possible, write an equation relating the variables.

   g. Draw some conclusions.

**17.** *Spring:* The length of a spring as a function of the weight that hangs from it — **You will need** a spring and several identical weights. Start by letting the spring hang freely. Measure its length. Then add the weights one by one, each time measuring the length of the spring as it stretches.

**18.** *Fall:* The time it takes for Lab Gear blocks to fall as a function of the number of blocks — **You will need** a stopwatch and 20 or more $x^2$-blocks. Line up $x^2$-blocks so that if the first one is pushed, each block will knock down the next block in succession.

**19.** *Summer:* The time it takes to do "the wave" as a function of the number of people involved. **You will need** a stopwatch. Decide on an order for the wave. Appoint a student (or the teacher) to be the timer. When the timer says "Go," take turns getting up and sitting down. Repeat the experiment for different numbers of people.

**20.** *Winter:* The height of an ice column as a function of the height of the corresponding water column — **You will need** some drinking straws, chewing gum, ice (or access to a refrigerator). Plug the bottom of a straw with gum. Fill it to a certain height with water. Mark and measure the height of the water column. Do it again with different amounts of water in other straws. Freeze them. Mark and measure the height of the column of ice.

**21.** Report Write an illustrated lab report on an experiment you conducted. This can be one of the ones presented in this section or another one of your own design. Include the data you collected, a graph, and an equation, if you found one. Describe the conditions in which you conducted the experiment, your expectations, and your conclusions.

# 12.A Equations from Data

Each of the tables below gives four $(x, y)$ pairs for a function. Each function is one of the following types and has an equation of the corresponding form.

| Type of Function | Form of Equation |
|---|---|
| direct variation | $y = mx$ |
| inverse variation | $y = k/x$ |
| linear | $y = mx + b$ |

For each table in problems 1 through 6,
  a. decide whether the function is direct variation, inverse variation, or linear;
  b. find the equation of the function.

**1.**

| x | y |
|---|---|
| 0.05 | 5 |
| 0.5 | 0.5 |
| 5 | 0.05 |
| 50 | 0.005 |

**2.**

| x | y |
|---|---|
| 0.05 | 0.002 |
| 0.5 | 0.02 |
| 5 | 0.2 |
| 50 | 2 |

**3.**

| x | y |
|---|---|
| 0.9 | 0.6 |
| 1.5 | 1.0 |
| 2.7 | 1.8 |
| 5.1 | 3.4 |

**4.**

| x | y |
|---|---|
| 200 | 125 |
| 100 | 62.5 |
| 120 | 75 |
| 320 | 200 |

**5.**

| x | y |
|---|---|
| 0.01 | 0.73 |
| 0.1 | 0.55 |
| 1.5 | -2.25 |
| 3 | -5.25 |

**6.**

| x | y |
|---|---|
| 4 | -2 |
| 8 | -1 |
| 18 | 1.5 |
| 25 | 3.25 |

**7.** Each of the following three tests can be used to recognize a certain type of function among direct variations, inverse variations, and linear functions. Match the test to the type of function. Make sure your answer works for problems 1-6.

  a. constant $xy$ product
  b. constant slope
  c. constant $y/x$ ratio

Because of measurement error, the numbers obtained in scientific experiments do not usually give perfect number patterns. For tables 8-10, find an equation that is approximately right.

**8.**

| x | y |
|---|---|
| 1.5 | 0.50 |
| 1.6 | 0.53 |
| 1.7 | 0.55 |
| 1.8 | 0.60 |
| 1.9 | 0.63 |
| 2.0 | 0.65 |

**9.**

| x | y |
|---|---|
| 12.5 | 6.8 |
| 13 | 6.5 |
| 13.5 | 6.3 |
| 14 | 6.1 |
| 14.5 | 5.9 |
| 15 | 5.6 |

**10.**

| x | y |
|---|---|
| 0.6 | 4.12 |
| 0.7 | 4.26 |
| 0.8 | 4.37 |
| 0.9 | 4.49 |
| 1.0 | 4.61 |
| 1.1 | 4.71 |

**11.** Report Summarize what you know about how to find the equation corresponding to experimental data, if it is one of the following types:
  • direct variation
  • linear function
  • inverse variation
Include examples. Explain both how to recognize the type of function and how to find the actual equation.

# LESSON 12.5 Modeling Motion

**You will need:**

graph paper

---

## AVERAGE SPEED

**Definition:** Average speed is total distance traveled divided by total travel time.

1. Joan goes to work at 6 A.M. She averages 60 mph on the interstate highway. She returns during rush hour, when she averages 15 mph. What is her average speed for the round trip if she travels 30 miles in each direction?

Many problems in this lesson can be understood better by making distance-time graphs, like this one about Joan's commute.

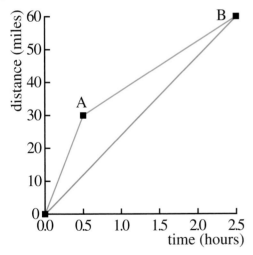

2. Explain how the coordinates of points A and B were obtained from the given information.

3. How does Joan's morning speed of 60 mph show up on the graph? Her return speed? Her average speed?

---

4. Joan calculated her average speed by adding the two speeds and dividing by 2.

$$(60 + 15)/2 = 37.5$$

Explain why this is wrong.

5. 🔑 Jill traveled for two hours at 30 mph and two hours at 60 mph. Jack traveled for 90 miles at 30 mph and for 90 miles at 60 mph. Which of them had an average speed of 45 mph? Which one did not? Explain.

6. **Generalization**

   a. I travel for $t$ hours at $v$ mph and $t$ more hours at $w$ mph. What is my average speed?

   b. I travel to work, which is $d$ miles away, at $v$ mph, and travel back at $w$ mph. What is my average speed?

---

## RELAY RACE

Alaberg High's Track Team has a relay race team. These tables show the times in seconds of the individual runners in the $4 \times 100$ meter race at the meet with the Lean County School. The runners are listed in running order.

| Alaberg | | Lean | |
|---|---|---|---|
| Mal | 12.2 | Neil | 12.1 |
| Cal | 12.0 | Neal | 12.3 |
| Hal | 12.4 | Alan | 12.2 |
| Zal | 11.4 | Allen | 10.9 |

7. Imagine you are the radio announcer for this event. Describe the teams' performances. Who was ahead at various times? How did it end up? What was the key to the winning team's victory?

**8. a.** Compare the median running times for the two teams.

**b.** Compare the mean running times for the two teams.

**c.** Which is more relevant to winning the race?

**9.** Find each runner's speed in m/sec.

**10.** Find the average speed of each team in m/sec.

**11.** Show how each student answered problem 10 and find their answers.

**a.** Andrea divided 100 by the mean running time for each team.

**b.** Beth divided 400 by the total time for each team.

**c.** Carolyn took the average of the individual members' speeds.

**12.** Summary Discuss the three methods presented in problem 11. Which ones are equivalent to each other? Which one is incorrect? Explain.

> **CATCH UP AND MEET**

**13.** Jane is traveling at 60 mph along a road. She has traveled for four hours when Joe catches up with her. How fast must Joe have been traveling if he left the same place one hour after Jane?

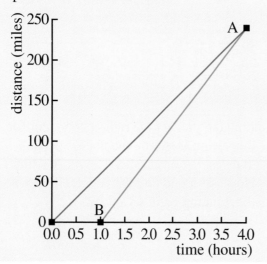

**14.** ☞ Look at the graph in problem 13. Explain how the coordinates of points A and B were chosen, and how the graph can help solve the problem.

**15.** Jim is traveling at 40 mph. Jorge leaves two hours later and travels at 50 miles per hour. How long until he catches up? How far have they gone?

**16.** Juan leaves at noon and travels at 45 mph. Jo leaves two hours later. How fast must she travel to catch up by:

**a.** 8 P.M.?      **b.** 8:30 P.M.?

**c.** 11 P.M.?      **d.** 💡 $H$ P.M.?

**17.** Jacquey and Gigi start out at the same time, traveling towards each other. Jacquey travels at 50 mph. Gigi travels at 40 mph. They start out 250 miles apart. When and where do they meet?

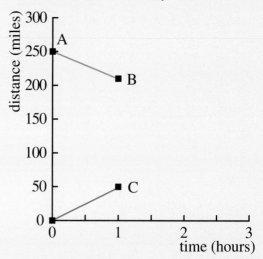

**18.** ☞ The graph shows Jacquey and Gigi's progress during the first hour. (Jacquey's graph starts at the origin.) Explain how the coordinates of points A, B, and C were obtained, and how to use a graph like this to solve problem 17.

**19.** Greg starts out going towards Cary, traveling 50 mph. Cary starts out two hours later going 40 mph, going towards Greg. If they are 250 miles apart to begin with, when and where do they meet?

## SAVING TIME

Paige travels to work so early that he meets hardly any traffic. He can drive at the speed limit the whole way. He wishes that the speed limit, which is 40 mph, would be raised so that he could sleep a little later in the morning.

20. How many minutes would Paige save if the speed limit were raised to 45 mph and he lives 30 miles from work?

21. Tara lives on the same road, 45 miles from work. How much time would she save?

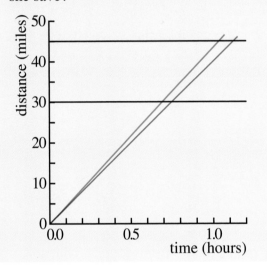

22. ⚷ Explain how you can use a graph like this one to think about problems 20 and 21.

23. Generalization How much time would be saved for people who live $d$ miles from work if the speed limit were raised from 40 to 45 mph?

24. If Leon lives 60 miles from work, to what would the speed limit have to be raised (from 40 mph) in order for him to save
    a. 6 minutes?     b. 12 minutes?

25. ⚷ Rina is taking a 60-mile trip. Which is greater: the time saved if she can travel 50 mph instead of 40 mph, OR the time saved if she can travel 60 mph instead of 50 mph? Explain.

# Gearing Up

In this lesson you will learn about the mathematics of gears. This will help you understand the decisions people have to make when they buy or design bicycles.

### BIG WHEELS

1. How far does a bicycle travel for every revolution of the wheel for each wheel diameter below?
   a. 20 in.      b. 27 in.
   c. 50 in.      d. 64 in.

Old-fashioned bicycles had huge front wheels. Most of these high-wheelers, as they were called, had a 50-inch front wheel and a 17-inch rear wheel, but some of the makers got carried away and built front wheels as high 64 inches! The pedals were in the center of the front wheels.

2. Why did bicycle makers make such big wheels?

Highwheelers had two drawbacks. First, the rider had to work very hard to get started, and most of these bicycles had to be pushed or dragged up hills. Second, their height made

them a dangerous and impractical means of transportation. The rider had to jump down from the seat when the bicycle stopped, hoping to land feet-first.

The invention of gears on bicycles was a key development. Gears allowed the rider to travel longer distances for each turn of the pedals, without requiring such big wheels.

### HOW GEARS WORK

**Example:** A bicycle has a chainwheel having 45 teeth and a rear sprocket having 15 teeth.

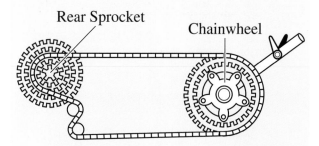

Rear Sprocket                    Chainwheel

Each time the chain passes over one tooth on the chainwheel, it also passes over one tooth on the rear sprocket. Therefore, the rear sprocket will go through three revolutions for every one revolution of the chainwheel.

3. 🔑 Explain why riding a 27-inch bicycle having these gears would be like riding an 81-inch bicycle in terms of the distance covered in one turn of the pedals.

**Definition:** The *gear ratio* is the ratio of the number of teeth on the chainwheel to the number of teeth on the rear sprocket.

4. If the gear ratio is 2.5, how many turns does the rear wheel make for each turn of the pedals?

A ten-speed bicycle has two chainwheels and five rear sprockets. Each combination of chainwheel and sprocket is a different gear.

5. Make a table to show how the gear ratio changes as a function of the number of teeth on the gears of a ten-speed bicycle, with two chainwheels having 40 and 54 teeth, and five rear sprockets having 14, 17, 22, 28, and 34 teeth.

|    | 14 | 17 | 22 | 28 | 34 |
|----|----|----|----|----|----|
| 40 | — | — | — | — | — |
| 54 | — | — | — | — | — |

6. **Generalization** Write the gear ratio ($g$) as a function of the number of teeth on the chainwheel ($c$) and the number of teeth on the rear sprocket ($r$).

### GEAR

**Definition:** The *gear* is the gear ratio multiplied by the diameter of the rear wheel. It gives the diameter of the wheel that would travel the same distance in one revolution of the pedals. (The unit of gear is inches, but it is usually omitted.)

**Example:** The gear ratio is 40/20, or 2, when using a chainwheel having 40 teeth and a rear sprocket having 20 teeth. On a bicycle having 26-inch wheels, the gear would be 2 × 26, or 52. This means that each turn of the pedals when the bicycle is in this gear would move the bike a distance equivalent to one turn of a 52-inch wheel.

7. If the gear is 52, how far would the bike travel with each turn of the pedals?

8. **Generalization**
   a. Write the gear ($G$) as a function of the number of teeth on the chainwheel ($c$), the number of teeth on the rear sprocket ($r$), and the size of the wheel ($w$).
   b. If the gear is $G$, how far would the bike travel with every turn of the pedals?
   c. Write a formula that gives the distance ($d$) that the bike would travel with each turn of the pedals as a function of $c$, $r$, and $w$.

### CADENCE

**Definition:** The *cadence* is the pace of pedaling.

A good cadence to maintain is 65 to 85 pedal revolutions per minute. Better cyclists like to maintain a cadence of 90 turns per minute.

9. Julio's ten-speed bike has wheels 27 inches in diameter. Its gears were described in problem 5. At a cadence of 90 pedal revolutions per minute, how fast, in miles per hour, would Julio be going in the highest gear? (Hint: Find a conversion factor to get directly from pedal revolutions per minute to miles per hour.)

10. If Julio knows his cadence, find a way for him to calculate his speed mentally in miles per hour when riding in the highest gear.

## DESIGN A BIKE

**11.** `Project` Design a bicycle. First describe the future owner of the bicycle and his or her needs. Will the rider be climbing steep hills? Be racing? Choose a size for the wheel, and the number of teeth for the gears of a 10-, 15-, or 18-speed bicycle. The following information may be helpful. Describe how each gear would most likely be used.

**Wheel diameters**
24, 26, and 27 inches are common.
**Teeth on the chainwheel**
24 to 58
**Teeth on the rear sprocket**
12 to 38
**Sample Gears**
• Very low gear, for climbing steep hills and for easy starts: 33
• Medium gear, for general use: 54
• Very high gear, for going downhill fast, and for racing: 100
**Progression**
Some cyclists like an approximately geometric progression of gears, because the common ratio makes the change feel the same from one gear to the next.

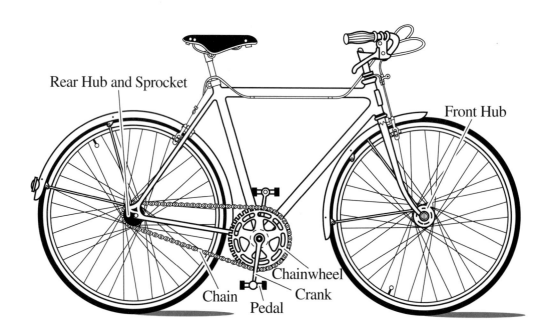

Rear Hub and Sprocket

Front Hub

Chain

Chainwheel

Crank

Pedal

*Chapter 12 Mathematical Modeling*

# Iterating Linear Functions

**You will need:**

graph paper

or function diagram paper

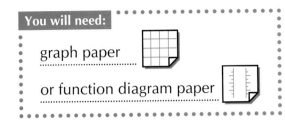

## TREE HARVESTING

Paul's Forestry Products owns two stands of trees. This year there are about 4500 trees in Lean County and 5500 in Cool County. So as not to run out of trees, the yearly harvesting policy at each location is to cut down 30% of the trees and then plant 1600 trees. For example, in Lean County this year they will cut 1350 trees and plant 1600 trees.

1. Make a table of values showing how many trees they would have at each location every year for nine years.

2. Describe the change in the number of trees at each location. Is it increasing or decreasing? Is it changing at a constant rate from year to year? What do you think will happen in the long run?

3. Write a formula that would give the number of trees next year in terms of the number of trees this year. (Use $y$ for next year's number and $x$ for this year's number. What you get is called a *recurrence equation*.)

4. How many trees would they have at each location after 30 years?

## DRUGS

To control a medical condition, Shine takes ten milligrams of a certain drug once a day. Her body gets rid of 40% of the drug in a 24-hour period. To find out how much of the drug she ends up with over the long run, we can use function diagrams.

5. If $x$ is the amount of the drug Shine takes per day, and $y$ is the amount that ends up in her body over the long run, explain why the recurrence equation is $y = 0.6x + 10$.

6. Make a table of values for the recurrence equation, using these values for $x$, the daily dose: 0, 5, 10, 15, 20, 25, 30, 35, 40.

Here is a function diagram for the recurrence equation.

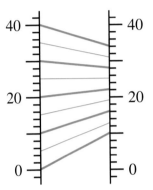

This function diagram can be repeated to show what happens over the long run. The linked diagrams show how the $y$-values for one become the $x$-values for the next.

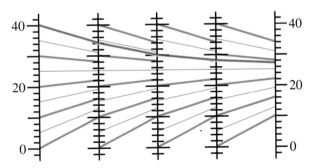

7. Use the diagram to predict what happens in the long run if Shine takes 10 mg a day of the drug after an initial dose of:
   a. 10 mg;  b. 25 mg;
   c. 40 mg.

8. Check your predictions by calculation.

Remember that instead of linked diagrams like in the figure, you could use a single function diagram of the function. Just follow an in-out line, then move horizontally across back to the *x*-number line; then repeat the process, using the in-out line that starts at that point.

---
SAVINGS
---

Glinda puts $50 a month into a savings account paying yearly compound interest of 6%.

**9.** What is the interest per month?

**10.** How much money will she have at the end of one year?

**11.** Write a recurrence equation for problem 10, expressing the amount in the account at the end of each month as a function of the amount the previous month.

**12.** Make a function diagram.

**13.** ◆— How does what happens in the long run for problem 10 differ from the problems in the previous sections? Explain.

**Definition:** To *iterate* a function means to use its output as a new input.

All the problems in this lesson involve iterating linear functions. We will use function diagrams and algebraic symbols to get a more general understanding of this kind of problem.

**14.** ◆— Describe the difference between function diagrams for $y = mx + b$ for the following:
a. $0 < m < 1$    b. $m = 1$
c. $m > 1$

---
THE FIXED POINT
---

**Definition:** A fixed point of a function is one in which the output is the same as the input.

**Example:** For the function $y = 7x - 12$, when the input is 2, the output is also 2.

**15.** What is the fixed point for each of the functions in problems 3 and 5? Why was it important in understanding the problems?

**16.** Find the fixed points.
a. $y = 3x - 6$    b. $y = 3x + 5$
c. $y = 3x$    d. $y = x$
e. $y = x + 3$    f. ◯ $y = x^2 - 2$

**17.** ◆— Function diagrams may help you think about these questions.
a. There is a linear function that has more than one fixed point. What is it? Explain.
b. What linear functions have no fixed points? Explain.

**18.** Generalization
a. Find a formula for the fixed point for the function $y = mx + b$. (Hint: Since the output is the same as the input, substitute *x* for *y* and solve for *x*.)
b. Explain why $m = 1$ is not acceptable in the formula you found. What does that mean in terms of the existence of the fixed point for equations of the form $y = x + b$?

---
ANALYZING THE SEQUENCES
---

When iterating a function, you get a sequence of numbers.

**19.** Exploration  Start with the equation $y = 2x + 3$. Change one number in the equation so that when iterating the function, starting with any input, you get
a. an arithmetic sequence;
b. a geometric sequence;
c. a sequence where the values get closer and closer to a fixed point.

Compare your answers with other students' answers.

**20.** **Generalization** When iterating $y = mx + b$, different things may happen, depending upon the value of the parameters. Find the values of $m$ and $b$ which lead to the following situations:

a. arithmetic sequences;

b. geometric sequences;

c. sequences where the values get farther and farther from the fixed point;

d. sequences where the values get closer and closer to the fixed point.

**21.** **Report** Summarize what you know about iterating linear functions. Include, but do not limit yourself to these topics.

- real-world applications
- use of function diagrams
- the fixed point
- these special cases:
  ◊ $b = 0$
  ◊ $0 < m < 1$
  ◊ $m = 1$
  ◊ $m > 1$

---

**DISCOVERY** **TWO RULERS**

Alice's ruler

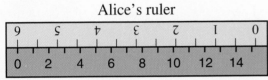

Oliver's ruler

Alice and Oliver lined up her inch ruler against his centimeter ruler, as in the above figure. This yielded the following table of numbers.

| x | y |
|---|---|
| 0 | 6.0 |
| 2 | 5.2 |
| 4 | 4.4 |
| 6 | 3.6 |

**22.** a. Graph these data.

b. What is the equation for $y$ in terms of $x$?

c. Interpret the slope and $y$-intercept in terms of the rulers.

Place an inch ruler and a centimeter ruler against each other so that they run in opposite directions.

**23.** Using the ruler arrangement you made as a source of $(x, y)$ pairs, make a table like Alice's and Oliver's. Then make a graph.

**24.** Write an equation for the function that shows the relationship between the numbers in your table.

**25.** Interpret the slope and $y$-intercept in your equation and graph in terms of your rulers and their positions.

# Representing Functions

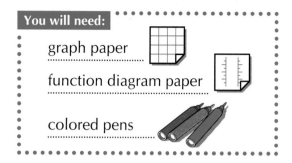

You will need:

graph paper

function diagram paper

colored pens

## POINTS AND LINES

As you know, an $(x, y)$ pair is represented as a point on a Cartesian graph and as an in-out line on a function diagram. In this section we will review how an equation of the form $y = mx + b$ is represented in these formats.

1.  For the function represented by this Cartesian graph,
    a.  write the equation;
    b.  draw a function diagram.

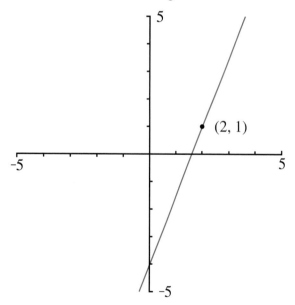

2.  Extend the in-out lines in the function diagram you made in problem 1. They should meet in one point, called the focus.

3.  ⚬━ What is the minimum number of lines you need to draw to find the focus? Explain.

Actually, a function of the form $y = mx + b$ can be represented by just the focus, as you will see in the next problem.

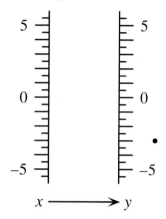

4.  The figure shows the focus of a certain function of the form $y = mx + b$.
    a.  Place a ruler on the focus, and find three in-out lines. Do not draw the lines, but keep a record of the $(x, y)$ pairs.
    b.  Find the equation.

5.  ⚬━ If you were to make a Cartesian graph of this function, what is the minimum number of points you would need to plot? Explain.

This table shows how points and lines appear in the two representations. Notice how points and lines are switched when going from one representation to the other.

| | Representation | |
|---|---|---|
| **Object** | on Cartesian graph | on function diagram |
| $(x, y)$ pair | one point | one line (in-out) |
| linear equation | one line | one point (the focus) |

*Chapter 12 Mathematical Modeling*

This graph shows $y = -3x$ and $y = -x + 2$.

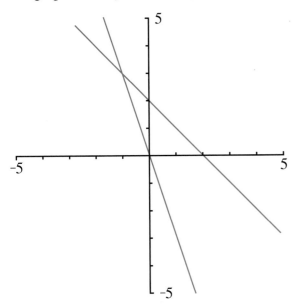

**6.** What point do the two lines have in common?

The function diagram shows the foci of $y = -3x$ and $y = -x + 2$. (Foci is the plural of focus.)

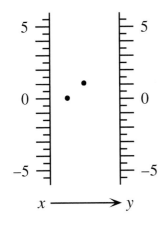

$$x \longrightarrow y$$

**7.** Check that the foci are placed correctly.

a. Place a ruler on the focus and find three in-out lines for each function. Do not draw the lines, but keep a record of the $(x, y)$ pairs.

b. Check that the $(x, y)$ pairs you found satisfy the equations.

**8.** If you were to draw an in-out line containing both foci, what $(x, y)$ pair would it represent?

**9.** ☞ How is the solution of a system of linear equations represented on:

a. a Cartesian graph?

b. a function diagram?

**10.** ☞ Explain how to solve this system by using a function diagram. (Hint: First find each focus, then find the solutions.)

$$\begin{cases} y = 0.5x + 2 \\ y = 2x - 1 \end{cases}$$

Because two lines meet in a point, the solution to a system of simultaneous equations is represented on a Cartesian graph by a point. Because two points determine a line, the solution to a system of linear equations is represented on a function diagram by a line (an in-out line).

| **Definition:** A *family* of functions is a group of functions that share a certain attribute.

**11.** All functions having equations of the form $y = 5x + b$ belong to the $m = 5$ family.

a. Sketch the graphs of two members of the family.

b. What do all graphs for this family have in common?

**12.** All functions having equations of the form $y = mx + 7$ belong to the $b = 7$ family.

a. Sketch the graphs of two members of the family.

b. What do all graphs for this family have in common?

All functions in the same $b$-family have foci that lie on the same in-out line.

13. These four functions are in the same *b*-family. For each one, draw in-out lines to find the focus and mark it with a colored pen or pencil. Do all four on the same diagram.
    a. $y = 0.5x - 2$    b. $y = 2x - 2$
    c. $y = -2x - 2$    d. $y = -0.5x - 2$

14. What is the family name for the functions in problem 13?

15. ⟜ Why do all the foci of the functions in problem 13 lie on the same in-out line? Which in-out line is it? Explain.

16. The foci for all functions in the family $b = -3$ also lie on one in-out line. Which line? Explain how you know.

Many *m*-families also have foci that lie on the same in-out line in a function diagram.

17. a. On a function diagram, find and mark the focus for $y = -2x + 3$.
    b. On the same function diagram, find and mark the focus for $y = -2x + 1$.
    c. Find and mark the focus for several other graphs of the form $y = -2x + k$.

18. ⟜ What is the family name for all the functions in problem 17? Explain why the foci are all on the same line. Describe the line.

19. ⟜ If two functions both have a focus on the same vertical line, what would their Cartesian graphs have in common?

20. 💡 What is the family name for all functions having focus half-way between the two number lines?

21. There is one *m* family for which the function diagrams have no focus, because the in-out lines do not meet. Which *m* family is this?

22. **Summary** On a function diagram, what is true of the foci of all linear functions in the same
    a. *m* family?    b. *b* family?

23. ⟜ The functions representing Charles's Law for gases in the graph in Lesson 4 form a family that is neither an *m* nor a *b* family. If you were to make function diagrams for them, the foci would all be on a certain in-out line. Which one? Explain.

# 12.B V-Shaped Graphs

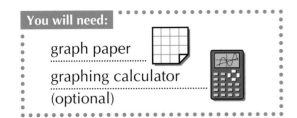

## THE SQUARE ROOT OF $x^2$

As you know, the radical sign means *the non-negative square root of.*

**1.** Make a table of values, and a graph, for the function $y = \sqrt{x^2}$. Use at least six values for $x$, including positive numbers, negative numbers, and zero.

**2.** Find a linear function that has the same graph as $y = \sqrt{x^2}$, when
   a. $x$ is positive;   b. $x$ is negative.

**3.** ➤ True or False? $\sqrt{x^2} = x$. Explain.

## ABSOLUTE VALUE

As you may remember, the absolute value of a number is the distance between that number and zero.

**4.** Repeat problems 1-3 for the function $y = |x|$.

Graph the functions in problems 5 through 10. Use separate axes for each one. Write each equation on its graph.

**5.** $y = |x| + 2$         **6.** $y = |x| - 2$

**7.** $y = -|x|$           **8.** $y = 2|x|$

**9.** $y = |x + 2|$        **10.** $y = |x - 2|$

**11.** **Exploration** Find equations of the form $y = A|x - H| + V$ for these four graphs.

a.
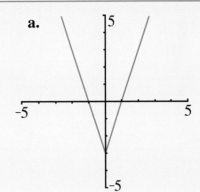

b.
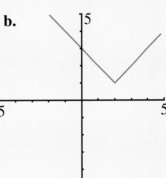

c.
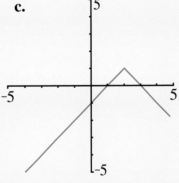

d.
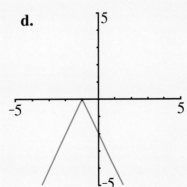

**12.** Report Write an illustrated report describing graphs of the form $y = A|x - H| + V$. Describe how each of the parameters $A$, $H$, and $V$ affects the graph. What are the slopes? Where is the vertex? What are the domain and range? Give examples, including both negative and positive values of all the parameters. ∎

**13.** ☞ Describe the plane's trip.

**14.** The equation of the graph is of the form $y = A|x - H| + V$. What are $A$, $H$, and $V$?

**15.** ☞ If the plane were going at 300 miles per hour,
   a. how would the graph be different?
   b. how would the equation be different?

### A ROUND TRIP

This graph shows a plane's trip. It was sighted passing over Alaberg at time $t = 0$.

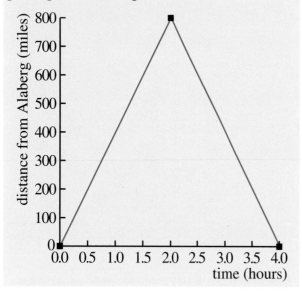

### REVIEW · LIKE TERMS

When combining terms involving fractions, it is sometimes useful to write the fractions with common denominators. However, it is often more convenient to use the method that is demonstrated in the following example.

**Example:**
$$\frac{x}{60} - \frac{11x}{70}$$
$$= \frac{1}{60}x - \frac{11}{70}x$$
$$= \left(\frac{1}{60} - \frac{11}{70}\right)x$$
$$= -0.14x$$

(A calculator was used for the last step.)

Combine like terms.

**16.** $\frac{2x}{3} - 4x$

**17.** $\frac{5x}{6} + \frac{7}{8} + \frac{9x}{4}$

**18.** $\frac{3x + 2}{5} - \frac{x}{2}$

# Essential Ideas

## FIRST CLASS STAMPS

This table shows the costs in cents of first-class stamps over the past sixty years. The dates indicate the year when there was an increase in the first-class rate.

| Year | Cost | Year | Cost |
|------|------|------|------|
| 1932 | 3 | 1975 | 13 |
| 1958 | 4 | 1978 | 18 |
| 1963 | 5 | 1981 | 20 |
| 1968 | 6 | 1985 | 22 |
| 1971 | 8 | 1988 | 25 |
| 1974 | 10 | 1991 | 29 |

Interpolation is not relevant since all the data are known within the given period. However extrapolation may be possible.

1.  Graph the data as a step function. For example, the cost was 3 cents from 1932 to 1957.

2.  In 1985 Barbara wanted to use the average cost increase in the period 1932-1985 to predict the cost of stamps in 1991.
    a.  What was the average yearly increase?
    b.  Based on this, what cost did she predict for 1991?

3.  In 1985 Sue used a computer to find the average percent increase over the 53-year period. The computer indicated that on the average, the cost went up by 3.8% a year. Based on this, what cost did she predict for 1991?

In 1991 they used the same methods to find the average increases over the 59-year period. Barbara found an average increase of 0.44 cents a year, and Sue found an average percent increase of 3.9% a year.

4.  Make a prediction for the cost of stamps in the year 1999 and 2032. Explain.

## THE MILE RUN

| Year | Time | Year | Time |
|------|--------|------|---------|
| 1868 | 4:29.0 | 1942 | 4:04.6 |
| 1868 | 4:28.8 | 1943 | 4:02.6 |
| 1874 | 4:26.0 | 1944 | 4:01.6 |
| 1875 | 4:24.5 | 1945 | 4:01.4 |
| 1880 | 4:23.2 | 1954 | 3:59.4 |
| 1882 | 4:21.4 | 1954 | 3:58.0 |
| 1882 | 4:19.4 | 1957 | 3:57.2 |
| 1884 | 4:18.4 | 1958 | 3:54.5 |
| 1894 | 4:18.2 | 1962 | 3:54.4 |
| 1895 | 4:17.0 | 1964 | 3:54.1 |
| 1911 | 4:15.6 | 1965 | 3:53.6 |
| 1911 | 4:15.4 | 1966 | 3:51.3 |
| 1913 | 4:14.6 | 1967 | 3:51.1 |
| 1915 | 4:12.6 | 1975 | 3:51.0 |
| 1923 | 4:10.4 | 1975 | 3:49.4 |
| 1931 | 4:09.2 | 1979 | 3:49.0 |
| 1933 | 4:07.6 | 1980 | 3:48.8 |
| 1934 | 4:06.8 | 1981 | 3:48.53 |
| 1937 | 4:06.4 | 1981 | 3:48.40 |
| 1942 | 4:06.2 | 1981 | 3:47.33 |

5. The table shows the world record for the mile run from 1868 to 1981. Plot the time *in seconds* as a function of year.

6. Use the median-median line method to fit a line.

7. What is the equation of your fitted line?

8. Richard Webster of Great Britain ran the mile in 4:36.5 in 1865. How does this compare with the time for 1865 predicted by your fitted line?

9. Steve Cram of Great Britain ran one mile in 3:46.31 in 1985. How does this compare with the time predicted by your fitted line?

10. a. According to your model, when would the mile be run in 0 seconds?
    b. For how many more years do you think your fitted line will be a good predictor of the time?

WIRES

When a metal wire changes temperature, it expands or contracts, according to the equation

$$L = L_0(1 + kT),$$

where $L$ is the length of the wire, $L_0$ is its length at 0°C, $T$ is the temperature, and $k$ depends on the metal. For copper, $k = 1.8(10^{-5})$.

11. A copper wire is 100.05 meters long at 40°C. If it is cooled to -10°C, how much will it shrink? (Hint: First find its length at 0°C.)

12. Two poles are 100 meters apart. They are connected by a 100.05-meter copper wire in the summer, when the temperature is 40°C. In the winter the temperature drops to -10°C.
    a. Explain why the wire breaks.
    b. How long should the wire be so as not to break in the winter?

A nickel-iron alloy is created. Measurements are made in a lab on a wire made of the alloy. It is found that a wire that is 10 meters long at 0°C expands by one half a millimeter at 100°C. The alloy is called *Invar*.

13. Find the value of $k$ for Invar.

14. Would an Invar wire that measures 100.01 meters at 40° C work to connect the poles in problem 12? Explain.

EQUATIONS FROM DATA

a.

| $x$ | $y$ |
|-----|-----|
| 0.4 | 15 |
| 0.6 | 10 |
| 0.8 | 7.5 |
| 1 | 6 |

b.

| $x$ | $y$ |
|-----|-----|
| 0.4 | 0.667 |
| 0.6 | 1.00 |
| 0.8 | 1.33 |
| 1 | 1.67 |

c.

| $x$ | $y$ |
|-----|-----|
| 0.4 | -4.4 |
| 0.6 | -2.6 |
| 0.8 | -0.8 |
| 1 | 1 |

15. Find an equation for each table. Hint: One is a direct variation, one an inverse variation, and one a linear function.

THE CAR TRIP AND THE BICYCLE TRIP

Reread **Thinking/Writing 2.B** (Chapter 2). The function diagram is shown below.

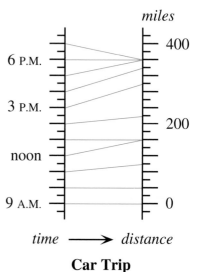

**Car Trip**

**16.** Make a Cartesian graph for the car trip, as best you can from the information given.

**17.** What is the car's average speed,
  a. if you include the time the car was stopped in the middle of the day?
  b. if you include only the driving time?

Reread **Thinking/Writing 4.A** (Chapter 4). The graph is shown below.

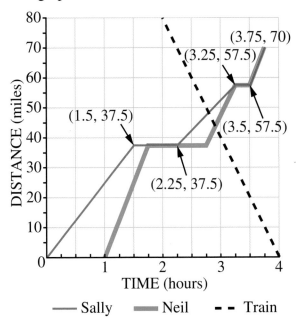

— Sally    ▬ Neil    - - Train

**18.** Repeat problem 17 for the van Neil drove.

**19.** If Neil were to make the return trip in the same length of time, but traveling at a constant speed and never stopping, what would be his speed?

**20.** a. Write an equation for Sally's graph during the leg of the trip when she and the train passed each other.

  b. Solve the system of equations consisting of the equations representing Sally's and the train's motion.

  c. Interpret the point of intersection.

For her asthma Lynne takes 360 mg of the drug *theophylline* twice a day. After 12 hours, 60% of the drug has been eliminated from her body.

**21.** Assume Lynne has $x_a$ mg of the drug in her body immediately after taking the dose. Explain why $y_a = 0.4y_a = 0.4x_a + 360$ is the recurrence equation that says how much will be in her body immediately after taking the next dose.

**22.** Assume she has $x_b$ mg of the drug in her body immediately before taking the dose. Explain why $y_b = 0.4(x_b + 360)$ is the recurrence equation that says how much will be in her body immediately before taking the next dose.

The amount of theophylline in Lynne's body is constantly changing, but the lowest amount (right before taking the drug) and the highest amount (right after) eventually approach a stable level.

**23.** Find that level, using tables, function diagrams, or equations. What is the level before taking the dose? What is it after?

# CHAPTER 13

The spiraling vortex of a whirlpool

## *Coming in this chapter:*

**Exploration** You want to make pens for Stripe, your pet zebra, and Polka Dot, your pet leopard. You have 100 feet of fencing. If you use all of it to make two pens of equal area, what is the biggest area possible?

# MAKING DECISIONS

# Rectangular Pens: Constant Perimeter

**You will need:**

graph paper

a graphing calculator
(optional)

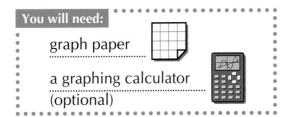

1. **Exploration** You want to make a rectangular pen for Stripe, your pet zebra. Even though Stripe takes many walks around town, you want to make sure she has as much space as possible inside the pen. You have 50 feet of fencing available. If you use all of it to make the pen, what is the biggest area possible? Find out by trying various dimensions for the pen.

## WIDTH AS A FUNCTION OF LENGTH

You have 28 feet of fencing to make a rectangular pen. There are many possible dimensions for this pen. One possible pen, 10 feet wide by 4 feet long, is shown below. In this section you will investigate how the length and width change in relation to one another if you keep the perimeter constant.

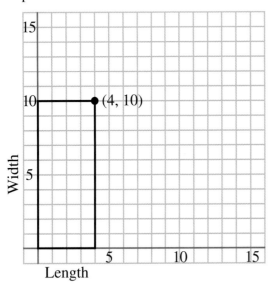

2. a. On graph paper, draw axes and at least six pens having a perimeter of 28.

   b. The upper right corner of the pen in the figure has been marked with a • and labeled with its coordinates. Do this for the pens you drew. Then connect all the points marked with a •. Describe the resulting graph.

3. a. Make a table showing all the coordinates on your graph. Look for a pattern and make three more entries in the table.

   b. Write an equation for the function described by your graph and table.

**Summary**

4. The point whose coordinates are (4, 10) is on the graph.

   a. What does the sum of these numbers represent in this problem?

   b. What does the product represent?

5. a. What is the greatest possible length of a pen? How can you see this on your graph?

   b. How many rectangles are possible if the dimensions are whole numbers? How many are possible otherwise?

   c. Explain why the graph should not be extended into quadrants II and IV.

6. If you increase the length by one foot, does the width increase or decrease? Does it change by the same amount each time? Explain.

## AREA AS A FUNCTION OF LENGTH

In the previous section you may have noticed that the area of the rectangles changed even though the perimeter remained constant. In this section you will investigate how the area changes as a function of length, if you keep the perimeter constant.

**7.** Write the area of the corresponding rectangle next to each of the points marked with a • on the graph from problem 2.

**8.** Make a graph of area as a function of length. Show length on the $x$-axis and area on the $y$-axis. Connect the points on your graph with a smooth curve. What kind of curve is it?

**9.** ⌐●

a. Label the highest point on your graph with its coordinates. Interpret these two numbers in terms of this problem.

b. Where does the graph cross the $x$-axis? What do these numbers mean?

c. If you increase the length by one foot, does the area increase or decrease? Does it change by the same amount each time? Explain.

**10.** Summary

a. Describe in words how you would find the area of the rectangular pen having perimeter 28 if you knew its length.

b. If the perimeter of a rectangular pen is 28 and its length is $L$, write an algebraic expression for its area in terms of $L$.

c. If you had 28 feet of fencing and wanted to make the largest possible rectangular pen, what would its length, width, and area be? Explain.

### Generalizations

**11.** Say the perimeter of a rectangle is $P$ and its length is $L$. Write the following expressions in terms of $P$ and $L$. (A sketch may help.)

a. an expression for the width

b. an expression for the area

**12.** Explain how to find the length that gives the maximum area. Write an algebraic expression for it in terms of $P$ only.

### PARABOLAS THROUGH THE ORIGIN

**13.** Graph each of the following functions, using graph paper. Since you will want to compare your graphs in the end, use the same pair of axes for all your graphs. Use a scale that will show values from –5 to 20 for $x$ and from –20 to 100 for $y$. This will allow you to see all four graphs clearly.

a. $y = x(8 - x)$    b. $y = x(15 - x)$
c. $y = x(12 - x)$   d. $y = x(20 - x)$

**14.** For each of the four parabolas in problem 13,

a. label the graph with its equation;

b. label the $x$-intercepts;

c. label the vertex.

**15.** Generalization

a. Describe the graph of a parabola having equation $y = x(b - x)$. Write expressions for the coordinates of its intercepts and vertex in terms of $b$.

b. Do these expressions work for negative values of $b$? Explain, using examples.

**16.** Graph.

a. $y = x(x - 8)$    b. $y = x(x - 15)$
c. $y = x(x - 12)$   d. $y = x(x - 20)$

**17.** How do the graphs differ from the ones in problem 3? Discuss the vertex and the intercepts.

**18.** Generalization

  a. Describe the graph of a parabola having equation $y = x(x - q)$. Write expressions for the coordinates of its intercepts and vertex in terms of $q$.

  b. Do these expressions work for negative values of $q$? Explain, using examples.

**19.** Graph $y = ax(x - 3)$ for:

  a. $a = 1$    b. $a = -1$

  c. $a = 2$    d. $a = -3$

**20.** ⬤━ What is the effect of $a$ on the position of:

  a. the vertex?

  b. the $x$-intercepts?

Find equations of the form $y = ax(x - q)$ for parabolas *through the origin*, with the given $x$-intercept and the vertex with the given $y$-coordinate.

| | | x-intercept | y-coordinate of vertex |
|---|---|---|---|
| **21.** | a. | 4 | 4 |
| | b. | 4 | 8 |
| | c. | 4 | 2 |
| | d. | 4 | -6 |
| **22.** | a. | 8 | 4 |
| | b. | 2 | 4 |
| | c. | -4 | 4 |
| | d. | -6 | -6 |

**REVIEW** *FIXED POINTS*

**23.** Find the fixed point for the function $y = 6x + 8$.

**24.** Solve the system: $\begin{cases} y = 6x + 8 \\ y = x \end{cases}$

**25.** ⬤━ Explain the statement: *To find the fixed points of a function, find the intersection of its graph with the line $y = x$.*

**26.** Test whether the statement is true by finding the fixed points of $y = x^2$.

# Advanced Penmanship

## PEN PARTITIONS

Assume that you have 50 feet of fencing to build a rectangular pen. You plan to use the garage wall as one side of the pen, which means you need to use your fencing for only three of the four sides. Since you are considering adopting more pets, you want to investigate what happens when you use some of the fencing to divide the pen into two or more parts by building partitions inside the pen, at a right angle to the wall.

1. Make a rough sketch of what this pen might look like,
   a. having no internal partitions;
   b. divided into two sections.

2. With no partitions, is it possible to get a square pen? If so, what are its dimensions?

3. With one partition, is it possible to get two square sections? If so, what are their dimensions?

Call the side of the pen parallel to the wall the *length,* and the distance between the wall and the side opposite the wall $x$.

4. Imagine you are dividing the pen into two parts. Make a table having three columns: $x$, the length, and the total area of the pen.

### Generalizations

5. Look for patterns in your table. Express algebraically as functions of $x$,
   a. the length;     b. the area.

6. What is the equation that expresses the length as a function of $x$, if the pen is divided into the given number of parts. (Make sketches. If you need to, make tables like those in problem 4.)
   a. 1          b. 3
   c. 4          d. $n$

7. Repeat problem 6, but this time find the area as a function of $x$.

## GRAPHS OF AREA FUNCTIONS

This section is about the graphs of functions like the ones you found in problem 7.

8. Using graph paper, graph each of the following functions. To make comparison easier, use the same graph, or at least the same scale, for all your graphs. To see all four graphs clearly, use a scale that will show values from −5 to 15 for $x$ and from −50 to 50 for $y$. When making a table of values, use both negative and positive values for $x$. Keep these graphs, because you will need them in the next section.
   a. $y = x(12 - x)$
   b. $y = x(12 - 2x)$
   c. $y = x(12 - 3x)$
   d. $y = x(12 - 4x)$

9. For each graph,
   a. label the graph with its equation;
   b. label the $x$-intercepts;
   c. label the vertex.

10. ⚷ Write a brief description comparing the four graphs. Describe how the graphs are the same and how they are different.

**11.** 💡 Without graphing, guess the vertex on the graph of $y = x(12 - 6x)$. Explain how you arrived at your guess.

### DIFFERENT FORMS

As you learned in Lesson 1 the equations of parabolas through the origin can be written in the form $y = ax(x - q)$.

**12.** For each parabola described in (a-d), find a function of the form $y = ax(x - q)$:

a. $x$-intercepts: 0 and 12, vertex: (6, 36)

b. $x$-intercepts: 0 and 6, vertex: (3, 18)

c. $x$-intercepts: 0 and 4, vertex: (2, 12)

d. $x$-intercepts: 0 and 3, vertex: (1.5, 9)

**13.** ⚷ How are the intercepts and the vertex related to the values of $a$ and $q$ in the equation $y = ax(x - q)$?

The equations in problems 8 and 12 have the same graphs. You can verify this by checking that they have the same vertices and intercepts, and in fact that for any $x$ they yield the same $y$. In other words, the equations are equivalent. We can use the distributive law to confirm this. For example, for problem 8a:

$$y = x(12 - x) = 12x - x^2$$

And for problem 12a:

$$y = -x(x - 12) = -x^2 + 12x$$

**14.** Show that the other three pairs of equations in problems 8b-d and 12b-d are equivalent.

It is possible to convert equations like the ones in problem 8 to the form $y = ax(x - q)$ by factoring. For example:

$$x(24 - 6x) = 6x(4 - x) = -6x(x - 4)$$

**15.** Fill in the blanks:

a. $x(24 - 2x) = 2x(_____)$

b. $x(24 - 3x) = -3x(_____)$

c. $x(24 - 4x) = \_\_\_(x - 6)$

**16.** Write in the form $y = ax(x - q)$ and find the vertex and the intercepts.

a. $y = x(12 - 6x)$

b. $y = x(50 - 5x)$

c. 💡 $y = x(50 - 3x)$

d. 💡 $y = x(50 - (n + 1)x)$

### MAXIMIZING AREA

**17.** If you have to use part of the 50 feet of fencing for a partition to divide the pen into two equal parts, what is the largest total area you can get for the enclosure? Explain how you got your answer, including a sketch and graph if necessary.

**18.** Solve problem 17 if you want to divide the pen into three equal parts.

**19.** 💡 Solve problem 17 if you want to divide the pen into $n$ equal parts.

**20.** Look at your solutions for problems 17, 18, and 19. In each case look at the shapes of the subdivisions of the pen having the largest area. Are they always squares? Are they ever squares? Does the answer to this depend on the value of $n$? Explain.

**21.** Look at your solutions for problems 17, 18, and 19. In each case look at how much of the fencing was used to construct the side parallel to the garage for the pen having maximum area. What fraction of the fencing was used to construct this side? Does the answer depend on the value of $n$? Explain.

**22.** Report Imagine you are the representative of a fencing company presenting information to a customer. Write a complete illustrated report, making clear who the customer is and what the pens are needed for. Explain how to maximize the area of the pens for a given amount of fencing. Discuss both divided and undivided pens.

# 13.3 The Zero Product Property

**You will need:**

graph paper

or a graphing calculator
(optional)

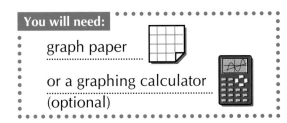

1. Given that you have 50 feet of fencing and that you can use the wall of the garage for the fourth side of your pen, what dimensions should you choose to make a rectangular pen having area 200 square feet? Solve by trial and error or by graphing. (There is more than one solution.)

This problem can be solved by writing the equation $x(50 - 2x) = 200$, where $x$ is the distance from the wall to the side opposite it. One way of doing it is to find the intersection of the graphs of $y = x(50 - 2x)$ and $y = 200$.

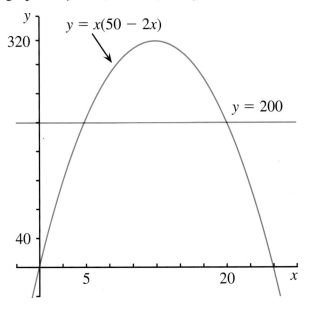

2. Use this method to find the dimensions for the following areas:
   a. 300          b. 250

Another method of solving this kind of problem is to write a quadratic equation and factor it, as explained in the following sections.

### ZERO PRODUCTS

3. 🔑 If $ab = 0$, which of the following is impossible? Explain.
   a. $a \neq 0$ and $b \neq 0$
   b. $a \neq 0$ and $b = 0$
   c. $a = 0$ and $b \neq 0$
   d. $a = 0$ and $b = 0$

**Zero Product Property:** When the product of two quantities is zero, one or the other quantity must be zero.

An equation like $(x + 6)(2x - 1) = 0$ can be solved using the zero product property. Since the product in the equation is zero, you can write these two equations.

$$x + 6 = 0 \quad \text{or} \quad 2x - 1 = 0$$

4. You know how to solve these equations. Write the solutions.

5. There are two solutions to the equation $(x + 6)(2x - 1) = 0$. What are they?

Solve these equations.

6. $(3x + 1)x = 0$

7. $(2x + 3)(5 - x) = 0$

8. $(2x - 2)(3x - 1) = 0$

## SOLVING QUADRATIC EQUATIONS

Some quadratic equations can be solved using the zero product property.

> **Example:** Find the values of $x$ for which
> $$x^2 + 6x = -5.$$
> First rewrite the equation so you can apply the zero product property.
> $$x^2 + 6x + 5 = 0$$
> In factored form, this is written:
> $$(x + 5)(x + 1) = 0.$$
>
> Since the product is 0, at least one of the factors must be 0. So $x + 5 = 0$ or $x + 1 = 0$.

**9.** What are the two solutions of the equation $(x + 5)(x + 1) = 0$?

> **Example:**
> Find the values of $x$ for which $6x^2 = 12x$.
> First rewrite the equation so that you can apply the zero product property.
> $$6x^2 - 12x = 0$$
> In factored form, this is written:
> $$6x(x - 2) = 0.$$

**10.** What are the two solutions to the equation $6x(x - 2) = 0$?

**11.** Factor and use the zero product property to solve these quadratic equations.
  a. $x^2 - x = 2$
  b. $2L^2 - L = 3$
  c. $W^2 + 10W + 16 = 0$
  d. $3M^2 + 30M + 48 = 0$

To solve problem 2a, write the equation:
$$x(50 - 2x) = 300$$
$$-2x^2 + 50x - 300 = 0$$
$$2x^2 - 50x + 300 = 0$$
$$x^2 - 25x + 150 = 0$$

**12.** Explain the four steps.

**13.** Factor the final equation and use the zero product property to solve it.

Unfortunately, most quadratic equations cannot easily be solved by factoring. In the next chapter you will learn a way that always works to solve quadratic equations.

## SYMMETRY

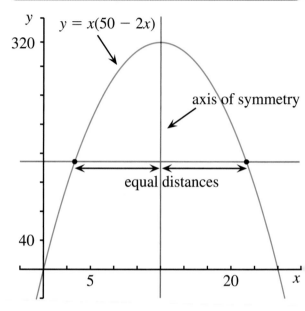

The vertical line through the vertex of a parabola is called its *axis of symmetry*.

**14.** How far is each $x$-intercept from the axis of symmetry in the preceding graph?

The $x$-intercepts are *equidistant* from the axis of symmetry. (They are at an equal distance from it.) As you can see in the figure, this is also true of any pair of points of the parabola that lie on the same horizontal line as each other.

**15.** Refer to the graph for problem 1.
  a. Show that the two solutions to problem 1 are equidistant from the axis of symmetry.
  b. Is this also true of the two solutions to problem 2a? What about problem 2b? Show your work.

### VERTEX AND INTERCEPTS

In an equation like $y = 2(x + 3)(x - 4)$, you can quickly find the intercepts and the vertex.

**16.** What is the value of $x$ at the $y$-intercept? Substitute this value for $x$ in the equation and find the $y$-intercept.

**17.** What is the value of $y$ at the $x$-intercepts? Substitute this value for $y$ in the equation and find the $x$-intercepts with the help of the zero product property.

**18.** If you know the $x$-intercepts, how can you find the $x$-coordinate of the vertex? Find it.

**19.** If you know the $x$-coordinate of the vertex, how can you find its $y$-coordinate? Find it.

**20.** Find the intercepts and vertex for:
a. $y = 0.5(x - 0.4)(x - 1)$
b. $y = 2(x + 3)(x + 4)$

**21.** ⚷ Explain how you would find the intercepts and vertex for a function of the form
$$y = a(x - p)(x - q).$$

**22.** Find the equation and the vertex for a parabola having the following intercepts:
a. $(3, 0)$, $(6, 0)$, $(0, 36)$
b. $(3, 0)$, $(6, 0)$, $(0, 9)$
c. $(-3, 0)$, $(-6, 0)$, $(0, -9)$
d. $(-3, 0)$, $(6, 0)$, $(0, 6)$

**23.** The vertex and one of the two $x$-intercepts of parabolas are given. Find the equation and the $y$-intercept.
a. vertex: $(2, -2)$; $x$-intercept: $(1, 0)$
b. vertex: $(1, -12)$; $x$-intercept: $(-1, 0)$
c. vertex: $(3, 4.5)$; $x$-intercept: $(6, 0)$

### DISCOVERY  TWO DEFINITIONS

**Definition:** The absolute value of a number is the distance between that number and zero.

Browsing through Ginger's calculus book, Mary and Martin noticed this definition:

**Definition:** $|x| = \begin{cases} x \text{ for } x > 0 \\ -x \text{ for } x < 0 \end{cases}$

"That $-x$ must be a misprint," Mary commented. "Absolute value can't be negative."

**24.** Report Write a letter to Mary explaining everything you know about absolute value. Restate the two definitions presented above in your own words. Using examples, explain why they are equivalent, and why Mary was wrong about the misprint.

# Rectangular Pens: Constant Area

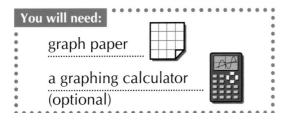

**You will need:**

graph paper

a graphing calculator
(optional)

1. **Exploration** You bought 45 square feet of artificial turf for the floor of Stripe's back-yard. You can cut it up any way you like, but you want to use all of it. Since you're almost broke (artificial turf is expensive) you would like to spend as little money as possible on fencing. What's the least amount of fencing you could buy and still make a rectangular pen that surrounded the artificial turf on all four sides? Find out by trying various dimensions for the pen.

## WIDTH AS A FUNCTION OF LENGTH

Suppose you want to make a rectangular pen having area 36.

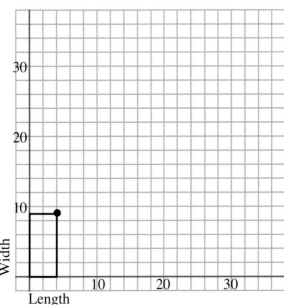

2. a. On graph paper draw a pair of axes and show five rectangular pens that would have an area of 36 square feet. The lower left corner should be at the origin. An example is shown in the figure.

   b. Mark with a • the upper right corner of each rectangle you drew. Then write in the coordinates of each of these points.

   c. Connect the •s. Do they lie in a straight line or on a curve? Describe any patterns you notice.

3. Make a table showing some of the coordinates on your graph. Look for a pattern in your coordinates and make three more entries in the table.

4. ⚷ Write an algebraic equation that expresses the width as a function of the length.

5. ⚷
   a. Would it be possible to have a pen having length greater than 30? 32? 36? Explain your answers, giving examples.

   b. Explain why your graph will never touch the x-axis or the y-axis.

   c. If you increase the length by one foot, does the width increase or decrease? Does it change by the same amount each time? Explain.

## PERIMETER LINES

In the previous section you probably noticed that the perimeter of the rectangles changed even though the area remained constant. In this section you will investigate how the perimeter varies as a function of length if you keep the area constant.

**6.** Write the perimeter of the corresponding rectangle next to each • you marked on the graph. Look for patterns.

Your graph should show pairs of points that correspond to the same perimeter. For example, (3, 12) and (12, 3) both correspond to the perimeter 30.

**7.** Connect (3, 12) and (12, 3) to each other by a straight line. Extend it to its intercepts. Interpret the intercepts in terms of this problem.

**8.** On your graph find two points that both correspond to a perimeter of 26. Repeat problem 7 for these points. Then find other pairs of points that both correspond to the same perimeter and repeat problem 7 for each of these pairs. What patterns do you see?

**9.** Use the graph to estimate the dimensions of a rectangle having area 36 and perimeter 36.

### PERIMETER AS A FUNCTION OF LENGTH

**10.** Make a graph of perimeter as a function of length. Show length on the $x$-axis and perimeter on the $y$-axis. Connect the points on your graph with a smooth curve. Describe the shape of the curve.

**11.** Label the lowest point on your graph with its coordinates. Interpret these two numbers in terms of the problem.

**Note:** The graph is *not* a parabola, and its lowest point is *not* called a *vertex*.

**12.** Explain why your graph will never touch the $x$-axis or $y$-axis.

**13.** If you increase the length by one foot, what happens to the perimeter? Can you tell whether it will increase or decrease? Does it increase or decrease by the same amount each time? Explain.

**14.** Summary
  a. For a fixed area of 36 square feet, explain in words how you would find the perimeter of the rectangular pen if you were given the length.
  b. If the area of a rectangular pen is 36 and its length is $L$, write an algebraic expression for its perimeter.
  c. If you had to enclose a rectangular area of 36 square feet and wanted to use the least amount of fencing, what would the length, width, and perimeter be? Explain.

### Generalizations

**15.** If the area of a rectangular pen is $A$ and its length is $L$,
  a. write an algebraic expression for its width in terms of $A$ and $L$;
  b. write an algebraic expression for its perimeter in terms of $A$ and $L$.

**16.** Explain how to find the length that gives the minimum perimeter. Write an algebraic expression for it in terms of $A$ only.

### NUMBER PUZZLES

**17.** Find two numbers $x$ and $y$ whose product is 75 and whose sum is 20. Explain your method.

**18.** Graph the equations $xy = 75$ and $x + y = 20$ on the same pair of axes. Find their point of intersection. How is this point related to your answer to problem 17?

**19.** Find two numbers whose product is 75 and whose sum is 23.75.

**20.** ⟸ If two numbers have a product of 75, what is the smallest value their sum could take? What is the largest? Explain.

# 13.A Business Applications

## MAXIMUM PROFIT

The Widget Company was trying to sell a widget for $24, but no one was buying. They decided to try to attract customers by reducing their prices. They found that for every $1 they lowered the price, they attracted ten customers.

| Price Reduction | Price | # of Customers | Gross Profit |
|---|---|---|---|
| $0 | $24 | 0 | $0 |
| $1 | $23 | 10 | $230 |
| $2 | $22 | 20 | $440 |

1.  a. Copy and extend the table for at least eight possible price reductions.
    b. If the price is $14, how many people will buy a widget? What will the gross profit be?
    c. If the price is lowered by $x$, how many people will buy a widget? What will the gross profit be?
    d. Make a graph showing how the gross profit depends on the price reduction. Put the price reduction on the $x$-axis and the profit on the $y$-axis.
    e. Interpret your graph. What price gives the most profit? Explain.
    f. Write an equation for your graph.

The Widget Company was trying to sell an item for $P$ dollars, and no one was buying it. They found that for every $1 they lower the price, they gain $C$ customers.

2.  If they lower the cost by $x$ and the gross profit is $y$, write an equation for $y$ in terms of $x$.

3.  Write an algebraic expression for:
    a. the amount by which the price should be reduced in order to maximize the profit;
    b. the maximum profit possible.

## MINIMUM COST

The Widget Company would like to ship 2000 widgets. They must be packaged in boxes of equal weight. (Each widget weighs one pound.) The L.A. Barge Company charges a basic rate of $100 per box for shipping. It also adds a surcharge to the total cost of the shipment that depends on the weight of the individual boxes, at the rate of $1 per pound.

> **Example:** If the widgets are packed in 10 boxes, each will weigh 200 lbs.
>
> | _Basic charge_ | _Surcharge_ | _Total_ |
> |---|---|---|
> | 10 boxes · $100 per box | $200 | $1200 |

4.  Explain, using examples of possible ways to package the 2000 widgets, how the L.A. Barge Company's policy guarantees that customers will not ship their goods in too many boxes, or in boxes that are too heavy.

5.  Write an algebraic expression for the cost of shipping the 2000 widgets, in terms of the number of boxes.

6.  What is the number of boxes that would be the cheapest way to ship the widgets? Explain how you get your answer. (Hint: You may use trial and error or graphing.)

7.  Using the cheapest way, how much does it cost per widget?

8.  Report Imagine you work for the Widget Company. Prepare an illustrated report to other employees about:
    a. the pricing of widgets and how to maximize profits, and
    b. the shipping of widgets and how to minimize cost.

# Packing and Mailing

**You will need:**

graph paper

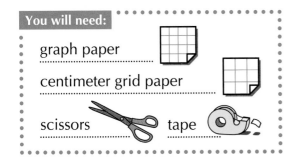

centimeter grid paper

scissors    tape

---

### MAXIMIZING VOLUME

You can make cardboard trays to hold 1-cm$^3$ cubes. Start with an 18-cm-by-18-cm piece of grid paper. Cut a square out of each corner and fold up the sides to form a tray.

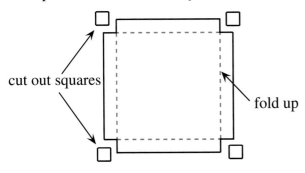

cut out squares

fold up

---

1. **Exploration** Work with other students to make as many different trays as you can by cutting square corners out of an 18-cm-by-18-cm piece of paper or cardboard. Figure out which tray holds the most cubes.

---

2. Make a table showing the side of the square corner that was cut out, the area of the base, and the number of cubes the tray would hold. (For example, if a 2-by-2 square is cut out at each corner, the area of the base should be 196 cm$^2$, and the tray should hold 392 cubes.)

3. 🔑 If the side of the square cut out of the corner is $x$,
   a. what is the area of the base?
   b. what is the volume of the tray?

4. Make a graph of the volume of the tray as a function of $x$. Include some fractional values of $x$.

5. What is the height of the tray that will give the maximum volume?

6. What are the $x$-intercepts of the graph? Interpret them in terms of this problem.

7. Draw a vertical line through the highest point on the graph. Are the $x$-intercepts equidistant from it?

8. Extend the graph in both directions by using a few more values for $x$ beyond the $x$-intercepts.

9. 🔑 Explain why the points you added in problem 8 do not represent the tray problem.

10. 🔑 Is the graph a parabola? Explain, giving as many reasons as you can for your answer.

---

11. **Generalization** Find the height which would give the maximum volume if the initial piece of paper had the following dimensions. You may want to use tables of values.
    a. 12 by 12        b. *S* by *S*

---

*13.5  Packing and Mailing*                                                   **469** ▲

## STORING CUBES

Suppose you want to make a cardboard tray for storing 100 centimeter cubes. The base does not have to be square.

12. **Exploration** What should the dimensions of the tray be so it will contain the least cardboard? Explain.

13. Repeat problem 12 for:
    a. 50 cubes;  b. 200 cubes;
    c. 500 cubes;  d. 1000 cubes.

14. **Project** Write an illustrated report explaining a strategy for solving this problem for *N* cubes.

## POSTAL REGULATIONS

The U.S. Postal Service will not mail by Priority Mail™ anything that weighs more than 70 pounds or exceeds 108 inches in combined length and girth. (The girth is the distance around, as shown in the figure.)

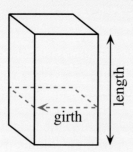

15. **Exploration** Find the dimensions for a box that would satisfy the Priority Mail™ requirements and would hold as large a volume as possible.

16. Suppose you want to mail a box full of 20-inch-long dowels. What are the dimensions of the rectangular box having the largest volume that would satisfy postal regulations and would accommodate the dowels?

17. Repeat problem 16, this time for 12-inch-long dowels.

18. **Project** A lumber company needs to pack dowels in boxes that can be sent by Priority Mail™. Boxes need to be designed to ship dowels of each length. Explain, with examples, how to find dimensions for such boxes that will allow the packing of the maximum number of dowels.

19. 💡 A shipping company has the following rules:
    • maximum length: 108 inches
    • maximum length plus girth: 130 inches
    In addition, they recommend two inches cushioning on all sides for fragile items. What is the largest volume possible for the contents of the package in the case of fragile items?

# Solving with Squares

In this chapter you have used quadratic functions to solve problems involving finding a maximum area. In the next chapter you will be faced with problems for which it will be useful to solve quadratic equations. In this lesson we start to prepare for this.

## EQUAL SQUARES

In Chapter 7, Lesson 7, you solved quadratic equations using the equal squares method. Some problems are easy to solve this way. For example,

$$x^2 - 10x + 25 = 16$$

can be written

$$(x - 5)^2 = 4^2$$

with a perfect square on each side.

1. Solve this equation. (Remember: There are two solutions.)

It is not necessary for the number on the right to be a perfect square, since you can take the square root of any nonnegative number.

**Example:**
$$x^2 - 10x + 25 = 7$$
$$(x - 5)^2 = 7$$
$$x - 5 = \sqrt{7} \text{ OR } x - 5 = -\sqrt{7}$$
$$x = 5 + \sqrt{7} \text{ OR } x = 5 - \sqrt{7}$$

Using your calculator, you can find decimal approximations for the two solutions:

$$x \approx 7.646 \text{ or } x \approx 2.354.$$

Solve these equations using the equal squares method. First give exact answers (using radicals if necessary); then find decimal approximations. Not all are possible.

2. $x^2 - 10x + 25 = 8$

3. $y^2 + 6x + 9 = 15$

4. $x^2 - 24x + 144 = 12$

5. $4r^2 - 4r + 1 = 6$

6. $9s^2 + 12s + 4 = 21$

7. $y^2 - 14y - 49 = -20$

## COMPLETING THE SQUARE

In this section you will learn how to turn certain quadratic equations into equal squares equations that you know how to solve.

8. Write the equation shown by this figure.

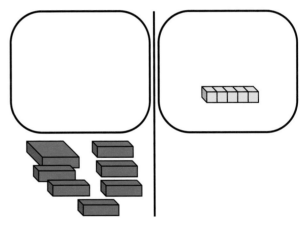

We will add the same quantity to both sides, so that the left side is a perfect square. This is called *completing the square*.

9. a. What number was added to both sides of the figure on the next page to make the left side a perfect square?

   b. Write the resulting equation.

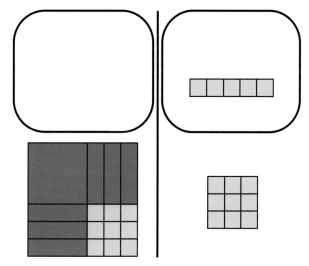

**10.** The right side can be simplified. The resulting equation is shown in the next figure. Write and solve this equation using the equal squares method. You should get two solutions.

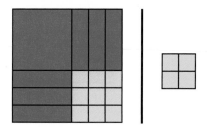

Complete the square to solve these equations. You will need to rearrange blocks and add or subtract the same amount on both sides in order to get equal squares.

**11.** $x^2 + 2x - 3 = 0$ **12.** $x^2 + 12x = -11$

**13.** $x^2 + 4x = 0$ **14.** $x^2 + 10x - 6 = 5$

**15.** $x^2 + 8x = 20$ **16.** $x^2 + 6x + 9 = 25$

**17.** Generalization Explain how to figure out what number to add to both sides of an equation of the form $x^2 + bx = k$ in order to get an equal squares equation. Use sketches and examples.

---

### SQUARE PRACTICE

Solve these equations by completing the square. Show all your work. Include a sketch showing the equal squares.

**18.** $x^2 + 8x = 33$ **19.** $x^2 + 4x = 96$

**20.** $x^2 + 6x = 55$ **21.** $x^2 + 10x = 56$

Solve these equations. Show your work.

**22.** $x^2 - 8x = 33$ **23.** $x^2 - 4x = 96$

**24.** $x^2 - 4x = -96$ **25.** $x^2 + x = 6$

Solve these equations. Show your work. Give exact answers, then find decimal approximations to the nearest hundredth.

**26.** $x^2 - 8x + 3 = 0$ **27.** $x^2 - 5x - 8 = 0$

**28.** $x^2 - 4x + 1 = 6$ **29.** $x^2 - 7x - 4 = 0$

### QUADRATIC EQUATIONS CHECKPOINT

Solve two of these equations by factoring (and the zero product property), and two by completing the square.

**30.** $x^2 + 18x = 0$ **31.** $x^2 + 5x = 2.75$

**32.** $x^2 + 2x - 8 = 0$ **33.** $x^2 + 7x + 12 = 0$

While it is somewhat cumbersome, completing the square is an important technique when dealing with quadratic expressions. Unlike factoring, you can use it to solve any quadratic equation. In addition, we will use completing the square repeatedly to get more understanding of quadratic functions and to develop more efficient ways to solve quadratic equations.

**34.** Find a quadratic equation having solutions 5 and -2.

**35.** 💡 Find a quadratic equation having solutions $2 + \sqrt{5}$ and $2 - \sqrt{5}$.

**36.** Multiply. $(x - (4 + \sqrt{3}))(x - (4 - \sqrt{3}))$ (Hint: Carefully remove the inside parentheses and then set up a three-by-three multiplication table.)

**37.** You should have obtained a quadratic expression in problem 36. Set it equal to zero, and solve the equation.

# LESSON 13.7 Finding the Vertex

**You will need:**

graph paper

graphing calculator
(optional)

In this lesson you will learn how to find the vertex of graphs of quadratic functions. This will help you solve quadratic equations.

## TRANSLATING A PARABOLA

Graph these functions on the same pair of axes. Use graph paper, even if you have a graphing calculator. For each one:

a. Graph the parabola.

b. Indicate the axis of symmetry with a dotted line, and label it with its equation.

c. Label the vertex with its coordinates.

**1.** $y = x^2 - 5$

**2.** $y = x^2 - 4x + 4$

**3.** $y = x^2 - 4x - 1$

> **Definition:** The graphs obtained by shifting the location of a given graph without changing its shape are called *translations* of the original graph.

The graphs you drew in problems 1 through 3 are all translations of the graph of $y = x^2$.

**4.** Which of the graphs you drew in problems 1 through 3 was obtained by shifting $y = x^2$

    a. horizontally?  b. vertically?

    c. both horizontally and vertically?

## VERTEX FORM

The vertex of the graph of $y = x^2$ is $(0, 0)$.
When the graph is shifted, the vertex is $(H, V)$.

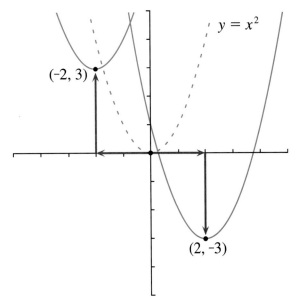

$y = x^2$

$(-2, 3)$

$(2, -3)$

• If $V$ is positive, the parabola $y = x^2$ has been shifted up; if $V$ is negative, it has been shifted down.

• If $H$ is positive, the parabola $y = x^2$ has been shifted to the right; if $H$ is negative, it has been shifted to the left.

The graph of each function below is a translation of $y = x^2$. For each function:

a. Make a rough sketch of the graph.

b. Show the translation with arrows, as in the preceding figure.

c. Label the vertex with its coordinates.

(If you have a graphing calculator, use it for these problems. However, you should record the graphs with sketches on graph paper.)

**5.** $y = x^2 + 4$

**6.** $y = (x - 6)^2 - 4$

**7.** $y = (x + 6)^2 - 4$

**8.** $y = (x + 6)^2 + 4$

**9.** $y = (x - 6)^2$

**10.** $y = (x - 6)^2 + 4$

**11.** Write the equation of a parabola that is a translation of $y = x^2$ and has
   a. a vertical distance of 8 and a horizontal distance of -3 ($H = -3$, and $V = 8$);
   b. a vertical distance of -4 and a horizontal distance of 5;
   c. 6 units to the left and 5 units down;
   d. 3 units to the right.

Earlier in this chapter you looked at equations of parabolas having the form $y = a(x - p)(x - q)$. That form was convenient for finding $x$-intercepts.

**12.** 🔑 Explain why the equations in problems 5-10 are in a form that makes it convenient to find the vertex by just looking at the equation.

The quadratic function $y = (x - H)^2 + V$ is said to be in *vertex form*.

**13.** 🔑 Explain why the $H$ in the vertex form equation is preceded by a minus, while the $V$ is preceded by a plus.

**14.** 🔑 The graph of $y = x^2$ meets the $x$-axis in one point. Give examples of translations of $y = x^2$ that meet the $x$-axis in the given number of points. Include explanations of how you chose different values of $H$ and/or $V$.
   a. 0 points        b. 1 point
   c. 2 points

### SITTING ON THE x-AXIS

The quadratic function $y = x^2 + bx + c$ is said to be in *standard form*.

For problems 15-21, consider these five equations:

$$y = x^2 + 6x \qquad y = x^2 + 6x + 5$$
$$y = x^2 + 6x + 8 \qquad y = x^2 + 6x + 9$$
$$y = x^2 + 6x + 12$$

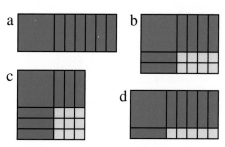

**15.** Match each Lab Gear figure with an equation from the list of five.

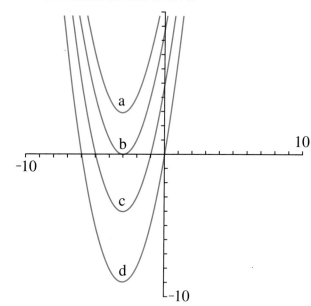

**16.** Match each parabola with an equation from the list of five.

**17.** 🔑 Explain how to identify the parabolas with the help of:
   a. the $y$-intercepts;
   b. the Lab Gear figures, combined with the $x$-intercepts and the zero product property.

**18.** 🔑 Explain why the graphs of perfect square quadratic equations have their vertices on the $x$-axis. (Hint: What is $V$?)

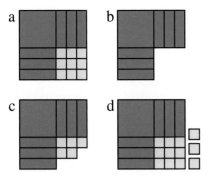

a   b

c   d

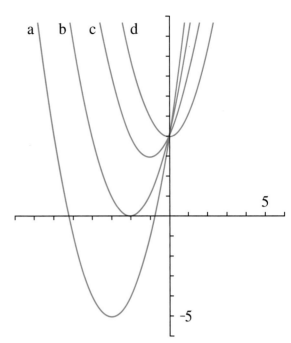

a  b  c  d

5

-5

**19.** Match each Lab Gear figure with the corresponding equation from the five given earlier.

**20.** Find *V* for each equation of the five.

**21.** ⊶ Explain how you can find *V*,
a. by looking at the Lab Gear figure;
b. by looking at the equation.

## STRADDLING THE *y*-AXIS

For problems 22-27, consider these four equations:

$$y = x^2 + 4 \qquad y = x^2 + 2x + 4$$
$$y = x^2 + 4x + 4 \qquad y = x^2 + 6x + 4$$

a     b

c     d

**22.** Match each Lab Gear figure with the corresponding equation from the four.

**23.** Match each equation with the correct graph.

**24.** ⊶ Explain why the graphs of equations of the form $y = x^2 + c$ have their vertex on the *y*-axis. (Hint: What is *H*?)

**25.** Find *H* for each equation in the list of four.

**26.** ⊶ Explain how you can find *H*,
a. by looking at the Lab Gear figure;
b. by looking at the equation.

**27.** a. What is *H* for any graph of an equation of the form $y = x^2 + 16x + c$?
b. What is *H* for any graph of an equation of the form $y = x^2 - 16x + c$?

**28.** Generalization Explain why, for graphs of equations in the form $y = x^2 + bx + c$, $H = -(b/2)$.

**29.** Report Write an illustrated report explaining how to find the vertex of a parabola if the equation is in:
a. the form $y = (x - p)(x - q)$;
b. vertex form;    c. standard form.

# Quadratic Equations: $x^2 + bx + c = 0$

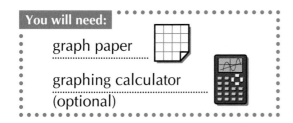

You will need:

graph paper

graphing calculator
(optional)

## FINDING THE x-INTERCEPTS

Earlier in this chapter you learned how to find the vertex after finding the x-intercepts. In this section you will learn how to find the x-intercepts after finding the vertex.

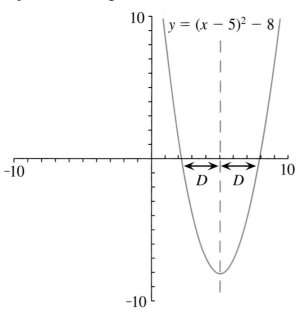

$y = (x - 5)^2 - 8$

1. **Exploration** As the figure shows, the x-intercepts are equidistant from the axis of symmetry. How can you tell how far they are from it? That distance is indicated by D on the figure. Is it possible to know the value of D by looking at the equation? Try several values for H and V in equations having the form $y = (x - H)^2 + V$. Look for a pattern.

The graph of each of the following quadratic functions is a translation of $y = x^2$. For each function:

  a. Make a rough sketch of the graph. Draw and label the axis of symmetry.

  b. Find H and V.

  c. Find exact values, not approximations, for the x-intercepts. (Set $y = 0$ and use the equal squares method.)

  d. Find D, the distance of each x-intercept from the line of symmetry.

2. $y = x^2 - 9$      3. $y = (x - 5)^2 - 9$

4. $y = (x - 9)^2 - 5$      5. $y = (x + 9)^2 - 5$

6. $y = (x + 9)^2 + 5$      7. $y = (x - 9)^2$

8. 🔑 Use patterns in problems 2-7 to explain how D and V are related.

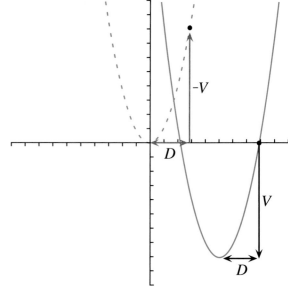

This figure shows D and V on a parabola that was translated from $y = x^2$. In this example, V was a negative number, and the translation was in a downward direction. The arrows representing D and V are also shown on the original parabola. (On $y = x^2$, the direction of the arrow for $V$ was reversed. What is shown is actually the opposite of $V$. This is indicated by the label $-V$. Since V is negative, $-V$ is positive.)

9. 🔑 Use the figure to explain why $-V = D^2$, and therefore $D = \sqrt{-V}$.

10. Summary Explain why the $x$-intercepts, when they exist, are equal to $H - \sqrt{-V}$ and $H + \sqrt{-V}$. ∎

### SOLVING QUADRATIC EQUATIONS

One way to solve the equation $x^2 + bx + c = 0$ is to find the $x$-intercepts of $y = x^2 + bx + c$. You can use a graphing calculator to find an approximate answer that way. For a precise answer, you can use what you learned in the previous section about how to find the $x$-intercepts from the vertex.

∎ **Example:** Solve $x^2 + 4x + 1 = 0$.

The solutions to the equation are the $x$-intercepts of $y = x^2 + 4x + 1$. We have shown that they are equal to $H - \sqrt{-V}$ and $H + \sqrt{-V}$. So all we have to do is find the values of $H$ and $V$. There are two ways to do that, outlined as follows:

*First method:* Find $H$ and $V$ by rewriting the equation $y = x^2 + 4x + 1$ into vertex form. This can be done by completing the square.

$$y = x^2 + 4x + 1 = \text{(a perfect square)} - ?$$
$$y = x^2 + 4x + 1 = (x^2 + 4x + \ldots) - ?$$
$$y = x^2 + 4x + 1 = (x^2 + 4x + 4) - 3$$

11. a. Explain the algebraic steps in the three preceding equations.
    b. Write $y = x^2 + 4x + 1$ in vertex form.
    c. Give the coordinates of the vertex.

*Second method:* Find $H$ and $V$ by first remembering that $H = -(b/2)$. In this case, $b = 4$, so $H = -(4/2) = -2$. H is the $x$-coordinate of the

vertex. Since the vertex is on the parabola, we can find its $y$-coordinate, $V$, by substituting -2 into the equation.

12. a. Find $V$. Check that it is the same value you found in problem 11.
    b. Now that you have $H$ and $V$, solve the equation.

13. 🔑 What are the advantages and the disadvantages of each method? Explain.

For each equation, find $H$ and $V$ for the corresponding function. Then solve the equations. There may be zero, one, or two solutions.

14. $y = x^2 + 6x - 9$    15. $y = x^2 - 6x + 9$

16. $y = x^2 - 6x - 9$    17. $y = x^2 + 6x + 12$

18. 🔑 How does the value of $V$ for the corresponding function affect the number of solutions? Explain.

### QUADRATIC EQUATIONS CHECKPOINT

As of now you know five methods to solve quadratic equations in the form $x^2 + bx + c = 0$. They are listed below.

I.  *On Graphing Calculators:* Approximate solutions can be found by looking for the $x$-intercepts of $y = x^2 + bx + c$.

II. *Factoring* and the zero product property can sometimes be used.

III. *Equal Squares:* First complete the square, then use the equal squares method.

IV. *Using Vertex Form:* Complete the square to get into vertex form, then use the fact that the solutions are equal to $H - \sqrt{-V}$ and $H + \sqrt{-V}$.

V.  *Using the Vertex:* Remember that for the function $y = x^2 + bx + c$, $H = -b/2$. Substitute into the equation to find $V$. Then use the fact that the solutions are $H - \sqrt{-V}$ and $H + \sqrt{-V}$.

**Caution:** In the next chapter you will learn another way to solve quadratic equations in the more general form $ax^2 + bx + c = 0$. Meanwhile you can solve them by dividing every term by $a$.

**Example:** Find an exact solution for:
$$x^2 - 6x + 2 = 0.$$

This does not seem to factor easily, which rules out Method II, and an exact solution is required, which rules out Method I. Luckily, Methods III-V always work on problems of this type. Using Method III:

$$x^2 - 6x + 2 = 0$$
$$(x^2 - 6x + 9) - 7 = 0$$
$$(x - 3)^2 - 7 = 0$$
$$(x - 3)^2 = 7$$

So $x - 3 = \sqrt{7}$ or $x - 3 = -\sqrt{7}$, and the solutions are $3 + \sqrt{7}$ and $3 - \sqrt{7}$.

19. Solve the same equation with Method IV or V. Check that you get the same answer.

Solve these equations. Use each of Methods II-V at least once. Give exact answers. The equations may have zero, one, or two solutions.

20. $x^2 - 4x + 2 = 0$

21. $x^2 + 8x - 20 = 0$

22. $x^2 - 14x + 49 = 0$

23. $x^2 - 16x + 17 = 0$

24. $x^2 + 9x = 0$

25. $x^2 + 9 = 0$

You have 40 square feet of artificial turf and 28 feet of fencing. Is it possible to use all your materials to build a rectangular pen?

1. Find the dimensions of a rectangle having area 40 and perimeter 28. (Hint: You may use trial and error, tables, or graphs.)

Problems like this one can be solved using algebra. The first step is to write some equations.

$$\begin{cases} LW = 40 \\ 2L + 2W = 28 \end{cases}$$

2. Explain how these equations express the given conditions for the pen.

3. Divide all the terms in the second equation by two, to make it simpler.

4. Use algebra to show how the equations can be combined into one of the following equations having just one variable:
   a. $L(14 - L) = 40$, or
   b. $L + \dfrac{40}{L} = 14$

5. Explain the following steps to transform the equation in problem 4b:

$$L + \frac{40}{L} = 14$$
$$L^2 + 40 = 14L$$
$$L^2 - 14L + 40 = 0$$

6. a. Use algebra to transform the equation in problem 4a into the same equation.
   b. Solve the equation.

7. a. The perimeter of a rectangle is 50. Write the area in terms of the length.
   b. The area of a rectangle is 60. Write the perimeter in terms of the width.

For each problem, 8-11, find the dimensions of the rectangle. Show your work and explain your method. Include a sketch labeled with the variables you use.

8. A rectangle has area 180 and perimeter 64.

9. A rectangle has area 126. The length is 25 more than the width.

10. A rectangle has perimeter 35, and its length is 4 times its width.

11. A rectangle has area 25, and its length is 4 times its width.

12. **Report** Hyru has 40 square feet of artificial turf. Valerie has 40 feet of fencing. They decide to use all their materials to build a rectangular pen. Write them a letter explaining as many methods as possible for finding appropriate dimensions for such a pen.

# ◆ Essential Ideas

## PERIMETER AND AREA

1. A rectangle has width $2x + 5$ and length $3x + 1$. What is the area, when the perimeter is 30?

2. The width of a rectangle is five less than the length. Write a formula for:
   a. the length in terms of the width;
   b. the width in terms of the length;
   c. the area in terms of the width;
   d. the perimeter in terms of the length.

3. The perimeter of a rectangle is 50.
   a. Find the dimensions that will give an area of 46.
   b. Find the dimensions that will give the largest possible area.

4. The circumference of a circle is 50. What is the area? (Hint: First find the radius.) Is it bigger or smaller than the area of the largest possible rectangle having perimeter 50?

5. ○
   a. Find the dimensions and the area of the largest possible rectangle that can be made with $P$ feet of fencing.
   b. Find the area of the circle that is surrounded by $P$ feet of fencing. (Hint: Start by expressing the radius in terms of $P$.)
   c. Which has greater area, the rectangle or the circle? Explain.

## FARES

6. A bus company takes people from a small town to and from a large city where they work. The fare is $4.00 per day, round trip. The company wants to raise its fare and has done a survey to find out if this will cause people to stop riding the bus. They estimate that for every 50 cents that they raise the fare, they will lose approximately 1000 customers. They now have 14,000 customers. Do you think they should raise their fare? If so, by how much? Explain.

7. A spaceship company charges its customers a basic fare of $50 million per light year for trips outside the solar system. However, to encourage long trips, it reduces the fare by $1 million for every light year a customer travels. For example, if a tourist travels five light years, her fare is reduced by $5 million. Her cost will be $45 million per light year for five light years, or $225 million. What is the most a person could ever pay for a trip on this spaceship? Explain.

## PARABOLAS AND INTERCEPTS

8. Which graphs have the same $x$-intercepts? Explain.
   a. $y = x(8 - x)$      b. $y = 2x(8 - x)$
   c. $y = x(2 - x)$      d. $y = x(8 - 2x)$
   e. $y = 3x(8 - 4x)$    f. $y = x(16 - 2x)$

9. Graph the following three functions on the same axes. Label $x$-intercepts, $y$-intercept, and the vertex of each parabola.
   a. $y = x(25 - 2x)$    b. $y = x(25 - x)$
   c. $y = 2x(25 - x)$

10. Pick one of the three functions in problem 9 and describe a real situation that would lead to the function. Tell what the variables represent. Make up at least two questions about the real situation that could be answered by looking at the graph you made in problem 9.

11. Write the equation of a parabola having $x$-intercepts at:

    a. $(0, 0)$ and $(2, 0)$;   b. $(-4, 0)$ and $(0, 0)$;

    c. $(-4, 0)$ and $(1, 0)$.

12. Compare the graphs of $y = 4x(x - 1)$, $y = 2x(2x - 2)$, and $y = x(4x - 4)$. Explain what you observe.

13. a. Find the equation of a parabola that has no $x$-intercepts.

    b. Find the equation of a parabola that has only one $x$-intercept.

    c. Find the equation of a graph that has three $x$-intercepts.

14. How many $x$-intercepts? Explain.

    a. $y = 2x + 1$      b. $y = x(4 - x)$

    c. $y = x^2 + 1$      d. $y = 3(x + 1)^2$

15. How many $x$-intercepts? Explain.

    a. $y = 8x - x^2$      b. $y = x^2 - x + 2$

    c. $y = 2x^2 + 12x + 18$

16. How many $x$-intercepts? Explain.

    a. $y = a(x - H)^2$      b. $y = a(x - H)^2 + 3$

    c. $y = a(x - H)^2 - 3$

## THE VERTEX

17. a. Write the equation of any parabola that crosses the $x$-axis at $(2, 0)$ and $(4, 0)$.

    b. Write the equation of any other parabola that crosses the $x$-axis at these two points.

    c. Find the coordinates of the vertices of both parabolas. Compare them. What is the same? What is different?

18. a. Write the equation of any parabola that crosses the $x$-axis at $(0, 0)$ and $(3, 0)$.

    b. Write the equation of a parabola that crosses the $x$-axis at $(0, 0)$ and $(3, 0)$ and has 9 as the $y$-coordinate of its vertex.

    c. Find an equation of any other parabola that has 9 as the $y$-coordinate of its vertex.

    d. Compare the three equations. What is the same? What is different?

19. Write three equivalent equations for the parabola that crosses the $x$-axis at $(2, 0)$ and $(0, 0)$ and has 6 as the $y$-coordinate of its vertex.

20. Find the equation of a parabola having:

    a. intercepts: $(6, 0)$, $(-2, 0)$, $(0, 4)$;

    b. vertex $(-1, -4)$; one intercept at $(1, 0)$;

    c. vertex $(-2, 0)$; one intercept at $(0, 2)$.

21. Find the coordinates of the vertex of the graph of:

    a. $y = -2(x - 5)(x + 8)$;

    b. $y = (x + 3)^2 - 6$;

    c. $y = x^2 + 4x - 7$.

22. Find the equation of a parabola that has a vertex having the following coordinates:

    a. $(2, 8)$          b. $(8, 64)$

23.

    a. Write the equation of a parabola that has $x$-intercepts $(p, 0)$ and $(-r, 0)$. How can you check that your answer is correct?

    b. What are the coordinates of the vertex?

## QUADRATIC EQUATIONS

24. Solve.

    a. $(x - 8)^2 + 6 = 0$    b. $(x - 8)^2 - 6 = 0$

    c. $(x + 8)^2 + 6 = 0$    d. $(x + 8)^2 - 6 = 0$

Solve.

25. $x^2 - 6 = 0$          26. $x^2 - 6x = 0$

27. $x^2 - 6x = -9$      28. $x^2 + 6x = -9$

29. $x^2 + 6x - 4 = 0$    30. $-4x + 2 = -x^2$

31. $-x^2 = 8x + 7$       32. $8x - x^2 = 7$

# CHAPTER  14

A futuristic spiral

## *Coming in this chapter:*

**Exploration** Make a paper rectangle that is similar to the smaller rectangle obtained by the following method:

    a. cutting the original rectangle in two equal parts;

    b. cutting off a square from the original rectangle.

What is the exact ratio of length to width for each of your rectangles?

# RATIOS AND ROOTS

# Rectangle Ratios

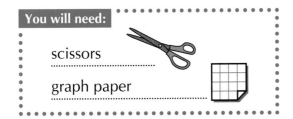

## HALF RECTANGLES

1. Take two identical rectangular pieces of paper. Fold one in half. Place it on top of the other piece. Is the folded half-rectangle similar to the original rectangle? Check with the diagonal test.

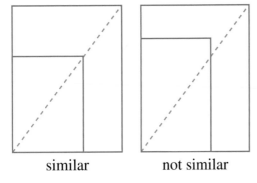

similar          not similar

2. **Exploration** Make a paper rectangle, such that the rectangle you get by folding it in half is similar to the original rectangle. What are the dimensions of your rectangle? (Hint: Remember that if two rectangles are similar, their length-to-width ratio must be the same. You may use trial and error on your calculators for different sizes.)

3. a. Sketch a 16-unit-by-12-unit rectangle on graph paper. What is the length-to-width ratio?

   b. Divide the rectangle in half to get one having length 12 and width 8. (The width of the original rectangle becomes the length of the new rectangle.) What is the length-to-width ratio?

c. Continue to divide the rectangle in half, calculating the ratio of length to width. Make a table like this one to record your data.

| Length | Width | *l/w* Ratio |
|--------|-------|-------------|
| 16 | 12 | — |
| 12 | 8 | — |

4. Describe any patterns you notice in your table.

5. a. Repeat problem 2 for three more rectangles. Keep a careful record of your data in tables. Look for patterns.

   b. Find some rectangles for which the length-to-width ratios do not change when you cut them in half.

6. 🔑 A rectangular sheet of paper is 1 foot wide and $x$ feet long. It is cut into two rectangles, each of which is $(1/2)x$ feet wide and 1 foot long.

   a. Illustrate this in a diagram.

   b. What is the length-to-width ratio in the original rectangle?

   c. What is the length-to-width ratio in each of the two new rectangles?

   d. If the rectangles are similar, we can write an equation setting the original ratio equal to the new ratio. Do this, and find the value of $x$. Show your calculations.

7. **Report** Summarize your findings from problems 1 through 6. Include sketches and examples. Describe any patterns you noticed. For the rectangles you found in problem 5b, what was the common ratio? What was the common ratio for the rectangle you found in problem 2?

## THE INTERNATIONAL PAPER STANDARD

In 1930 an international standard was established for paper sizes, called the *A-series*. The basic size is A0, which is one square meter in area. If you fold it in half, you get paper of size A1. You can fold A1 in half to get A2, fold A2 in half to get A3, etc. The dimensions of A0 were chosen so that *all paper sizes in the series are similar to each other and to A0.*

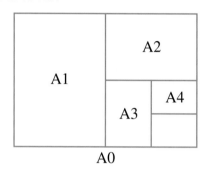

A0

**8.** 💡 Find the dimensions, to the nearest millimeter, of A0 and A1.

## DYNAMIC RECTANGLES

The special rectangles you discovered in the previous section each have the property that half of the rectangle is similar to the whole. They are examples of a group of rectangles, called *dynamic rectangles*, that are very useful to artists and designers. Dynamic rectangles have the property that when you cut them into a certain number of equal parts, each of the parts is similar to the whole.

The rectangle below is divided into three parts, each one of which is similar to the original rectangle.

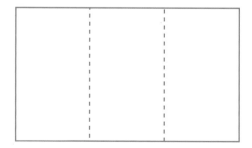

We can express this similarity by writing two equal ratios.

$$\frac{L}{W} = \frac{W}{\frac{1}{3}L}$$

Multiplying both sides of the equation by $W$:

$$W\left(\frac{L}{W}\right) = W\left(\frac{W}{\frac{1}{3}L}\right)$$

$$L = \frac{W^2}{\frac{1}{3}L}$$

and then by $\frac{1}{3}L$, we get the equation:

$$\frac{1}{3}L^2 = W^2$$

**9.** Show how to find $L$, the length of the original rectangle, if the width is the following:

a. 1        b. 2        c. $W$

**10.** What is the ratio of length to width in each of the rectangles in problem 9?

Dynamic rectangles are named for their ratio of length to width. These two rectangles are both called $\sqrt{5}$ rectangles because the ratio of length to width in each of them is $\sqrt{5}$.

**11.** 🔑 Into how many equal parts would you divide a $\sqrt{5}$ rectangle in order to make each of the parts similar to the original rectangle? Explain how you figured this out, showing your work.

**12.** A rectangle is divided into seven parts, each of which is similar to the original rectangle.

    **a.** Give possible dimensions (length and width) for the rectangle.

    **b.** Give another set of possible dimensions.

    **c.** What is the ratio of length to width?

**13.** ⚷ A rectangle having width one unit is divided into $n$ equal parts, each of which is similar to the original rectangle.

**a.** To find the length $x$ of the original rectangle, Tara wrote:

$$\frac{x}{1} = \frac{1}{\frac{1}{n}x}$$

Explain why Tara wrote this proportion.

**b.** Solve this equation for $x$.

**c.** Summarize your results in words.

**14.** Research Many artists and designers use mathematics. Do some research to find out why dynamic rectangles are so useful in art and design. Then make your own design based on dynamic rectangles.

---

**DISCOVERY** *INTERESTING NUMBERS*

**15.** Find a number that is one more than its reciprocal.

**16.** Find a number that is one less than its square.

**REVIEW** *NUMBERS AND THEIR RECIPROCALS*

If possible, find or estimate the number described. Explain how you found it. (If there is more than one number that fits the description, try to find as many as possible.)

**17.** The number equals its reciprocal.

**18.** The number is four more than its reciprocal.

**19.** The number is one more than twice its reciprocal.

**20.** The number does not have a reciprocal.

# Simplifying Algebraic Fractions

**You will need:**

Lab Gear

## ADDING OR SUBTRACTING EQUAL AMOUNTS

1. **Exploration** What happens if you add or subtract equal amounts to or from the numerator and the denominator of a fraction? How can you tell whether the value of the fraction will increase, decrease, or remain the same? Make up several examples to see what happens, then make a generalization.

To model fractions with the Lab Gear, you can use the workmat turned on its side. Instead of representing an equals sign, the straight line in the middle now represents the fraction bar.

Edith and Anna modeled the fraction $\frac{4x + 16}{4x}$ with the Lab Gear, as shown below.

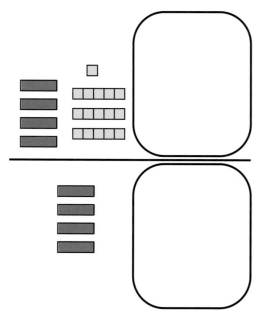

"This is an easy problem," said Edith. "There's a $4x$ in both the numerator and the denomina-

tor, so I can get rid of them. The simplified fraction is 16."

Anna didn't think Edith's method was right. She decided to check Edith's answer by substituting.

2. Calculate the value of the expression $\frac{4x + 16}{4x}$ for several different values for $x$. Do all values of $x$ make this fraction equal to 16? Does any value of $x$ make it equal to 16? Explain.

3. ⚷ Explain why you cannot simplify a fraction by subtracting the same number from the numerator and the denominator. Give examples.

## COMMON DIMENSIONS AND DIVISION

As you know, to simplify a fraction, you *divide numerator and denominator by the same number*. This is still true of algebraic fractions.

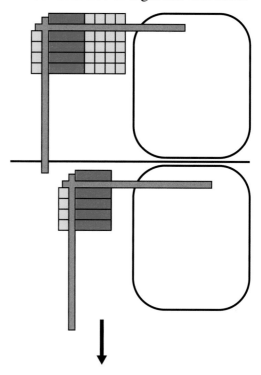

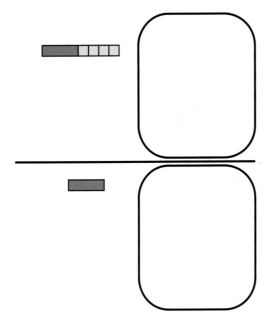

Repeat problem 5 for the following figures.

**6.**

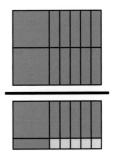

**7.**

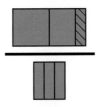

**4.** Study the previous figure.
  a. What are the numerator and the denominator divided by?
  b. What is the simplified fraction?

Sometimes, as in the figure below, the numerator and denominator rectangle are seen to have a common dimension, which is the common factor we divide by to get the simplified fraction.

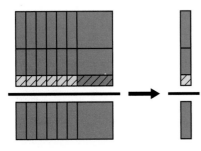

**5.** Study the preceding figure.
  a. Write the original fraction.
  b. Show what the numerator and denominator must be divided by to simplify the fraction.
  c. Write the simplified fraction.

**8.**

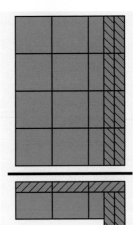

### SIMPLIFYING FRACTIONS

Sometimes it is necessary to factor the numerator and the denominator in order to see the common factors.

▍**Example:** Simplify: $\dfrac{x^2 + 3x + 2}{x^2 + 5x + 6}$

Factor: $\dfrac{(x + 2)(x + 1)}{(x + 2)(x + 3)}$

Divide both numerator and denominator by the common factor, $(x + 2)$. The simplified fraction is: $\dfrac{x + 1}{x + 3}$.

The following example is done with the Lab Gear.

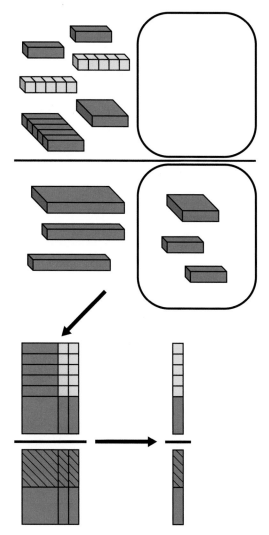

**9.** 🔑 Explain the process shown in the figure, using words and algebraic notation.

If possible, simplify these fractions.

**10.** $\dfrac{3x + 12}{x^2 + 4x}$    **11.** $\dfrac{x^2 + 10x + 25}{2x + 10}$

**12.** $\dfrac{7x + 5}{7x}$    **13.** $\dfrac{2d + 3}{d + 3}$

### ZERO IN THE DENOMINATOR

When we substitute 2 for $x$ in the fraction $\dfrac{3x - 1}{x - 2}$, the denominator has the value zero. Since division by 0 is undefined, we say that the fraction is undefined when $x = 2$.

For what value or values of $x$ (if any) is each fraction undefined?

**14.** $\dfrac{2x}{x - 6}$    **15.** $\dfrac{x - 6}{x + 6}$

**16.** $\dfrac{3}{2x + 6}$    **17.** $\dfrac{x^2 + 2}{x^2 - 6x + 8}$

### ALWAYS, SOMETIMES, NEVER

Since $\dfrac{x^2 + 12x + 20}{x + 2}$ can be written

$$\dfrac{(x + 10)(x + 2)}{x + 2},$$

we can write:

$$\dfrac{x^2 + 12x + 20}{x + 2} = x + 10$$

**18.** 🔑 Explain why the preceding equality is not true when $x = -2$.

**19.** 🔑 Explain why it's true when $x \neq -2$.

**20.** For what value(s) of $x$ is

a. $\dfrac{2x - 3}{8x - 12} \neq \dfrac{1}{4}$?

b. $\dfrac{x^2 - 9}{x - 3} = x + 3$?

Tell whether each equation 21-23 is always true or only sometimes true. If it is only sometimes true, give the values of $x$ for which it is *not* true.

**21.** $\dfrac{8x}{4} = 2x$

**22.** $\dfrac{x^2 - 1}{8x - 8} = \dfrac{(x + 1)}{8}$

**23.** $\dfrac{5 - 5x}{2x^2 - 2} = \dfrac{-5}{2x + 2}$

Tell whether each equation 24-26 is always, sometimes, or never true. If it is sometimes true, give the values of $x$ that make it true.

**24.** $\dfrac{5x - 5}{5} = 5x$

**25.** $\dfrac{5x - 5}{5} = x - 5$

**26.** $\dfrac{x^2 - 10}{5} = x^2 - 2$

## 14.3 Fractions and Equations

1. **Exploration** Wanda always enjoyed the math tests Mr. Stevens gave every Friday. She especially liked the tests on fractions. Here is the test she took on Friday the 13th. Try to find the problems she did wrong. If necessary, substitute numbers. If you can, show her how to do them correctly.

a. $\frac{2x}{5} - \frac{x}{3} = \frac{x}{2}$

b. $\frac{x}{5} + \frac{x}{5} = \frac{2x}{10}$

c. $\frac{x}{5} \cdot \frac{x}{5} = \frac{x^2}{25}$

d. $\frac{2x}{5} \cdot \frac{5}{2x} = 1$

e. $\frac{x}{5} + \frac{5}{x} = 2$

f. $\frac{M}{5} = \frac{10M}{50}$

g. $\frac{2M + 4}{M + 2} = 2$

### COMPLICATING FRACTIONS

Sometimes it is useful to *complicate* fractions instead of simplifying them. For example, here are some more complicated fractions that are equivalent to $\frac{2x}{5}$.

a. $\frac{4x^2}{10x}$     b. $\frac{2xy}{5y}$     c. $\frac{8x + 2x^2}{20 + 5x}$

2. What was $\frac{2x}{5}$ multiplied by to give each one of the fractions? Sketch a Lab Gear fraction for part (a).

3. Write three fractions that are equivalent to $2/(x - 3)$. Check the correctness of a classmate's fractions.

4. Write a fraction that is equivalent to $\frac{x + 2}{5}$ that has the following:

a. a denominator of 10

b. a denominator of $5x + 15$

c. a numerator of $4x + 8$

d. a numerator of $3x^2 + 6x$

5. If possible, write a fraction that is equivalent to $\frac{y + x}{4x}$ that has the following:

a. a denominator of $8xy$

b. a denominator of $6x^2$

c. a numerator of $-2y - 2x$

d. a numerator of $3y + x$

6. Write a fraction equivalent to 2 that has $5a^2$ as a denominator.

7. Write a fraction equivalent to 1 that has $b$ as a denominator.

8. Write a fraction equivalent to $b$ that has $b$ as a denominator.

9. Write a fraction equivalent to $x$ that has $x^2$ as a denominator.

### COMMON DENOMINATORS

To add or subtract fractions having unlike denominators, you first have to find a common denominator.

10. a. Write a fraction equivalent to $\frac{b}{3}$ having a denominator of $6a^2$.

b. Add $\frac{b}{3} + \frac{c}{6a^2}$.

11. Write two fractions whose sum is $\frac{2x + 5}{10x}$.

12. a. Write a fraction equivalent to $\frac{bc}{5a}$ having a denominator of $5ac$.

13. Find a common denominator and add or subtract.

a. $\frac{1}{4x} + \frac{1}{10x^2}$     b. $\frac{5}{xy} - \frac{1}{x^2}$

*Chapter 14 Ratios and Roots*

### FROM QUADRATICS TO FRACTIONS

Tara was trying to solve $x^2 + 4x - 6 = 0$ with the zero product property. She couldn't figure out a way to factor the trinomial. Then she had an idea. She wrote:

$$x^2 + 4x = 6$$
$$x(x + 4) = 6$$

Tara was still thinking about the zero product property. She wrote:

$$x = 6 \text{ or } x + 4 = 6$$

**14.** 🔑 Explain why Tara's reasoning is incorrect. (Why does this method work when one side of the equation is 0?)

When Tara saw her mistake, she tried another method. She divided both sides by $x$.

$$x(x + 4) = 6$$
$$x + 4 = \frac{6}{x}$$

Then she was stuck. Her teacher suggested that she use trial and error, so she made this table.

| $x$ | $x + 4$ | $\frac{6}{x}$ |
|---|---|---|
| 1 | 5 | 6 |
| 2 | 6 | 3 |
| 1.5 | 5.5 | 4 |
| 1.25 | 5.25 | 4.8 |
| 1.13 | 5.13 | 5.31 |

**15.** Continue the table and find a value of $x$ that, when substituted into both sides of the equation, will give the same value
  a. to the nearest tenth;
  b. to the nearest hundredth.

**16.** The quadratic equation that Tara was solving has two roots. Approximate the other root to the nearest hundredth.

**17.** Solve the equation $x^2 + 5x - 3 = 0$ using trial and error. (You do not need to do it in the same way as Tara.) Approximate each solution to the nearest hundredth.

**18.** Confirm your solution by using a method you learned in Chapter 13.

### FROM FRACTIONS TO QUADRATICS

Rewrite each equation as an equivalent quadratic equation. Then try to solve it. Show each step.

**19.** $x + 4 + \frac{3}{x} = 0$    **20.** $2m + \frac{4}{m} = 9$

**21.** $4x = \frac{1}{x}$    **22.** $L - 4 = \frac{20}{L}$

**23.** $\frac{1}{x} = x + 1$    **24.** $\frac{4}{x} = x + 1$

# LESSON 14.4 Finding the Vertex

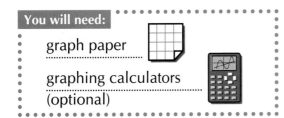

**You will need:**

graph paper

graphing calculators (optional)

Knowing more about quadratic functions and their graphs will help you understand and solve quadratic equations. In particular, it is useful to know how to find the vertex and the x-intercepts of quadratic functions in the following two forms:

- *Intercept form:* $y = a(x - p)(x - q)$
- *Standard form:* $y = ax^2 + bx + c$

## DIFFERENT SHAPES

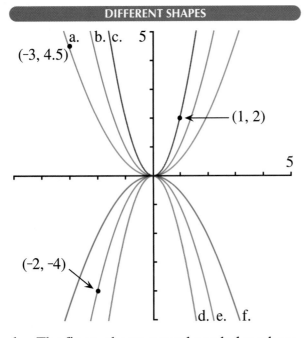

1. The figure shows several parabolas whose x-intercepts, y-intercept, and vertex are all (0, 0). Match each one with an equation:

$y = x^2$     $y = 0.5x^2$     $y = 2x^2$

$y = -x^2$     $y = -0.5x^2$     $y = -2x^2$

2. What is the value of $a$ for the parabolas on the following figure?

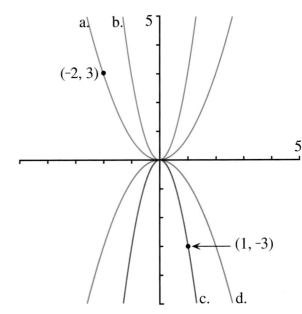

3. Which among the parabolas in problems 1 and 2 is most open? Most closed? How is this related to the value of $a$?

4. Write the equation of a parabola that lies entirely between parabolas 1a and 1b.

5. Describe the graph of:
   a. $y = -0.01x^2$;    b. $y = 100x^2$.

6. **Summary** Explain the effect of the parameter $a$, in the function $y = ax^2$, on the shape and orientation of the graph.

## INTERCEPT FORM

As you learned in Chapter 13, when the equation is in intercept form, you can find the vertex from the x-intercepts, which are easy to locate.

7. Try to answer the following questions about the graph of $y = 2(x - 3)(x + 4)$ without graphing.
   a. What are the x- and y-intercepts?
   b. What are the coordinates of the vertex?

**8.** | Generalization |

    a. What are the *x*- and *y*-intercepts of
$y = a(x - p)(x - q)$? Explain.

    b. Explain in words how to find the vertex
if you know the intercepts.

**9.** 💡 The figure shows the graphs of several
parabolas. Write an equation for each one.
(Hint: To find *a*, use either the *y*-intercept
or the vertex and algebra or trial and
error.)

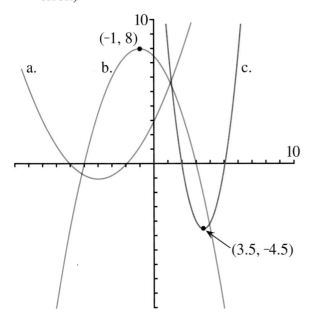

**10.** For each equation, tell whether its graph is
a smile or a frown parabola, without
graphing. Explain your reasoning.

    a. $y = 9(x - 8)(x - 7)$

    b. $y = -9(x - 8)(x - 7)$

    c. $y = 9(8 - x)(x - 7)$

    d. $y = 9(8 - x)(7 - x)$

**11.** 🔑 If you know all the intercepts and the
vertex of $y = 3(x - p)(x - q)$, explain
how you would find the intercepts and the
vertex of $y = -3(x - p)(x - q)$.

### STANDARD FORM

When the equation is in standard form,
$y = ax^2 + bx + c$, it is more difficult to find
the location of the vertex. One particularly
easy case, however, is the case where $c = 0$.

**12.** 👓 Explain why when $c = 0$, the
parabola goes through the origin.

**13.** Find the vertex of $y = 2x^2 + 8x$.
(Hint: Factor to get into intercept form.)

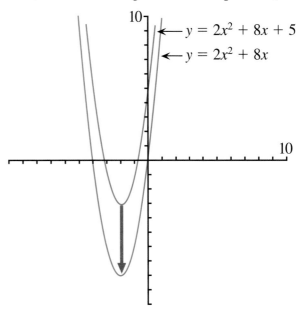

**14.** 🔑 How are the two graphs related?
Compare the axis of symmetry and the
*y*-intercept.

**15.** 👓 How is the graph of $y = 2x^2 + 8x - 3$
related to them?

**16.** Find the equation of any other parabola
whose vertex is directly above or below
the vertex of $y = 2x^2 + 8x$.

### FINDING *H* AND *V*

**Example:** Find the coordinates $(H, V)$ of the
vertex of the graph of $y = 3x^2 - 18x + 7$.

• $y = 3x^2 - 18x$ is the vertical translation
for which $V = 0$. By factoring, we see it is
equal to $y = x(3x - 18)$.

• To find the *x*-intercepts of $y = 3x^2 - 18x$,
we set $y = 0$. By the zero product
property, one *x*-intercept is 0. To find the
other, we solve the equation $3x - 18 = 0$,
and get $x = 6$.

• Since the *x*-intercepts are 0 and 6, and the
axis of symmetry for both parabolas is
halfway between, it must be 3. So $H = 3$.

- Substitute 3 into the original equation to see that the $y$-coordinate of the vertex is:
$$V = 3(3)^2 - 18(3) + 7 = -20.$$
So the coordinates of the vertex for the original parabola are $(3, -20)$.

17. For each equation, find $H$ and $V$. It may help to sketch the vertical translation of the parabola for which $V = 0$.
    a. $y = x^2 + 6x + 5$
    b. $y = 2x^2 + 6x + 5$
    c. $y = 3x^2 - 6x + 5$
    d. $y = 6x^2 - 6x + 5$

**Generalizations**

18. What is the equation of a parabola through the origin that is a vertical translation of $y = ax^2 + bx + c$?

19. Show how to find the axis of symmetry of:
    a. $y = ax^2 + bx$;
    b. $y = ax^2 - bx$.

20. Explain why the $x$-coordinate of the vertex of the parabola having equation $y = ax^2 + bx + c$ is
$$H = -\frac{b}{2a}.$$

**SAME SHAPE**

The parameter $a$ determines the shape of the parabola. The graphs of all equations in standard form that share the same value for $a$ are translations of the graph of $y = ax^2$.

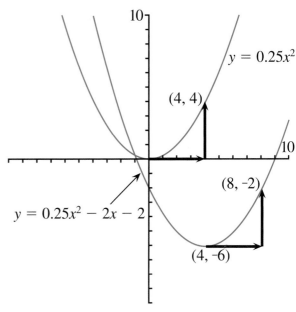

For example, the two parabolas in the figure have equations with $a = 0.25$. Therefore they have the same shape, as the following exercise shows.

21. 🔑
    a. Show algebraically that starting at the vertex, and moving 4 across and 4 up, lands you on a point that satisfies the equation in both cases.
    b. If you move 2 across from the vertex, show that you move up the same amount to get to the parabola in both cases.

You have a long rectangular sheet of metal, having width $L$ inches. You intend to fold it to make a gutter. You want to find out which of the folds shown in the figure will give the maximum flow of water. This depends on the area of the cross-section of the gutter; a bigger area means better flow.

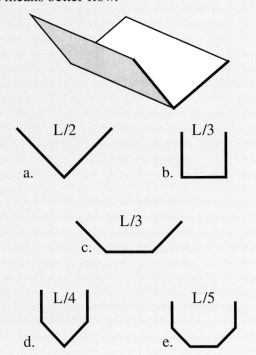

1. Find the area of the cross-section for the examples shown in the figure. (All angles are 90 or 135 degrees. All sides in each cross-section are of equal length. Hint: Divide the areas into rectangles and right triangles that are half-squares.) Which cross-section has the greatest area?

2. You may try the same shapes with different dimensions. For example, for cross-section b, you could have a height of $L/4$, and a width of $L/2$. Try to increase the areas for cross-sections b, c, d, and e by choosing different values for the different segments. (Remember that the sum of all the lengths must be $L$.)

3. **Report** Figure out the best design for a gutter. Write an illustrated report on your research, explaining clearly how you arrived at your conclusions. You need not limit yourself to the shapes given here.

# A Famous Formula

## STANDARD FORM OF A QUADRATIC

**Definition:** A quadratic equation is said to be in *standard form* if it is in the form:
$$ax^2 + bx + c = 0.$$

In Chapter 13 you learned several methods to solve quadratics in the case where $a = 1$. If you divide all the terms of a quadratic equation in standard form by $a$, you can solve it with those methods.

**Example:** Solve $3x^2 + 5x - 4 = 0$.
Divide both sides by 3:
$$x^2 + \frac{5}{3}x - \frac{4}{3} = \frac{0}{3}$$
$$x^2 + \frac{5}{3}x - \frac{4}{3} = 0.$$

Since $a = 1$, the solutions are $H \pm \sqrt{-V}$. In this case:
$$H = -b/2 = -5/6.$$

Find $V$ by substituting $H$ for $x$ in the equation.
$$V = \left(\frac{-5}{6}\right)^2 + \left(\frac{5}{3}\right)\left(\frac{-5}{6}\right) - \frac{4}{3}$$
$$= \frac{25}{36} - \frac{25}{18} - \frac{4}{3}$$
$$= \frac{25}{36} - \frac{50}{36} - \frac{48}{36}$$
$$= \frac{-73}{36}$$

So the solutions are:
$$-\frac{5}{6} + \sqrt{\frac{73}{36}} \text{ or } -\frac{5}{6} - \sqrt{\frac{73}{36}}$$

The two solutions can be written as one expression:
$$-\frac{5}{6} \pm \sqrt{\frac{73}{36}}$$

where the symbol $\pm$ is read *plus or minus*. It is also possible to write it as a single fraction:
$$-\frac{5}{6} \pm \sqrt{\frac{73}{36}} = -\frac{5}{6} \pm \frac{\sqrt{73}}{6} = \frac{-5 \pm \sqrt{73}}{6}$$

Solve. (Hint: You may divide by $a$, then use any of the methods from Chapter 13.)

1. $2x^2 + 4x - 8 = 0$

2. $-x^2 + 4x + 8 = 0$

3. $3x^2 + 4x - 4 = 0$

4. $-3x^2 + 8x + 8 = 0$

## FINDING THE x-INTERCEPTS

You already know how to find the vertex of a quadratic function in standard form. In this section you will learn how to find the $x$-intercepts from the vertex.

The following figure shows the graph of the function $y = ax^2 + bx + c$, which is a translation of $y = ax^2$, whose graph is also shown. The coordinates of the vertex are $(H, V)$. $D$ is the distance from the $x$-intercepts to the axis of symmetry. When $a = 1$, we found that $D = \sqrt{-V}$. What is $D$ in the general case?

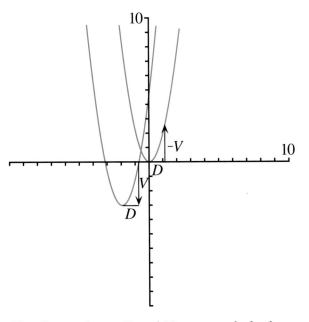

The figure shows $D$ and $V$ on a parabola that was translated from $y = ax^2$. In this example, $V$ was a negative number, and the translation was in a downward direction. The arrows representing $D$ and $V$ are also shown on the original parabola. (On $y = x^2$, the direction of the arrow for $V$ was reversed. What is shown is actually the opposite of $V$. This is indicated by the label $-V$. Since $V$ is negative, $-V$ is positive.)

5. 🗝 Use the figure to explain why $-V = aD^2$.

6. 🗝 Express $D$ in terms of $V$ and $a$.

7. 🗝 This formula is different from the one we had found in the case where $a = 1$. Explain why this formula works whether $a = 1$ or $a \neq 1$.

The $x$-intercepts, when they exist, are equal to $H \pm D$. It follows from the value of $D$ found in the previous section that the solutions to the quadratic equation $ax^2 + bx + c = 0$ are given by the formula:

$$H \pm \sqrt{-\frac{V}{a}} \, .$$

Therefore, one way to solve a quadratic equation in standard form is first to find $H$ and $V$. In Lesson 2 you learned how to express $H$ in terms of $a$ and $b$. Then $V$ can be found by substituting $H$ into the equation.

> **Example:** Solve $2x^2 + 8x - 7 = 0$.

Solutions:

$$H \pm \sqrt{-\frac{V}{a}} = -2 \pm \sqrt{-\frac{-15}{2}} = -2 \pm \sqrt{7.5}$$

Solve.

8. $2x^2 + 6x - 8 = 0$

9. $-x^2 + 6x + 8 = 0$

10. $3x^2 + 6x + 1 = 0$

11. $-3x^2 + 6x + 8 = 0$

As you know, $H = -b/(2a)$. The following problem uses that fact to find a formula for $V$ in terms of $a$, $b$, and $c$.

12. 💡 Substitute $-b/(2a)$ into $ax^2 + bx + c$ to find the $y$-coordinate of the vertex as a single fraction in terms of $a$, $b$, and $c$.

If you did problem 12 correctly, you should have found that:

$$V = \frac{-b^2 + 4ac}{4a} \, .$$

13. 💡 To find a formula for the solutions of the quadratic equation in standard form in terms of $a$, $b$, and $c$, substitute the expressions for $H$ and $V$ into the expression

$$H \pm \sqrt{-\frac{V}{a}} \, .$$

If you did this correctly, you should have found that the solutions are:

$$-\frac{b}{2a} \pm \sqrt{\frac{b^2 - 4ac}{4a^2}}$$

**14.** 💡 Show that this simplifies to:

$$\frac{-b \pm \sqrt{b^2 - 4ac}}{2a}$$

This expression is the famous *quadratic formula*. It gives the solutions to a quadratic equation in standard form in terms of $a$, $b$, and $c$. You will find it useful to memorize it as follows: "The opposite of $b$, plus or minus the square root of $b$ squared minus $4ac$, all over $2a$."

Solve these equations. (If you use the quadratic formula, you are less likely to make mistakes if you calculate the quantity $b^2 - 4ac$ first.)

**15.** $2x^2 + 6x - 4 = 0$

**16.** $-x^2 + 6x + 4 = 0$

**17.** $3x^2 + 6x - 4 = 0$

**18.** $-3x^2 + 7x - 4 = 0$

**19.** Report What are all the methods you know for solving quadratic equations? Use examples.

---

### DISCOVERY A TOUGH INEQUALITY

On Friday night when Mary and Martin walked into the G. Ale Bar, Ginger gave them a challenging inequality. "This stumps some calculus students," she said, "but I think you can figure it out."

**20.** Solve Ginger's inequality: $3 < 1/x$. Check and explain your solution.

### REVIEW RECTANGLES

**21.** The length of a rectangle is 10 more than the width. Write a formula for:
   a.  the width in terms of the length;
   b.  the area in terms of the length;
   c.  the perimeter in terms of the width.

**22.** A rectangle has width $3x + 1$ and length $6x + 2$. Find the perimeter when the area is 200.

# Translations of $y = ax^2$

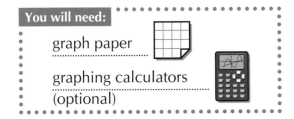

**You will need:**

graph paper

graphing calculators (optional)

## VERTEX FORM

In Chapter 13 you learned that the parameters $H$ and $V$ in the equation $y = (x - H)^2 + V$ represent the coordinates of the vertex of a parabola which is a translation of the one with equation $y = x^2$. This is easy to generalize to any equation in the form $y = a(x - H)^2 + V$, even when $a \neq 1$.

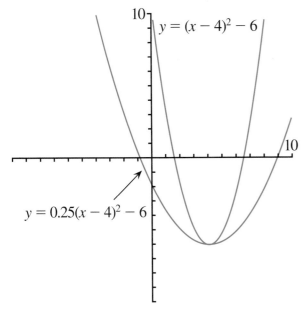

The two parabolas shown in the figure have the same vertex.

1. Write the equation of a parabola having the same vertex as both in the figure that is
   a. more open than either;
   b. more closed than either;
   c. between the two.

2. 🔑
   a. Explain why the lowest value for the quantity $(x - 4)^2$ is 0.
   b. Explain how it follows that the lowest point for both parabolas must be for $x = 4$.

3. Write the equation of the parabola that has the same shape as $y = 0.25x^2$ having vertex (-3, 2).

4. Find the equation of a parabola that is a translation of $y = 5x^2$ having vertex (4, -2).

5. The following questions are about the function $y = 6(x + 5)^2 - 4$.
   a. What are the coordinates of the vertex of its graph?
   b. What is the equation of the parabola of the same shape having the vertex at the origin?
   c. What is the equation of the frown parabola having the same shape, and the vertex at the origin?
   d. What is the equation of the frown parabola having the same shape and vertex?

6. **Summary** What do you know about the shape and vertex of the graph of $y = a(x - H)^2 + V$?

## MORE ON EQUAL SQUARES

Use the equal squares method to solve each equation. Notice how the solutions of the first equation in each pair differ from the solutions of the second equation.

7. a. $x^2 - 9 = 0$
   b. $4x^2 - 9 = 0$

**8.** a. $x^2 - 6 = 0$

    b. $9x^2 - 6 = 0$

**9.** a. $(x - 3)^2 - 5 = 0$

    b. $16(x - 3)^2 - 5 = 0$

**10.** a. $(x + 2)^2 - 7 = 0$

     b. $3(x + 2)^2 - 7 = 0$

**11.** Generalization

    a. Describe how the roots of the second equation in each pair differ from the roots of the first equation.

    b. Use the equal squares method to find a general formula for the solutions of the equation $a(x - H)^2 + V = 0$. Explain.

If you did problem 11 correctly, you should have found the same formula as in Lesson 5.

$$H \pm \sqrt{-\dfrac{V}{a}}$$

**COMPLETING THE SQUARE**

You can change a quadratic equation from standard form to vertex form by completing the square. When $a \neq 1$, it is more difficult, but it can still be done.

**Example:** Write $y = 3x^2 + 6x - 9$ in vertex form.

Then complete the square for the quantity inside the parentheses:
$$y = 3(x^2 + 2x + 1 - 1 - 3)$$

Finally, distribute the 3:
$$y = 3(x + 1)^2 - 12$$

So $H = -1$ and $V = -12$. You can check that this was done correctly by finding $H$ and $V$ using the method from Lesson 4:

$$V = 3(-1)^2 + 6(-1) - 9 = -12$$

The same method for completing the square is used even when $a$ is not a common factor.

**Example:** Write $y = 3x^2 + 5x - 7$
Factor the 3:
$$y = 3\left(x^2 + \dfrac{5}{3}x - \dfrac{7}{3}\right)$$

Complete the square:
$$y = 3\left(x^2 + \dfrac{5}{3}x + \dfrac{25}{36} - \dfrac{25}{36} - \dfrac{7}{3}\right)$$
$$= 3\left(\left(x + \dfrac{5}{6}\right)^2 - \dfrac{109}{36}\right)$$

Distribute the 3:

So $H = -5/6$ and $V = -109/12$.

**12.** Check that $H$ and $V$ were found correctly.

Complete the square.

**13.** $y = 3x^2 + 6x + 9$

**14.** $y = -2x^2 + 5x + 8$

**15.** $y = 2x^2 - 5x + 3$

**THE QUADRATIC FORMULA, AGAIN**

Let us write $y = ax^2 + bx + c$ in vertex form by completing the square.

Factor the $a$:
$$y = a\left(x^2 + \dfrac{b}{a}x + \dfrac{c}{a}\right)$$

Complete the square:
$$y = a\left(x^2 + \dfrac{b}{a}x + \dfrac{b^2}{4a^2} - \dfrac{b^2}{4a^2} + \dfrac{c}{a}\right)$$
$$= a\left(\left(x + \dfrac{b}{2a}\right)^2 + \dfrac{-b^2 + 4ac}{4a^2}\right)$$

Distribute the $a$:
$$y = a\left(x + \dfrac{b}{2a}\right)^2 + \dfrac{-b^2 + 4ac}{4a}$$

So $H = \frac{-b}{2a}$, and $V = \frac{-b^2 + 4ac}{4a}$ as we saw in Lesson 5.

Finally, if we solve the equation

$$a\left(x + \frac{b}{2a}\right)^2 + \frac{-b^2 + 4ac}{4a} = 0$$

by the equal squares method, we get:

$$a\left(x + \frac{b}{2a}\right)^2 = \frac{b^2 - 4ac}{4a}$$

$$\left(x + \frac{b}{2a}\right)^2 = \frac{b^2 - 4ac}{4a^2}$$

So:

$$x + \frac{b}{2a} = \pm\sqrt{\frac{b^2 - 4ac}{4a^2}}$$

$$x = \frac{-b}{2a} \pm \frac{\sqrt{b^2 - 4ac}}{2a}$$

$$x = \frac{-b \pm \sqrt{b^2 - 4ac}}{2a}$$

---

### DISCOVERY  EGYPTIAN FRACTIONS

The ancient Egyptians used only those fractions having 1 for the numerator.

**16.** Find the sum. Look for patterns.

   a. $\frac{1}{5} + \frac{1}{20} = \frac{1}{?}$   b. $\frac{1}{3} + \frac{1}{6} = \frac{1}{?}$

   c. $\frac{1}{4} + \frac{1}{12} = \frac{1}{?}$

**17.** Use the above pattern to predict these missing denominators.

   a. $\frac{1}{7} + \frac{1}{?} = \frac{1}{6}$   b. $\frac{1}{?} + \frac{1}{30} = \frac{1}{5}$

   c. $\frac{1}{10} + \frac{1}{90} = \frac{1}{?}$

**18.** Write three more problems having the same pattern as above.

**19.** Generalization

   a. Write an algebraic statement to describe the pattern you found in #16. Use expressions in terms of $D$ for $m$ and $n$ in the equality.

$$\frac{1}{m} + \frac{1}{n} = \frac{1}{D}$$

   b. Use algebra to check that your statement is an identity.

**20.** Find $x$. Look for patterns.

   a. $\frac{1}{2} + \frac{1}{3} + \frac{1}{6} = \frac{1}{x} + \frac{1}{x}$

   b. $\frac{1}{4} + \frac{1}{5} + \frac{1}{20} = \frac{1}{x} + \frac{1}{x}$

**21.** Use the above pattern to express the following fractions as a sum of Egyptian fractions. Check your answers.

   a. $\frac{2}{5}$      b. $\frac{2}{7}$

**22.** Generalization

   a. Write an algebraic statement to describe the pattern.

   b. Use algebra to check that your statement is an identity.

---

# Equations and Numbers

In this lesson we will discuss quadratic functions and equations in standard form, $y = a^2 + bx + c$ and $ax^2 + bx + c = 0$.

### HOW MANY x-INTERCEPTS?

A quadratic equation may have 2, 1, or 0 real number solutions, depending on the number of *x*-intercepts on the graph of the corresponding function.

1.  Sketch a parabola for whose equation:
    a. $a > 0$ and $c < 0$
    b. $a < 0$ and $c > 0$

2.  ⬤━ Explain why a parabola for which *a* and *c* have opposite signs must intersect the *x*-axis.

3.  Sketch a parabola to explain why if $a > 0$ and $V < 0$ there are two *x*-intercepts.

4.  Fill the table with the number of *x*-intercepts for a quadratic function with the given signs for *a* and *V*. Justify each answer with a sketch.

|         | $V < 0$ | $V = 0$ | $V > 0$ |
|---------|---------|---------|---------|
| $a > 0$ | 2       | —       | —       |
| $a < 0$ | —       | —       | —       |

(We do not consider the case $a = 0$, since then the function is no longer quadratic.)

5.  How many *x*-intercepts are there if:
    a. $V = 0$?
    b. *V* and *a* have the same sign?
    c. *V* and *a* have opposite signs?

In Lesson 6 you found that $V = \dfrac{-b^2 + 4ac}{4a}$.

**Definition:** The quantity $b^2 - 4ac$, which appears under the radical in the quadratic formula, is called the *discriminant*, which is sometimes written $\Delta$ (the Greek letter *delta*).

6.  Explain why we can write $V = -\Delta/(4a)$.

### HOW MANY SOLUTIONS?

It turns out that the discriminant allows us to know the number of solutions of a quadratic equation. Refer to the table in problem 4 to answer the following questions.

7.  If $\Delta = 0$, what is *V*? How many solutions are there?

8.  If $\Delta > 0$,
    a. and $a > 0$, what is the sign of *V*? How many solutions are there?
    b. and $a < 0$, what is the sign of *V*? How many solutions are there?

9.  If $\Delta < 0$,
    a. and $a > 0$, what is the sign of *V*? How many solutions are there?
    b. and $a < 0$, what is the sign of *V*? How many solutions are there?

The quadratic formula can be written:
$$\frac{-b \pm \sqrt{\Delta}}{2a}$$

10. **Summary** Using the quadratic formula, explain why,
    a. if $\Delta = 0$ there is only one solution;
    b. if $\Delta < 0$ there are no real solutions;
    c. if $\Delta > 0$ there are two real solutions.

11. ⬤━ Explain why if *a* and *c* have opposite signs, the discriminant cannot be negative.

## SUM AND PRODUCT OF THE SOLUTIONS

12. In the case where there are two solutions

$$x_1 = \frac{-b + \sqrt{\Delta}}{2a} \text{ and } x_2 = \frac{-b - \sqrt{\Delta}}{2a},$$

a. what is $x_1 + x_2$?
b. what is the average of $x_1$ and $x_2$? (How is this related to the axis of symmetry?)
c. what is $x_1 \cdot x_2$?

The sum of the solutions of a quadratic equation is $S = -b/a$, and the product is $P = c/a$. This provides a quick way to check the correctness of the solutions to a quadratic.

> **Example:** Phred solved the quadratic equation $2x^2 + 5x - 8 = 0$ and got $\frac{-5 \pm \sqrt{89}}{2}$.
> To check the correctness of the answer, he added the two roots, hoping to get $S = -b/a = -5/2$. Conveniently, the $\sqrt{89}$ disappeared:
> $$\frac{-5 + \sqrt{89}}{2} + \frac{-5 - \sqrt{89}}{2} = \frac{-10}{2}$$
> Since $-10/2 \neq -5/2$, Phred must have made a mistake.

Solve, and check the correctness of your answers, with the help of $S$ and $P$ (or by substituting in the original equation).

13. $2x^2 + 5x - 8 = 0$

14. $2x^2 - 8x + 5 = 0$

15. $-8x^2 + 3x + 5 = 0$

16. $-2x^2 - 5x - 1 = 0$

## KINDS OF NUMBERS

The first numbers people used were whole numbers. It took many centuries to discover more and more types of numbers. The discovery of new kinds of numbers is related to the attempt to solve more and more equations. The following equations are examples.

a. $x + 2 = 9$    b. $x + 9 = 2$
c. $2x = 6$    d. $6x = 2$
e. $x^2 = 9$    f. $x^2 = 10$
g. $x^2 = -9$

17. Pretend you know about only the *natural numbers*. (These are the positive whole numbers.) List the equations a-f that can be solved.

18. Pretend you know about only the *integers*. (These are positive and negative whole numbers and zero.) List the equations a-f that can be solved. Find one that has two solutions.

19. Pretend you know about only the *rational numbers*. (These are all fractions, positive, negative, and zero. Of course, integers are included, since for example $3 = 6/2$.) List the equations a-f that can be solved.

20. The *real numbers* include all rational and irrational numbers. Which equations can be solved if you know about all the real numbers?

Natural numbers, integers, rational numbers, and real numbers can all be found on a one-dimensional number line. However, to solve equation (g), you need to get off the number line. The solution is a *complex number*, and it is written $3i$. The number $i$ is a number one unit away from 0, but off the number line. It is defined as a number whose square is -1:

$$i^2 = -1.$$

Complex numbers cannot be shown on a line. They require a two-dimensional number plane. You will learn more about them in future math classes.

21. Create an equation whose solution is
    a. a natural number;
    b. an integer, but not a natural number;
    c. a rational number, but not an integer;
    d. an irrational number.

22. Create an equation that has no real number solution.

23. **Research** Find out about complex numbers.

# The Golden Ratio

### 14.8

**You will need:**

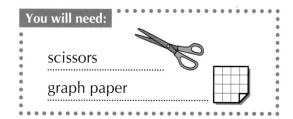

scissors

graph paper

---

## THE GOLDEN RECTANGLE

1.  Take two identical rectangular pieces of paper. Cut a square off one end of one of them, as shown in the figure. Is the remaining rectangle similar to the original one? Check with the diagonal test.

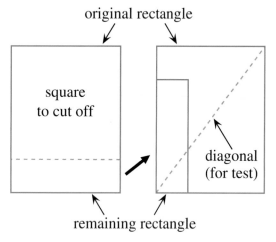

original rectangle

square to cut off

diagonal (for test)

remaining rectangle

2.  **Exploration** Make a paper rectangle, such that the rectangle that remains after cutting off a square is similar to the original rectangle. What are the dimensions of your rectangle? (Hint: Remember that if two rectangles are similar, their length-to-width ratio must be the same. You may use trial and error on your calculators for different sizes, or write and solve equations.)

**Definitions:**

- A *golden rectangle* is one that satisfies the following property: If you cut a square off one end of the rectangle, the remaining rectangle is similar to the original one.

- The ratio of the longer to the shorter side of a golden rectangle is called the *golden ratio*.

Golden rectangles and the golden ratio are used frequently in art, design, and architecture.

3.  What is the length-to-width ratio of the rectangle you found in problem 2? Compare your answer with your classmates' answers.

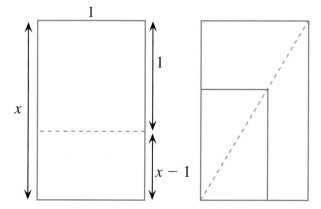

This figure shows a golden rectangle (on the left). To find the exact value of the golden ratio, we will write and solve an equation about the similar rectangles shown (on the right).

4.  🗝 Explain why $\frac{x-1}{1} = \frac{1}{x}$ .

5.  Solve the equation.

There should be two solutions. The positive one is the golden ratio.

6.  What is the exact value of the golden ratio?

7.  What is the golden ratio, rounded to the nearest one thousandth?

8.  What is the reciprocal of the golden ratio, rounded to the nearest one thousandth?

**Notation:** The golden ratio is often represented by the Greek letter φ (*phi*).

## A SPECIAL SEQUENCE

A Fibonacci-like sequence is one in which each term is the sum of the previous two. A geometric sequence is one in which the ratio of consecutive terms is constant. We will try to create a sequence that is geometric and Fibonacci-like at the same time.

9. 🗝 Consider the sequence $1, k, k^2, k^3, \ldots$. Explain why it is a geometric sequence. What is its common ratio?

10. 🗝 Explain why, if $1, k, k^2, k^3, \ldots$ were a Fibonacci-like sequence, we would have $1 + k = k^2$.

11. Find a number $k$ that satisfies the equation $1 + k = k^2$. Explain your reasoning.

In problems 9-11, you have shown that the sequence $1, \varphi, \varphi^2, \varphi^3, \ldots$ is geometric and starts out as a Fibonacci-like sequence, since its third term is the sum of the first two. It remains to show that if you add the second and third terms, you get the fourth, if you add the third and fourth, you get the fifth, and so on. More generally, we need to show that if you add the $(n + 1)^{th}$ term and the $(n + 2)^{th}$ term, you get the $(n + 3)^{th}$ term.

12. Use algebra to explain why if $1 + k = k^2$, then $k + k^2 = k^3$.

13. 🗝 Multiply both sides of $1 + k = k^2$ by $k^n$. Use the result to show that the sequence $1, \varphi, \varphi^2, \varphi^3, \ldots$ is Fibonacci-like.

## GOLDEN WINDOWS

Some architects think that rectangular windows look best if their sides are in the ratio of approximately $\varphi$.

14. Imagine that you must make "golden windows" out of square panes. Since the sides must be whole numbers, you will not be able to have an exact golden rectangle, so try to find the dimensions of a few windows having whole number sides in a ratio close to $\varphi$.

Many architects use consecutive numbers in the Fibonacci sequence: 1, 1, 2, 3, 5, 8, 13, … as the dimensions of windows and other rectangles. (Example: 3 by 5, or 5 by 8.)

15. Make a sequence of the ratios of consecutive Fibonacci numbers: 1/1, 2/1, 3/2, 5/3, 8/5, 13/8, …. Are the ratios greater or less than the golden ratio? What is the trend in the long run?

16. a. Plot the points (1, 1), (1, 2), (2, 3), (3, 5), (5, 8), (8, 13), ….
    b. Graph the line $y = \varphi x$.
    c. Describe the position of the points in relation to the line.

17. Plot the points $(1, \varphi), (\varphi, \varphi^2), (\varphi^2, \varphi^3), \ldots$ and the line $y = \varphi x$. Compare the graph with the one in problem 16.

18. **Research** Read about the golden ratio, the golden rectangle, and the Fibonacci sequence. Write a report on what you learn.

# 14.B Up and Down Stream

The L.A. Barge Company operates boats on canals, lakes, and rivers. One of their boats, the *Huck Finn*, moves at a maximum rate of 11 mi/hr in still water. The boat regularly does a round trip on the Leumas River, going 32 miles upstream, and returning. The river flows at a rate of 2 mi/hr.

To calculate the total time for the round trip, you need to use the formula

$$\text{distance} = \text{rate} \cdot \text{time}.$$

Assuming the boat goes at its maximum rate, it goes upstream at a rate of $(11 - 2)$ mi/hr, and it goes downstream at a rate of $(11 + 2)$ mi/hr.

1. What is the total time for the round trip? Assume a one-hour stop before heading back.

2. What is the average speed
   a. with a stop?
   b. without a stop?

3. True or False? Since the boat goes upstream on the way there, and downstream on the way back, the effect of the current is cancelled, and the trip takes as long as it would on a lake. Explain.

4. How long does the upstream portion of the trip take? How about the downstream portion?

For problems 5 and 6 assume the boat moves at a rate of $r$ miles per hour in still water.

5. What would its rate be in terms of $r$,
   a. going upstream if the river is moving at 2 miles per hour?
   b. going downstream if the river is moving at $c$ miles per hour?

6. If the river is moving at 3 miles per hour,
   a. how long does the upstream portion of the trip take in terms of $r$?
   b. how long does the downstream portion of the trip take in terms of $r$?
   c. how long does the whole trip take in terms of $r$?

7. How fast should the boat go (still water rate), if the L.A. Barge Co. wants to conserve fuel, but needs to make the round trip (including a one-hour stop) in:
   a. 13 hours?     b. 8 hours?

An airplane flies from Alaberg to Bergala with a headwind of 20 miles per hour and returns with a tailwind of 20 miles per hour. The plane stopped in Bergala for an hour. The whole trip took 4 hours. The towns are 500 miles apart.

8. How long did each portion of the trip take?

9. Create a problem involving currents, winds, or moving sidewalks that requires solving a quadratic equation. Solve your problem.

# ◆ Essential Ideas

1. The A.B. Glare Window Store sells a two-pane window, especially designed so that the panes have the same dimensions as each other, and the whole window has the same proportions as each pane. If the horizontal dimension of the window is 36 inches, what is the vertical dimension, to the nearest inch? Make a sketch and show your work.

2. The A.B. Glare Window Store sells two models of two-pane windows, such that one pane is square and the other is rectangular. The rectangular pane has the same proportions as the whole window. Both models have a horizontal dimension of 36 inches. Make a sketch and show your work as you answer the following question: What are the dimensions of the rectangular pane, if its longer dimension is
   a. horizontal?    b. vertical?

3. Dwight was simplifying $\dfrac{x+2}{x}$. He said, "I can't get rid of the $x$'s in the numerator and denominator." He wrote $\dfrac{x+2}{x} = 2$.

   Did Dwight correctly simplify $\dfrac{x+2}{x}$? Is his statement always, sometimes, or never true?

If possible, simplify the fractions.

4. $\dfrac{xy+y}{y}$      5. $\dfrac{3x+3y}{x^2-y^2}$

6. $\dfrac{3a+3b}{4a+4b}$      7. $\dfrac{6}{6x-6}$

8. $\dfrac{x^2+5x}{x^2+4x}$      9. $\dfrac{2x+2y}{3x+3y}$

Tell whether each expression is always, sometimes, or never true.

10. $\dfrac{3x+5}{3x} = 5$      11. $\dfrac{3x+3y}{x+y} = 6$

12. $\dfrac{3x+3y}{x+y} = 3$      13. $\dfrac{3x+y}{y} = 3x$

14. Write a fraction having a denominator of $6y$ that is equivalent to:
    a. 1/6      b. $x$

15. Write a fraction having a denominator of $y$ that is equivalent to:
    a. $6x$      b. $6xy$

16. a. Write a fraction equivalent to $3/x$ having $xy$ as a denominator.
    b. Write a fraction equivalent to $5/y$ having $xy$ as a denominator.
    c. Add $3/x$ and $5/y$. (Hint: To add, you need a common denominator.)

17. a. Write a fraction that is equivalent to $x$ having $x$ as a denominator.
    b. Add $x + 1/x$. (Hint: Find a common denominator.)

Put on the same denominator.

18. $x^2 + \dfrac{b}{a}x + \dfrac{c}{a}$      19. $-\dfrac{b^2}{4a^2} + \dfrac{c}{a}$

On a test Joel solved the quadratic equation $6x^2 = 12x$ using this method:

| | |
|---|---|
| Divide both sides by $x$: | $\dfrac{6x^2}{x} = \dfrac{12x}{x}$ |
| Simplify fractions: | $6x = 12$ |
| Divide both side by 6: | $\dfrac{6x}{6} = \dfrac{12}{6}$ |
| The answer is | $x = 2.$ |

Joel's teacher, Mr. Letter, wrote this on his paper:

> There are two solutions to this equation. You missed one of them because you divided by 0.

Joel was puzzled. "I divided by $x$, and then by 6 " he thought. "I never divided by 0."

**20.** 🔑 Can you explain what Mr. Letter meant? Can you solve the equation correctly?

**MYSTERY PARABOLAS**

Make a rough sketch showing two parabolas having the features described. Some of your parabolas should be frowns and others smiles; some should be more open, some less. Label each parabola with:

    a. its equation;
    b. its axis of symmetry;
    c. its $x$-intercepts (exact values);
    d. its vertex.

**21.** The parabola has $x$-intercepts at 2 and -4.

**22.** The parabola has vertex (3, -5).

**23.** The parabola has an $x$-intercept at $\sqrt{5}$ and is symmetric with respect to the $y$-axis.

**24.** The parabola has an $x$-intercept at $1 - \sqrt{6}$ and has the line $x = 1$ as its axis of symmetry.

**25.** The parabola has an axis of symmetry at $x = 5$ and $y$-intercept 3.

**PARABOLA FEATURES**

**26.** Give the vertex, $x$-, and $y$-intercepts of:
    a. $y = 2(x + 3)^2 - 9$
    b. $y = 4(x - 5)(x + 1)$
    c. $y = 6x^2 - 7x - 8$

**27.** How many $x$-intercepts?
    a. $y = -2(x + 3)^2 - 9$
    b. $y = -4(x - 2)$
    c. $y = 6x^2 + 7x + 8$

**FROM FRACTIONS TO QUADRATICS**

Rewrite each equation as an equivalent quadratic equation. Then solve the equation. Show your work.

**28.** $w + 9 = \frac{10}{w}$      **29.** $L + 3 = 2 + \frac{6}{L}$

**30.** $L - 4 = \frac{32}{L}$      **31.** $\frac{1}{x} = x - 1$

Solve these equations. They have zero, one, or two solutions.

**32.** $\frac{4}{x} + x = -4$      **33.** $\frac{1}{x} + \frac{2}{x} = \frac{3}{x}$

**34.** $1 = \frac{1}{x} + \frac{1}{x^2}$

**WRITE AN EQUATION**

**35.** Write a quadratic equation that has the following solutions:
    a. 4 and -2
    b. $\sqrt{5}$ and $-\sqrt{5}$
    c. $1 + \sqrt{5}$ and $1 - \sqrt{5}$

**36.** Write a quadratic equation that has the solution -6.

**37.** Write a quadratic equation that has no real number solutions.

**Absolute value** The absolute value of a number $x$ is the distance from $x$ to 0 on the number line.

**Absolute zero** The temperature for which the volume (of gases) would be zero—the lowest possible temperature.

**Acute angle** An angle whose measure is less than a right angle.

**Acute triangle** A triangle that contains three acute angles.

**Adding zero** Adding the same quantity to both sides of an equation, or to the plus and minus area on a workmat, is the technique of adding zero.

**Area** The size of a surface expressed in square units.

**Arithmetic sequence** In an arithmetic sequence the difference between consecutive terms is always the same. It is called the *common difference*.

**Associative Law** For all real numbers $a$, $b$, and $c$, Addition: $a + (b + c) = (a + b) + c$., i.e., quantities can be grouped in any way. Multiplication: $a \cdot (b \cdot c) = (a \cdot b) \cdot c$., i.e., factors can be grouped in any way.

**Average speed** The total distance traveled divided by total travel time.

**Axis** In the Cartesian coordinate system, the horizontal number line is the $x$-axis. The vertical number line is the $y$-axis.

**Axis of symmetry** If the graph of a parabola is folded so that its two sides coincide, the line on which the fold occurs is the axis of symmetry.

**Bounce ratio** The bounce-height to drop-height ratio.

**Cadence** The pace of pedaling (a bicycle).

**Cartesian coordinate system** The Cartesian coordinate system is the technique of using horizontal and vertical axes and graph points to make geometric representations of algebraic equations. It is named for Descartes, the French mathematician and philosopher.

**Chunking** The process of grouping bits of information into a single piece of information. Also treating an entire algebraic expression as one variable.

**Coefficient** In a term, the coefficient is the numeric factor of the term or number that is multiplied by the variable.

**Commutative Law** For any real numbers $a$ and $b$, Addition: $a + b = b + a$. Multiplication: $ab = ba$.

**Completing the square** When you add the same quantity to both sides of a quadratic equation (and make a perfect square), you are completing the square.

**Complex number** A complex number cannot be shown on a number line. It requires a two-dimensional number plane.

**Compound inequality** An inequality that contains more than one inequality symbol.

**Constant** A term having no variables.

**Constraints** A constraint is a condition necessary when solving an equation.

**Conversion factor** In the case of unit conversion, the proportionality constant (the number by which you multiply) is the conversion factor.

**Coordinates** In the Cartesian coordinate system, the numbers in an ordered pair, i.e., $(x, y)$ are used to locate a point on a plane.

**Degree of an expression** The degree of an expression, in terms of the Lab Gear, is the lowest dimension in which you can arrange the blocks.

**Density** Density is equal to weight per unit of volume.

**Discriminant** The discriminant is the quantity $b^2 - 4ac$ that appears under the radical in the quadratic formula, sometimes written as the Greek letter delta, $\Delta$.

**Distributing the minus sign** When you write an equivalent expression without parentheses you are distributing the minus sign.

**Distributive Law** For any real numbers $a$, $b$, and $c$, of multiplication over addition: $a(b + c) = ab + ac$ and $(b + c)a = ba + ca$. of multiplication over subtraction: $a(b - c) = ab - ac$ and $(b - c)a = ba - ca$.

**Domain (of a function)** The set of values that the input can take.

**Dynamic rectangles** Dynamic rectangles have the property that half of such a rectangle is similar to the whole.

**Equivalent equations** If equations in two variables have the same graph on the Cartesian coordinate system, they are called equivalent equations.

**Euclidean distance** The straight-line distance between two points.

**Evaluating expressions** When you evaluate an expression, you replace each variable in it by a given value and then simplify the result.

**Experiment** An example of an experiment would be one roll of a pair of dice. Each different possibility of a result is an *outcome*. An *event* is one or more outcomes.

**Exponential growth** Involves repeated multiplication by a number.

**Exponentiation** or **Raising to a power** The operation of multiplying a number by itself repeatedly. The number multiplied is the *base*. The number of factors is the *exponent*.

**Extrapolation** When you know data points and use them to predict data values at a later or earlier time, the process is called extrapolation.

**Eyes** The points of intersection of the grid lines inside a polyomino are eyes.

**Factor (noun), Common** A common factor divides each term in a polynomial evenly.

**Factor (verb)** To write as a product.

**Fair** A game is fair if each of the players is equally likely to win.

**Family (of functions)** A group of functions that share a certain attribute.

**Fixed point** If an in-out line is horizontal, its input is a fixed point.

**Focus** Point where all in-out lines meet, if extended to the left or right.

**Function** A relation that assigns to each member of its *domain* exactly one member, its *range*.

**Gear** The gear ratio multiplied by the diameter of the rear wheel (of a bicycle).

**Gear ratio** The ratio of the number of teeth on the chainwheel (of a bicycle) to the number of teeth on the rear sprocket.

**Geometric sequence** In a geometric sequence each term is obtained from the previous term by multiplying by a constant amount, the common ratio.

**Golden ratio** The ratio of the longer to the shorter side of a golden rectangle is the golden ratio.

**Golden rectangle** A golden rectangle satisfies this property: If you cut a square off one end of the rectangle, the remaining rectangle is similar to the original rectangle.

**Group** A set of elements, together with an operation, that satisfies certain rules.

**Hypotenuse** The side of a right triangle that is opposite the right angle.

**Identity** An equation that is true for all values of the variables.

**Inequalities** An inequality is a mathematical sentence that contains an inequality symbol between two expressions, e.g. $2 < 6$, $x + 4 > 5$.

**Input-Output Tables** In such tables, $x$ is the number that is put in, and $y$ is the number that comes out. Each table has a rule that allows you to get $y$ from $x$.

**Integer** Any positive or negative whole number and zero.

**Intercepts of graphs**
$x$-intercept: The point where it crosses the $x$-axis.
$y$-intercept: The point where it crosses the $y$-axis.
Intercept form: $y = a(x - p)(x - q)$

**Interpolation** When you know data points and use them to determine data values between those points, the process is called interpolation.

**Inversely proportional** You can say that $y$ is inversely proportional to $x$ if the product of $x$ and $y$ is constant. Algebraically, $xy = k$ or $y = k/a$ for some constant $k$.

**Iterating functions** To iterate a function means to use its output as a new input.

**Lattice line** A line having equation $x = b$ or $y = b$, where $b$ is an integer.

**Lattice point** A point on the Cartesian plane having integer coordinates.

**Legs** The two sides of the right angle in a right triangle.

**Like terms** Terms whose variable factors are the same.

**Linear combination** The equation obtained by adding constant multiples of two equations together.

**Magnification** In function diagrams that have a focus, changes in $y$ can be found by multiplying the changes in $x$ by a number, called the magnification. Also called *rate of change*.

**Mean** The average of a set of values.

**Median** The middle value of a set of values.

**Numbers**
Rational: A rational number is any number that can be expressed as the ratio of two integers in the form $a/b$ where $b \neq 0$.
Irrational: An irrational number is a real number that cannot be written in the form $a/b$ where $a$ and $b$ are integers.
Natural: Natural numbers are the numbers we count with: 1, 2, 3, 4,…etc.
Real: Real numbers include all rational and irrational numbers.

**Observed probability** Can be represented graphically by the slope of the line through the origin and the corresponding data point.

**Obtuse angle** An obtuse angle is greater than a right angle.

**Obtuse triangle** An obtuse triangle contains an obtuse angle.

**Order of operations** A rule for the order in which operations are to be done.
1) Compute within grouping symbols;
2) Compute powers;
3) Multiply and divide in order from left to right;
4) Add and subtract in order from left to right.

**Origin** The point at which the axes of a graph cross; point $(0, 0)$ in the Cartesian coordinate system.

**Parabola** The graph of a quadratic equation $ax^2 + bx + c = 0$; $a \neq 0$ is a parabola.

**Parameter** A constant or variable in a mathematical expression which distinguishes specific cases. In $y = a + bx$, $a$ and $b$ are the parameters.

**Perimeter** The perimeter of a figure is the distance around it.

**Pi** Pi, $\pi$, is approximately equal to the number 3.1415926536. The formula for the area of a circle is $\pi r^2$. ($r$ is the radius of the circle.)

**Plaintext** The text of a message, before it is encoded.

**Polycubes** You can create polycubes by joining cubes together face-to-face. Polycubes are the three-dimensional equivalent of *polyominoes*.

**Polynomial function** A function of the form $y =$ a polynomial.

**Polynomials** A polynomial is a monomial or a sum of monomials.
Monomial: An expression that is the product of numerals and variables.
Binomial: A polynomial having two terms.
Trinomial: A polynomial having three terms.

**Polytans** Shapes created by combining tans.

**Power** A number that can be named using exponential notation.

**Power of a product law** It states that $x^a y^a = (xy)^a$ as long as $x$ and $y \neq 0$.

**Power of a ratio law** It states that $x^a/y^a = (x/y)^a$ as long as $x$ and $y \neq 0$.

**Prime factorization** Prime factorization occurs when you write a whole number as a product of prime factors.

**Prime number** An integer greater than one that has no factors other than one and itself.

**Probability** The probability of an event is interpreted to mean the relative frequency with which an event occurs if the experiment is repeated many times.

**Product of powers law** States that $x^a \cdot x^b = x^{a+b}$ as long as $x \neq 0$.

**Pythagorean theorem** In all right triangles, if $a$ and $b$ are the lengths of the legs and $c$ is the length of the hypotenuse, then $a^2 + b^2 = c^2$.

**Quadrant** In the Cartesian coordinate system, the axes divide the system into four parts, called quadrants.

**Quadratic formula** A formula for finding the solutions of a quadratic equation $ax^2 + bx + c = 0$. The formula is $x = \dfrac{-b \pm \sqrt{b^2 - 4ac}}{2a}$

**Quadratic function** A second-degree polynomial function.

**Radical**
Radical sign: The symbol $\sqrt{\ }$.
Radical expression: An expression written under the radical sign.

**Range** (of a function) The set of values the output can take.

**Rate of change of a function** The rate of change of a function is the ratio between the change in $y$ and the change in $x$.
rate of change = change in $y$/change in $x$
It is often called *magnification*.

**Ratio of powers law** It states that $x^a/x^b = x^{a-b}$ as long as $x \neq 0$.

**Rational expression** The quotient of two polynomials.

**Rationalizing the denominator** Simplifying a radical expression so that there are no radicals in the denominator and only whole numbers or variables in the radicand.

**Reciprocals** Two expressions are reciprocals if their product is one. Also called the *multiplicative inverse*.

**Relative frequency** The relative frequency of successes is the ratio of successes to trials.

**Repeating decimal** A decimal in which the same number or group of numbers repeats endlessly.

**Right triangle** A right triangle contains one angle of 90 degrees.

**Rise** The units of altitude gained for every 100 units moved in a horizontal direction (the run).

**Run** Distance moved in the horizontal direction when dealing with grade and slope.

**Scientific notation** A number expressed as the product of a power of 10 and a numeral greater than or equal to 1 but less than 10.

**Sequence** An ordered list of numbers or expressions, called *terms*.

**Similarity** Two figures are similar if all the dimensions of one can be obtained by multiplying the dimensions of the other by the same number. This number is called the *ratio of similarity*.

**Simple radical form** Writing the square root of a whole number as a product of a whole number and the square root of the smallest possible whole number.

**Simultaneous equations** Two or more equations for which you must find a common solution.

**Slope** A number telling how steeply a line slants; the ratio of rise to run.

**Slope-intercept form** $y = mx + b$

**Solving an equation** When you find all the values of a variable that make an equation true, you are solving an equation.

**Standard form equation** $ax^2 + bx + c = 0$

**Step function** May be shown by a graph. The end points of the steps may be filled in (closed circles) or hollow (open circles).

**Subjective probability** Subjective probability is assigned to an event according to a person's own knowledge, beliefs, or information.

**Surface area** The surface area of a figure (for example, a cube) is the number of unit squares it would take to cover all its faces.

**Tan** In the world of geometric puzzles, a tan is half a unit square (cut along the diagonal).

**Tangent** A line that touches a graph at only one point is tangent to the graph.

**Taxicab distance** The taxicab distance between two points in the Cartesian plane is the length of the shortest path between them that consists of only horizontal and vertical segments.

**Terminating decimal** A decimal that can be written in decimal form with a finite number of digits.

**Terms** An expression that is the product of numerals and variables.

**Theoretical probability** Can be represented graphically as a line through the origin.

**Translations (of groups)** A graph obtained by shifting the location of a given graph without changing its shape is called a translation of the original graph.

**Variable** A letter or other symbol used to represent a number or numbers.

**Vertex of an angle** The "corner" of a geometric figure is the vertex. The plural is *vertices*.

**Vertex form of quadratic function** The quadratic function $y = (x - H)^2 + V$ in vertex form.

**Volume of solids** The volume of a solid is the number of unit cubes it would take to build it.

**Zero product property** It states that when the product of two quantities is zero, one or the other quantity must be zero.

# INDEX

De Morgan, Augustus, 229
Denominator
   common, 490
   rationalizing, 352
   zero in, 489
Density, 137–138
Dependent variable, 436–437
Descartes, Rene, 84
Diagonal, on geoboard, 404–405
Diameter, area and, 144
Dice game, 409–411
Dicube, 31
Difference
   absolute value of, 329
   of perfect squares, 383
     factoring, 255
Dimension, 5, 15–17
   finding, 479
   lowest, 18
Diophantus, 229
Direct variation, 138, 146–147
Discount, 217
Discrete graph, 152–153
Discriminant, 502
Distance, 328–330
   Euclidean, 328–329
   finding from coordinates, 332
   on geoboard, 279–280, 334
   skidding, 350
   taxicab, 328–329
   vs. speed, 126
   vs. time, 125–126, 156
Distributing, 189
   the minus sign, 87
Distributive law, 172–173
   division and, 172–173, 220
   of division over addition and subtraction, 173
   minus and, 87, 182–85
   multiplication of polynomials and, 99
   of multiplication over addition and subtraction, 52–53
Distributive law, radical expressions and, 351
Division
   distributive law and, 172–173, 220
   function diagram and, 68
   model for, 101
   multiplication and, 97–99
   of radicals, 337–338
   shortcut, 102
   solving linear equations with, 227–229
   by zero, 108
Division symbol, 97
Division table, 145
Domain, 342
Domino, 4
Domino problem, 25
Double negative, 84–86
Downstairs block, 183
Dynamic rectangle, 485–486

### E

Electron, weight of, 325
Equal power, 313–314
Equal ratio, 121
Equal squares, 265, 471, 499–500

Equation(s)
   from data, 438
   equivalent, 228–229, 376
   from graphs, 128
   identities and, 215–216
   linear, 134, 389–390
     parameters for, 381–382
     solving, 211–213, 261
     standard form of, 381–383
   from patterns, 127
   with percents, 307
   points and, 128
   quadratic, 476–478
     fractions and, 490–491
     real number solutions for, 502
     simplifying, 488–489
     solving, 261–263, 477, 497
       with zero product property, 463–464
     standard form of, 496
     sum of solutions of, 503
     $x$–intercepts for, 476–477
   recurrence, 445
   simultaneous, 374, 387–388, 449
     system of, 376–379
   solving, 106–107, 211–213
     addition and subtraction and, 221–223
     multiplication and division and, 227–229
   with squares, 264–266
   writing, 106
Equidistant, 464
Equivalent equations, 228–229, 376
Equivalent fractions, 115
Eratosthenes, 274
Estimating, 140–141
   population, 349
Euclid, 328
Euclidean distance, 328–329
Euler, Leonhard, 76
Evaluating, 11–12
Even number, 192
Event, 410
   probability of, 413
Experiment, 409
Exponent, 56
   fractional, 348
   laws of, 314, 322, 349
   multiplication and, 276
   negative, 317–319
   1/2, 348–349
   zero, 267–268
Exponential growth, 303, 317–318
   midpoint of, 346
Exponential notation, 56
Exponentiation, 56
   calculator, 272
   commutative, 269
   order of operations and, 129
Expression
   algebraic, comparing, 225
   degree of, 18
   evaluating, 11–12
   radical, 335, 351–352
   rational, 231–233
     comparing, 231
     equivalent, 231–232
   simplifying, 209–210

Extrapolation, 427–428
Eyes, 72

### F

Factor, 174
   common, 181
     greatest, 181
Factoring, 180–181
   difference of squares, 255
   polynomials, 259
   prime, 406
   of third-degree polynomials, 175
   of trinomials, 174–175
Fahrenheit temperature, converting to Celsius, 104, 390
Fahrenheit temperature scale, 103–104
Fair, 409
Family of functions, 449–450
Feet per second, 148
Fibonacci, 333
Fibonacci number, 59
Fibonacci sequence, 505
Finding $x$, 12
Fixed point, 118, 289, 446, 460
Flip, 198
Focus, 289
Formula
   area, 157–158
   Pick's, 158
   quadratic, 497–498, 500–501
   speed by, 126
Fraction(s), 401–402
   combining terms involving, 452
   complicating, 490
   as decimals, 401
   decimals as, 401–402
   equivalent, 115
   lattice points and, 404
   quadratic equations and, 490–491
   radicals and, 352
   rationalizing, 352
   simplifying, 172–173, 488–489
Fractional exponent, 348
Frequency, relative, 412–413
Frown parabola, 178
Function(s), 61
   area, 146–147
   coding, 92
   combined, 109–111
   constant product, 169–171
   constant sum, 167
   domain of, 342
   families of, 449–450
   fixed point of, 118, 446, 460
   inverse, 110–111
   linear, 296–298
     iterating, 445–447
   opposite, 105
   perimeter, 69–70
   polynomial, 129–130
   polyomino, 72–73
   quadratic, 177–179
     intercept form of, 492–493
     standard form of, 474, 493
     vertex of, 492–494
     $x$-intercepts of, 496–497
   range of, 342
   reciprocal, 105
   representing, 448–450